ESSENTIALS OF MODERN
ORGANIC CHEMISTRY

REINHOLD CHEMISTRY TEXTBOOK SERIES

Consulting Editors: HARRY H. SISLER CALVIN A. VANDERWERF
University of Florida *Hope College*
Gainesville, Florida *Holland, Michigan*

BONNER AND CASTRO—*Essentials of Modern Organic Chemistry*
DAY AND SELBIN—*Theoretical Inorganic Chemistry*
DRAGO—*Physical Methods in Inorganic Chemistry*
FAIRLEY AND KILGOUR—*Essentials of Biological Chemistry, Second Edition*
FIESER AND FIESER—*Advanced Organic Chemistry*
FIESER AND FIESER—*Topics in Organic Chemistry*
HEFTMANN—*Chromatography, Second Edition*
HEFTMANN AND MOSETTIG—*Biochemistry of Steroids*
KLINGENBERG AND REED—*Introduction to Quantitative Chemistry*
LINGANE—*Analytical Chemistry of Selected Metallic Elements*
LUDER—*A Different Approach to Thermodynamics*
MEYER—*Food Chemistry*
MORTIMER—*Chemistry: A Conceptual Approach*
NECKERS—*Mechanistic Organic Photochemistry*
REID—*Principles of Chemical Thermodynamics*
SANDERSON—*Inorganic Chemistry*
SMITH AND CRISTOL—*Organic Chemistry*

Selected Topics in Modern Chemistry
Harry H. Sisler and Calvin A. VanderWerf, EDITORS

BREY—*Physical Methods for Determining Molecular Geometry*
CHELDELIN AND NEWBURGH—*The Chemistry of Some Life Processes*
EYRING AND EYRING—*Modern Chemical Kinetics*
HILDEBRAND—*An Introduction to Molecular Kinetic Theory*
KIEFFER—*The Mole Concept in Chemistry*
MOELLER—*The Chemistry of the Lanthanides*
MORRIS—*Principles of Chemical Equilibrium*
MURMANN—*Inorganic Complex Compounds*
O'DRISCOLL—*The Nature and Chemistry of High Polymers*
OVERMANN—*Basic Concepts of Nuclear Chemistry*
ROCHOW—*Organometallic Chemistry*
RYSCHKEWITSCH—*Chemical Bonding and the Geometry of Molecules*
SISLER—*Electronic Structure, Properties, and the Periodic Law*
SISLER—*Chemistry in Non-Aqueous Solvents*
SONNESSA—*Introduction to Molecular Spectroscopy*
STRONG AND STRATTON—*Chemical Energy*
VANDERWERF—*Acids, Bases, and the Chemistry of the Covalent Bond*
VOLD AND VOLD—*Colloid Chemistry*

CONSULTING EDITORS' STATEMENT

MODERN organic chemistry is constructed upon a well-developed intellectual framework of compelling beauty and fascination. The science of
organic chemistry has come of age. No longer is the subject an impene-
trable jungle of unrelated facts, but rather a stately mansion soundly built
upon comprehensive unifying concepts and sweeping interlocking ideas.

In recent years the architecture of organic chemistry has been so clearly
and consistently established that no longer should the student be denied
the opportunity to view the subject as an exciting intellectual achievement.
The time has come, we believe, when he, too, *can* and *should* be taught
to explore the grand edifice of organic chemistry as a challenging adventure
of the mind. This is precisely the contribution which the authors of
Essentials of Modern Organic Chemistry are making. We at Reinhold are
honored to present this text, because we believe that its special contribution heralds a notable advance in teaching and learning for the terminal
course in organic chemistry.

Professors Bonner and Castro hold distinguished records as master
teachers and active research workers in organic chemistry, one at a noted
private university, the other at an outstanding state college. Out of their
broad experience, they have become convinced that the student of organic
chemistry can best be taught the subject on a broad, conceptual basis.
More than that, they have found that such an approach adds exhilaration
and stimulus to active participation in the learning adventure.

Teachers and students, alike, who enjoy the use of *Essentials of Modern
Organic Chemistry* will, we are confident, prove that they are right.

CALVIN A. VANDERWERF
HARRY H. SISLER

ESSENTIALS OF

ORGANIC

WILLIAM A. BONNER

Professor of Chemistry
Stanford University
Stanford, California

MODERN
CHEMISTRY

ALBERT J. CASTRO

Professor of Chemistry
San Jose State College
San Jose, California

REINHOLD PUBLISHING CORPORATION
A Subsidiary of Chapman-Reinhold/New York, London, Amsterdam

To Our Wives

Preface

RECENT important and exciting developments in organic chemistry have led us to feel the need for a modern and challenging textbook. Furthermore, as we encounter students with a better foundation in basic chemistry, we feel that a rigorous, updated treatment of organic chemistry should prove vital and stimulating. We believe that today's beginning student is equipped both to grasp the modern theoretical concepts underlying organic chemistry and to appreciate recent technical advances in the subject. Accordingly, we have emphasized principles, mechanisms, and modern techniques throughout the text, and have left a good portion of the traditional factual matter for learning later if needed.

Certain distinguishing features of the present text merit comment. It is written with the view that all students enrolled in the lecture course may not take the accompanying laboratory. Accordingly, early chapters are devoted to isolation and purification procedures (including vapor phase and thin layer chromatography) and to characterization techniques (including mass, nuclear magnetic resonance, infrared, and ultraviolet spectrometry). Those not enrolled in laboratory work thereby gain an appreciation for the important methods of organic chemistry, and the laboratory student is aided as well. Aliphatic and aromatic compounds are integrated, resulting in an economy of presentation and permitting the early introduction of the latter class of compounds in accompanying laboratory work. A brief introduction to mechanisms of organic reactions and other theoretical features is presented early in the text. These concepts are then used as a framework that is employed throughout the text and expanded at proper points. Natural products, medicinal substances, and other important types of compounds representative of particular structures are interwoven throughout the text, and a separate chapter is devoted to carbohydrates, amino acids, proteins, and other natural products.

In deciding upon the reactions to be included, two criteria have been employed: (1) Does the reaction illustrate a basic principle or concept? (2) Is the reaction of practical value in the laboratory or in commerce? Thus many of the traditional reactions treated in organic texts in the past have been omitted, and only their more efficient modern counterparts are included. At the same time, however, in the overall choice of subject matter we have been cognizant of the differences in emphasis stressed by different teachers and have tried to include sufficient choice so that the text is not unduly restrictive. Concomitantly, there has resulted an increase in the subject matter presented over that found in most other introductory texts. We believe that the advantages to the teacher and student of a broad choice in subject matter are obvious.

The text is profusely illustrated, although illustrations are limited only to those which are pertinent to a better understanding or appreciation of the topic under consideration. For the benefit of both teacher and student each chapter is followed by an extensive supplementary reading list referring to pertinent articles in the *Journal of Chemical Education* and *Scientific American*. A number of questions of graded difficulty for each chapter are provided at the back of the text.

We are indebted, for their helpful comments, to Drs. Harry S. Mosher, Arthur Kornberg, and Hubert S. Loring of Stanford University and Drs. Ronald Watanabe, Harold J. DeBey, and George A. McCallum of San Jose State College, each of whom read portions of our manuscript, and to Dr. James A. Marshall of Northwestern University, who read the entire manuscript. For the artwork, illustrations, and equations we are grateful to Mrs. Allison Scott-Cassel and Mrs. Tatiana Hunter. Those photographs not bearing acknowledgment were prepared by one of us (W.A.B.); for the others we express appreciation to the firms or individuals listed. In particular, we are grateful to Mrs. Elisabeth H. Belfer of the Reinhold Publishing Corporation for her patience, encouragement, and editorial assistance.

The authors solicit your suggestions for improvement of the text.

W. A. B.
A. J. C.

To the Student

LEARNING organic chemistry—and many other subjects—may be approached in two ways: we may learn the subject, or we may learn merely *about* the subject. Learning *about* a subject involves relatively passive reading or listening in order to become more or less acquainted with its principal content. Learning a subject, however, implies active participation in the manipulation of the intellectual and physical tools which the particular discipline employs. You may learn a little *about* organic chemistry by merely reading this text. To obtain a preliminary operational knowledge of the subject, however, you must devote both time and thought to the questions for each chapter.

The study of organic chemistry is much like that of a foreign language. First, a good deal of memory work is required—an essential feature for which no apology can be made. Second, the nomenclature and symbolism of organic chemistry are much akin to vocabulary and alphabet, but will prove rather more precise. Third, general organic reactions are analogous to the grammatical syntax of a foreign language, and "exceptions to the rules" prove to be very important in both disciplines. A necessary skill for organic chemistry is the facile ability to apply *general* equations and principles to particular problems in varying contexts. This need to go "from the general to the particular" is perhaps the most difficult aspect of the subject at the outset, much as the most difficult exercise at the start of a foreign language is the conversion of vocabulary and grammatical rules into correct and meaningful sentences. The chapter questions are graded in difficulty and are designed to develop this facility.

There is no single technique which minimizes the effort required in mastering organic chemistry, or, for that matter, any other subject. Some students find that careful rewriting of their lecture and reading material is a useful learning aid. Some discover that "flash cards" of names, equations, and reaction conditions are equally helpful. Others find that working in small groups, with extensive cross-questioning, is useful in clarifying concepts and developing optimum answers to questions having a multitude of answers. The common feature in all of these learning techniques is *active participation*, without which an operational understanding of organic chemistry is impossible.

Contents

Preface   ix

To the Student   xi

1. Introduction: The Nature of Organic Chemistry   1

1-1. Historical Background and Contemporary Setting   1-2. The
Unique Chemical Character of Carbon   1-3. Sources and Transformations of Organic Compounds

2. Some Basic Principles and Concepts   8

2-1. Organic Chemical Formulas   2-2. The Chemical Bond
2-3. Comparison of Organic and Inorganic Compounds   2-4. Principal Series of Organic Compounds   2-5. Functional Groups
2-6. Homologous Series   2-7. Isomerism   2-8. Stereoisomerism and
Stereochemistry   2-9. Bond Energies   2-10. Isotopes of Carbon

3. Isolating and Purifying Organic Compounds   37

3-1. Extraction   3-2. Distillation   3-3. Sublimation   3-4. Crystallization   3-5. Chromatographic Methods   3-6. Ion Exchange
3-7. Criteria of Purity

4. Determining Molecular Structures   55

4-1. Elemental Analyses   4-2. Empirical and Molecular Formulas
4-3. Molecular Weight   4-4. Functional Groups   4-5. Degradative
Reactions   4-6. Interaction of Radiant Energy with Matter
4-7. Spectrometers   4-8. Infrared Spectrometry   4-9. Visible and

Ultraviolet Spectrometry   4-10. Nuclear Magnetic Resonance Spectrometry   4-11. Mass Spectrometry   4-12. X-Ray Diffraction
4-13. Confirmatory Synthesis

5.   Resonance and Molecular Orbitals   **85**

5-1. Resonance   5-2. Molecular Orbitals   5-3. Orbital Hybridization

6.   Organic Reactions and Their Intermediates   **96**

6-1. Types of Organic Reactions   6-2. Reaction Mechanisms and Reaction Intermediates   6-3. Experimental Conditions and Reaction Mechanisms   6-4. Some Aspects of Free Radicals   6-5. Lewis Acids and Bases   6-6. Some Aspects of Carbonium Ions   6-7. Some Aspects of Carbanions   6-8. Energy Relations during Chemical Reactions

7.   Hydrocarbons—Alkanes   **119**

7-1. Classes of Hydrocarbons   7-2. Nomenclature   7-3. Physical Properties of Alkanes   7-4. Sources and Uses of Alkanes—The Petroleum Industry   7-5. Synthesis of Alkanes   7-6. Reactions of Alkanes

8.   Hydrocarbons—Alkenes   **143**

8-1. Nomenclature   8-2. Sources and Physical Properties of Alkenes   8-3. Synthesis of Alkenes   8-4. Reactions of Alkenes   8-5. Dienes and Polyenes

9.   Hydrocarbons—Alkynes and Cycloalkanes   **183**

ALKYNES

9-1. Nomenclature and Physical Properties of Alkynes   9-2. Acetylene and Naturally Occurring Alkynes   9-3. Synthesis of Alkynes   9-4. Reactions of Alkynes

CYCLOALKANES

9-5. Sources, Occurrence, and Uses of Cycloalkanes   9-6. Ring Strain and Geometry of Cycloalkanes   9-7. Synthesis of Cycloalkanes   9-8. Reactions of Cycloalkanes

Contents

10. Aromatic Hydrocarbons   **215**

10-1. Structure, Nomenclature, and Physical Properties of Aromatic Hydrocarbons   10-2. Sources of Aromatic Compounds   10-3. Synthesis of Aromatic Compounds   10-4. Reactions of Aromatic Hydrocarbons   10-5. The Mechanism of Electrophilic Aromatic Substitution   10-6. Polysubstitution; Orientation Effects in Electrophilic Substitutions   10-7. Nucleophilic and Free Radical Aromatic Substitution 10-8. Structure of Benzene Derivatives   10-9. Non-Benzenoid Aromatic Derivatives   10-10. Heterocyclic Compounds

11. Alcohols, Alkyl Halides, and Ethers   **248**

ALCOHOLS

11-1. Nomenclature of Alcohols   11-2. Physical Properties and Characterization of Alcohols   11-3. Hydrogen Bonding
11-4. Sources and Uses of Alcohols   11-5. Synthesis of Alcohols
11-6. Polyhydric Alcohols   11-7. Reactions of Alcohols   11-8. Reactions of Glycols   11-9. Phenols

ORGANIC HALIDES

11-10. Nomenclature, Physical Properties, and Characterization of Halides   11-11 Synthesis of Organic Halides   11-12. Reactions of Organic Halides   11-13. Structure and Reactivity of Organic Halides

ETHERS

11-14. Nomenclature, Physical Properties, and Characterization of Ethers   11-15. Occurrence and Uses of Ethers   11-16. Synthesis of Ethers   11-17. Reactions of Ethers

SULFUR ANALOGS OF ALCOHOLS AND ETHERS

11-18. Mercaptans   11-19. Sulfides

12. Aldehydes and Ketones   **298**

12-1. Nomenclature of Aldehydes and Ketones   12-2. Physical Properties and Characterization of Aldehydes and Ketones   12-3. Synthesis of Aldehydes and Ketones   12-4. Synthesis of Aldehydes
12-5. Synthesis of Ketones   12-6. Industrial Synthesis of Aldehydes and Ketones   12-7. Reactions of Aldehydes and Ketones   12-8. α,β--Unsaturated Aldehydes and Ketones   12-9. Quinones   12-10. Tropolones   12-11. Epoxides

13. Carboxylic Acids and Their Derivatives   **344**

CARBOXYLIC ACIDS

13-1. Nomenclature and Physical Properties of Carboxylic Acids
13-2. Acidity of Carboxylic Acids   13-3. Synthesis of Carboxylic Acids   13-4. Reactions of Carboxylic Acids

ACYL HALIDES

13-5. Preparation and Properties of Acyl Halides

CARBOXYLIC ACID ANHYDRIDES

13-6. Preparation and Properties of Carboxylic Acid Anhydrides

CARBOXYLIC ESTERS

13-7. Nomenclature and Physical Properties of Esters   13-8. Natural
Esters   13-9. Soaps and Detergents   13-10. Synthesis of Esters
13-11. Reactions of Esters

CARBOXAMIDES

13-12. Preparation and Properties of Carboxamides

NITRILES

13-13. Preparation and Properties of Nitriles

ORTHO ACIDS AND ESTERS

13-14. Organic Ortho Acids and Esters

HYDROXY ACIDS AND LACTONES

13-15. Hydroxy Acids and Lactones

DICARBOXYLIC ACIDS

13-16. Preparation, Properties, and Uses of Dicarboxylic Acids

KETO ACIDS AND KETO ESTERS

13-17. Preparation and Properties of Keto Acids and Esters
13-18. Malonic and Acetoacetic Ester Synthesis

PEROXY ACIDS AND DERIVATIVES

13-19. Preparation and Uses of Peroxy Acids and Acyl Peroxides

SULFUR AND NITROGEN ANALOGS OF CARBOXYLIC ACIDS

13-20. Typical Sulfur and Nitrogen Analogs

SULFONIC ACIDS AND THEIR DERIVATIVES

13-21. Preparation and Uses of Sulfonic Acids and Derivatives

ORGANIC OXIDATION-REDUCTION REACTIONS

13-22. Balancing Organic Oxidation-Reduction Reactions
13-23. The Mechanism of Organic Oxidations

14. **Organic Nitrogen Compounds**   **397**

AMINES

14-1. Nomenclature of Amines   14-2. Structure of Ammonia and
Amines   14-3. Physical Properties of Amines   14-4. Basicity of
Amines   14-5. Characterization of Amines   14-6. General Synthesis
of Amines   14-7. Synthesis of Primary Amines   14-8. Synthesis of
Secondary Amines   14-9. Synthesis of Tertiary Amines   14-10. Re-
actions of Amines

QUATERNARY AMMONIUM SALTS AND BASES

14-11. Preparation and Properties of Quaternary Ammonium Derivatives   14-12. Pyrolysis of Quaternary Ammonium Derivatives   14-13. A Problem in Structure Determination

NITRO COMPOUNDS

14-14. Nomenclature and Uses of Nitro Compounds   14-15. Structure and Physical Properties of Nitro Compounds   14-16. Synthesis of Nitro Compounds   14-17. Reactions of Aliphatic Nitro Compounds   14-18. Reactions of Aromatic Nitro Compounds

AROMATIC DIAZONIUM AND DIAZO COMPOUNDS

14-19. Formation of Diazonium Salts   14-20. Diazonium Salt Reactions with Loss of Nitrogen   14-21. Diazonium Salt Reactions with Retention of Nitrogen   14-22. Dyestuffs

MISCELLANEOUS NITROGEN COMPOUNDS

14-23. Isonitriles and Related Compounds   14-24. Urea, Cyanamide, and Guanidine   14-25. Isocyanates and Related Products

15. Optical Isomerism   454

15-1. Plane Polarized Light   15-2. Optical Activity   15-3. The polarimeter; Optical Rotation   15-4. Optically Active Organic Compounds   15-5. The Cause of Optical Activity   15-6. Optical Activity in Compounds with No Asymmetric Carbon Atom   15-7. Molecules with Several Asymmetric Carbon Atoms   15-8. Resolution of Racemic Modifications   15-9. Formation of Racemic Modifications   15-10. Relative Configuration   15-11. Absolute Configuration   15-12. Mechanism and Stereochemistry of Substitution Reactions   15-13. Stereoselective Syntheses and Asymmetric Syntheses   15-14. Optical Rotatory Dispersion   15-15. The Origin of Optically Active Compounds

16. Natural Products   493

CARBOHYDRATES

16-1. Classes and Properties of Carbohydrates   16-2. Structures of Aldoses and Ketoses   16-3. Stereochemical Configurations of Aldoses   16-4. Determination of Carbohydrate Configurations   16-5. Ring Structure of Sugars   16-6. Ring Size in Cyclic Sugars   16-7. Configuration at the Anomeric Center   16-8. Reactions of Monosaccharides   16-9. Disaccharides   16-10. Structure Determination of Disaccharides and Trisaccharides   16-11. Polysaccharides   16-12. Photosynthesis

AMINO ACIDS

16-13. Nomenclature of Amino Acids   16-14. Essential Amino Acids
16-15. Zwitterion Structure of Amino Acids   16-16. The Isoelectric
Point   16-17. Synthesis of Amino Acids   16-18. Reactions of Amino
Acids

PROTEINS AND PEPTIDES

16-19. Classification of Proteins   16-20. Some Properties of Proteins
16-21. Isolation and Purification of Proteins   16-22. Molecular
Weights of Proteins   16-23. Determination of Protein Structures
16-24. Structure of Oxytocin   16-25. Conformation of Proteins
16-26. Synthesis of Peptides   16-27. Enzymes   16-28. Depsipeptides

NUCLEIC ACIDS AND NUCLEOTIDES

16-29. Components of Nucleic Acids   16-30. Structure of Nucleic
Acids   16-31. Function of Nucleic Acids

STEROIDS

16-32. Cholesterol and Other Sterols   16-33. Bile Acids   16-34. Sex
Hormones   16-35. Corticosteroids   16-36. Steroid Sapogenins
16-37. Cardiac Glycosides and Toad Poisons   16-38. Stereochemistry of Steroids   16-39. Steroids in Medicine

ALKALOIDS

16-40. Extraction and Structure Elucidation of Alkaloids
16-41. Phenylalkylamine Derivatives   16-42. Pyrrolidine Derivatives
16-43. Piperidine Derivatives   16-44. Pyridine-Pyrrolidine and Pyri-
dine-Piperidine Derivatives   16-45. Alkaloids with Condensed Ring
Systems

TERPENES

16-46. The Isoprene Rule   16-47. Classification of Terpenes
16-48. Monoterpenes   16-49. Sesquiterpenes   16-50. Diterpenes
16-51. Triterpenes   16-52. Tetraterpenes—The Carotenoids
16-53. Biogenesis of Natural Products

Questions   593

Index   635

ESSENTIALS OF MODERN
ORGANIC CHEMISTRY

CHAPTER 1 # Introduction:
The Nature of Organic Chemistry

WHAT IS "organic chemistry" and why is it important? Briefly, organic
chemistry is the body of knowledge concerned with the chemical and to
some extent the physical properties of the broad group of compounds containing the element carbon. The importance of the subject can best be
illustrated by considering some of the areas in which it impinges upon our
daily lives.

The chemical substances which make up the tissues of our bodies, as
well as the foods which nourish them, contain carbon and are hence organic in nature. The same is true of the vitamins, hormones, and other
dietary factors our bodies require, and of most of the medicines we use.
The concern with organic chemistry of both the medical profession and
other branches of the biological sciences (bacteriology, zoology, etc.) is
thus obvious, and the related subject "biochemistry" has arisen to study
the chemical transformations (principally organic) which occur within all
living organisms. The clothes we wear, the dyestuffs we use to make these

1

esthetically pleasing, many of our insecticides, and the petroleum products used in our automobiles are all organic in nature. Even our mass distribution, communication, and entertainment enterprises rely heavily on organic materials in their products and processes. Indeed, it is impossible to think of an aspect of our daily life which is not influenced in one way or another by the broad subject of organic chemistry.

1-1. Historical Background and Contemporary Setting

Let us briefly examine organic chemistry from the standpoint of its development into a separate scientific discipline and its position in the contemporary setting of science and technology. The use and modification of organic materials extend back to the earliest recorded history. Typical examples include the structural use of wood, the fermentation of natural sugars into alcoholic beverages, the preparation of writing material by the ancient Egyptians from the pith of the papyrus plant (*Cyperus papyrus*, a tall sedge native to Egypt and adjacent countries), the preparation of dyestuffs from different plants, and the formulation of medications from plant and animal sources. Thus, the blue dye indigo was formerly derived from plants of the *Indigofera* species and from woad (*Isatis tinctoria*), while cochineal (carminic acid) is still obtained from the female of the cochineal insect (*Coccus cacti*), which is found on cactus in Central America and Mexico. Interestingly, Shen Nung, Chinese scholar and emperor of the 28th century B.C., compiled a book of herbs and observed the antifebrile action of the plant Ch'ang Shan, which is now known to contain antimalarial alkaloids.

During the Middle Ages the development of organic chemistry was delayed by the alchemists' search for a means (the philosophers' stone) of transmuting baser metals into gold. Such investigations led to our earliest systematic knowledge of many metals and inorganic compounds, but fostered no similar knowledge of organic materials. It is of interest that a designation for the element carbon is absent from alchemical symbols. A parallel concern with longevity (the elixir of life), however, gradually fostered the emergence of the iatrochemists of the 16th century, whose principal objective was the preparation of medicines. The investigations of Paracelsus, van Helmont, and others of this era, involving the distillation of herbs, resins, and similar plant materials, led to preliminary knowledge of organic substances and to the accepted early 19th century definition of organic chemistry as the chemistry of those substances derived from plant and animal sources. Chemists of this period believed that a "vital force" in nature was essential for the formation of organic compounds. This belief was not unreasonable, since a variety of individual organic compounds had been prepared from a number of animal and vegetable sources, but never, as of that time, from inorganic precursors. Examples of such natural products included malic acid from apples, tartaric acid from grapes, oxalic acid from wood sorrel, gallic acid from gallnuts, and glycerol and "fatty acids" from oils and fats of vegetable and animal origin. The vital force theory was shown to be untenable in 1828 when the German chemist Friedrich Wöhler showed that ammonium cyanate, a representative inorganic substance, could be converted by heat into urea, an organic compound isolable from urine. This and subsequent similar discoveries led to the gradual abandonment of the vital force theory by the mid-19th century.

A major advance in organic chemistry came about during the late 18th century from the research of the French chemist Antoine Lavoisier, who discovered that combustion consists of the chemical combination of a combustible substance with oxygen of the air, that the combustion of organic compounds invariably produces carbon dioxide and water, and that such compounds must therefore contain carbon and hydrogen. Later investigators showed that organic compounds also frequently contain oxygen, nitrogen, and sulfur, and less commonly a few other elements. By 1848 the currently accepted definition of organic chemistry as "the chemistry of carbon-containing compounds" had been established. Because of their properties and also for historical reasons, however, a few carbon-containing compounds are not included among organic substances. Inorganic substances such as carbon dioxide, potassium cyanide, and sodium carbonate are much less numerous and cause no difficulty with regard to the above definition.

Today we recognize five major divisions of chemistry: analytical chemistry, biochemistry, inorganic chemistry, organic chemistry, and physical chemistry. The demarcations between these divisions are by no means sharp, however, and such specialties as isotope chemistry, surface chemistry, and electrochemistry cut quite generally across two or more of the five fields. Furthermore, the broad field of chemical engineering, which applies chemical reactions, techniques, and theory ultimately to utilitarian objectives, also encompasses each of the arbitrary divisions of chemistry. Organic chemistry thus confronts us today as one of several "basic" chemical disciplines which are highly interrelated and complexly interwoven with one another.

Finally, the student will occasionally encounter the expressions "fundamental" (or "pure") chemistry and "applied" chemistry. It is worthwhile considering briefly the meanings and limitations of these terms. Fundamental studies are those whose objective is simply the discovery of new knowledge, with no concern as to its possible future practical application.

Applied chemistry, on the other hand, has the objective of applying existing chemical knowledge or art for the realization of specific practical objectives. As one might imagine, however, these artificial distinctions often vanish in practice. Thus pure research may turn out to have almost immediate practical application (as in the discovery of penicillin), while the efforts of applied research have often led to new accumulations of basic knowledge (as in the fields of dyestuffs and catalysis).

1-2. The Unique Chemical Character of Carbon

Although the earth's crust, oceans, and atmosphere contain less than 0.1 per cent carbon, making this element only the twelfth most abundant, the number of "known" organic compounds (those whose molecular structure has been established; see Section 2-1) far exceeds that of all known inorganic compounds. The prolific nature of carbon is illustrated by a comparison of the numbers of known hydrides of elements in the first row of the periodic table:

Element	He	Li	Be	B	C	N	O	F
Number of known hydrides	0	1	1	7	over 2300	6	2	1

There are probably more known organic compounds than there are words in the English language (about one million), and thousands of new organic compounds are described each year. Like the population of a large city, the exact number of organic compounds is unknown, nor is there an upper limit on the number theoretically possible. Furthermore, carbon is the key element around which the very process of life itself is built, a role which could be played by probably no other element. What features give carbon this unique status among the hundred-odd elements of the periodic table?

The carbon atom is tetravalent (has four valences), as represented simply in 1-1. For the moment, think of valences as hooks which can attach to the "valence hooks" of other atoms, producing a chemical bond between the atoms. Thus a carbon atom may unite with four monovalent atoms to give the molecule symbolized in 1-2. It may also unite with a second carbon (1-3), a third carbon (1-4), and so on, forming "chains" of carbon

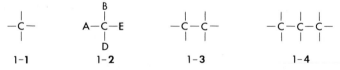

atoms. As will be immediately apparent, not only is it possible for carbon to form chains of any arbitrary length, but also a given number of carbon atoms can be assembled in a variety of ways. Thus, five carbon atoms might be joined in a number of different arrangements, four of which are shown in 1-5. The "unfilled" valences of each carbon atom in 1-3 through

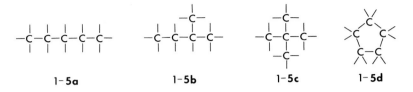

1-5a   1-5b   1-5c   1-5d

1-5 may, of course, unite with the free valences of other atoms such as hydrogen, oxygen, nitrogen, sulfur, or halogen. Bonds to such atoms may in principle be formed at any one or more arbitrary positions in the "straight chain," "branched chain," or "ring" carbon skeletons illustrated. Furthermore, rings such as 1-**5d** may themselves be attached to other rings, giving rise to the possibility of "polycyclic" ring systems. While the above considerations will be developed in more rigorous detail in subsequent chapters, we may now readily appreciate from this brief description the vast structural complexities which are possible among organic molecules. This complexity is well illustrated by consideration of morphine, the most important constituent of opium, whose structure (arrangement of atoms) is shown below. The ability of carbon (not shared to the same extent by any other element) to "combine with itself" in an infinite variety of arrangements is the most basic characteristic making this element unique among all others. The vastness and diversity of organic chemistry are the consequences of this uniqueness.

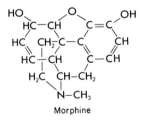

Morphine

1-3. Sources and Transformations of Organic Compounds

Organic substances are available from two sources, either directly from naturally occurring raw materials or through preparation from other substances (synthesis). Natural sources of organic raw materials are of great variety, and may be either living or nonliving. Several examples of organic compounds from living sources have been cited in Section 1-1. Other examples include quinine from the bark of the cinchona tree, penicillin from the mold *Penicillium chrysogenum*, cholesterol from gallstones, and squalene from shark liver oil, to mention but a few of importance. Petroleum (including natural gas) and coal, which represent the residue of life which existed on earth millions of years in the past, constitute the important nonliving sources of organic compounds. The extensive heating (coking) of coal affords coal tar, from which literally hundreds of such commercially important organic substances as benzene, naphthalene, and phenol may be obtained. The distillation and "cracking" of crude petroleum likewise provide numerous individual organic compounds, as well as such complex mixtures as gasoline, kerosene, and paraffin. The so-called "bulk" organic chemicals of industry come almost invariably from such natural sources.

The conversion of one organic compound into another by suitable chemical reactions provides another major source of specific organic substances. Such conversions may involve the building up of a desired large molecule by combination of two or more smaller molecules or the degradation (breakdown) of a larger molecule into a desired smaller one. In both instances the conversion is referred to as an "organic synthesis." A large fraction of the known organic compounds have been obtained only synthetically, and are not found among natural sources. The so-called "fine" chemicals of the pharmaceutical and dyestuff industries, for example, are mainly synthetic, as are also many of the fibers used in modern fabrics. Many other important organic chemicals are available both naturally and synthetically, and indeed the two sources occasionally compete economically. The question of whether or not synthetic products are "better" than those from natural sources is usually beside the point. In the case of an individual pure substance there are no differences whatsoever in the physical, chemical, or pharmacological properties between natural and synthetic varieties. Thus the vitamin C from citrus fruit is identical in all respects with that synthesized commercially from the sugar L-sorbose—each, after all, has the same chemical identity. It is true, however, that trace impurities in either the synthetic or natural product may materially alter one or more of its properties. In the case of nonidentical substances, such as natural wool versus synthetic nylon, the superiority of one over the other can be assessed only with regard to a particular property or group of properties being compared.

In practice, both commercial and laboratory syntheses may involve a single transformation (step), two steps, or a series of steps, as illustrated in the following equation:

$$A \rightarrow B \rightarrow C \rightarrow D \rightarrow E \rightarrow \ ----- \ \rightarrow X$$

In this sequence the final product, X, is said to be synthesized from A, and the products B, C, D, and E are referred to as intermediates. A synthesis of cortisone (a drug used to treat inflammations and allergies, rheumatic arthritis, and other diseases) from deoxycholic acid (a normal constituent of human bile) involves the preparation of over thirty intermediates! It is understandable that, in commercial syntheses at least, organic chemists attempt to conserve both time and money by devising syntheses requiring a minimum number of steps.

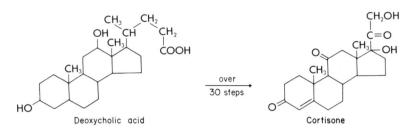

Deoxycholic acid

over
30 steps

Cortisone

SUPPLEMENTARY READING

Vitalism
1. "The Liebig-Pasteur Controversy—Vitality without Vitalism," G. E. Hein, *J. Chem. Educ.*, **38,** 614 (1951).
2. "Wöhler and the Vital Force," L. Hartman, *J. Chem. Educ.*, **34,** 141 (1957).
3. "Wöhler and the Overthrow of Vitalism," E. Campaigne, *J. Chem. Educ.*, **32,** 403 (1955).

CHAPTER 2

Some Basic Principles and Concepts

THERE ARE a number of theoretical principles underlying the subject of organic chemistry, many of which are discussed in subsequent chapters. Here we turn our attention to some of the simpler basic principles and concepts in order that they may be put to immediate use.

2-1. Organic Chemical Formulas

By the term "formula" the chemist means a symbolic expression representing the composition or constitution of a substance. There are several types of formulas which are used by chemists. A formula which merely indicates the *relative number* of different kinds of atoms in a molecule is called an **empirical formula**. Thus the empirical formula of both formaldehyde and glucose is CH_2O, or more properly, $(CH_2O)_n$. A formula which tells the *actual number* of each kind of atom in a molecule (and hence also the molecular weight) is called a **molecular formula**. Thus the molecular formula of formaldehyde is CH_2O (mol. wt. 30), while that of glu-

8

cose is $(CH_2O)_6$, or $C_6H_{12}O_6$ (mol. wt. 180). Empirical and molecular formulas represent the first stage of systematic chemical information about a substance, and the means by which the chemist obtains this important preliminary type of information will be discussed in Chapter 4.

Such formulas, however, clearly tell us nothing about the *arrangement* of the atoms in a molecule, and provide by themselves very little basis for interpreting or predicting chemical behavior. Consider the molecular formulas of some typical naturally occurring substances: quinine, $C_{20}H_{24}O_2N_2$; streptomycin, $C_{21}H_{39}N_7O_{12}$; strychnine, $C_{21}H_{22}O_2N_2$; α-tocopherol (vitamin E), $C_{29}H_{50}O_2$; vitamin B_{12}, $C_{63}H_{90}O_{14}N_{14}PCo$. How do we explain the fact that these substances have widely different chemical, physical, and physiological properties? What, indeed, are the valences of the elements of such compounds? Imagine the impotence of the organic chemist of the early 19th century when he tried to interpret the widely differing behavior of various organic substances in terms of such molecular formulas! The situation is roughly analogous to trying to deduce the rules and tactics of football, knowing only the names and numbers of the players as printed in the program, and never seeing the game.

This was the unsatisfactory state of affairs until 1859, when the German chemist August Kekulé proposed a brilliant but simple **structural theory** which rationalized the maze of existing molecular formulas and provided the cornerstone for the future development of organic chemistry. Kekulé assumed that, regardless of the complexity of the organic molecule, each carbon atom always has the normal valence of four which is apparent in such simple molecular formulas as CH_4, CCl_4, and CO_2. Hydrogen and halogens were assumed to have a valence of one, oxygen and sulfur two, and nitrogen three. Dashes were attached to the symbols of the different elements to indicate graphically the valence of each atom, as shown in Table 2-1. When two atoms were joined together in a molecule, Kekulé used one or more common dashes between their symbols to indicate the utilization of one or more valences in forming a chemical bond between

Table 2-1. Kekulé Valence Notation

Valence			
1	2	3	4
—H	—O— —S—	—Ṇ—	—Ç̧—
—Cl	=O =S	=N—	=C—
—Br		≡N	≡C—

Table 2-2. Kekulé Structures of Some Simple Organic Compounds

Compound	Molecular Formula	Kekulé Structural Formula
Methane	CH_4	$H-\overset{\displaystyle H}{\underset{\displaystyle H}{C}}-H$
Ethane	C_2H_6	$H-\overset{H}{\underset{H}{C}}-\overset{H}{\underset{H}{C}}-H$
Ethylene	C_2H_4	$\overset{H}{\underset{H}{}}C=C\overset{H}{\underset{H}{}}$
Carbon dioxide	CO_2	$O=C=O$
Hydrogen cyanide	HCN	$H-C\equiv N$
Ammonia	NH_3	$H-N\overset{H}{\underset{H}{}}$

the atoms in question. Applying these simple conventions, **structures** of organic molecules could for the first time be pieced together, as illustrated in Table 2-2. By the **structural formula** of a molecule, we mean a Kekulé representation delineating the relative positions and correct valences of all of the atoms in the molecule. The interpretation of the chemical behavior of more complex molecules in terms of Kekulé's conventions has permitted chemists to deduce structural formulas of great complexity indeed. Structural formulas provide the basis for describing and predicting the behavior of all organic compounds, and underlie all theoretical interpretations of organic phenomena. So important is Kekulé's contribution that modern organic chemistry would be literally impossible without it.

To save time and space, organic chemists have adopted a variety of useful shorthand conventions for writing Kekulé structures. Some of these shortcuts, which will become second nature in time, are illustrated by the following equivalent ways of writing the structural formulas of 1-butanol, $C_4H_{10}O$; 1-propylamine, C_3H_9N; and cyclohexanol, $C_6H_{12}O$. Structural formulas of these abbreviated types will be used throughout the remainder

$H-\overset{H}{\underset{H}{C}}-\overset{H}{\underset{H}{C}}-\overset{H}{\underset{H}{C}}-\overset{H}{\underset{H}{C}}-O-H$ $CH_3-CH_2-CH_2-CH_2-OH$ $CH_3CH_2CH_2CH_2OH$ $CH_3(CH_2)_3OH$

1 – Butanol

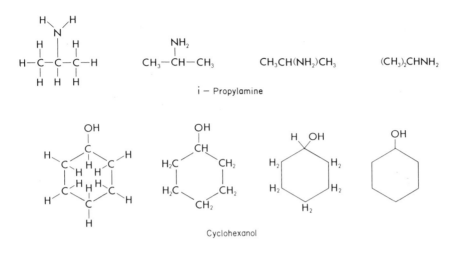

i – Propylamine

Cyclohexanol

of this text. Note the increasing abbreviation in going from left to right in each of the examples.

2-2. The Chemical Bond

As mentioned above, the dashes connecting atoms in a Kekulé structural formula represent chemical bonds between these atoms. Let us now examine briefly the interpretation of chemical bonds in terms of present-day terminology. According to modern theory, the atom consists of a nucleus containing positively charged protons (p) and uncharged neutrons (n), surrounded by a "cloud" of negatively charged electrons (e) equal in number to the protons in the nucleus. The electrons occupy "shells" surrounding the nucleus, the first (K shell) capable of containing 2 electrons, the second (L shell) 8 electrons, and the third (M shell) 18 electrons. The electrons are essentially "weightless" (0.05 per cent of the mass of the proton or neutron), and the bulk mass of the atom therefore resides in its nucleus. Figure 2-1 shows the constituents of the atoms of the principal isotopes of the first eighteen elements in the periodic table. Atoms whose outer electron shells are filled (the noble gases: He, Ne, Ar, etc.) are generally chemically inert, although a few compounds of such elements are known. Examples include krypton tetrafluoride, xenon di- and tetra-fluorides, and radon fluoride. Atoms with incompletely filled electron shells, on the other hand, are chemically reactive and will form bonds to other atoms by processes which involve the transfer of electrons to and from their outer electron shells. There are two main processes of this sort: *electron transfer*, leading to **ionic bonds**, and *electron sharing*, leading to **covalent bonds.**

I	II	III	IV	V	VI	VII	VIII
$_1H^1$ 1, 0, 0							$_2He^4$ 2, 0, 0
$_3Li^7$ 2, 1, 0	$_4Be^9$ 2, 2, 0	$_5B^{11}$ 2, 3, 0	$_6C^{12}$ 2, 4, 0	$_7N^{14}$ 2, 5, 0	$_8O^{16}$ 2, 6, 0	$_9F^{19}$ 2, 7, 0	$_{10}Ne^{20}$ 2, 8, 0
$_{11}Na^{23}$ 2, 8, 1	$_{12}Mg^{24}$ 2, 8, 2	$_{13}Al^{27}$ 2, 8, 3	$_{14}Si^{28}$ 2, 8, 4	$_{15}P^{31}$ 2, 8, 5	$_{16}S^{32}$ 2, 8, 6	$_{17}Cl^{35}$ 2, 8, 7	$_{18}Ar^{40}$ 2, 8, 8

Subscript = atomic number; number of protons in nucleus; positive charge on nucleus
Superscript = mass number of principal isotope of element
Difference between superscript and subscript = number of neutrons in nucleus
Three numerals = number of electrons in K, L, and M shells, respectively

Figure 2-1. Partial Periodic Table of the Elements

a. Ionic Bonds. Ionic bonds form between elements at opposite sides of the periodic table (group I or II with group VI or VII). An example of electron transfer forming an ionic bond is shown in Figure 2-2, which illustrates the hypothetical formation of the salt lithium fluoride from its elements. The lithium atom donates its one L-shell electron, becoming lithium ion, $Li^\oplus$, which is electronically equivalent to (**isoelectronic** with) helium. Fluorine accepts the electron into the lone vacancy in its L shell, becoming fluoride ion, $F^\ominus$, which is isoelectronic with neon. The energy required to remove the outer electron from lithium is more than compensated by that liberated when fluorine completes its outer shell. There is therefore a net liberation of energy during the electron transfer, and an ionic bond results. The actual "bond" in such salts is the electrostatic attraction between the positively charged cation and the negatively charged anion.

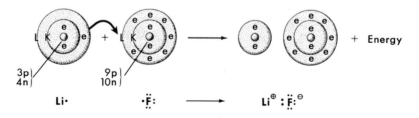

Figure 2-2. Hypothetical Formation of Lithium Fluoride

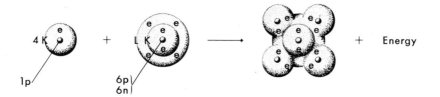

Figure 2-3. Hypothetical Formation of Methane

b. Covalent Bonds. Bond formation involving elements toward the middle of the periodic table occurs by the process of electron sharing. The resulting bond is called a covalent bond. Again, each atom involved achieves the electronic shell structure of its nearest noble gas neighbor, and energy is again liberated in the process. Covalent bond formation between one carbon and four hydrogen atoms during the hypothetical formation of methane, CH_4, is shown in Figure 2-3. Note that the carbon atom in methane has attained the electronic structure of neon, while each hydrogen atom becomes isoelectronic with helium. An equivalent representation of methane formation is shown in the first equation below, where each dot in the symbols represents an outer shell valence electron. The remaining equations in similar notation illustrate the hypothetical formation of carbon tetrachloride, CCl_4; water, H_2O; molecular chlorine, Cl_2; and carbon dioxide, CO_2, from their elements. Such "electron dot" for-

$$4 \, H\cdot \; + \; \cdot\overset{\cdot}{\underset{\cdot}{C}}\cdot \; \longrightarrow \; H\!:\!\overset{H}{\underset{H}{C}}\!:\!H \; \equiv \; H\!-\!\overset{\displaystyle H}{\underset{\displaystyle H}{\overset{|}{\underset{|}{C}}}}\!-\!H$$

Methane

$$\cdot\overset{\cdot}{\underset{\cdot}{C}}\cdot \; + \; 4\cdot\overset{\cdot\cdot}{\underset{\cdot\cdot}{C}}l\!: \; \longrightarrow \; :\!\overset{\cdot\cdot}{\underset{\cdot\cdot}{C}}l\!:\!\overset{:\overset{\cdot\cdot}{C}l:}{\underset{:\overset{\cdot\cdot}{C}l:}{C}}\!:\!\overset{\cdot\cdot}{\underset{\cdot\cdot}{C}}l\!: \; \equiv \; Cl\!-\!\overset{\displaystyle Cl}{\underset{\displaystyle Cl}{\overset{|}{\underset{|}{C}}}}\!-\!Cl$$

Carbon tetrachloride

$$2 \, H\cdot \; + \; \cdot\overset{\cdot\cdot}{\underset{\cdot\cdot}{O}}\cdot \; \longrightarrow \; H\!:\!\overset{\cdot\cdot}{\underset{\cdot\cdot}{O}}\!:\!H \; \equiv \; H\!-\!O\!-\!H$$

Water

$$:\!\overset{\cdot\cdot}{\underset{\cdot\cdot}{C}}l\cdot \; + \; \cdot\overset{\cdot\cdot}{\underset{\cdot\cdot}{C}}l\!: \; \longrightarrow \; :\!\overset{\cdot\cdot}{\underset{\cdot\cdot}{C}}l\!:\!\overset{\cdot\cdot}{\underset{\cdot\cdot}{C}}l\!: \; \equiv \; Cl\!-\!Cl$$

Chlorine

$$2 \, \overset{\cdot\cdot}{\underset{\cdot\cdot}{O}}\!: \; + \; :\!C\!: \; \longrightarrow \; \overset{\cdot\cdot}{\underset{\cdot\cdot}{O}}\!:\!:\!C\!:\!:\!\overset{\cdot\cdot}{\underset{\cdot\cdot}{O}} \; \equiv \; O\!=\!C\!=\!O$$

Carbon dioxide

mulas depicting molecules with covalently bonded atoms were first proposed by Lewis and Langmuir in 1919, and are now in quite common
usage for illustrating the positions of shared and unshared electron pairs in
molecules. Note that in the final covalent structures each atom has a completed octet of electrons (eight dots) around it, save hydrogen, which has
two electrons. We see that a dash between two atoms in a Kekulé structural formula represents a covalent bond formed by a pair of shared electrons, and is depicted by a pair of "electron dots" in Lewis-Langmuir
terminology. A more sophisticated account of covalent bonding is reserved
for Chapter 5.

  c. Coordinate Covalent Bonds.   In the normal covalent bond discussed
above, each atom contributed one electron to the shared pair forming the
bond between them. An alternative way for two atoms to bond covalently
is for one of the atoms to furnish *both* electrons for the bond, and for the
other atom to accept both, each atom again thereby completing its octet.
The bond resulting from such a donor-acceptor process is called a **dative**,
coordinate covalent, or **semipolar** bond. The process may be illustrated
by considering the reaction of ammonia with boron fluoride. Since nitro-

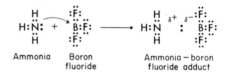

| Ammonia | Boron fluoride | Ammonia–boron fluoride adduct |

gen donated both of its electrons to the bond, it must acquire a partial
positive charge (symbolized by δ^+) in the final product. Since the boron
atom accepted *both* electrons, it acquires a partial negative charge (δ^-) in the
adduct. Dative bonds, sometimes written as short arrows, for example,
$H_3N{\rightarrow}BF_3$, clearly have associated with them both ionic and covalent
character; that is, the strength of the bond originates both from forces of
electrostatic attraction and from electron sharing.

  d. Ionic Character of Bonds.   When two *unlike* atoms share an electron
pair, the resulting bond between them is not actually the "pure" covalent
type idealized on page 13. It is characterized, rather, by a varying degree of
ionic character; that is—as with dative bonds—it is actually partially
ionic. To understand this, consider the C–F bond in methyl fluoride, CH_3F,
and the effect of the nuclear charges of the carbon and fluorine atoms on
its shared pair of electrons. As illustrated below, the nine positively

$$\left.\begin{matrix}6p\\6n\end{matrix}\right\{\ \ H{:}\overset{\overset{\delta^+ H}{\ \ }}{\underset{H}{C}}\ :\ \overset{\delta^-}{\underset{\cdot\cdot}{\overset{\cdot\cdot}{F}}}{:}\ \left\}\begin{matrix}9p\\10n\end{matrix}\right.$$

charged protons of the fluorine will attract the negatively charged pair of bonding electrons more strongly along the bond axis than will the mere six protons of the carbon nucleus, resulting in a displacement of the pair toward the fluorine nucleus. This great **electronegativity** (total attraction of the atomic nucleus for electrons) of fluorine results in an electrical charge separation along the bond, and a corresponding amount of ionic character in the bond. Such a bond is called a **partially ionic** bond, and the charge separation is said to constitute an **electric dipole**—again designated by the partial charge symbols, δ^+ and δ^-. Note that the negative end of the dipole lies toward the more electronegative atom (fluorine). Since nuclear charges (and hence electronegativities) of different atoms vary, all covalent bonds between *unlike* atoms will be partially ionic. The greater the difference in the electronegativities of the two bonded atoms, the greater will be the amount of ionic character in a given covalent bond. Electronegativities increase across each horizontal row of the periodic table from metallic to nonmetallic elements (that is, from left to right in a horizontal column, from bottom to top in a vertical column).

Semipolar bonds of the above types have associated with them characteristic **dipole moments**. When placed in an electric field, molecules containing semipolar bonds tend to align themselves in the direction of the electric field (Figure 2-4). The torque tending to align the molecule parallel to the field is the product of the dipole moment (μ) times the electric field strength (E). Numerically, the dipole moment is the product of the magnitude of the negative electric charge (δ^-) times the average distance between the positive and negative charges in the semipolar bond. Dipole moments may be determined experimentally by several methods, and their magnitudes provide insight into the relative electronegativities of atoms and the extent of ionic contributions to semipolar covalent bonds.

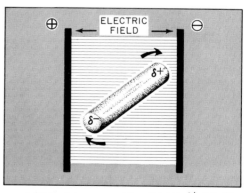

Figure 2-4. Schematic Representation of Dipole Moment

$\mu = \delta^-$ X distance separating charges, δ^+ and δ^-

e. *Multiple Bonds.* When two atoms mutually share more than one pair of electrons, the resulting covalent bond is said to be multiple. If two pairs of electrons are shared, we have a **double bond** between the atoms; if three pairs, a **triple bond**. Electron dot and Kekulé formulas for typical double- and triple-bonded structures are shown below. Note that each

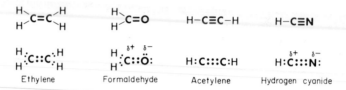

| Ethylene | Formaldehyde | Acetylene | Hydrogen cyanide |

atom in the molecule (save hydrogen) has its completed octet of electrons and that when the two multiply bonded atoms are different, the bond is again semipolar, with the negative end of the dipole toward the most electronegative atom.

2-3. Comparison of Organic and Inorganic Compounds

There are a number of striking differences in properties between most organic compounds and most inorganic compounds. These differences arise from the fact that the majority of inorganic substances are salts— for example, sodium chloride (table salt)—while organic compounds are usually nonsalts—for example, sucrose (table sugar). Some of the outstanding contrasts between these two classes of compounds are listed in Table 2-3. It should be emphasized that these statements are generalizations, and the student will immediately think of numerous exceptions to them. They are nevertheless valid for the majority of compounds in each class.

Table 2-3.   Contrasts in Properties

Property	Most Inorganic Compounds (Salts)	Most Organic Compounds (Nonsalts)
Physical state	Solid	Solid, liquid, gas
Combustibility	Do not burn	Usually burn in air
Melting point	Very high	Low (below 250°)
Boiling point	Nonvolatile	Low (below 300°)
Solubility in water	Soluble	Insoluble
Solubility in organic solvents	Insoluble	Soluble
Electrical conductivity	Conducting when melted or dissolved in water	Nonconducting

With the exception of combustibility, the differences in properties listed in Table 2-3 are explainable in terms of the differences in types of bonding in the two classes of substances. Generally speaking, the atoms of inorganic compounds are linked by ionic bonds, while organic compounds are co-valently bonded. The ability of oppositely charged ions of inorganic salts to conduct an electric current, in contrast to the inability of uncharged covalent molecules, is understandable. As regards solubility, those in-organic salts which are soluble in water dissolve with ionization. In the process the ions are *hydrated* by water molecules and energy is released:

$$M^{\oplus}X^{\ominus} + (x+y)H_2O \longrightarrow M^{\oplus}\cdot(H_2O)_x + X^{\ominus}(H_2O)_y + Energy$$

Salt crystal   Hydrated ions

Covalent molecules do not ionize in water and hydrate only negligibly, if at all, and are therefore water insoluble. The solid physical state, high melting point, and low volatility of inorganic compounds, furthermore, result from their highly stable crystal lattices, which arise through the strong electrostatic attractions of the cations and anions of ionic salts. The weaker forces of attraction between the molecules of covalent com-pounds, on the other hand, lead to less stable crystal lattices, lower melting points, and higher volatilities. What are these intermolecular forces of attraction (association) operating between covalent molecules? They are called **van der Waals forces** and are of two types: **permanent dipole attractions** and **induced dipole attractions**. Permanent dipole attractions exist between semipolar covalent molecules and arise as a result of the attraction between the positive and negative ends of the permanent dipoles in the semipolar bonds of adjacent molecules, as typified with methyl fluoride in Figure 2-5. Induced dipole attractions arise when two nonpolar

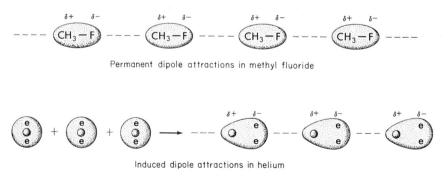

Permanent dipole attractions in methyl fluoride

Induced dipole attractions in helium

Figure 2-5. Van der Waals Forces between Covalent Molecules

molecules come close to one another. The outer electrons of one molecule or atom repel those of an adjacent molecule or atom, inducing a charge separation (**polarization**). The resulting dipoles in turn induce similar polarization of more nearby molecules, and the electrically opposite ends of the induced dipoles attract one another exactly as do permanent dipoles. Induced dipole attractions are illustrated schematically with the helium atom in Figure 2-5. It is understandable that van der Waals forces of inter-molecular attraction in organic solids made up of covalent molecules should be much weaker than the full electrostatic attractions between the ions of inorganic salt crystals.

2-4. Principal Series of Organic Compounds

The million or so known organic compounds can be divided into two major groups: the **acyclic series** and the **cyclic series**. As indicated in the names, the first group contains compounds whose molecular structures are noncyclic or open chained, while the cyclic series includes compounds which contain one or more rings of atoms in their structures. There are numerous examples, of course, of compounds having structural features common to both series. Cyclic compounds are further subdivided into the **carbocyclic** and the **heterocyclic series**. The former group contains rings made up only of carbon atoms, while heterocyclic compounds have rings containing one or more noncarbon (hetero) atoms as well. Cyclic com-

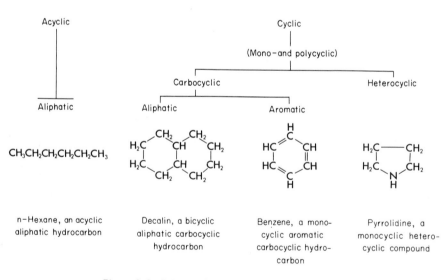

Figure 2-6. *Principal Series of Organic Compounds*

pounds may be further classified as **monocyclic, bicyclic, tricyclic,** etc., depending on how many individual carbocyclic or heterocyclic rings the molecules contain. Carbocyclic compounds containing benzene rings (Figure 2-6) are said to belong to the **aromatic series,** while acyclic as well as nonaromatic carbocyclic compounds belong to the **aliphatic series.** These relationships and some typical examples are shown in Figure 2-6. Note that compounds containing only carbon and hydrogens are called **hydrocarbons.**

2-5. Functional Groups

One of the most important concepts in organic chemistry is that of the functional group. A functional group is an atom or an aggregate of atoms in a molecule whose presence confers upon the molecule, whatever the remainder of its structure may be, a unique chemical behavior characteristic of the functional group. To illustrate, consider the three compounds A, B, and C in Figure 2-7. Each contains the formyl group, —CH=O, characteristic of aldehydes. These three compounds show similar chemical behavior. For example, the formyl group of each may be *reduced*, (H), to yield representative members of another class of compounds called alcohols, all of which contain —OH as their functional group. Similarly, each aldehyde may be *oxidized*, (O), to a corresponding carboxylic acid containing the —COOH function. Finally, each aldehyde will react with hydrox-

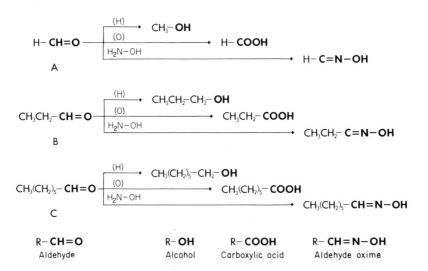

Figure 2-7. Examples of Functional Group Behavior

ylamine, $H_2N—OH$, to produce members of a class of compounds called oximes, whose functional group is $—CH=N—OH$. It is apparent at once that each of the above chemical transformations is quite independent of the particular group attached to the $—CH=O$ function. We see, in other words, that the common chemical characteristics shared by aldehydes are due to the behavior of the formyl group, and not to the remainder of the molecule. In the same way alcohols, carboxylic acids, and oximes each show their own unique chemical properties, determined in each case only by the characteristic behavior of the specific functional groups, $—OH$, $—COOH$, and $—CH=N—OH$, respectively. The distinctive chemical behavior of different functional groups thus gives rise to *classes* of organic compounds. Members of each class share common chemical properties which are determined by their common functional group and which differ from the properties characteristic of other classes.

Since chemical behavior of classes is essentially independent of the

Table 2-4. Some Functional Groups and Their Corresponding Classes of Compounds

FUNCTIONAL GROUP		CLASS	
Structure	Name	General Formula	Name
$-OH$	Hydroxyl	$R-OH$	Alcohol
$-NH_2$	Amino	$R-NH_2$	Amine
$-OR$	Alkoxyl	$R-OR$	Ether
$-X^a$	Halo	$R-X$	Alkyl halide
$-CH=CH-$	Alkene	$RCH=CHR$	Alkene, olefin
$-C\equiv C-$	Alkyne	$R-C\equiv C-R$	Alkyne, acetylene
$-CH=O$	Formyl	$R-CH=O$	Aldehyde
$-\overset{\parallel}{\underset{O}{C}}-$	Carbonyl	$R-\overset{\parallel}{\underset{O}{C}}-R$	Ketone
$-C\overset{\nearrow OH}{\searrow O}$	Carboxyl	$R-C\overset{\nearrow OH}{\searrow O}$	Carboxylic acid
$-C\overset{\nearrow OR}{\searrow O}$	Alkoxycarbonyl	$R-C\overset{\nearrow OR}{\searrow O}$	Ester
$-C\overset{\nearrow NH_2}{\searrow O}$	Carboxamide	$R-C\overset{\nearrow NH_2}{\searrow O}$	Amide
$>C=N-$	Imino	$R_2C=N-R$	Imine
$-C\equiv N$	Cyano	$R-C\equiv N$	Nitrile
$-N\overset{\nearrow O}{\searrow O}$	Nitro	$R-NO_2$	Nitroalkane

[a] X designates Cl, Br, or I (chloro, bromo, or iodo) functions; the corresponding classes of compounds are alkyl chlorides, bromides, and iodides. The designation X does not include F, since the properties of alkyl fluorides, R—F, are frequently different from those of other alkyl halides.

carbon skeleton attached to a functional group, it is often convenient to depict various classes of compounds in general terms. In the aliphatic series, the symbol R is used to designate an **alkyl group**, which is obtained by removal of one hydrogen atom from the formula of an aliphatic hydrocarbon. In the aromatic series, Ar designates an **aryl group** obtained by removing a hydrogen from the formula of an aromatic hydrocarbon. Thus in the aliphatic series, aldehydes, alcohols, carboxylic acids, and oximes may be generalized as $R—CH=O$, $R—OH$, $R—COOH$, and $R—CH=N—OH$, respectively, while in the aromatic series these classes are designated as $Ar—CH=O$, $Ar—OH$, $Ar—COOH$, and $Ar—CH=N—OH$. It should be emphasized that in certain specific cases the properties of the individual functional groups may be modified to a certain extent by the nature of the R or Ar group to which they are attached, and in some cases these effects may be considerable. Table 2-4 shows the structures of the more important functional groups and the classes of compounds corresponding to them.

2-6. Homologous Series

A homologous series is a group of compounds wherein the only formal difference among individual members is the number of methylene, CH_2, groups which they contain. Figure 2-8 shows the structures of the first several members of three homologous series: normal (straight-chain) alkanes, alkyl chlorides, and carboxylic acids.

Alkanes	Alkyl Chlorides	Carboxylic Acids
$C_n H_{2n+2}$	$C_n H_{2n+1}—Cl$	$C_n H_{2n+1}—COOH$
CH_4	$CH_3—Cl$	$H—COOH$
$CH_3 CH_3$	$CH_3 CH_2—Cl$	$CH_3—COOH$
$CH_3 CH_2 CH_3$	$CH_3 CH_2 CH_2—Cl$	$CH_3 CH_2—COOH$
$CH_3 CH_2 CH_2 CH_3$	$CH_3 CH_2 CH_2 CH_2—Cl$	$CH_3 CH_2 CH_2—COOH$
• • •	• • •	• • •
$CH_3(CH_2)_n CH_3$	$CH_3(CH_2)_n—Cl$	$CH_3(CH_2)_n—COOH$
RH	R—Cl	R—COOH

Figure 2-8.   Examples of Homologous Series

The molecular formulas of adjacent members in each homologous series are seen to differ by only a CH_2 group, and the members of such series are called **homologs**. Note how the molecular formula for each series may be expressed algebraically. Homologous series may be written for each of the classes of compounds having different functional groups in Table 2-4, and it is evident that members of a given homologous series must have similar chemical properties. Physical properties, however, vary from one homolog to another in any such series.

2-7. Isomerism

When two or more compounds have *identical molecular formulas but different structural formulas*, the compounds are said to be **isomers** of each other, and the phenomenon of their coexistence is referred to as **isomerism**. Isomers are readily distinguishable from each other since, being distinct chemical individuals they have different chemical and/or physical properties. Several types of isomerism are recognized, depending upon the type of molecular structural difference giving rise to the isomers.

a. Skeletal Isomerism. This type of isomerism arises as a result of the different permissible sequences of carbon atoms which may make up a Kekulé structure, as illustrated in the structural formulas of three isomeric C_5 hydrocarbons, the pentanes. Note that the only structural differences

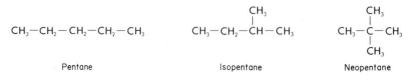

$CH_3-CH_2-CH_2-CH_2-CH_3$	$CH_3-CH_2-CH-CH_3$	CH_3-C-CH_3
Pentane	Isopentane	Neopentane

in these isomers are the arrangements of the carbon skeletons. The structures of the cyclic pentane isomers also show differences in skeletal arrangement. We note, however, that—although they are also pentanes (C_5 hydrocarbons)—the cyclic group is not isomeric with the acyclic. The

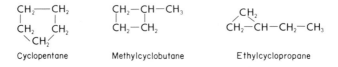

Cyclopentane	Methylcyclobutane	Ethylcyclopropane

molecular formula of the acyclic pentane isomers is C_5H_{12}, whereas that of the cyclic isomers is C_5H_{10}. Among open-chain compounds, skeletal isomerism is sometimes referred to as **chain isomerism**.

As the number of carbon atoms in a molecule increases, the number of possible isomers increases astronomically. Table 2-5, for example, shows the theoretical number of skeletal isomers possible for aliphatic hydrocarbons of increasing carbon contents. Only through the nonanes, C_9H_{20}, have all of the theoretically possible isomers actually been prepared. In no cases ever have more isomers been found than the number predicted on the basis of Kekulé's structural theory.

Table 2-5.   Isomers of Aliphatic Hydrocarbons

Number of Carbon Atoms	Molecular Formula	Theoretical Number of Isomers
4	C_4H_{10}	2
5	C_5H_{12}	3
6	C_6H_{14}	5
7	C_7H_{16}	9
8	C_8H_{18}	18
9	C_9H_{20}	35
10	$C_{10}H_{22}$	75
20	$C_{20}H_{42}$	366, 319
30	$C_{30}H_{62}$	4, 111, 846, 763
40	$C_{40}H_{82}$	6.25×10^{13}

b. Positional Isomerism.   This type results from the possibility of attaching functional groups at structurally nonequivalent positions on a carbon skeleton. Suppose we replace one of the hydrogen atoms of the hydrocarbon butane, $CH_3CH_2CH_2CH_3$, with a hydroxyl group. Numbering the carbons in the butane chain and performing this replacement at the end carbon (C1), we obtain an alcohol called 1-butanol. If we replace a hydrogen at C2 with —OH, we get the isomeric alcohol 2-butanol, which differs in the *position* of its hydroxyl group. Notice that if we perform the replacement at C3, however, we do not obtain a third isomer. The two representations shown for 2-butanol are structurally identical, as can be seen by rotating either structure horizontally through 180°.

$$\overset{4}{C}H_3-\overset{3}{C}H_2-\overset{2}{C}H_2-\overset{1}{C}H_2-OH$$

1 – Butanol

$$CH_3-CH_2-\underset{\underset{OH}{|}}{CH}-CH_3$$

2 – Butanol

$$CH_3-\underset{\underset{OH}{|}}{CH}-CH_2-CH_3$$

2 – Butanol

c. Functional Isomerism.   This type arises in certain cases of molecules having different functional groups. Ethyl alcohol contains the hydroxyl group, for example, while methyl ether has the methoxy group, —OCH_3.

The two compounds are isomeric because of their common molecular formula, C_2H_6O. Similarly, acetone and propionaldehyde are functional isomers, as are acetic acid and methyl formate.

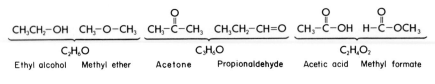

CH₃CH₂–OH	CH₃–O–CH₃	CH₃–C–CH₃	CH₃CH₂–CH=O	CH₃–C–OH	H–C–OCH₃

$$C_2H_6O \qquad\qquad C_3H_6O \qquad\qquad C_2H_4O_2$$

Ethyl alcohol   Methyl ether   Acetone   Propionaldehyde   Acetic acid   Methyl formate

2-8. Stereoisomerism and Stereochemistry

The structural formulas which we have drawn so far have been flat and two dimensional. Like any form of matter, however, molecules are three dimensional, and some aspects of their behavior can be understood only by taking this into account. Isomers which differ in their three-dimensional structures are called **stereoisomers** or **stereomers**. **Stereochemistry** is that segment of chemistry concerned with the three-dimensional aspect of molecular structure and its effect on chemical behavior. Stereochemical representations, therefore, must be rendered as perspective drawings or as three-dimensional models.

a. The Tetrahedral Carbon. On the basis of evidence to be discussed in Chapter 15, J. H. van't Hoff and J. A. LeBel proposed independently in 1874 that the carbon atom must be *tetrahedral;* that is, the four bonds of carbon must be directed toward the four corners of an imaginary tetrahedron encompassing it. This is illustrated in Figure 2-9, where the Kekulé formula (*A*) for methane is contrasted with tetrahedral representations (*B* and *C*). In *C* the heavy line projects out from the paper, the dotted line projects behind the paper, and the two solid lines are in the plane of the paper. Modern investigations of organic compounds by electron diffraction techniques have confirmed the tetrahedral three-dimensional structure of the carbon atom, and have shown that the **bond angle** between any two atoms attached to carbon is close to 109°28′, the regular tetrahedral angle.

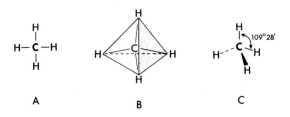

A   B   C

Figure 2-9. Flat and Tetrahedral Representations of Methane

b. Bond Angles and Bond Lengths. Just as with carbon, the covalent bonds associated with other elements are spatially oriented in characteristic ways. Thus any molecule which has a sequence of three atoms in it will have a particular **bond angle** associated with the central atom in the sequence. Figure 2-10 shows some typical bond angles observed in several covalent compounds. Bond angles are not completely invariant, but may undergo slight deformations (up to $10°$ or so) as the spatial requirements of the substituents on the central atom vary. Note in Figure 2-10, for example, the $6°$ difference in the oxygen bond angles of water and methyl ether, CH_3—O—CH_3, whose CH_3 groups are bulkier than the smaller H atoms of water.

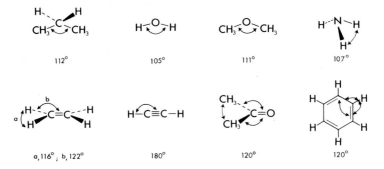

Figure 2-10. Typical Bond Angles in Some Covalent Molecules

The distance between the nuclei of two bonded atoms is called the **bond length** or **bond distance**. These distances depend not only upon the atoms themselves, but also upon the functional groups in which the atoms partake. Thus the carbon-carbon bond lengths vary (Table 2-6) depending on whether we have singly, doubly, or triply bonded structures, as do also the carbon-oxygen and carbon-nitrogen bond lengths. Note that the bond distances become progressively shorter in multiply bonded systems. For example, the carbon to carbon double and triple bond distances prove to be roughly 87 and 78 per cent, respectively, of the carbon to carbon single bond distance. Since the energy required to stretch or compress a bond is higher than that required to bend bonds, bond lengths typically show less variation from their usual values than do bond angles. Bond lengths and bond angles prove to be important for understanding and interpreting the behavior of organic compounds stereochemically. Each can be measured with high accuracy by electron diffraction and spectroscopic techniques.

Table 2-6. Some Covalent Bond Lengths

Bond	Typical Compound	Bond Length, Å
C to C	CH_3-CH_3	1.54
	$CH_2=CH_2$	1.33
	Benzene	1.39
	$HC\equiv CH$	1.20
C to O	CH_3-OH	1.43
	$(CH_3)_2C=O$	1.22
C to N	CH_3-NH_2	1.47
	$CH_3CH=NOH$	1.29
	$CH_3C\equiv N$	1.16
C to H	CH_3CH_2-H	1.07
O to H	CH_3O-H	0.96

c. Molecular Models. For examining the three-dimensional features of molecules, molecular models are usually more revealing than perspective drawings. Three types of molecular models widely used by organic chemists for stereochemical visualization are shown in Figure 2-11, where each model shows the methane molecule. *A* is a **ball-and-stick** model; *B* is a plastic **Dreiding** model, which is built to scale to show relative interatomic distances; and *C* is a **Hirschfelder** model, which is scaled to show the relative size of each atom (van der Waals radius) as determined by X-ray and electron-diffraction measurements. Each type of model has its own utility for particular stereochemical problems, and we shall refer to them, or their perspective equivalents, frequently.

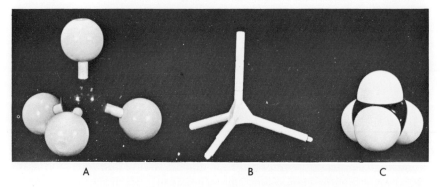

A   B   C

Figure 2-11. Types of Molecular Models

d. Optical Isomerism. Certain very important conclusions arise from the tetrahedral nature of carbon. In the first place, Kekulé structures such as 2-**1a** and 2-**1b** below, having three different groups (H, A, and B) attached to carbon, do not represent position isomers. This is immediately obvious in perspective (2-**1c** and 2-**1d**), where it is seen that the two structures are identical except for their orientation in space; 2-**1c** may be *superimposed* on 2-**1d** if it is merely rotated through 120° around the axis of its

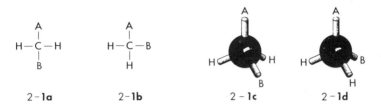

2-**1a** 2-**1b** 2-**1c** 2-**1d**

C–A bond, whereupon the positions of all atoms in each structure are seen to be the same. If there are *four different* groups attached to a carbon atom, however, the situation is different. We see that such a structure (2-**2a**) has a mirror image structure (2-**2b**) which is *not superimposable* on it; that is, there is no way that structure 2-**2b** can be rotated in space such that it can be superimposed on 2-**2a**. In this respect structures 2-**2a** and 2-**2b** are similar to right and left hands. Such nonsuperimposable, mirror-image structures are called **enantiomers**. Whenever a carbon atom has four dif-

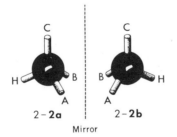

2-**2a**   2-**2b**

Mirror

ferent groups or atoms attached to it, two enantiomeric structures are possible and therefore two stereoisomers will exist. For reasons to be discussed in Chapter 15, each enantiomer shows the phenomenon of **optical activity** (rotation of the plane of polarization of polarized light), and such enantiomers are therefore also referred to as **optical isomers**. As we shall see, one enantiomer rotates the plane of polarization of polarized light to the right, and the other enantiomer rotates the plane equally to the left.

An equimolar mixture of two enantiomers is called a **racemic mixture** or a **racemate**. Racemates are **optically inactive**, since the optical activity due to one enantiomer is exactly canceled by that of the other enantio-

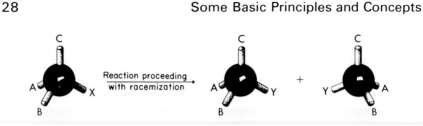

Figure 2-12. Reaction Proceeding with Racemization

mer. A chemical reaction which involves the conversion of an optically active compound into an optically inactive racemic product is said to proceed with complete **racemization,** as typified in Figure 2-12.

A carbon atom bearing four *different* substituents is called an **asymmetric carbon,** and is often designated by an asterisk, as shown in 2-**3.**

2-**3**

Molecules containing asymmetric carbon atoms may thus exist as enantiomers, but molecules with fewer than four different substituents on the carbon atom ordinarily may not. The student should convince himself that the mirror image of a structure such as 2-**1c** is superimposable on structure 2-**1d,** and that enantiomerism is therefore impossible in such structures.

e. Geometric Isomerism. We have seen some of the experimentally determined geometric aspects of carbon-carbon double bonds in Table 2-6 and Figure 2-10. In accord with such data, the stereochemical features of a hydrocarbon such as 2-butene, CH_3—CH=CH—CH_3, can be represented by the molecular models shown in Figure 2-13 and by the perspective drawings 2-**4a** and 2-**4b.** Notice that there are two ways in which the CH_3 groups can be attached to the doubly bonded carbons—either on the same side of the plane of the double bond (equivalent in 2-**4a** and 2-**4b** to the plane of the paper), or on opposite sides. Now, a very important feature of double bonds is their rigidity or *lack of free rotation.* Thus structure 2-**4a** cannot be converted into 2-**4b** by rotating one carbon atom through 180°

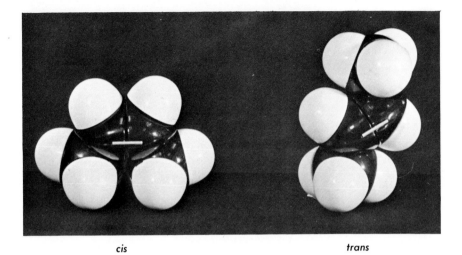

cis   trans

Figure 2-13. Molecular Models of cis-*2-Butene and* trans-*2-Butene*

with respect to the other. The situation is analogous to the boards shown nailed together in Figure 2-14. The doubly nailed structures are not interconvertible by rotation, whereas the singly nailed boards can be rotated with respect to one another. Thus structures 2-**4a** and 2-**4b** represent two stereoisomers, in that they are two distinct structures which vary in their nonequivalent and noninterconvertible spatial arrangements. Such stereoisomers are called **geometric** or **cis-trans** isomers, 2-**4a** being the *cis* (Latin, on this side) isomer and 2-**4b** the *trans* (Latin, across) isomer. Although made possible by restricted rotation about the double bond, geometric isomerism is found only when the two substituents on each doubly

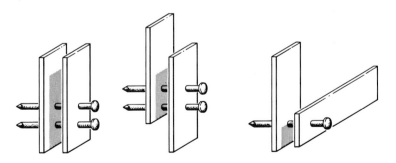

Figure 2-14. Analogy to Restricted Rotation and Free Rotation

bonded carbon are different. Structures 2-**5a** and 2-**5b**, for example, are not geometric isomers; they are identical, as is obvious if we merely turn one molecule over. Note that this operation does *not* interconvert true *cis*-

2-**5a**   2-**5b**

trans isomers such as 2-**4a** and 2-**4b**. Geometric isomerism is also possible in cyclic structures, as shown with *cis*- and *trans*-1,2-dichlorocyclopentanes in Figure 2-15. Here again the structures are noninterconvertible because

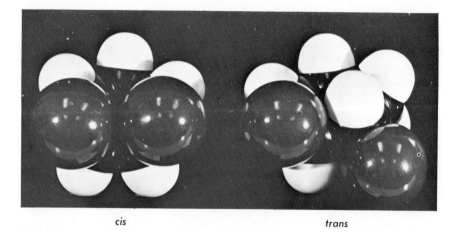

cis   trans

Figure 2-15. Molecular Models of cis- *and* trans-*1,2-Dichlorocyclopentanes*

of the restricted rotation imposed by the ring skeleton. The nail and board analogy in Figure 2-16 illustrates this stereochemical principle.

Figure 2-16. Analogy to Restricted Rotation in Cyclic Structures

f. Conformations of Molecules. The restricted rotation characteristic of double bonds is not ordinarily found in single bonds. Rather (see Figure 2-14), singly bonded atoms or groups in molecules may rotate with respect to one another about the bond axis. This type of **free rotation** for the two methyl groups of ethane, CH_3—CH_3, is shown in Figure 2-17. Perspective

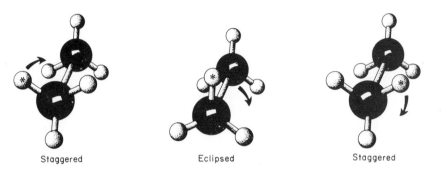

Staggered   Eclipsed   Staggered

Figure 2-17. Free Rotation of Methyl Groups in Ethane

drawings for such rotations are often cumbersome, and the essential features are shown better by **Newman projection formulas**, such as those shown for ethane in Figure 2-18. Different arrangements of atoms in a molecule which are interconvertible by mere rotation about a single bond are called **conformations.** Thus in Figure 2-18, the ethane molecule is shown to rotate internally about its C—C bond from a **staggered** conformation through 60° to an **eclipsed** conformation, and then through another 60° to an equivalent staggered conformation—and so forth, in either direction.

In an important sense, however, such internal rotations are not strictly "free." In going from the staggered to the eclipsed conformation in ethane,

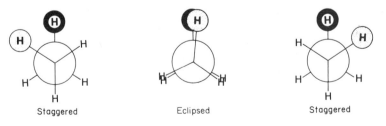

Staggered   Eclipsed   Staggered

Figure 2-18. Newman Projections for Conformations of Ethane

for example, the hydrogen atoms on each carbon are clearly being brought into closer proximity. In short, we are "squeezing together" not only their intrinsic bulk but also their negatively charged bonding electrons and positively charged nuclei. Ethane thus resists free rotation, and energy must be put into the molecule to force it through its higher-energy, transitory eclipsed conformations. This **energy barrier** to free rotation (energy difference between eclipsed and staggered conformations) amounts to about 3 kcal/mole for ethane. With larger or more polar (that is, more or less electronegative) substituents than hydrogen, such repulsive forces ("nonbonded interactions") will clearly be even stronger, and the barrier to free rotation will be even greater. Ordinarily such energy barriers are overcome by the thermal (collision) energy available to all molecules at room temperature, and internal molecular rotations about single bonds occur freely and randomly. At very low temperatures or with very bulky substituents, however, rotation about C—C single bonds may actually be prevented. Thus at low temperatures the two conformational isomers (2-**6a** and 2-**6b**) of tetrabromoethane, Br_2CH—$CHBr_2$, may be recognized

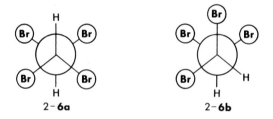

separately, but they interconvert on warming up. The term **conformational analysis** is applied to the interpretation of chemical behavior in terms of the conformations of the molecules involved. This approach is becoming increasingly important to theoretical organic chemistry.

2-9. Bond Energies

Another important characteristic associated with individual bonds is their strength. **Bond strength** or **bond energy** is defined as the amount of energy required to break a bond in a molecule **homolytically**, that is, into uncharged fragments.

$$A{:}B \ + \ Energy \ \longrightarrow \ A{\cdot} \ + \ B{\cdot}$$

Note that each fragment from the rupture takes with it one of the original bonding electrons. The reverse of this process (the formation of A:B from the fragments, A· and B·) *liberates* the same amount of energy, which is referred to as the **heat of formation** of the bond. Bond energies vary among different types of bonds, as well as with the structural environment in which the bond is situated. They may be estimated by quantitative measurements of the heats of chemical reactions (calorimetry) and by spectroscopic methods. Such data are very useful in interpreting and predicting the course of organic reactions. Table 2-7 lists some typical covalent bond energies.

Table 2-7. Some Covalent Bond Energies

Bond	Bond Energy, kcal/mole	Bond	Bond Energy, kcal/mole
H—H	104	C—H	99
Cl—Cl	58	C—Cl	81
Br—Br	46	C—Br	68
I—I	36	C—I	51
H—Cl	103	C—C	83
H—Br	88	C=C	146
H—I	71	C≡C	200
H—O	111	C—O	86
		C=O	178
		C—N	73

2-10. Isotopes of Carbon

Many elements exist in several modifications—called **isotopes**—which have different mass numbers. There are three isotopes of hydrogen: protium (ordinary hydrogen), $_1H^1$; deuterium, $_1H^2$; and tritium, $_1H^3$, having, respectively, 0, 1, and 2 neutrons in the nucleus along with the single proton. Hydrogen and deuterium are stable isotopes, whereas tritium is radioactive, having a **half-life** of about 30 years (that is, 50 per cent of a given sample disintegrates by radioactive decay within 30 years). Carbon comprises five isotopes of mass numbers 10, 11, 12, 13, and 14. C^{10} and C^{11} have been prepared only artificially by nuclear transformations and are radioactive (half-lives 9 seconds and 21 minutes, respectively). C^{12} and C^{13} are stable isotopes, and both are naturally occurring. The ordinary carbon of organic compounds and carbonate minerals is a mixture of C^{12} and C^{13} in a ratio of about 99 to 1, the exact value depending somewhat upon the source. The rarer C^{13} isotope may be concentrated by appropriate fractionation techniques, and organic compounds "enriched" in C^{13} may be prepared for special purposes. C^{14} is a radioactive isotope which occurs only insignificantly in nature, its natural abundance in ordinary carbon being only 10^{-14} per cent. It can be conveniently produced artifically, however, by bombardment of nitrogen compounds with neutrons in the atomic pile. Its very long half-life (about 5000 years) and its convenient detection through the β rays (electrons) which it emits on disintegrating into N^{14} make it a most useful isotope for organic and biochemical "tracer" experiments. Examples of such applications will be discussed in future chapters.

$$\text{Formation of } C^{14}: \quad {}_7N^{14} + {}_0n^1 \longrightarrow {}_6C^{14} + {}_1H^1$$

$$\text{Disintegration of } C^{14}: \quad {}_6C^{14} \longrightarrow {}_7N^{14} + {}_{-1}e^0$$

One nonchemical application of carbon isotopes which is worth considering briefly is the technique of **radiocarbon dating**, which is of importance in historical and anthropological studies. A low level of C^{14} is maintained naturally in all carbonaceous material exposed to atmospheric conditions by equilibration with the small amount (10^{-14} per cent) of $C^{14}O_2$ in the atmosphere. Suppose an ancient artifact—a papyrus scroll, for example—were sealed off in a tomb or cave from such equilibration. Without a source of fresh C^{14}, the C^{14} content of the artifact would diminish by radioactive decay at the known rate of about 1.3×10^{-6} per cent per year. By measuring the C^{14} content of such an artifact, therefore, it is possible to tell within a margin of about 200 years how long the radioactive decay process has been in progress, or how long the object has been sealed off from fresh $C^{14}O_2$. This radiocarbon dating technique has confirmed with striking agreement the ages, based on historical and anthropological information, of a number of objects of historical importance, and Professor W. F. Libby of the University of California at Los Angeles received the Nobel Prize (1960) for its development. At the present time, complete equipment for carbon dating of samples up to 45,000 years old is commercially available.

Although the chemical reactions of all isotopes of a given chemical element are similar, the rates at which these reactions occur vary slightly. In general, reactions involving bonds to a light isotope of an element proceed faster than the same reactions involving bonds to a heavier isotope. The rate of reaction of the light isotope species divided by the rate of the reaction of the heavy isotope species is called the **isotope effect**. Such effects are rather small. C^{12}/C^{14} rate ratios are about 1.01, for example, and H^1/H^2 rate ratios are around 1.05. Isotope effect studies have become increasingly important because they provide theoretical information about chemical reactions which has proved inaccessible by other means.

SUPPLEMENTARY READING

Structure
1. "The Origin of the Theory of Chemical Structure," G. V. Bykov, *J. Chem. Educ.*, **39,** 220 (1962).
2. "The Experimental Basis of Kekulé's Valence Theory," E. N. Hiebert, *J. Chem. Educ.*, **36,** 320 (1959).
3. "Foundations of the Structural Theory," H. C. Brown, *J. Chem. Educ.*, **36,** 104 (1959).
4. "August Kekulé and the Birth of the Structural Theory of Organic Chemistry," O. T. Benfey, *J. Chem. Educ.*, **35,** 21 (1958).
5. "The Evolution of Valence Theory and Bond Symbolism," H. Mackle, *J. Chem. Educ.*, **31,** 618 (1954).

Isomerism, Stereoisomerism, and Conformation
1. "Stereoisomerism of Carbon Compounds," W. K. Noyce, *J. Chem. Educ.*, **38,** 23 (1961).
2. "Conformational Analysis in Mobile Systems," E. L. Eliel, *J. Chem. Educ.*, **37,** 126 (1960).
3. "Aspects of Isomerism and Mesomerism, I, II and III," R. L. Bent, *J. Chem. Educ.*, **30,** 220, 284, 328 (1953).
4. "The Chemical Properties of the Methyl Group," P. D. Bartlett, *J. Chem. Educ.*, **30,** 22 (1953).

Bond Angles, Bond Lengths, and Bond Energies
1. "Principles of Chemical Bonding," R. T. Sanderson, *J. Chem. Educ.*, **38,** 382 (1961).
2. "Lone Pair Electrons," G. W. A. Fowles, *J. Chem. Educ.*, **34,** 187 (1957).
3. "Some Aspects of Organic Molecules and their Behavior. II. Bond Energies," O. Reinmuth, *J. Chem. Educ.*, **34,** 318 (1957).

Carbon Isotopes
1. "The Early History of Carbon-14," M. D. Kamen, *J. Chem. Educ.*, **40,** 234 (1963).
2. "Uses of Isotopes in Organic Chemistry," D. A. Semenow and J. D. Roberts, *J. Chem. Educ.*, **33,** 2 (1956).
3. "Dating with Carbon-14," J. L. Kulp, *J. Chem. Educ.*, **30,** 432 (1953).
4. "Tracer Isotopes in Biochemistry," C. M. Bergen, *J. Chem. Educ.*, **29,** 84 (1952).

CHAPTER 3

Isolating and Purifying Organic Compounds

THE ISOLATION and purification of organic compounds are critical features of any laboratory investigation in organic chemistry, whether it be concerned with the determination of the structure of a natural product, the synthesis of an antibiotic, or the fundamental study of an organic reaction. The procedures used in isolation and purification are often understandably similar since the process of isolation is in essence one of purification. A number of the procedures used in the research laboratory are also adaptable to large-scale industrial use, while others—because of their nature—are limited to the smaller scale of laboratory operations. The choice of a particular process for isolation or purification is governed by the physical or chemical nature of the material at hand, with the important restriction that the process itself must not chemically alter the desired final product. In this chapter we shall examine briefly some of the physical methods which organic chemists employ to isolate and purify the compounds which concern them. Chemical isolation and purification procedures are also employed, but these are more specific and will be discussed at appropriate points in subsequent chapters.

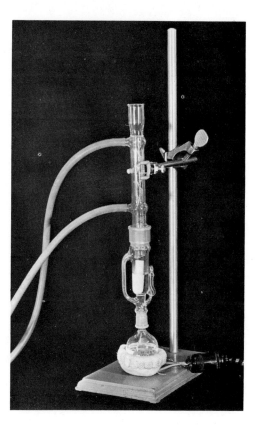

Figure 3-1. Soxhlet Extraction Apparatus

3-1. Extraction

The process of extraction is one of the most useful general techniques for isolation and purification. It involves treatment of the raw material with an appropriate solvent which, ideally, will dissolve only the desired constituent, leaving unwanted material undissolved. Filtration of the extract from the undissolved residue, followed by evaporation of the solvent from the extract, yields the isolated constituent. This ideal situation is seldom encountered, however; more usually a crude product is obtained which requires further purification.

For the *continuous* extraction of solid samples, it is convenient to use a **Soxhlet extractor** (Figure 3-1). The procedure is as follows. An appropriate solvent is boiled from a flask, and its vapors are condensed above the sample, which is contained in a porous "thimble." The hot condensate leaches the sample as it fills the thimble, and the resulting solution siphons

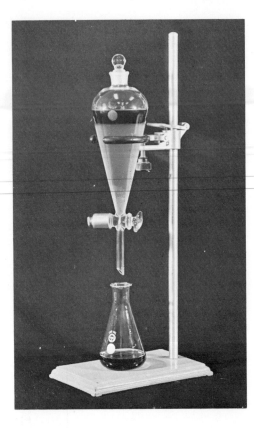

Figure 3-2. Separatory Funnel

back into the boiling flask when the thimble chamber has become full. This action repeats itself over and over, thereby concentrating the extract in the solution contained in the boiling flask.

Organic compounds in aqueous solutions are commonly extracted by vigorously shaking the solution with an immiscible organic solvent in a separatory funnel (Figure 3-2). The immiscible layers are allowed to settle, and the organic layer, containing the organic compound in solution, is separated by partially draining the funnel, then is evaporated free of solvent.

3-2. Distillation

A pure liquid has a characteristic boiling point which varies with external pressure. Water, for example, boils at 100° at atmospheric pressure, 151° at 5 atmospheres pressure, 80° at 0.5 atmosphere, and 46° at 0.1

atmosphere.* Other substances also have individual boiling points which become progressively lower as the external pressure decreases. The process of distillation involves conversion of a liquid to its vapor by boiling, condensation of the vapor back to liquid by cooling, and collection of the condensed liquid. Substances may be separated by distillation on the basis of differences in their boiling points, the lower-boiling component of a mixture tending to distill first. **Simple distillation** may be accomplished with the apparatus illustrated in Figure 3-3. The efficiency of simple distilla-

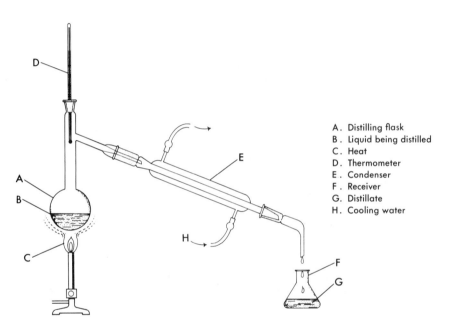

A. Distilling flask
B. Liquid being distilled
C. Heat
D. Thermometer
E. Condenser
F. Receiver
G. Distillate
H. Cooling water

Figure 3-3. Simple Distillation Apparatus

tion for the separation of a liquid mixture, however, is usually not very high. Suppose that we distill a mixture of benzene (b.p. 80°) and toluene (b.p. 110°) in the apparatus shown in Figure 3-3. We would observe that the initial temperature of the vapor is about 80° and that the initial distillate is almost pure benzene. As distillation proceeds, the vapor temperature rises continuously, and the distillate proves to be a mixture of increasing toluene content. At the end of the distillation the vapor temperature approaches 110°, and the distillate is almost pure toluene. By collecting

* All temperatures quoted in this text are given as °C.

small fractions of distillate at the beginning and end of the distillation, we will have effected a substantial separation of the two components. The process is inefficient, however, because the large intermediate fraction is still a mixture of both components; that is, simple distillation is ineffective for the separation of liquid components having boiling points which are reasonably similar.

This inefficiency can be largely overcome by placing a **fractionating column** between the distillation flask and the "take-off" to the condenser (Figure 3-4). Distillation of mixtures performed with such an apparatus is referred to as **fractional distillation.** A typical laboratory fractionating

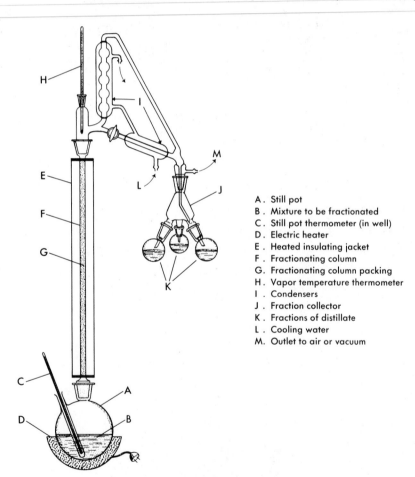

A. Still pot
B. Mixture to be fractionated
C. Still pot thermometer (in well)
D. Electric heater
E. Heated insulating jacket
F. Fractionating column
G. Fractionating column packing
H. Vapor temperature thermometer
I. Condensers
J. Fraction collector
K. Fractions of distillate
L. Cooling water
M. Outlet to air or vacuum

Figure 3-4. Fractional Distillation Apparatus

Figure 3-5A. A Fractionating Column (Center) Used in Petroleum Refining (courtesy Standard Oil Company of California)

column consists of a long glass tube filled with an inert packing (glass helices, for example) which provides a large surface area. It is apparent that redistillation of the first fraction from the simple distillation described above would provide an initial distillate even richer in benzene than the first fraction from which it was derived. This "redistillation" occurs automatically in a fractionating column, which can be thought of as providing a continuous series of distillations and condensations. Thus as benzene–toluene vapors, for example, boil up into the column, the higher-boiling toluene tends to condense on the packing and flow back into the distillation flask, while the vapors of the lower-boiling benzene remain uncondensed in the column and pass over into the condenser. With a column of sufficient length and careful temperature control, liquids boiling only a few degrees apart can be efficiently separated by fractional distillation. This technique is particularly important in the petroleum industry, where crude petroleum is distilled into a number of fractions of increasing boiling point range (Figure 3-5A). From these fractions, pure compounds can be obtained by further processing (see Section 7-4).

Figure 3-5B. Fractionating Columns in a Modern Distillation Laboratory (courtesy United States Steel Corporation)

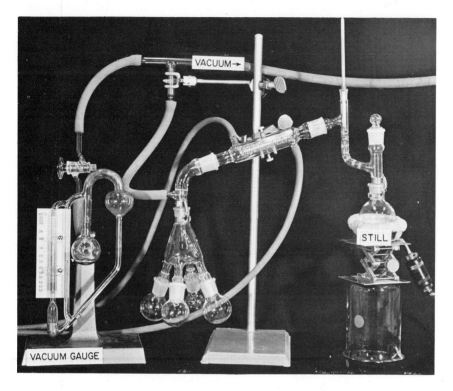

Figure 3-6. Laboratory Apparatus for Vacuum Distillation

Compounds which decompose at temperatures involved during distillation at atmospheric pressure can frequently be distilled without decomposition at reduced pressure, where they boil at a lower temperature. This widely employed technique of **vacuum distillation** is accomplished by evacuating the distillation apparatus with a vacuum pump while conducting the distillation (Figure 3-6).

Compounds which are *immiscible* with water and which have an appreciable vapor pressure near 100° may be isolated or purified by a technique known as **steam distillation,** which involves distillation of the compound *with water*, usually while passing steam through the mixture. Since water and the compound of interest are immiscible, each exerts its vapor pressure *independently* of the other, in contrast to ordinary distillation. As a result, the *sum* of the vapor pressures of water and the compound of interest equals atmospheric pressure below 100°, and the two components distill together when the mixture boils. Condensation of the vapors affords an aqueous mixture from which the desired compound may be separated by

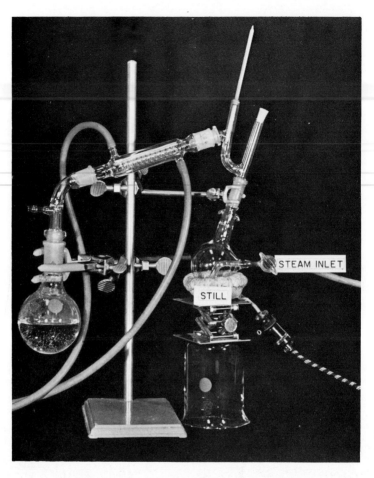

STEAM INLET

STILL

Figure 3-7. Laboratory Apparatus for Steam Distillation

filtration or extraction. One type of laboratory apparatus for steam distillation is shown in Figure 3-7.

3-3. Sublimation

Sublimation is a procedure applicable to some solids which is analogous to distillation of liquids. The solid being **sublimed** is converted directly (without melting) to its vapor by heating, whereupon the vapors are condensed back to the solid by cooling. Not all solids have a sufficiently high vapor pressure to sublime, but those which do may be readily separated

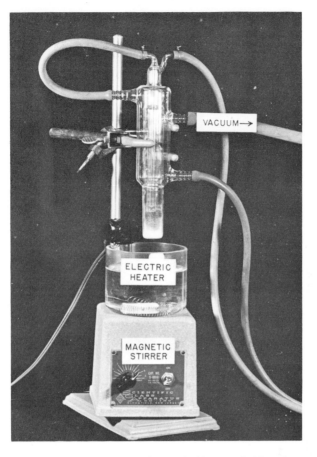

Figure 3-8. Laboratory Apparatus for Vacuum Sublimation

from nonvolatile impurities by this method. The process may be carried out at atmospheric or reduced pressure. A familiar example of sublimation is the disappearance of snow, without melting, on a cold, sunny winter day. Figure 3-8 illustrates a typical laboratory sublimation apparatus.

3-4. Crystallization

A **saturated solution** of a substance is a solution in which no more of the solute will dissolve at the prevailing temperature and in which the dissolved and undissolved solute are in equilibrium. The concentration of a solute in a saturated solution increases with increasing temperature, except

Figure 3-9. Laboratory Apparatus for Vacuum Filtration

in a few abnormal cases. In the process of **crystallization**, which is the most widely used method for purifying solids, an impure solid is dissolved in a minimum volume of boiling solvent (for example, water, benzene, ethyl alcohol), and the hot, saturated solution is allowed to cool gradually. As the temperature falls, the solubility of the solute decreases and it crystallizes from solution. The crystals are filtered (Figure 3-9) from the "mother liquors," rinsed with pure solvent, and allowed to dry. Ideally, the concentration of an impurity will not exceed its saturation point in the cooled solution, and the impurity therefore remains dissolved in the mother liquors. In practice, however, some of the impurity may crystallize with the desired substance, which must thereupon be recrystallized further to achieve satisfactory purification. In a variation of the above procedure, a solution which is less than saturated is allowed to evaporate slowly at room temperature. As the solvent evaporates, the saturation point of the solution is reached and the solute begins to crystallize from solution.

3-5. Chromatographic Methods

a. Column Chromatography. This extremely powerful and versatile separation technique, first described by the botanist Tswett in 1906, suffers
only the unfortunate practical limitation of rather small-scale operation.
Again, the principles involved are simple. Certain chemically inert solid
substances (**adsorbents**, such as silica, alumina, charcoal), in a finely
powdered form of large surface area, have the property of weakly binding
(**adsorbing**) to their surfaces a wide variety of compounds. Furthermore,
the tenacity with which different compounds are adsorbed by a given
adsorbent varies from one compound to another. Suppose we place such
an adsorbent into a glass tube (**chromatographic adsorption column**;
Figure 3-10) and place on top of the adsorbent a mixture of two compounds, A and B, which require separation. Now suppose we add a
suitable solvent to the top of the column and allow it to percolate down
through the adsorbent. The solvent, of course, dissolves A and B and tends
to wash each through the column. However, the binding forces of the

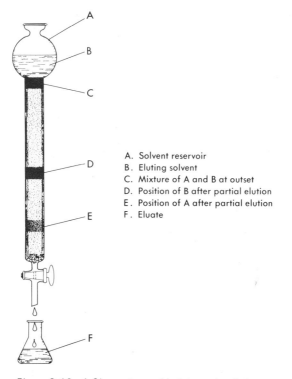

A. Solvent reservoir
B. Eluting solvent
C. Mixture of A and B at outset
D. Position of B after partial elution
E. Position of A after partial elution
F. Eluate

Figure 3-10. A Chromatographic Adsorption Column

adsorbent toward A and B tend to hold them back. Moreover, since these adsorption forces are different for A and B, each will be held back to a different degree. If A is less strongly adsorbed then B, it will be washed through (**eluted** from) the column more readily than B, and the latter, moving at a slower rate, will be eluted only after percolation of additional solvent. By evaporation of the solvent from those fractions of the washings (**eluate**) which contain A or B, the two substances may be recovered in a state of complete purity.

A variation of this technique may be used with mixtures of colored compounds, which form visible colored bands as they are eluted down the column at different rates. When the bands are well separated on the column, the adsorbent is extruded mechanically, the bands are cut apart, and the individual component in each band is recovered by solvent extraction. Also, very small amounts of colored impurities may be removed from a colorless compound by filtering its solution through a thin bed of an adsorbent such as charcoal which selectively adsorbs the colored impurities; the filtrate will contain only the pure colorless compound.

b. Thin Layer Chromatography. This technique is a very useful adaptation of the column method of chromatographic separation. Here the adsorbent (usually containing an inert adhesive) is spread in a uniformly thin layer over a glass plate. A small quantity of a solution of the mixture to be separated is "spotted" on one end of the plate, and the plate is placed, that end down, in contact with solvent so as not to cover the spot. The adsorbent acts as a blotter and the solvent gradually creeps up the dry portion of the plate, separating the mixture exactly as described above. When the solvent has climbed to near the top of the adsorbent the plate is removed, dried, and finally sprayed with appropriate chemicals to render the separated spots visible. The **chromatogram** (Figure 3-11) immediately shows by its separate spots the number of components in the mixture, and the R_f **value** of each spot (distance of spot from origin divided by distance of the solvent front from origin) can be used diagnostically to identify the separate components by making R_f comparisons with authentic samples under similar conditions. The components may be recovered, if desired, by solvent extraction of those portions of the adsorbent in an unsprayed chromatogram which, by comparing with the sprayed chromatogram, is known to contain them.

c. Paper Chromatography. This important variation of adsorption chromatography is widely used by biochemists. The process is similar to thin layer chromatography, except that a strip of filter paper acts as the adsorbent. More delicate separations may be achieved by **two-dimensional paper chromatography.** Here the paper chromatogram is eluted with one solvent as described above, then is removed, allowed to dry,

Figure 3-11. A Developed Thin Layer Chromatogram

turned through 90°, and eluted with a second solvent. This causes additional component separation along axes at right angles to the original.

    d. Gas Chromatography.   An extremely important and effective separation technique applicable to liquids is known as gas chromatography, vapor phase chromatography, or, more properly, gas-liquid partition chromatography. It is so superior in its efficiency to fractional distillation that it has rendered that method obsolete for small-scale separations. Unfortunately, like column chromatography, its application to large-scale separations is difficult, and at present it is employed only as a powerful laboratory tool. The principles of its operation are somewhat similar to those described for column chromatography. The **gas chromatographic column** (Figure 3-12) consists of a jacketed (for temperature control), packed tube attached to a gas (usually helium) inlet, a sample inlet, and a detector chamber. The tube packing consists of a porous, inert powder (for example, crushed firebrick) impregnated with an oil (such as silicone or petroleum jelly). Helium is passed through the heated column, and a small sample of the liquid mixture to be separated is injected into the

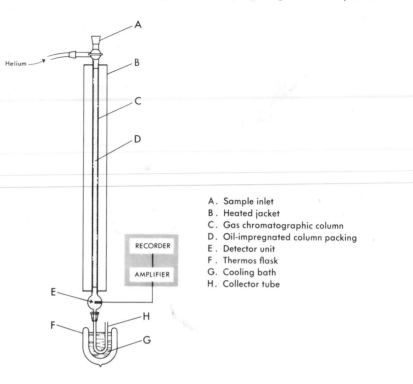

Helium

RECORDER

AMPLIFIER

A. Sample inlet
B. Heated jacket
C. Gas chromatographic column
D. Oil-impregnated column packing
E. Detector unit
F. Thermos flask
G. Cooling bath
H. Collector tube

Figure 3-12. Schematic Diagram of a Gas Chromatographic Column

helium stream. The mixture volatilizes, and the helium sweeps the vapors down the column. The vapors, however, tend to be held back by partially dissolving in the oil phase. Because of their different solubilities in the oil phase, the various components of the mixture are held back to different extents, and ultimately separate into clearly defined "bands" of vapor as they pass down the column with the helium stream. As each "band" passes into the detector chamber (the details of which need not concern us), its presence is registered graphically on an automatic recorder. When the component has passed through the chamber, the recorder again registers zero until the next "band" passes the detector (Figure 3-13). By chilling the exit stream of helium at appropriate times, each individual component can be condensed and collected as it passes from the apparatus. The inventors of this technique, A. J. P. Martin and R. L. M. Synge of England, received the Nobel Prize in 1952 for its discovery. Figure 3-14 illustrates a "preparative" gas chromatography unit capable of handling the practical upper limit of sample size (about 10 ml).

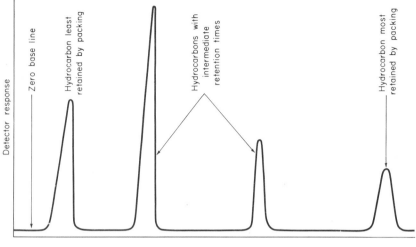

Figure 3-13. Vapor Phase Chromatogram of a Hydrocarbon Mixture

Figure 3-14. Laboratory Apparatus for Preparative Gas Chromatography

3-6. Ion Exchange

Ion exchange is important to the organic chemist because it provides a means of separating water-soluble organic compounds from accompanying water-soluble inorganic salts. **Ion exchange resins** are insoluble, high molecular weight substances having ionic groups as an integral part of their molecular structure. When in contact with solutions containing inorganic ions such resins will exchange their hydrogen and hydroxyl ions for the inorganic cations and anions in the solution. Thus, if an aqueous solution of sodium chloride ($Na^\oplus$ and $Cl^\ominus$) and sucrose (table sugar; nonionic $C_{12}H_{22}O_{11}$) is permitted to percolate through the proper ion exchange column, the eluate will be simply an aqueous solution of sucrose, the sodium chloride being exchanged onto the resin. Such applications make ion exchange an important technique both in the laboratory and in industry, where the method is used primarily for water softening (removing inorganic salts from water). The action of an ion exchange column is diagrammed in Figure 3-15.

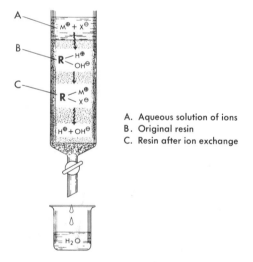

A. Aqueous solution of ions
B. Original resin
C. Resin after ion exchange

Figure 3-15. Principle of Ion Exchange Column

3-7. Criteria of Purity

What do we mean by a "pure compound"? A pure compound, simply, is one which contains no other substance with it; that is, it is *chemically homogeneous*. Reduced to practice, a compound is said to be pure when no physical, chemical, or biological test reveals the presence of a contaminant. The most useful criteria of purity are (1) chromatographic behavior showing a single substance and (2) constancy of the physical properties of the sample. As an example of the latter, if a solid compound melts over the same characteristic narrow temperature range before and after recrystallization, it is considered pure. If not, recrystallization (or other purification) is continued until a constant and sharp melting point is obtained. Despite such constancy of physical properties, a compound may occasionally still be impure. Chromatographic techniques are fortunately so sensitive, however, that their application in one manner or another will almost invariably reveal the presence of an impurity. Melting point, boiling point, and refractive index are the three physical constants most widely employed in estimating the purity of a compound. They are also useful in *characterizing* compounds, that is, in establishing their identity. Other physical properties such as ultraviolet, infrared, proton magnetic resonance, and mass spectra are also used as criteria both of purity and of identity, as will be discussed in the following chapter.

SUPPLEMENTARY READING

General
1. "Analytical Separation," S. Dal Nogare and L. W. Safranski, *J. Chem. Educ.*, **35,** 14 (1958).
2. "The Nature of Separation Processes," H. G. Cassidy, *J. Chem. Educ.*, **27,** 241 (1950).
3. "Methods of Separation and Tests for Purity," H. G. Cassidy, *J. Chem. Educ.*, **23,** 427 (1946).

Extraction
1. "Efficiency in Extraction with Solvents," J. G. Sharefkin and J. M. Wolfe, *J. Chem. Educ.*, **21,** 449 (1944).

Distillation
1. "History of Distillation," A. J. Leibmann, *J. Chem. Educ.*, **33,** 166 (1956).
2. "Batch Distillation," J. P. W. Houtman and A. Husain, *J. Chem. Educ.*, **32,** 529 (1955).
3. "Efficiency of Fractional Distillation Columns," A. C. Buck, *J. Chem. Educ.*, **21,** 475 (1944).

Crystallization
1. "The Early History of Crystallization," H. M. Schoen, C. S. Grove, Jr., and J. A. Palermo, *J. Chem. Educ.*, **33,** 373 (1956).
2. "Crystallization of Organic Compounds from Solution," H. Svanoe, *J. Chem. Educ.*, **27,** 549 (1950).

Chromatography
1. "The Nature of Chromatography," H. G. Cassidy, *J. Chem. Educ.*, **33,** 482 (1956).
2. "Chromatography," W. H. Stein and S. Moore, *Scientific American*, March, 1951.
3. "Chromatography," edited by E. Heftmann, Reinhold Publishing Corp., New York, 1961.

Gas Chromatography
1. "Gas Chromatography," R. L. Pecsok, *J. Chem. Educ.*, **38,** 212 (1961).
2. "Gas Chromatography," R. A. Keller, *Scientific American*, October, 1961.
3. "Gas Chromatography—The Fine Touch in Separations," L. W. Safranski and S. Dal Nogare, *Chemical and Engineering News*, **39,** 102 (June 26, 1961).

Ion Exchange
1. "Industrial Applications of Ion Exchange Resins," R. M. Wheaton and R. E. Anderson, *J. Chem. Educ.*, **35,** 59 (1958).
2. "Ion Exchange," H. F. Walton, *J. Chem. Educ.*, **23,** 454 (1946).

CHAPTER 4

Determining Molecular Structures

THE STRUCTURAL FORMULA of chlorophyll-a, $C_{55}H_{72}N_4O_5Mg$, one of the key substances in the process of photosynthesis by plants (Section 16-12), is the

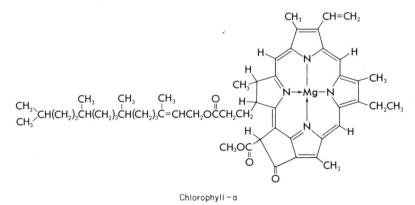

Chlorophyll – a

culmination of years of outstanding chemical research by R. Willstätter, H. Fischer, A. Stoll, J. B. Conant, and others which began in the early years of this century. The monumental achievement of these workers, equipped with little more than test tubes and their native talents, is seen in the full confirmation of their structural deductions by the equally brilliant complete syntheses of chlorophyll-a by R. B. Woodward at Harvard University and M. Strell at the University of Munich in 1960. Using different synthetic routes and working independently, these later workers announced their results just weeks apart—but years after the structure had been deduced. Imagine the staggering problems involved in deducing the location and nature of each one of the 137 atoms in the chlorophyll-a molecule, as well as in devising a synthesis which will put each of these atoms together in the correct arrangement! What sort of techniques does the organic chemist use to obtain information which allows the deduction of such a complex molecular structure? In this chapter we shall examine briefly the more important chemical and physical techniques of structural investigation.

4-1. Elemental Analyses

Following the isolation and purification of a substance (Chapter 3), the first problem confronting the organic chemist concerned with establishing the structure of an organic compound is that of determining which elements are present in the compound, and in what relative amounts. Since organic compounds may contain—in addition to carbon and hydrogen—such elements as oxygen, nitrogen, sulfur, and halogen, qualitative tests for extraneous elements are conducted at the outset. A typical procedure involves fusing the organic material with molten sodium, whereby nitrogen in the molecule is converted into cyanide ion, sulfur to sulfide, and halogens to halide ions. The presence or absence of these ions in the fusion mixture is then established by ordinary qualitative analytical tests. Oxygen is tentatively assumed to be present, and the presence of other elements may be established, if necessary, by additional qualitative tests. Having determined *what* elements are present in the compound, the chemist next undertakes a **quantitative analysis** to establish *how much* of each element is present. From such data the empirical formula for the compound may be deduced.

a. Carbon and Hydrogen. The quantitative analysis for carbon and hydrogen is accomplished using a technique and apparatus (Figures 4-1 and 4-2) originally developed by the German chemist J. Liebig in 1831. A carefully weighed sample of the organic compound (*C* in Figure 4-2) is

Figure 4-1. Apparatus for Quantitative Determination of Carbon and Hydrogen

placed in a combustion tube (A) and vaporized by heating in a furnace (B_1). The vapors are swept by a stream of oxygen through a heated copper oxide packing (D at B_2), which accomplishes the quantitative oxidation of the carbon and hydrogen to carbon dioxide and water. The water vapor is absorbed from the oxygen stream in a weighed tube (E) containing Dehydrite ($Mg(ClO_4)_2$), and the carbon dioxide is absorbed in a weighed tube (F) containing Ascarite (asbestos impregnated with sodium hydroxide). By the weight gains of these tubes, the exact amounts of carbon dioxide and water produced during the combustion are determined. This

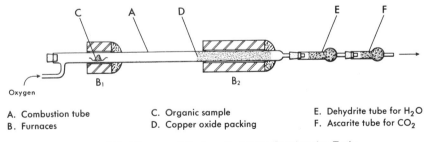

| A. Combustion tube | C. Organic sample | E. Dehydrite tube for H_2O |
| B. Furnaces | D. Copper oxide packing | F. Ascarite tube for CO_2 |

Figure 4-2. Diagram of Carbon-Hydrogen Combustion Train

information permits calculation of the percentages of carbon and hydrogen in the organic compound, as illustrated in the following example.

Example: A pure liquid sample, containing no extraneous elements (except possibly oxygen), is placed in a 0.53908 gram platinum boat, which on re-weighing weighs 0.57612 gram. The sample is ignited, and the previously weighed absorption tubes are reweighed. The 5.47531 gram CO_2 absorption tube now weighs 5.54132 grams; the 6.43336 gram H_2O absorption tube now weighs 6.46039 grams. Calculate the percentages of carbon and hydrogen in the sample.

Total wt.	0.57612 g	Total wt.	5.54132 g	Total wt.	6.46039 g
Boat	0.53908 g	CO_2 tube	5.47531 g	H_2O tube	6.43336 g
Sample	0.03704 g	CO_2	0.06601 g	H_2O	0.02703 g

$$\% \text{ C} = \frac{\text{Wt. of C in sample}}{\text{Wt. of sample}} \times 100$$

$$\text{Wt. of C in sample} = \text{Wt. of } CO_2 \times \frac{\text{At. wt. of C}}{\text{Mol. wt. of } CO_2}$$

$$= \text{Wt. of } CO_2 \times \frac{12.01}{44.01}$$

$$\% \text{ C} = \frac{\text{Wt. of } CO_2}{\text{Wt. of sample}} \times \frac{12.01}{44.01} \times 100 = \frac{0.06601}{0.03704} \times \frac{12.01}{44.01} \times 100$$

$$= 48.64\%$$

$$\% \text{ H} = \frac{\text{Wt. of } H_2 \text{ in sample}}{\text{Wt. of sample}} \times 100$$

$$\text{Wt. of } H_2 \text{ in sample} = \text{Wt. of } H_2O \times \frac{\text{Mol. wt. of } H_2}{\text{Mol. wt. of } H_2O}$$

$$= \text{Wt. of } H_2O \times \frac{2.016}{18.016}$$

$$\% \text{ H} = \frac{\text{Wt. of } H_2O}{\text{Wt. of sample}} \times \frac{2.016}{18.016} \times 100 = \frac{0.02703}{0.03704} \times \frac{2.016}{18.016} \times 100$$

$$= 8.16\%$$

Note that the carbon and hydrogen analyses total only 56.80 per cent and that the compound showed no qualitative tests for extraneous elements. The remainder of the molecule therefore (as in the typical case) must be made up of oxygen. We may thus achieve a quantitative analysis for oxygen by difference. The complete analysis of the present compound is therefore: C, 48.64 per cent; H, 8.16 per cent; O, 43.20 per cent.

b. Other Elements. Quantitative analytical methods are also available for the accurate determination of other elements frequently present in organic compounds. Nitrogen is most generally determined by the **Dumas method** (Figure 4-3), which consists of oxidizing the weighed sample by heating with copper oxide in a stream of carbon dioxide. The combustion gases are swept into a *nitrometer* (inverted microburet) filled with 50 per cent potassium hydroxide solution, which absorbs the carbon dioxide but not the nitrogen. The volume of residual nitrogen in the nitrometer is then read, and the weight of this volume of nitrogen is calculated, whereupon

$$\% \, N = \frac{\text{Wt. of N}_2}{\text{Wt. of sample}} \times 100$$

Sulfur and halogen are determined by fusing the weighed organic sample with sodium peroxide in a *Parr bomb*, whereby the carbon and hydrogen are oxidized to carbon dioxide and water, respectively, the sulfur is con-

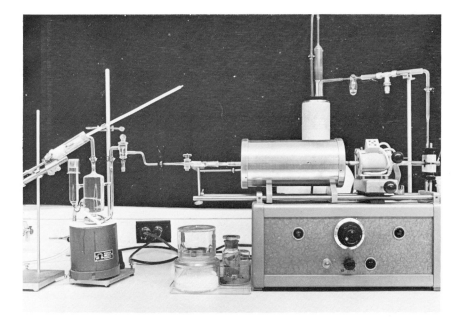

Figure 4-3. Apparatus for Determination of Nitrogen by the Dumas Method

verted to sodium sulfate, and the halogen to sodium halide. In sulfur determinations the dissolved fusion mixture is acidified and treated with barium chloride, and the precipitated barium sulfate is collected and weighed. The percentage of sulfur in the sample is calculated from the relationship

$$\% \text{ S} = \frac{\text{Wt. of BaSO}_4}{\text{Wt. of sample}} \times \frac{\text{At. wt. of S}}{\text{Mol. wt. of BaSO}_4} \times 100$$

For halogen, the acidified fusion mixture is treated with silver nitrate, and the precipitated silver halide is filtered and weighed, permitting calculation of the percentage of halogen (X) by the relationship

$$\% \text{ X} = \frac{\text{Wt. of AgX}}{\text{Wt. of sample}} \times \frac{\text{At. wt. of X}}{\text{Mol. wt. of AgX}} \times 100$$

The percentage of oxygen in an organic compound may actually be determined by direct analysis, but is usually estimated by difference, as in the example above, that is,

$$\% \text{ O} = 100.0 - (\text{sum of \%'s of all other elements})$$

4-2. Empirical and Molecular Formulas

We recall (Section 2-1) that an empirical formula for a substance defines the ratio of the different kinds of atoms present, while a molecular formula also describes exactly how many of each kind of atom are present. Complete and accurate analytical data, obtained as described above, are extremely important to the organic chemist because from such data both the empirical formula and (if the molecular weight is known) the molecular formula of an organic compound may be deduced. The calculations involved are simple, and may be illustrated by continuing our example from above.

Example: A compound has the analysis: C, 48.64 per cent; H, 8.16 per cent; O, 43.20 per cent. Calculate its molecular formula. Atomic weights: C, 12.01; H, 1.008; O, 16.00.

a. Divide the percentage of each element by its atomic weight:

$$\text{C:} \quad \frac{48.64}{12.01} = 4.05 \qquad \text{H:} \quad \frac{8.16}{1.008} = 8.09 \qquad \text{O:} \quad \frac{43.20}{16.00} = 2.70$$

b. Divide each quotient by the smallest. This gives the ratios of all the atoms.

$$\text{C:} \quad \frac{4.05}{2.70} = 1.5 \qquad \text{H:} \quad \frac{8.09}{2.70} = 3.0 \qquad \text{O:} \quad \frac{2.70}{2.70} = 1.0$$

c. Convert the quotients from Step *b* to whole numbers. In this example multiply each quotient by 2.

C: $1.5 \times 2 = 3$ H: $3.0 \times 2 = 6$ O: $1.0 \times 2 = 2$

This gives the atomic ratios in terms of whole numbers; that is, $C/H/O = 3{:}6{:}2$. The empirical formula is thus $(C_3H_6O_2)_n$, where $n = 1, 2, 3, 4$, etc. Possible molecular formulas will thus be $C_3H_6O_2$, $C_6H_{12}O_4$, $C_9H_{18}O_6$, $C_{12}H_{24}O_8$, etc.

d. Check your calculation by calculating the theoretical percentage composition for the formula $C_3H_6O_2$.

$$
\begin{aligned}
3 \times \text{at. wt. of C} &= 36.03 \\
6 \times \text{at. wt. of H} &= 6.05 \\
2 \times \text{at. wt. of O} &= 32.00 \\
\text{Mol. wt.} &= \overline{74.08}
\end{aligned}
$$

$$\% \, C = \frac{36.03}{74.08} \times 100 = 48.64 \qquad \% \, H = \frac{6.05}{74.08} \times 100 = 8.16$$

$$\% \, O = \frac{32.00}{74.08} \times 100 = 43.20$$

Note that the theoretical analysis agrees quite precisely with the actual analytical figures originally obtained, thus indicating the correctness of our empirical formula.

The empirical formula in the above example, $(C_3H_6O_2)_n$, has the corresponding molecular weights of 74, 148 (2×74), 222 (3×74), etc., for $n = 1, 2, 3$, etc. Clearly, if we can measure the actual molecular weight of the substance experimentally, we can establish the value of n in the empirical formula and thus determine the molecular formula. If our measured molecular weight proved to 150 ± 5, for example, we would know that $n = 2$ and that the molecular formula in the above case was $C_6H_{12}O_4$.

4-3. Molecular Weight

The molecular weight of an organic compound may be determined by one of several available techniques. We recall that the boiling point of a solution of a nonelectrolyte (for example, sucrose) in water is higher than the boiling point of pure water and that the freezing point of such a solution is lower than that of pure water. Furthermore, one gram molecular weight of such a nonelectrolyte dissolved in 1000 grams of water causes a boiling point elevation of $0.52°$ and a freezing point lowering of $1.86°$. Organic solutes dissolved in organic solvents behave in a similar way. Thus by establishing quantitatively the **boiling point elevation,** the **freezing point depression,** or the **melting point depression** of a solution of an organic compound in an appropriate organic solvent, we may readily determine the molecular weight of the compound. The equations giving these relationships are the following:

$$\text{Mol. wt.} = \frac{K_{bp}}{\Delta t} \times \frac{\text{Wt. of compound}}{\text{Wt. of solvent}} \times 1000$$

$$\text{Mol. wt.} = \frac{K_{fp}}{\Delta t'} \times \frac{\text{Wt. of compound}}{\text{Wt. of solvent}} \times 1000$$

where K_{bp} and K_{fp} = the **molal boiling point constant** and the **molal freezing point constant** (independently measurable)

Δt and $\Delta t'$ = the observed boiling point elevation and freezing point depression (in °C)

The constants K_{bp} and K_{fp} for several organic solvents useful in molecular weight determinations are listed in Table 4-1.

Table 4-1. Solvents Used for Molecular Weight Determination

Solvent	Boiling point, °C	K_{bp}	Freezing point, °C	K_{fp}
Acetic acid	118	3.07	16.7	3.86
Benzene	80	2.53	5.5	5.12
Cyclohexane	81	2.79	6.5	20.0
Camphor	—	—	178.4	37.7

Example: 0.333 gram of propionic acid, $C_3H_6O_2$, was dissolved in 10.00 grams of acetic acid. The freezing point of the solution was 14.86°, whereas that of pure acetic acid is 16.70°. The molal freezing point constant for acetic acid is 3.86. Calculate the molecular weight of propionic acid and compare with its known formula weight.

$$\text{Mol. wt.} = \frac{3.86}{16.70 - 14.86} \times \frac{0.333}{10.00} \times 1000 = 70$$

Formula weight for $C_3H_6O_2$ = 74

Note: This agreement is about as good as is observed in such determinations.

Boiling point and freezing point molecular weight determinations are probably the most widely used methods, although, as noted in the above example, the precision of such measurements is not too great. High precision is not usually required, however, to establish the value for n in an empirical formula such as $(C_3H_6O_2)_n$, since an approximate molecular weight serves to distinguish unambiguously between n = 1, 2, 3, etc. Neverthe-

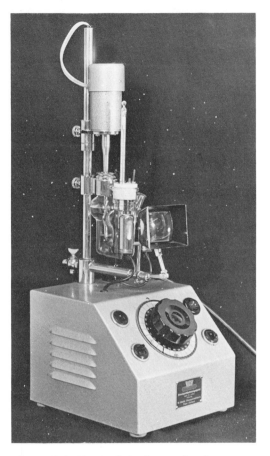

Figure 4-4. Melting Point Depression Apparatus
for Molecular Weight Determination

less other methods are also available, the most accurate being mass
spectrometry, which is described in Section 4-11. Typical laboratory apparatus for the determination of molecular weights by melting point depression is shown in Figure 4-4.

4-4. Functional Groups

We have seen above that analytical and molecular weight determinations provide the basis for establishing the molecular formula of an unknown organic compound. Having this basic information, the chemist next
undertakes to establish the structure of the compound—that is, the ar-

rangement in which all of the atoms in the molecular formula are joined—bearing in mind Kekulé's valence rules (Section 2-1). The arrangements of some of the atoms in the molecule may be established by determining what functional groups (Section 2-5) are present. To illustrate, let us consider several structural possibilities for the molecular formula $C_3H_6O_2$. If we can establish, for example, that a carboxyl group (—COOH) is present in the molecule, then CHO_2 out of $C_3H_6O_2$ is accounted for, leaving only C_2H_5 unaccounted. According to Kekulé's rules, C_2H_5 can be only CH_3CH_2—, and 4-1 is the only structure possible. Alternatively, if an ester function (—COOR) can be shown to be present, 4-2 would be a structural possibility. Similarly, if a ketone, $>C=O$, and a hydroxyl, —OH, function were present, structure 4-3 would be required; while an aldehyde, —CH=O, together with a hydroxyl function would necessitate 4-4 as the structure. How many additional structures may be written for $C_3H_6O_2$?

CH₃CH₂-**COOH**   CH₃-**COOCH₃** $CH_3-\overset{\overset{O}{\|}}{C}-CH_2-OH$ HO-CH₂CH₂-**CH=O**

4-1   4-2   4-3   4-4

The presence or absence of each individual functional group in a molecule may usually be established by applying a series of simple and relatively unambiguous qualitative chemical tests to the unknown sample. For example, neutralization and CO_2 evolution on treatment with sodium bicarbonate indicates the presence of a carboxylic acid, —COOH, or sulfonic acid, —SO_3H, function, while formation of a solid precipitate with hydroxylamine (Section 2-5) is characteristic of an aldehyde or ketone function. Alternatively, or as confirmation, the presence of individual functional groups in the molecule may be revealed by the powerful technique of infrared spectrometry, as described in Section 4-8.

4-5. Degradative Reactions

In establishing the structure of a large and complicated organic molecule, the chemist may next apply one or more of a wide variety of degradative reactions, with the objective of breaking the molecule apart into two or more smaller molecular fragments. After isolating and identifying each of these fragments (whose structures are hopefully already known), he then attempts to visualize a complete original structure which would logically yield such fragments as a result of the particular degradative technique employed. The number of possible degradative reactions which the chemist has at his disposal is quite large, but only a few may yield useful information in a particular case. He therefore selects those which, on the basis of his total knowledge regarding functional groups present in the molecule, will have the greatest likelihood of successful application. As an illustration of the principles involved in degradative work, consider the following example.

Example: A low-boiling hydrocarbon isolated from gasoline is found to have the molecular formula C_4H_8. Several qualitative tests as well as its infrared spectrum reveal the presence of an olefin function, $>C=C<$. Its degradative reaction with ozone (ozonolysis) affords the fragments acetone and formaldehyde. What is the structure of the olefin?

Applying Kekulé's valence rules, we observe that there are only three olefin structures corresponding to C_4H_8, namely 4-5, 4-6, and 4-7. Now, ozonolysis is a reaction which brings about the breakdown of olefins into aldehydes and ketones as follows:

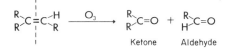

Let us examine the course of ozonolysis for each of the three possible structures under consideration:

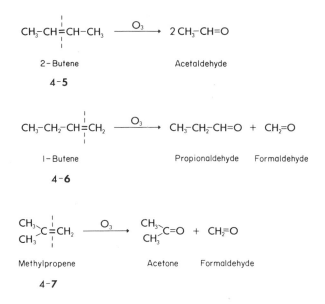

Clearly, the observed isolation of acetone and formaldehyde on ozonolysis uniquely establishes the structure of the unknown olefin C_4H_8 as methylpropene (4-7), since the other theoretically possible structures would afford different degradation products.

4-6. Interaction of Radiant Energy with Matter

To understand the basis of the important modern spectrophotometric techniques used by chemists for structural investigations, it is necessary to digress and briefly review the quantum mechanical nature of the interaction of electromagnetic radiation with matter. We are all familiar with one form of such radiation, namely, visible light. Ordinary light, like all other forms of electromagnetic radiation, consists of an electromagnetic wave (vibration) which travels in a straight line at a uniform velocity (3×10^{10} cm/sec in a vacuum), the direction of wave vibration being perpendicular to the direction of its propagation. Furthermore, ordinary light embodies a number of different "components," each having a different wavelength (color). The familiar dispersion of white light into its colored components by passage through a glass prism (Figure 4-5) illus-

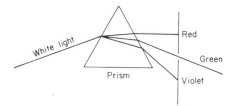

Figure 4-5. Dispersion of White Light into Its Spectral Components

trates this point. In contrast, monochromatic electromagnetic radiation (Figure 4-6) contains only a single wavelength component. Reasonably

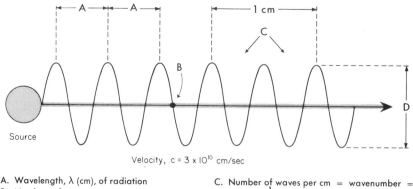

Velocity, $c = 3 \times 10^{10}$ cm/sec

A. Wavelength, λ (cm), of radiation
B. Number of waves passing per second = frequency, ν (sec^{-1})
C. Number of waves per cm = wavenumber = $1/\lambda$ (cm^{-1})
D. Amplitude, proportional to intensity of radiation

Figure 4-6. Schematic Diagram of Monochromatic Radiation

monochromatic visible light may be obtained by passing light from a prism through a very narrow slit (Figure 4-5).

The wavelength of electromagnetic radiation varies over extremely broad limits, depending upon its source. Thus the electromagnetic radiation from a radio broadcasting station has very long wavelengths compared to the radiation from a flashlight bulb. The **electromagnetic spectrum**, so to speak, is a catalog of such wavelengths. Table 4-2 lists the wavelengths, frequencies (in wavenumbers, that is, waves per cm), and energies within the practical limits of the electromagnetic spectrum. Notice that there is a ratio of 10^{14} between the shortest and longest wavelengths shown at each end of the spectrum. This is equivalent to the ratio between one inch and a billion miles!

Table 4-2. The Electromagnetic Spectrum

Region of Spectrum	Wavelength, cm	Wavenumber, cm^{-1}	Energy, erg
Radio broadcasting	10^4	10^{-4}	2×10^{-20}
Radar	10	10^{-1}	2×10^{-17}
Infrared			
Longest heat waves	3×10^{-2}	33	6.6×10^{-15}
Shortest infrared	7×10^{-5}	1.4×10^4	2.8×10^{-12}
Visible			
Red	7.5×10^{-5}	1.3×10^4	2.7×10^{-12}
Green	5×10^{-5}	2×10^4	4×10^{-12}
Violet	4×10^{-5}	2.5×10^4	5×10^{-12}
Ultraviolet			
Long	4×10^{-5}	2.5×10^4	5×10^{-12}
Short	10^{-5}	10^5	2×10^{-11}
X rays			
Long	10^{-7}	10^7	2×10^{-9}
Short	10^{-9}	10^9	2×10^{-7}
γ rays	2×10^{-10}	5×10^9	10^{-6}

We see in Table 4-2 that each wavelength of electromagnetic radiation has a particular energy associated with it. Now, quantum theory tells us that, in addition to its wave nature, electromagnetic radiation also consists of discrete **quanta** ("packets" of energy), and that the energy (ergs) associated with each quantum of a particular wavelength is given by the simple relation:

$$E = h\nu = \frac{hc}{\lambda} = \frac{1.98 \times 10^{-16}}{\lambda}$$

where E = energy (ergs) per quantum of radiation
       h = Planck's constant = 6.6×10^{-27} erg $\times$ second
       ν = frequency of light (number of waves passing a point per second)
       c = velocity of radiation = 3×10^{10} cm/sec
       λ = wavelength of radiation (cm)

With this equation it is possible to calculate the energy per quantum for electromagnetic radiation of any wavelength, and we see at once (Table 4-2) that the shorter the wavelength, the greater the energy associated with the radiation. We are now in a position to understand the interaction of radiation of various wavelengths with matter.

Let us consider a simple nonlinear molecule made up of just three atoms, A, B, and C, held together with single bonds. Such a molecule, like mole-

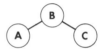

cules in general, is not a rigid, stationary structure, but is in a state of violent and ceaseless motion owing to the impact of other molecules, etc. Think of the bonds momentarily as springs, and try to imagine the different types of motion prevailing *within* the molecule itself—aside from the translational and rotational motions of the molecule as a whole. In particular, the molecule may have the internal motions of vibration (A back and forth against B, and C against B, both in phase and out of phase) and

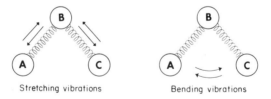

Stretching vibrations   Bending vibrations

of bending (A back and forth toward C). In large and complex molecules, where "twisting" and "wagging" motions also occur, the number of modes of internal motion clearly becomes very large indeed. Now, the theories of quantum mechanics tell us that such motions are not random, but rather are **quantized**; that is, *each particular motion has a unique and characteristic energy* associated with it. In addition, each such motion also has associated with it one or more similarly quantized *excited states* of higher characteristic energy, to which the motion may be "excited" by putting energy into the system. Excitation will occur, however, only when *the energy put into the system exactly corresponds to the difference in energy between the original "ground* *state" motion and the "excited state" motion.* Thus the characteristic vibration between atoms A and B in the hypothetical molecule above, for example, may be put into a vibrationally excited state by saturating the molecule with energy equal to the difference in the energies of the ground state A-B vibration and the excited state A-B vibration. The discrete difference in energy between the two states may be likened to the discrete increment of energy which is utilized in climbing from one step of a staircase to the next. Not only are the vibrational, rotational, and bending motions within a molecule quantized, but the electron systems which make up the bonds of molecules are energetically quantized as well. Thus if we allow electromagnetic radiation to impinge upon a molecule, the radiation will be *absorbed* provided that its energy (Table 4-2) exactly corresponds to the difference in the ground and excited state energies for some motion within the molecule, and the molecule will in turn be "excited" with respect to that particular motion.

Different portions of the electromagnetic spectrum have energies which correspond to the excitation energies characteristic of different types of molecular motions. Infrared radiation, for example, has energies bracketing the vibrational and bending excitation energies of bonds, visible and ultraviolet lights have energies in the range of electronic excitation energies of bonding electrons, while radar frequencies correspond in energy to the tumbling and spinning acrobatics of a molecule. With the wide range of energies available in the electromagnetic spectrum (Table 4-2), it is not surprising that all modes of molecular motion—in principle, at least—may be examined by studying the interaction of radiation with matter.

4-7. Spectrometers

The interaction of electromagnetic radiation with matter is studied in an instrument called a **spectrometer**. Such instruments have been constructed to make use of most of the regions of the electromagnetic spectrum, and those covering the infrared, visible, and ultraviolet regions, in particular, are widely available commercially. The construction and operating details of spectrometers vary, depending upon the portion of the electromagnetic spectrum which they cover, but the basic principles behind each type are quite similar.

The spectrometer ordinarily consists of a radiation source (A in Figure 4-7) which can supply monochromatic radiation having a wavelength which can be varied continuously. The radiation is split into two parallel beams of equal intensity. One of these passes through the sample (B) under investigation, resulting in a beam having intensity I; the other is the reference beam (intensity I_0). The sample and reference beams then

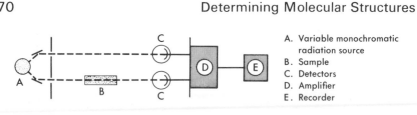

A. Variable monochromatic
   radiation source
B. Sample
C. Detectors
D. Amplifier
E. Recorder

Figure 4-7. Schematic Diagram of a Spectrometer

strike detectors (C), each of which gives an electrical signal proportional
to the intensity of the radiation falling upon it. These signals in turn are
led into an amplifier (D), where their difference is amplified and fed into
a chart recorder (E). If the wavelength (energy) from the source is such
that absorption by the sample occurs, the consequent difference in intensities of the two beams reaching the detectors is measured and recorded for
the wavelength in question. Such absorption measurements are automatically made and plotted over the entire spectrum of wavelengths covered by
the instrument. The resulting graph is known as the **absorption spectrum**
of the substance under investigation in this spectral region. The graph
may show absorbance ($\log_{10} I_0/I$; Figure 4-8), transmittance (I/I_0), or per
cent transmittance ($I/I_0 \times 100$; Figure 4-9) of the radiation as a function
of either wavelength or wavenumber. Those wavelengths or frequencies at
which the molecule absorbs electromagnetic radiation are referred to as
absorption bands. Structural units in a molecule which give rise to particular absorption bands are called **chromophores.** Absorption bands
may occur in various regions of the spectrum, depending upon the particular type of molecular or electronic excitation being caused by the radiation.
With appropriate spectrometers we may measure infrared, visible, and
ultraviolet absorption spectra, as well as microwave (radar), X-ray, and

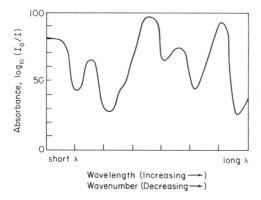

*Figure 4-8. Representative Absorp-
tion Spectrum*

γ-ray spectra. Each spectral region furnishes its own type of information about the molecule under investigation.

4-8. Infrared Spectrometry

The measurement of infrared absorption in the spectral region from 5000 to 625 wavenumbers (cm^{-1}) constitutes a technique so powerful and revealing that it provides—literally in minutes—structural information which might take hours or days to obtain by ordinary chemical methods. As mentioned above, absorption in this region arises from stretching, bending, and wagging excitations of the molecule. The particular value of infrared spectra lies in the fact that absorption bands between 5000 and about 1450 cm^{-1} are characteristic of individual functional groups within the molecule. As seen in Table 4-3, each type of functional group has associated with it a unique and rather narrow range of infrared absorption frequencies. Furthermore, the exact absorption frequency within each range varies slightly depending on the type of substituent attached to the functional group. The tremendous importance of these facts is obvious. The chemist can determine not only the types of functional groups present in a molecule, but also something about their immediate structural environment, by merely measuring and interpreting the infrared spectrum. Another very important application of infrared spectrometry is in establishing the identity of two substances. Over the entire infrared region, and particularly between 1450 and 650 cm^{-1} (the "fingerprint region," where absorption is particularly characteristic of the individual molecule), the spectrum of each individual organic compound (with very few special exceptions) is literally as unique as is the fingerprint of an individual human.

Table 4-3. Some Typical Infrared Absorption Frequencies

Functional Group (Chromophore)	Absorption Frequency Range, cm^{-1}
—OH	3100–3600
—OR	1050–1260
—NH$_2$	3150–3400
$>C=C<$	1600–1650
—CH=O	1700–1730
$>C=O$	1670–1710
—COOH	1700, 2500–3000
—COOR	1720–1740, 1100–1310

Thus if the infrared spectra of two substances are absolutely identical in all respects, we have the most conclusive evidence available that the substances are in fact identical. Figure 4-9 illustrates a typical infrared spectrum, and Figure 4-10 shows a commercial infrared spectrometer.

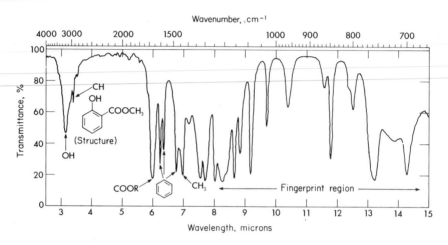

Figure 4-9. Infrared Spectrum of Methyl Salicylate (Oil of Wintergreen)

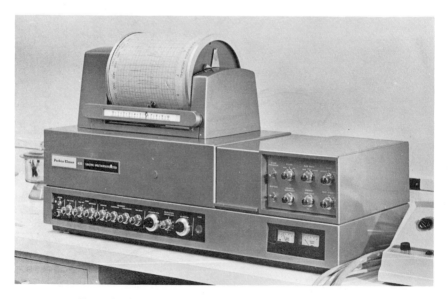

Figure 4-10. Infrared Spectrometer Used in Organic Research

4-9. Visible and Ultraviolet Spectrometry

The absorption of visible and ultraviolet light by molecules, a consequence of electronic excitations, is especially valuable in the investigation of unsaturated linkages and aromatic systems. The region of the spectrum from the visible (750 mμ (red) to 400 mμ (violet)) down into the ultraviolet (about 195 mμ) may be readily and rapidly scanned using commercially available visible-ultraviolet spectrometers (Figure 4-11). Absorption bands in this region are generally far fewer in number, broader, and less characteristic than infrared bands. Nevertheless, the occurrence of such bands in particular wavelength regions and at characteristic intensities is again diagnostic of specific types of groups (chromophores) within the molecule. Hence, visible-ultraviolet spectrometry is widely used as a diagnostic tool, particularly in conjunction with infrared data. Ultraviolet and visible spectra can also be used for quantitative analytical purposes (as can infrared, with less precision), since the intensity of absorption at a given wavelength is proportional to the quantity of absorbing material in solution (Beer's law).

Figure 4-11. Visible-Ultraviolet Spectrometer

4-10. Nuclear Magnetic Resonance Spectrometry

Nuclear magnetic resonance (NMR) spectrometry, involving the use of radiofrequency radiation, has come into widespread use since about 1960. Despite the complexity and relatively high cost ($20,000 to $50,000) of commercial NMR spectrometers, the structural information available from NMR spectra is so important and so unique that laboratories the world over are finding this tool increasingly indispensable. F. Bloch of Stanford University and E. M. Purcell at Harvard University, codiscoverers of the principles underlying NMR spectrometry, shared the Nobel Prize in 1952 for their discovery.

The principles of NMR spectrometry differ slightly from those of ordinary spectrometry in that they involve the interaction of radiation with the *nuclei* of certain atoms in the molecule, rather than with the molecule itself or its bonding electrons. The nuclei of all isotopes having an odd atomic or mass number (e.g., $_1H^1$, $_6C^{13}$, $_7N^{15}$, $_9F^{19}$) have associated with them a **magnetic moment** along the axis of their rotation, roughly analogous to the mechanical moment associated with a spinning top. In the presence of an external magnetic field, as between the poles of a powerful magnet, these magnetic moments tend to align themselves parallel to, and in a direction either with (C) or against (D), the magnetic field (Figure 4-12). Now, as with a compass in the earth's magnetic field, the more favorable (lower) energy state is that wherein the nuclear magnetic moments are aligned with (C) the external field, and the higher energy state involves alignment against (D) the field. Because of thermal agitations, however, there is only a small preponderence of the magnetic moments aligned in the lower energy orientation. The energy difference between the two types of orientation depends upon the particular nucleus involved and upon the strength of the external magnetic field, and proves to be within the radiofrequency range of energies. By putting radiofrequency energy into such a system (Figure 4-12), it is therefore possible to "flip" some of the nuclear

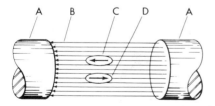

A. Magnet poles
B. Direction of magnetic field
C. Magnetic moment oriented with field
D. Magnetic moment oriented against field

Figure 4-12. Orientation of Nuclear Magnetic Moments in a Magnetic Field

magnetic moments from the lower energy orientation into the higher energy one, provided that the radiofrequency energy exactly corresponds to the energy difference between the two orientation states. This condition is referred to as **nuclear magnetic resonance**. An NMR spectrometer (Figure 4-13) permits the measurement of those values of external magnetic field strength at constant radiofrequency energy (or those values of radiofrequency energy at constant external field strength) at which the condition of nuclear magnetic resonance exists for various atomic nuclei.

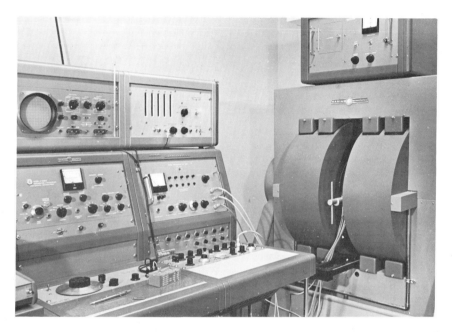

Figure 4-13. Nuclear Magnetic Resonance Spectrometer

Among the various nuclei having nuclear magnetic moments, the proton is the most important to the organic chemist, and instruments are therefore constructed for studying proton magnetic resonance alone. An important feature of the NMR spectrum of the proton, as well as of other nuclei capable of nuclear magnetic resonance, is that the exact position (that is, exact value of external magnetic field strength at a fixed radiofrequency) of the NMR signal depends upon the electronic environment of the proton. The bonding electrons about the proton "shield" it, so to speak, from the external magnetic field, and the extent of this shielding differs in different electronic environments. Therefore, the *resonance con-*

dition for the hydrogen nucleus occurs at different magnetic field strengths depending upon the type of atom or group to which the hydrogen atom is attached. This phenomenon, referred to as the **chemical shift**, is strikingly apparent in the NMR spectrum of ethyl alcohol (Figure 4-14), where we see that the proton NMR signal occurs at different magnetic field strengths depending upon whether the hydrogen atom is attached in the —OH, the —CH_2—, or the —CH_3 group. Furthermore, the areas under the three NMR bands for CH_3—CH_2—OH are in the ratio of 1:2:3, indicating that the low-field band is due to NMR of the —OH proton, the midfield band to NMR of the two —CH_2— protons, and the high-field band to NMR of the three —CH_3 protons. These NMR band assignments can be confirmed by substituting deuterium for the various hydrogen atoms in CH_3—CH_2—OH. With CH_3—CH_2—OD, for example, the low-field NMR band in Figure 4-14 disappears, since the NMR band position for the deuterium nucleus is far removed from that of the proton.

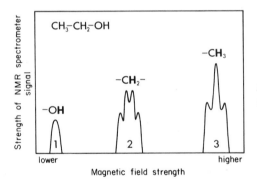

Figure 4-14. NMR Spectrum of Ethyl Alcohol, CH_3—CH_2—OH

The structural importance of this powerful technique should now be obvious. As with other types of spectra, tables have been developed which correlate the positions of proton NMR signals with structural units within the molecule. Thus, by measuring and interpreting the NMR spectrum of an organic compound, the chemist can deduce not only *where* hydrogen atoms are attached to the carbon skeleton of the molecule, but also *how many* hydrogen atoms are attached at each position. The interpretation of **spin-spin splitting**, which is exemplified in the "fine structure" of the —CH_2— and —CH_3 bands of CH_3—CH_2—OH and which is caused by the mutual interaction (**coupling**) of the nuclear magnetic moment of one proton with that of a neighboring proton, provides even more subtle information about organic molecular structures. NMR spectrometry may also be adapted for quantitative analysis, and, as with other spectral methods, the entire NMR spectrum can be scanned and recorded automatically in a matter of minutes.

4-11. Mass Spectrometry

For several decades after its invention by F. W. Aston in 1919, the mass spectrometer was used only by physicists, and as late as 1940 there were probably less than a dozen such instruments in the world. Since about 1960, however, there has been growing recognition of mass spectrometry's unusual power and versatility for the solution of structural problems in organic chemistry. Thus, despite their novelty, intricacy, and cost, mass spectrometers are becoming increasingly utilized by chemists in the major organic research centers of the world.

A mass spectrometer (Figure 4-15) is an instrument which distinguishes between ions of different mass to charge (m/e) ratios, and simultaneously measures the relative abundance of each ionic species. The principles of this instrument, which differ widely from those of other spectrometers, are illustrated in Figure 4-16. Vapors (A) of the compound under investigation are admitted (B) into an evacuated ionization chamber (C), where their molecules are subjected to energetic electron bombardment (E) and are thereby converted into positive ions (F) of varying mass to charge ratios. An electrical potential accelerates their movement toward a negatively charged plate (G), where they escape through a slit and form a posi-

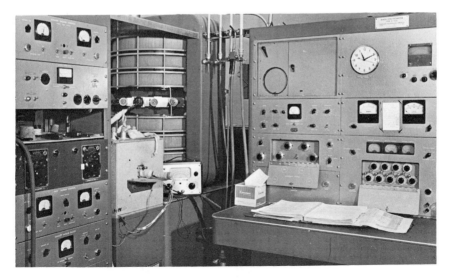

Figure 4-15. A Mass Spectrometer

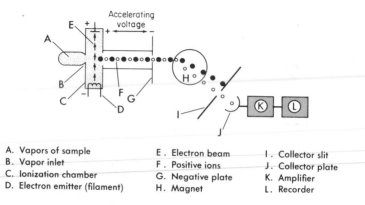

A. Vapors of sample	E. Electron beam	I. Collector slit
B. Vapor inlet	F. Positive ions	J. Collector plate
C. Ionization chamber	G. Negative plate	K. Amplifier
D. Electron emitter (filament)	H. Magnet	L. Recorder

Figure 4-16. Schematic Diagram of a Mass Spectrometer

tive ion beam, which is then diverted by the magnetic field of a powerful magnet (H). Ions with a greater mass per unit charge are diverted less than those with a smaller m/e ratio. By varying the accelerating potential or the magnetic field strength of H, ions of a particular m/e value may be focused on the collecter slit (I) and its accompanying collector plate (J). The ensuing "ion current" in J, which is proportional to the intensity of the focused ion beam, is amplified (K) and automatically recorded (L). The resulting **mass spectrum** is obtained as a series of discrete and increasing m/e values. If the positive charge on each ion sorted by the mass spectrometer is unity ($e = 1$), as is usually the case, the mass spectrum consists of a series of **mass numbers** of all of the positive ions produced by electron bombardment of the substance vaporized into the ionization chamber (C).

The electron bombardment of methane (Figure 4-17) in the mass spectrometer, for example, results in the loss of one electron and concomitant formation of a **parent ion**, CH_4^+, having $m/e = 16$. One or more hydrogen atoms are also lost by *fragmentation*, giving varying amounts of CH_3^+, CH_2^+, CH^+, and C^+, having $m/e = 15$, 14, 13, and 12, respectively. A small

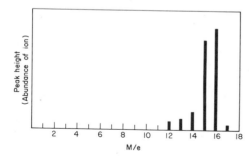

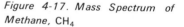

Figure 4-17. Mass Spectrum of Methane, CH_4

amount of $m/e = 17$ is also observed, owing to the approximately 1 per cent natural abundance of $C^{13}H_4$ in methane. Note that m/e of the parent ion gives the exact molecular weight of the compound. The relative amounts of each of the fragment ions give a **fragmentation pattern** which is typical for methane. With larger and more complicated molecules we again observe a parent ion peak and a typical fragmentation pattern of smaller peaks. This pattern will be more complex, however, as fragment ions may be formed from carbon-carbon bond rupture as well as from carbon-hydrogen bond rupture, and a richer variety of ionic fragments will result. Mass spectrometers are available which will permit the examination of compounds having molecular weights as high as 1000. In using mass spectrometric data to attack a structural problem, the organic chemist attempts to recognize the parent ion (which is not always the most abundant), to deduce the structure of each of the fragment ions, and to visualize how these fragments must have been fitted together in the parent molecule prior to its decomposition in the mass spectrometer.

4-12. X-Ray Diffraction

The technique of X-ray diffraction, development of which some five decades ago earned for Sir W. H. Bragg and his son, W. L. Bragg, the Nobel Prize in physics in 1915, is today becoming increasingly important to the chemist as a means of determining the structures of complex organic molecules. So powerful is the method in principle that it may one day largely supplant other physical methods as a means of structure determination. Its major limitations, however, are its complexity and its applicability only to crystalline materials. The method is based on the fact that crystalline substances (organic or inorganic) possess extremely regular periodic sequences of atoms within their characteristic crystal structures. Each such representative periodic array of atoms in the crystal is referred to as a **unit cell**, and each adjacent unit cell has all of its constituent atoms in the same relative positions in space (Figure 4-18). Now, when a beam of monochromatic X rays (whose wavelength is comparable to the inter-

Figure 4-18. Atoms in a Crystal Lattice

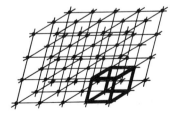

Crystal lattice   Unit cell

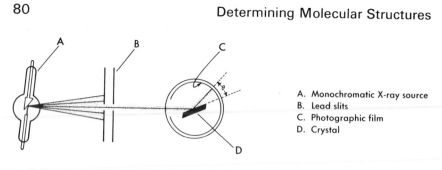

A. Monochromatic X-ray source
B. Lead slits
C. Photographic film
D. Crystal

Figure 4-19. Schematic Diagram of X-ray Camera

atomic spacings in the unit cell) impinges upon a crystal at an appropriate angle to one of the regular "planes" of atoms in the crystal lattice, it is strongly reflected at the same angle, provided that the angle satisfies the **Bragg equation**:

$$n\lambda = 2d \sin \theta$$

where d = spacing between interatomic planes
    θ = angle of reflected beam
    λ = wavelength of X ray
    n = "order of reflection," that is, 1, 2, 3, . . .

Experimentally, the angle θ may be measured photographically using a special circular camera, within which the crystal under examination may be rotated through any desired angle, so as to pick up reflections from all

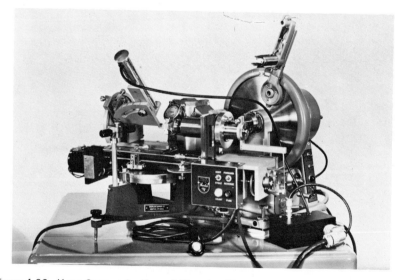

Figure 4-20. X-ray Camera for X-ray Diffraction Measurements (Norelco Single Crystal Diffractometer, manufactured by Philips Electronic Instruments, Mount Vernon, N.Y.)

different atomic planes within its lattice (Figures 4-19 and 4-20). Since all arbitrary planes of atoms in the crystal lattice cause their own characteristic reflection, the final X-ray-diffraction pattern (photographic image from the camera) consists of a symmetrical array of spots on the photographic film. The positions of these spots are related to the positions of the reflecting atomic planes in the crystal, and the spot intensities are related to the intensities of the X-ray beam reflected from each plane of atoms (Figure 4-21). These intensities, in turn, are determined by the atomic number of the atoms in the reflecting planes; the heavier the atom, the more intense the reflected spot. Such diffraction patterns are unique and characteristic for each crystalline substance and therefore, like infrared spectra, may be used for identification purposes.

By a complex mathematical analysis of the positions and intensities of the various spots in the X-ray-diffraction patterns obtained along all three crystal axes, the X-ray crystallographer next attempts to deduce a three-dimensional projection ("contour map") of electron densities within the unit cell. Electron densities are greatest at the positions of atomic nuclei, less along bonds between atoms, and zero elsewhere within the· unit cell. The three projections of electron density of a simple five-atom tetrahedral molecule might look like those shown in Figure 4-22. The superimposed projections then afford a three-dimensional picture of the electron density distribution throughout the unit cell, or in other words, a picture of the position in space of each atom in the unit cell. Knowing from supplementary data the number of separate molecules in the unit cell, the structure of each molecule then follows. The technique of X-ray crystallo-

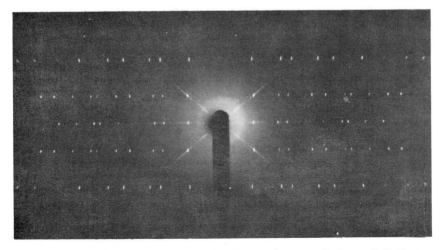

Figure 4-21. Representative X-ray Diffraction Pattern (courtesy Professor C. O. Hutton, Stanford University)

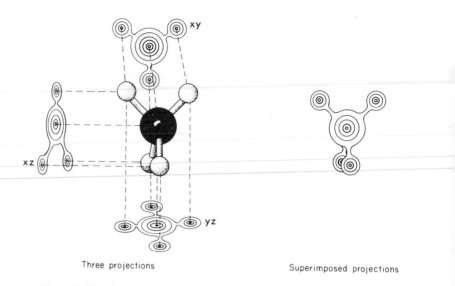

Three projections   Superimposed projections

Figure 4-22. Electron Density "Contour Map" of a Tetrahedral Molecule

graphic structure determination is mathematically complex, specialized, and tedious, but, with the aid of modern electronic computers, is beginning to come into more widespread use for the solution of complex structural and stereochemical problems. The elucidation of the structure of vitamin B_{12}, $C_{63}H_{90}N_{14}O_{14}PCo$, by X-ray diffraction for which (among other contributions in the field) Dr. Dorothy C. Hodgkin of Oxford Uni-

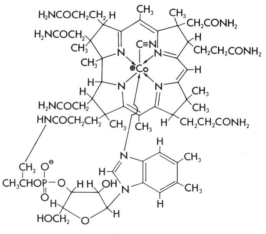

Vitamin B_{12}

versity was awarded the Nobel Prize in 1964—is one of the crowning achievements of the method.

4-13. Confirmatory Synthesis

As indicated in the previous sections, the organic chemist approaches a structural problem by a variety of techniques: analytical, chemical, and physical. With data from all these sources he is able ultimately to write a unique structural formula for an unknown substance which is consistent with all of the known facts of its behavior. When he can do this, he tentatively "knows" the structure of the compound.

The structural conclusions reached by the above methods, however, are never considered *absolutely* definitive until the structure has been "confirmed" by an independent synthesis of the compound in question. Assuming the structure to be as he believes it, the organic chemist next undertakes to synthesize the same molecule from smaller molecules of established structures—utilizing only those chemical reactions which are known to proceed in an unambiguous fashion. If the physical, chemical, and biological properties of the synthetic product prove *identical in all respects* with those of its nonsynthetic counterpart, then the structure of the latter is said to be "confirmed by synthesis." The ingenuity of the synthetic organic chemist may be severely taxed in such efforts, and the "known" structures of a number of complex molecules have not yet been confirmed by synthesis.

It should be stated at this point that the term **total synthesis** implies that the compound in question has been synthesized starting with its elements. In 1963 W. S. Johnson and co-workers at Stanford University achieved the 22-step synthesis of the pregnancy-controlling hormone progesterone from the coal tar derivative 1,6-dihydroxynaphthalene. Since

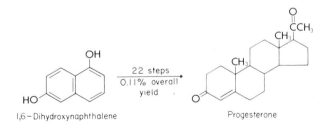

1,6−Dihydroxynaphthalene · 22 steps 0.11% overall yield · Progesterone

this naphthalene derivative may be synthesized from its elements, the total synthesis of progesterone was in principle accomplished. In contrast, in a **partial synthesis** one or more of the starting materials has not yet been obtainable, directly or indirectly, from the elements.

SUPPLEMENTARY READING

Infrared and Ultraviolet Spectrometry
1. Spectrometric Identification of Organic Compounds," R. M. Silverstein and G. C. Bassler, *J. Chem. Educ.*, **39,** 546 (1962).
2. "Infrared Spectroscopy: A Chemist's Tool," G. C. Pimentel, *J. Chem. Educ.*, **37,** 651 (1960).
3. "The Origin of Characteristic Group Frequencies in Infrared Spectra," D. A. Dows, *J. Chem. Educ.*, **35,** 629 (1958).
4. "Chemical Analysis by Infrared," B. Crawford, *Scientific American*, October, 1953.
5. "Infrared Spectroscopy as an Organic Analytical Tool," R. C. Gore, *J. Chem. Educ.*, **20,** 223 (1943).
6. "Ultraviolet Absorption Spectroscopy," I. M. Klotz, *J. Chem. Educ.*, **22,** 328 (1945).

NMR Spectrometry
1. "Characteristic NMR Spectral Positions for Hydrogen in Organic Structures," E. Mohacsi, *J. Chem. Educ.*, **41,** 38 (1964).
2. "Nuclear Magnetic Resonance Spectroscopy," J. D. Roberts, *J. Chem. Educ.*, **38,** 581 (1961).
3. "NMR Spectroscopy as an Analytical Tool in Organic Chemistry," J. C. Martin, *J. Chem. Educ.*, **38,** 286 (1961).
4. "How Amateurs Can Build a Simple Magnetic Resonance Spectrometer," C. L. Stong, *Scientific American*, April 1959.
5. "Magnetic Resonance," G. E. Pake, *Scientific American*, August, 1958.
6. "Nuclear Magnetic Resonance," H. L. Richter, *J. Chem. Educ.*, **34,** 618 (1957).

Mass Spectrometry
1. "Mass Spectrometry," S. E. Wiberley and D. A. Aikens, *J. Chem. Educ.*, **41,** A75 (1964).
2. "The Use of Mass Spectrometry in Organic Analysis," E. L. Eliel, T. J. Prosser, and G. W. Young, *J. Chem. Educ.*, **34,** 72 (1957).
3. "The Mass Spectrometer," O. C. Nier, *Scientific American*, March 1953.
4. "A Model Mass Spectrometer," F. J. Norton, *J. Chem. Educ.*, **25,** 677 (1948).

CHAPTER 5

Resonance and
Molecular Orbitals

ALTHOUGH SUITABLE for showing gross structural features of molecules, Kekulé and electron dot representations of chemical bonds (Section 2-2) suffer several serious inadequacies. Such representations fail, for example, (1) to explain the difference in chemical reactivity (bond energy) of the two bonds in multiple bond linkages such as $>C=C<$ and $>C=O$; (2) to explain and correlate the geometrical aspects of different types of bonds; and (3) to describe the peculiar chemical inertness observed in certain types of molecules (benzene, for example). To overcome these and other difficulties, two major theories have been developed—the **resonance theory** and the **molecular orbital theory.** Each theory is based on the principles of quantum mechanics, and each strives to give a sharper and more inclusive description of the nature of chemical bonding. Let us next examine briefly some of the qualitative aspects of each of these theories, in order to be able to apply their concepts in later chapters.

5-1. Resonance

Consider the structure of benzene, C_6H_6, which in Kekulé notation (5-1) has three C—C single bonds and three C=C double bonds. On the basis of this structure we would expect benzene to show chemical behavior typical for compounds containing >C=C< linkages (alkenes) and to show three normal C—C and three normal C=C bond distances. Actually, in contrast to the chemically reactive alkenes, benzene is strikingly inert. Furthermore, electron diffraction studies have shown that all of the carbon-carbon bond distances in benzene are identical, and are intermediate (1.39 Å) between the normal C—C bond length (1.54 Å) and the normal C=C bond length (1.33 Å). The resonance theory accounts for these and other anomalies by postulating that the "true" structure of benzene is neither of the two equivalent Kekulé formulas, but rather a **resonance hybrid** of both. This hybrid state is designated by double-headed arrows (↔) written between all possible Kekulé structures, as shown in 5-2. An alternative representation of hybrid structure of benzene involves a circle written inside of the benzene hexagon (5-3). Representations 5-2 and 5-3 imply that all of the C—C bonds in benzene are equivalent and are neither true single nor true double bonds, but rather hybrid bonds intermediate between the two extremes.

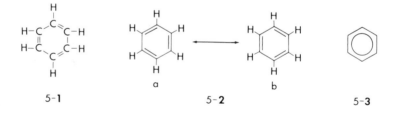

5-1   5-2   5-3

Whenever it is possible to write more than one Kekulé (or electron dot) structure for a molecule, without changing the relative positions of its atoms and without violating the rules of covalence maxima for the atoms, the actual structure of the molecule—according to resonance theory—is a resonance hybrid of all of the different Kekulé structures which can be written. (The covalence maximum for H is 2 electrons; for elements in the first row of the periodic table, 8 electrons; for second row elements, possibly higher. Thus in SF_6 the covalence maximum is 12.) The distinction between the symbol ↔ designating a hybrid state and the symbol ⇌ used to indicate mobile equilibria should be emphasized. If we write A ⇌ B, the symbol implies that both A and B exist as such in a mixture, and are rapidly transforming back and forth into one another. An actual motion of some atom within the molecule is invariably implied, as in the following example.

When we write A ⟷ B, on the other hand, we are designating a single substance whose structure is neither A nor B, but rather a hybrid in between. By way of analogy, a mule is a hybrid of a horse and a donkey. It is forever a mule, and does not alternate between being a horse and being a donkey. Thus we might write "mule = horse ⟷ donkey," but *never* "mule = horse ⇌ donkey."

In resonance such as A ⟷ B, the individual Kekulé structures which designate the hybrid are called **canonical structures**. Generally, a resonance hybrid will have more than two canonical structures, and these ordinarily make unequal contributions to the hybrid. We might imagine additional canonical structures (5-4) contributing to the benzene hybrid. On

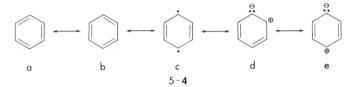

theoretical grounds structures 5-**4c, d**, and **e** (each of which represents but one of equivalent forms of such types) will be less important than the Kekulé structures (5-**4a** and 5-**4b**), and will make a smaller total contribution to the resonance hybrid. Similarly, the contribution of the charged structure (5-**5b**) to the carbonyl hybrid (5-**5**) will be less important than that of the uncharged canonical structure (5-**5a**). Structures 5-**5c** and 5-**5d** depict resonance contributions to the excited state of the carbon group and presumably make little contribution to its ground state.

It is not always obvious by inspection, however, which canonical structures of a hybrid will make the most significant contributions to it. Furthermore, higher energy structures (for example, diradical or charge-separated), which may be unimportant contributors to the "ground state" of the molecule (as when the substance is stored in a dark bottle at room temperature), may become important in an "activated state" of the molecule, as during a chemical reaction or on irradiation with ultraviolet light.

Thus ionic canonical structures (5-**6b** and 5-**6c**) of the ethylene hybrid (5-**6**) are important during some of its addition reactions, and diradical structures (5-**6d**) come into play during its absorption of ultraviolet light, although the ground state contribution is principally the normal Kekulé structure (5-**6a**).

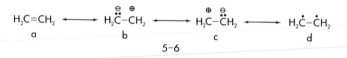

An important consequence of resonance is that the stability of a resonance hybrid is greater than that of any of the individual canonical structures which can be written for it. For example, the total energy of the benzene hybrid is lower than the total energy of the two classical Kekulé structures by some 36 kcal/mole (Figure 5-1). The difference in energy between the hybrid and the most stable canonical structure is referred to as the **resonance energy** of the molecule, and benzene is said to be "stabilized" by a resonance energy of 36 kcal/mole. Such resonance energies may be

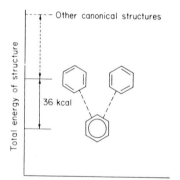

Figure 5-1. Resonance Energy of Benzene

determined experimentally by measuring heats of combustion or heats of hydrogenation. To illustrate, an individual double bond in a molecule will react with hydrogen in the presence of a catalyst (Section 8-4a) with the liberation of about 31 kcal/mole of heat energy,

$$R-CH=CH-R + H_2 \xrightarrow{\text{Catalyst}} R-CH_2-CH_2-R + 31 \text{ kcal}$$

while a molecule containing two isolated double bonds liberates about 62 kcal/mole during hydrogenation. In other words, heats of hydrogenation are approximately additive in simple alkenes. The heat of hydrogenation of cyclohexene is 28.6 kcal/mole. Accordingly, the heat of hydrogenation of cyclohexatriene (one of the classical Kekulé structures of benzene) should be 3 × 28.6 = 85.8 kcal/mole. Experimentally, however, the observed heat of hydrogenation of benzene is only 49.8 kcal/mole. The difference between the theoretical and experimental heats of hydrogenation (85.8 − 49.8 = 36.0 kcal/mole) is regarded as the resonance energy by which the benzene molecule is stabilized. Similar experiments and reasoning involving heats of combustion lead to a comparable value for the resonance energy of benzene.

    Cyclohexene   Cyclohexatriene

5-2. Molecular Orbitals

The regions in space just outside the nucleus of the atom where the probability of finding the atom's electrons is greatest are called **atomic orbitals**. The electron shells (K, L, M in Figure 2-1) about the nucleus contain groups of these atomic orbitals. Each orbital (designated as s, p, d, f) has a unique energy associated with it, can contain a maximum of two electrons, and varies in its shape and spatial orientation. The K shell consists of a single orbital, called 1s. The L shell contains four orbitals, 2s, $2p_x$, $2p_y$, and $2p_z$. The M shell contains nine atomic orbitals, one 3s, three 3p, and five 3d. The manner in which the K- and L-shell orbitals are filled with electrons in forming the first ten elements of the periodic table is illustrated in Table 5-1. Note that (1) s orbitals are filled before

Table 5-1. Electron Distribution for the First Ten Elements of the Periodic Table

Element	Number of Electrons	K Shell 1s	L Shell 2s	$2p_x$	$2p_y$	$2p_z$
H	1	1				
He	2	2				
Li	3	2	1			
Be	4	2	2			
B	5	2	2	1		
C	6	2	2	1	1	
N	7	2	2	1	1	1
O	8	2	2	2	1	1
F	9	2	2	2	2	1
Ne	10	2	2	2	2	2

p orbitals; (2) two electrons cannot occupy a p orbital until all p orbitals have at least one electron each; and (3) no orbital may contain more than two electrons.

The s orbitals are spherically symmetrical about the nucleus. That is, if we picture the nucleus at the center of a three-dimensional coordinate system (Figure 5-2), the probability of finding an s electron in a spherical shell will rise uniformly in all directions to a maximum, then will gradually diminish uniformly in all directions. In the hydrogen atom the position of greatest probability for the location of the $1s$ electron is in a sphere symmetrical about the nucleus and 0.53 Å in radius. The three p orbitals comprise dumbbell-shaped regions in space at right angles to one another along the x, y, and z axes (Figure 5-2). These each have a **nodal plane** at the nucleus, where the probability of the electron's location is zero. Most of the elements found in organic molecules have their electrons in the $1s$, $2s$, and $2p$ orbitals; higher d and f orbitals are utilized by elements further down in the periodic table.

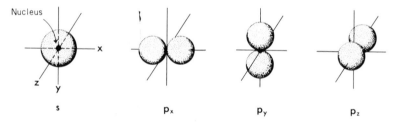

Figure 5-2. s *and* p *Atomic Orbitals*

Bonding between atoms occurs when they come into close enough proximity for their orbitals to interpenetrate one another, or *overlap*. Thus when two hydrogen atoms are brought close enough together to permit overlap of their $1s$ orbitals, their two electrons pair and go into a single orbital encompassing both nuclei (Figure 5-3). A pair of electrons encompassing two or more nuclei is said to occupy a **molecular orbital.** As with atomic orbitals, a molecular orbital may not contain more than two electrons. The molecular orbital represents a lower energy state for the system than do two separate atomic orbitals at the characteristic internuclear distance. Energy is therefore liberated during the overlap, and a stable covalent bond is formed.

A molecular orbital which is symmetrical about two nuclei, in the manner shown for H_2 in Figure 5-3, is called a sigma (σ) molecular orbital. The two electrons in it are called σ **electrons**, and the bond is referred to as a σ **bond**. A σ bond exists as long as the molecular orbital is of the type described, regardless of the nature of the atomic orbitals (s or p) whose overlap produced it. A second type of molecular orbital of importance to organic chemists is the so-called pi (π) orbital, which contains π **electrons** and gives rise to π **bonds**. In contrast to σ orbitals, the π orbital has a nodal plane, analogous to the nodal plane in a p atomic orbital. π orbitals are discussed in greater detail below.

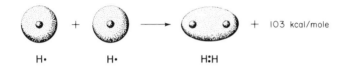

$$H\cdot \qquad H\cdot \qquad H\colon H$$

Figure 5-3. Overlap of 1s *Orbitals in Formation of* H_2

5-3. Orbital Hybridization

On examining the electron distribution in the carbon atom (Table 5-1), we note that the $2s$ atomic orbital is filled, and that the $2p_x$ and $2p_y$ atomic orbitals contain one electron each. We might anticipate, therefore, that carbon would be divalent, forming bonds by overlap involving only its two partially filled p orbitals. There is a tendency, however, for atoms to make maximum use of their available orbitals for bond-forming purposes, and to do this **hybrid atomic orbitals** may be invoked during orbital overlap and bond formation. **Hybridization** thus involves the "promotion" of existing ground state atomic orbitals to new hybrid atomic orbitals during the process of orbital overlap. In the case of carbon, hybridization may occur in three ways, and the choice is governed simply by the number of atoms which are to be bonded to the particular carbon atom involved.

When a carbon atom combines with four other atoms, **tetragonal hybridization** occurs. The four L-shell electrons of carbon are promoted one each into four "sp^3" atomic orbitals, which then overlap with the orbitals of the four combining atoms to form four covalent bonds of the σ type. The sp^3 orbitals and their resulting σ bonds are tetrahedrally oriented, such that the positive nuclei of all of the atoms attached to carbon are as far apart as possible. Tetrahedral hybridization of the atomic orbitals of carbon is illustrated in the hypothetical formation of methane from the elements in Figure 5-4.

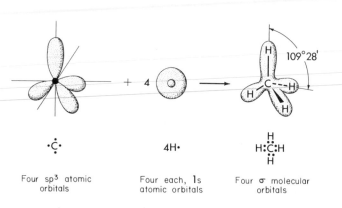

| Four sp^3 atomic orbitals | Four each, 1s atomic orbitals | Four σ molecular orbitals |

Figure 5-4. Hypothetical Formation of Methane

When carbon combines with three other atoms, **trigonal hybridization** occurs. Three of the L shell electrons are promoted to "sp^2" atomic orbitals, the fourth electron remaining in a p atomic orbital. The three sp^2 orbitals overlap with the orbitals of the three combining atoms to form three σ molecular orbitals and three σ bonds, while the remaining p atomic orbital of carbon overlaps the p orbital of one of the adjacent atoms to form a π bond. This gives rise to the double bond so frequently encountered in organic chemistry. Again, the positive nuclei of all of the atoms involved situate themselves as far apart as possible, resulting in the familiar coplanarity and 120° geometry of double-bonded systems (Section 2-8b). Minimum distance π-orbital overlap explains the lack of free rotation about the double bond, and the existence of *cis* and *trans* isomers. These principles are illustrated in Figure 5-5, where the hypothetical formation of ethylene from two carbon and four hydrogen atoms is shown in stepwise fashion. Note that the nodal plane in the π orbital is coincident with the common plane of the five σ bonds.

When carbon forms bonds with two other atoms, **digonal hybridization** occurs, utilizing two "sp" hybrid atomic orbitals and two p atomic orbitals. In acetylene, H—C≡C—H, for example, each carbon is joined to one carbon and one hydrogen atom. One sp hybrid orbital of carbon overlaps the 1s orbital of hydrogen, while the second sp orbital overlaps one of the sp orbitals of the second carbon atom, forming two σ molecular

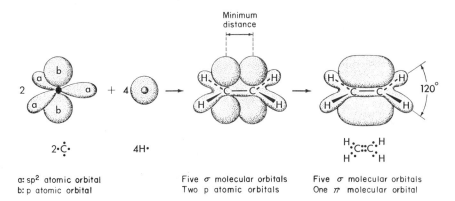

Figure 5-5. Hypothetical Stepwise Formation of Ethylene

orbitals—one to carbon and one to hydrogen. The remaining two perpendicular p atomic orbitals on each of the carbon atoms then overlap to form two cylindrically symmetrical π molecular orbitals with nodal planes at right angles to each other. sp hybrid orbitals form bonds $180°$ apart, giving rise to the "linear" geometry of acetylene and other triple-bonded structures. Figure 5-6 illustrates the hypothetical bond formation steps involved.

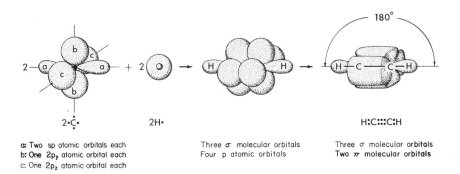

Figure 5-6. Hypothetical Stepwise Formation of Acetylene

Turning our attention finally to benzene, we note that there are six carbon atoms, each one bonded to three other atoms. One would expect, therefore, that each carbon atom would utilize sp^2 hybrid atomic orbitals in its σ bonds to hydrogen and its two adjacent carbon atoms, leaving a

p atomic orbital at each carbon to be utilized in a π molecular orbital. Now, clearly, the p orbital remaining on each of the six carbon atoms may overlap with the p orbital on either adjacent carbon atom with equal ease. There being six such p-orbital electrons, the result is the formation of three π molecular orbitals, each containing two paired electrons, as illustrated in Figure 5-7. The first of these has a nodal plane in the plane of the benzene

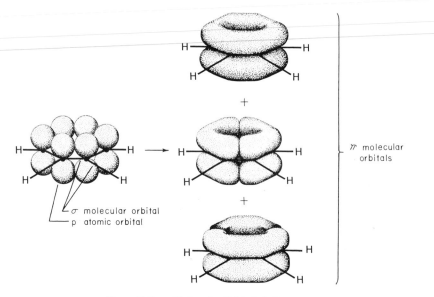

Figure 5-7. π Molecular Orbitals in Benzene

ring only, while the second and third π orbitals have nodal planes per-pendicular to the plane of the ring as well. The measurable geometry of the benzene molecule (flat, regular hexagon; hydrogen atoms making 120° angles with the carbon atoms once removed) is in full accord with the molecular orbital picture of it. The inertness of benzene as compared to ethylene—that is, the stability of the benzene π-electron system as compared to that of ethylene—is explained in terms of **delocalization energy** (equivalent to resonance energy), arising as a consequence of the very large and symmetrical molecular orbitals available to the π electrons of benzene.

SUPPLEMENTARY READING

Resonance

1. "A Physical Picture of Covalent Bonding and Resonance in Organic Chemistry," C. R. Noller, *J. Chem. Educ.*, **27,** 504 (1950); **32,** 23 (1955).
2. "The Concept of Resonance in Elementary Organic Chemistry," A. Gero, *J. Chem. Educ.*, **29,** 82 (1952).
3. "Predicting Reactions of a Resonance Hybrid from Minor Canonical Structures," A. Gero, *J. Chem. Educ.*, **31,** 136 (1954).
4. "About a Machistic Theory in Chemistry and Its Propogandists," V. M. Tatevskii and M. I. Shakhparanov, *J. Chem. Educ.*, **29,** 13 (1952).

Molecular Orbitals

1. Reference 1 above.
2. "Pi and Sigma Bonding in Organic Molecules—An Experiment with Models," K. B. Hoffman, *J. Chem. Educ.*, **37,** 637 (1960).
3. "Distribution of Atomic *s* Character in Molecules and Its Chemical Implications," H. A. Bent, *J. Chem. Educ.*, **37,** 616 (1960).
4. "The Principle of Minimum Bending of Orbitals," G. H. Stewart and H. Eyring, *J. Chem. Educ.*, **35,** 550 (1958).
5. "Atomic and Molecular Orbital Models," F. L. Lambert, *J. Chem. Educ.*, **34,** 217 (1957).
6. "Orbital Models," G. W. A. Fowles, *J. Chem. Educ.*, **32,** 260 (1955).

CHAPTER 6

Organic Reactions
and Their Intermediates

IN THIS CHAPTER we shall examine some general aspects of organic reactions, reserving for later chapters an amplification of the concepts here introduced, additional specific examples of reaction types, and more intimate details of reaction mechanisms.

6-1. Types of Organic Reactions

It is helpful for us to recognize that most organic reactions may be classified as belonging to one of the relatively small number of types listed in Figure 6-1. The specific reactions which we shall encounter throughout the remainder of this book will generally be found to fall into one or more of these types or to be logical analogs of them.

Substitution reactions, also referred to as **displacement** reactions, are said to occur when one atom or group in a molecule is displaced by another atom or group. **Elimination** reactions are characterized by the *intramolecular* loss of a small molecule from a larger one, with simultaneous

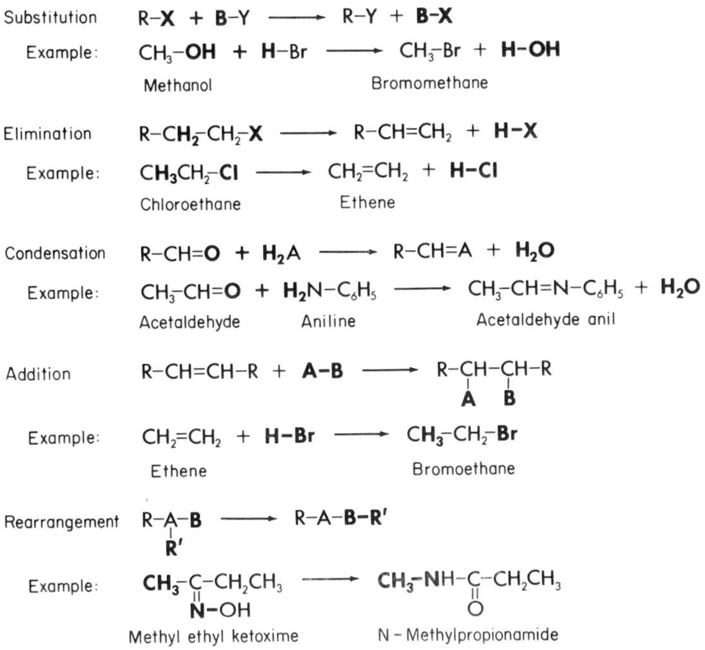

Substitution $R–X + B–Y \longrightarrow R–Y + \mathbf{B–X}$

Example: $CH_3–\mathbf{OH} + \mathbf{H–Br} \longrightarrow CH_3–Br + \mathbf{H–OH}$

      Methanol   Bromomethane

Elimination $R–CH_2–CH_2–X \longrightarrow R–CH=CH_2 + \mathbf{H–X}$

Example: $CH_3CH_2–Cl \longrightarrow CH_2=CH_2 + \mathbf{H–Cl}$

      Chloroethane   Ethene

Condensation $R–CH=O + H_2A \longrightarrow R–CH=A + \mathbf{H_2O}$

Example: $CH_3–CH=O + H_2N–C_6H_5 \longrightarrow CH_3–CH=N–C_6H_5 + \mathbf{H_2O}$

      Acetaldehyde   Aniline   Acetaldehyde anil

Addition $R–CH=CH–R + \mathbf{A–B} \longrightarrow R–\underset{\underset{A}{|}}{C}H–\underset{\underset{B}{|}}{C}H–R$

Example: $CH_2=CH_2 + \mathbf{H–Br} \longrightarrow CH_3–CH_2–\mathbf{Br}$

      Ethene   Bromoethane

Rearrangement $R–\underset{\underset{R'}{|}}{A}–B \longrightarrow R–A–B–R'$

Example: $CH_3–\underset{\underset{\mathbf{N}–OH}{\|}}{C}–CH_2CH_3 \longrightarrow CH_3–NH–\underset{\underset{O}{\|}}{C}–CH_2CH_3$

      Methyl ethyl ketoxime   N–Methylpropionamide

Figure 6-1. General Types of Organic Reactions

formation of a multiple-bond linkage in the larger molecule. In **condensation** reactions, a small molecule (usually H_2O) is eliminated *intermolecularly* from two or more larger molecules. **Addition** reactions, which are the reverse of elimination reactions, involve the addition of one molecule across a multiple bond in another molecule. **Rearrangement** reactions proceed with a reshuffling of the sequence of atoms in a molecule and lead to products having a new structure. The reactions of a given organic compound may involve one of the above reaction types singly, or may involve a sequence of two or more of these types occurring consecutively. In some cases such reactions proceed spontaneously on mere contact of the reactants, but more frequently catalysts are required to bring them about.

6-2. Reaction Mechanisms and Reaction Intermediates

When we examine the types of reactions in Figure 6-1, we notice that each reaction involves the rupture of existing bonds in the reactants and the formation of new bonds in the products. How do such bond-breaking and bond-making processes occur? This question leads us into the consideration of reaction mechanisms, a challenging theoretical field which has occupied the attention of organic chemists intensively during the past several decades. By the **mechanism** of a chemical reaction we mean the actual series of discrete steps which are involved in the transformation of reactants into products. The understanding of reaction mechanisms has been clarified by the recognition of three major bond cleavage processes. Let us consider the hypothetical molecule $CH_3:X$, and imagine the possible ways in which the bond between the carbon atom and the group X may be broken. These are illustrated in Figure 6-2. It is exciting to learn that each of these types of bond cleavage may be observed experimentally.

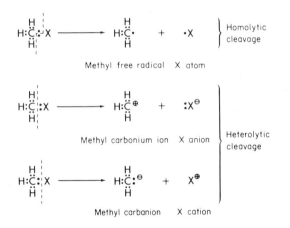

Figure 6-2. *Bond Cleavage Processes*

In **homolytic bond cleavage**, one electron of the bonding pair goes with each of the departing groups, resulting in two electrically neutral fragments, atoms and/or **free radicals.** We see that both the atom and the free radical are uncharged electrically, and that each characteristically has one unpaired electron. Alkyl free radicals are designated in general terms by the symbol R·. **Heterolytic bond cleavages** result in charged fragments. When the two bonding electrons leave the organic group and remain with the departing substituent X, the resulting organic fragment—which has only six paired electrons (electrons with opposite spins) and bears a positive charge at its carbon center—is called a **carbonium ion.** Carbonium ions are symbolized generally as $R^{\oplus}$. Heterolytic cleavage wherein the two bonding electrons remain with the organic group result in a **carbanion**, $R:^{\ominus}$, which has eight paired electrons and bears a negative charge on its carbon center. Analogous heterolytic and homolytic cleavage processes apply also to other chemical bonds, leading similarly to positively or negatively charged ionic fragments (for example, $R:\ddot{S}^{\oplus}$ and $R:\ddot{O}:^{\ominus}$) or to neutral free radicals (such as $R:\ddot{O}\cdot$).

The fragments resulting from the above bond cleavage processes are highly reactive, and ordinarily react *very* rapidly (within small fractions of a second) with other molecules in their environment. Under these circumstances such species thus constitute **transitory intermediates** in the progress of a reaction from reactants to products. They are too short lived to be examined by customary physical or chemical methods, and their intervention during a chemical reaction can only be inferred indirectly. In fact, sometimes the discrete intermediate does not become fully developed during the progress of a reaction, but is only approached or approximated (see S_N2 reactions; Section 11-12d). Occasionally, however, because of structural peculiarities (see Sections 6-4a, 6-6a, 6-7) and in proper environments, such intermediates may have lower reactivities and long enough lifetimes to be studied as individual chemical entities. Reactions whose pathways involve carbonium ion intermediates are said to proceed by a carbonium ion mechanism, reactions involving free radical intermediates by a free radical mechanism, and so on.

Studies commenced in the 1930's have led to the recognition of a fourth type of transitory reaction intermediate, namely, the **carbenes.** The fragment $CH_2:$, called carbene or methylene, can be thought of as arising by a homolytic fission of the following sort.

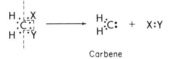

Carbene

Although not as important generally as carbonium ions, carbanions, and free radicals, carbene and substituted carbene intermediates have been found to intervene in a number of special organic reactions to be discussed in later chapters.

6-3. Experimental Conditions and Reaction Mechanisms

There are characteristic experimental conditions which favor each of the two major types of reaction mechanism—ionic or free radical—open to organic reactants. These are summarized in Table 6-1. The criteria listed are quite general, so that if a reaction occurs under one set of conditions and not the other, evidence is at hand for the type of mechanism which the reaction is following.

Table 6-1. Experimental Characteristics of Ionic and Free Radical Reactions

Ionic	Free Radical
1. Occur in solution, and only very rarely in the gas phase.	1. Occur in the gas phase or in non-polar solvents.
2. Occur in polar solvents; reactions influenced by the polarity of the solvent.	2. Catalyzed and initiated by light and by substances (e.g., peroxides) which are known to decompose with the formation of free radicals.
3. Catalyzed by acids and bases.	
4. Reaction rates increased by increasing temperature. Rates not affected by light, free radical sources, or free radical inhibitors.	3. Many occur only at high temperatures.
	4. Reaction rates not greatly influenced by variation in temperature. Rates of gas phase reactions influenced by the shape and size of the reaction vessel.
5. Generally not autocatalytic; that is, reaction rates are uniform and regular throughout the course of the reaction.	5. Reactions inhibited or prevented by the presence of free radical "scavengers" (e.g., hydroquinone).
	6. Reactions often autocatalytic, showing a characteristic induction period and proceeding with an increasing rate once started.

6-4. Some Aspects of Free Radicals

We learned above that free radicals may be long lived or transitory, depending upon their structure and environment. Let us next consider in more detail how stable and transient free radicals may be generated, the factors which determine their stability, and their stereochemical features. In subsequent chapters we shall encounter additional methods for producing free radicals and examine the fascinating variety of reactions which transient free radicals may undergo.

a. Stable Free Radicals. In 1900 M. Gomberg at the University of Michigan attempted to prepare a then unknown compound, hexaphenylethane, by a rational method. His product, however, proved to be unusually reactive and to have none of the anticipated properties of the desired hydrocarbon, which he was subsequently able to prepare only by rigorously excluding air from his reaction mixture. Gomberg soon recognized that the expected hexaphenylethane had partially dissociated into two **triphenylmethyl radicals**, which reacted rapidly with oxygen in the air to form colorless triphenylmethyl peroxide, $(C_6H_5)_3C-O-O-C-(C_6H_5)_3$. Upon exclusion of air, a mobile equilibrium existed between undissociated hexaphenylethane and the free radical. Freshly prepared

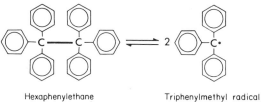

Hexaphenylethane	Triphenylmethyl radical
(Colorless solution in benzene)	(Orange solution in benzene)

solutions of hexaphenylethane in benzene were colorless, but rapidly became orange as dissociation progressed. The color could be reversibly intensified by warming the solution and diminished by cooling it, and the free radical present reacted avidly with oxygen, chlorine, bromine, and iodine. Subsequent investigations by physical methods, chiefly spectro-

$$2 \ (C_6H_5)_3C\cdot \quad \begin{array}{c} \xrightarrow{\ O_2\ } (C_6H_5)_3C-O-O-C(C_6H_5)_3 \\ \text{Triphenylmethyl peroxide} \\ \xrightarrow{\ X_2\ } 2 \ (C_6H_5)_3C-X \\ \text{Triphenylmethyl halide} \end{array}$$

metric and magnetic, have abundantly established the correctness of Gomberg's interpretation, and many stable free radicals of analogous types have been prepared. Owing to the odd electron, a free radical is **paramagnetic**—that is, it is attracted into a magnetic field—and the measurement of the **magnetic susceptibility** of solutions of stable free radicals gives a measure of their degree of dissociation. It has been found that a 0.07 per cent solution of hexaphenylethane in benzene contains 18 per cent triphenylmethyl radical at 13° and 42 per cent at 43°.

The carbon-carbon bond strength in ethane is about 83 kcal/mole, whereas that between the central carbons of hexaphenylethane is only about 11 kcal/mole. How can we explain the instability of hexaphenyl-ethane and the stability of the triphenylmethyl radical? Several factors are important. Dissociation is promoted by the extreme crowding which exists between the six large phenyl groups attached to two adjacent carbon atoms in hexaphenylethane; this bulk factor is referred to as a **steric effect**. The stability of the radical itself is explained by its existence as a resonance hybrid, with its odd electron distributed over the three aro-

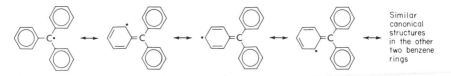

Figure 6-3. Canonical Structures for the Triphenylmethyl Radical Hybrid

matic rings. We see (Figure 6-3) that the odd electron becomes effectively "lost" in the resonance hybrid, and is therefore less available for bond formation during association. Only those structures which are a resonance hybrid of a large number of canonical forms are able to exist as stable free radicals, and when the possibilities for additional canonical structures increase, the extent of dissociation of the hexaarylethane is even greater. Thus hexa-*p*-diphenylethane is more than 70 per cent dissociated in solution, and the solution is deep purple. Furthermore, the sp^2 hybridization

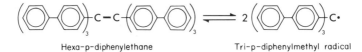

Hexa-p-diphenylethane   Tri-p-diphenylmethyl radical

and 120° geometry of the triphenylmethyl radical provide greater "elbow room" for the bulky phenyl groups than do the sp^3 bonds and 109.5° bond angles of the undissociated hexaphenylethane. Thus steric factors also help to explain both the stability and ease of formation of triarylmethyl radicals.

b. Transient Free Radicals. In 1929 F. Paneth in Germany obtained the first clear-cut evidence for transient alkyl free radicals. When tetramethyllead, $Pb(CH_3)_4$, vapors were heated in an evacuated quartz tube through which hydrogen was flowing (Figure 6-4), a lead mirror formed where the tube was heated, and ethane, CH_3CH_3, was found in the exit gas stream. If the tube were then heated "upstream" from an existing mirror, a new mirror formed, the original mirror vanished, and tetramethyllead was found in the exit gas stream. Since the likely stable products of such de-

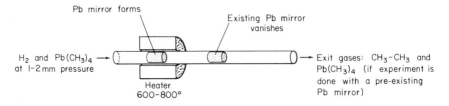

Figure 6-4. Paneth's Discovery of Transient Methyl Radicals

composition (H_2, CH_4, CH_3CH_3, $CH_2{=}CH_2$, and $HC{\equiv}CH$) had no effect on lead mirrors, Paneth concluded that the tetramethyllead must have decomposed into metallic lead and free methyl radicals. The methyl radicals could then combine with each other to form ethane, or react with a pre-existing mirror to regenerate tetramethyllead:

Mirror formation: $Pb(CH_3)_4 \xrightarrow{\ 600-800°\ } Pb\ +\ 4\ CH_3\cdot$

Ethane formation: $2\ CH_3\cdot \xrightarrow{\hspace{2cm}} CH_3{:}CH_3$

Mirror removal: $4\ CH_3\cdot\ +\ Pb \xrightarrow{\hspace{2cm}} Pb(CH_3)_4$

By measuring the rate of disappearance of lead mirrors located at different distances from the heater (Figure 6-4), and knowing the flow rate of hydrogen through the tube, Paneth was able to calculate that the **half-life** of such methyl radicals was about 0.006 second. By the half-life of a substance we mean the time required for one-half of it to react. Paneth and others have since investigated higher alkyl radicals ($R\cdot$) and found them also to be extremely reactive and short lived.

Alkyl radicals are classed as **primary, secondary,** or **tertiary,** depending upon whether the carbon atom at the radical site is attached to two (or three), one, or no hydrogen atoms. While vastly less stable than the tri-

Primary free radicals	Secondary free radical	Tertiary free radical

arylmethyl radicals discussed above, these types of alkyl radicals vary in their relative stability, and it has been found from free radical reactions that the order of stability of alkyl radicals is: tertiary > secondary > primary. Related to and paralleling the stability of free radicals is their relative ease of formation, which again follows the pattern: tertiary > secondary > primary. Thus, other things being equal, a tertiary free radical will form more readily as a reaction intermediate than will a secondary or primary radical. One explanation for the relative stabilities of alkyl radicals involves the concept of **hyperconjugation** or **no-bond resonance**. The no-bond canonical structures for representatives of the three radical types are illustrated in Figure 6-5. These canonical structures imply that there is something less than a full covalent bond between the indicated carbon and hydrogen atoms in the radical hybrid. Just as with ordinary resonance (Chapter 5), the greater the number of possible canonical structures for no-bond resonance, the more the odd electron is delocalized and the greater is the stability of the radical. Thus tertiary radicals, with greater possibilities for hyperconjugation, are more stable than secondary,

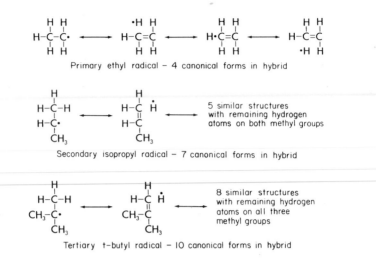

Figure 6-5. Canonical Forms of Alkyl Radical Hybrids

which, in turn, are more stable than primary. The relative ease of forming tertiary, secondary, and primary free radicals is reflected in the bond strengths of bonds whose heterolytic cleavage yields such radicals, as illustrated in Table 6-2.

Table 6-2. Some Bond Dissociation Energies for Homolytic Bond Cleavage

	Bond Strength, kcal/mole	Radical Formed
CH_3—H	101	Primary
CH_3CH_2—H	98	Primary
$(CH_3)_2CH$—H	89	Secondary
$(CH_3)_3C$—H	85	Tertiary
CH_3—Br	67	Primary
CH_3CH_2—Br	65	Primary
$(CH_3)_2CH$—Br	59	Secondary

c. *The Configuration of Free Radicals.* A variety of stereochemical investigations indicate that the three groups attached to carbon in a free radical are ordinarily trigonally oriented, with sp^2 hybridization (Figure 6-6). Such hybridization allows for stabilization of the radical by resonance or by hyperconjugation. Other experiments, however, involving

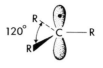

Figure 6-6. Trigonal Hybridization in a Free Radical

radicals where sp^2 hybridization is impossible, suggest that—in contrast to carbonium ions (see Section 6-6c)—free radicals may also exist with tetragonal sp^3 hybridization.

6-5. Lewis Acids and Bases

The understanding of ionic organic reactions involving carbonium ion or carbanion intermediates has been aided by the concept of generalized acids and bases developed by G. N. Lewis at the University of California around 1923. Lewis proposed the following very broad and extremely useful definitions:

 An **acid** *is any species (molecule or ion) which is capable of accepting a pair of electrons from another molecule or ion.*

 A **base** *is any species capable of donating a pair of electrons to another molecule or ion.*

 An **acid-base reaction** *(neutralization) is the sharing of an electron pair of a base with an acid, with formation of a coordinate covalent bond.*

Some typical generalized acid-base reactions are shown in Table 6-3.

Table 6-3. Lewis Acids and Bases

Acid	Base	Product
$H^{\oplus}$ +	$:\!\overset{..}{\underset{..}{O}}\!:\!H^{\ominus}$	$H\!:\!\overset{..}{\underset{..}{O}}\!:\!H$
$H^{\oplus}$ +	$H\!:\!\overset{..}{\underset{..}{O}}\!:\!H$	$H\!:\!\overset{..}{\underset{H}{O}}\!:\!H^{\oplus}$
$H^{\oplus}$ +	$R\!:\!\overset{..}{\underset{..}{O}}\!:\!H$	$R\!:\!\overset{..}{\underset{H}{O}}\!:\!H^{\oplus}$
$H^{\oplus}$ +	$:\!\overset{..}{\underset{..}{Cl}}\!:^{\ominus}$	$H\!:\!\overset{..}{\underset{..}{Cl}}\!:$
$H^{\oplus}$ +	$:\!\overset{H}{\underset{H}{N}}\!:\!H$	$H\!:\!\overset{H}{\underset{H}{N}}\!:\!H^{\oplus}$
$Cl\!:\!\overset{Cl}{\underset{Cl}{Al}}$ +	$:\!\overset{..}{\underset{..}{Cl}}\!:^{\ominus}$	$Cl\!:\!\overset{Cl}{\underset{Cl}{Al}}\!:\!Cl^{\ominus}$
$F\!:\!\overset{F}{\underset{F}{B}}$ +	$R\!:\!\overset{..}{\underset{..}{O}}\!:\!R$	$F\!:\!\overset{F}{\underset{F}{B}}\!:\!\overset{\delta-}{\underset{R}{O}}\!:\!R^{\delta+}$

Note that acids are either cations or neutral molecules with unfilled outer electron orbitals, whereas bases are anions or neutral molecules with unshared electrons in an outer orbital. Accordingly, the products of such reactions may be positively charged, negatively charged, or neutral, depending upon the natures of the participating acid and base.

An important corollary to the above definitions is that the "electron-rich" part of one molecule or ion will be attracted to a site of low electron density in another molecule. Conversely, an "electron-poor" part of one molecule or ion will be attracted to a site of high electron density in another molecule. Reactants which seek a site of low electron density in another molecule are called **nucleophiles** (Greek, nucleus lover), and are exemplified by Lewis bases. Reactants which seek a point of high electron density are called **electrophiles**, and Lewis acids fall into this category. We shall see that the above terms and concepts are widely applied in the description and understanding of organic reactions having ionic mechanisms.

6-6. Some Aspects of Carbonium Ions

We shall examine next a few general aspects of carbonium ions, reserving for later chapters more detailed examples of their modes of formation and their various reaction paths. As with free radicals, carbonium ions may be classed as stable or transient, depending upon the duration of their existence. Structural features within the carbonium ion again determine their stability and lifetime.

a. Stable Carbonium Ions. When triphenylchloromethane, a white, covalent solid, is dissolved in the electrically nonconducting solvent, liquid sulfur dioxide, an orange-colored solution results, which readily conducts an electric current. Clearly, the covalent chloride has ionized on dissolving, producing a triphenylmethyl carbonium ion and a chloride ion.

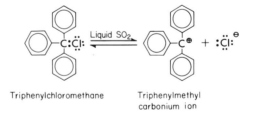

Triphenylchloromethane   Triphenylmethyl
                                 carbonium ion

Similarly, when the white, crystalline alcohol triphenylmethanol is dissolved in sulfuric acid, an orange-colored solution is obtained, which shows a molal freezing point depression four times that expected for a solution of undissociated triphenylmethanol. This is attributed to ionization of the alcohol in the sulfuric acid solvent, with the formation of a triphenylmethyl carbonium ion, according to the sequence of reactions in Figure 6-7. Note that in the first step the alcohol acts as a Lewis base, that dissociation of the cation of its resulting "salt" generates the triphenylmethyl carbonium ion in the second step, and that the net reaction yields four ionic fragments. Furthermore, when the yellow sulfuric acid solution is diluted with water, the yellow color vanishes and unaltered triphenylmethanol is regenerated (via a reversal of step 2).

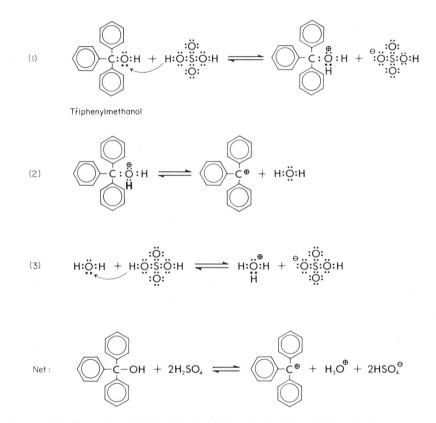

Figure 6-7. Formation of Triphenylmethyl Carbonium Ion from Triphenylmethanol

The stability of the triphenylmethyl carbonium ion is again explained in terms of resonance; that is, the positive charge on the ion is actually not localized on the central carbon atom, but rather is distributed uniformly throughout the three adjacent aromatic rings. The ten canonical structures

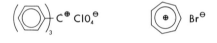

Figure 6-8. Canonical Structures for the Triphenylmethyl Carbonium Ion Hybrid

of the resonance hybrid making up this ion are shown in Figure 6-8. Carbonium ions are generally stable when their structures permit such an extensive delocalization of their positive charge, and many analogous triarylmethyl carbonium ions are known, some even as stable, solid salts. Triphenylmethyl perchlorate, for example, exists as a red, crystalline solid, while tropylium bromide is a yellow solid. The latter salt is insoluble

Triphenylmethyl perchlorate   Tropylium bromide

in ether, but soluble in water (see Table 2-3). The seven completely equivalent canonical structures for the tropylium ion hybrid are illustrated in Figure 6-9.

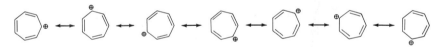

Figure 6-9. Canonical Structures for the Tropylium Ion Hybrid

b. Transient Carbonium Ions. Carbonium ions lacking extensive resonance stabilization, like their free radical analogs, are known only as transitory intermediates in certain organic reactions. Short-lived carbonium ions may be generated by the action of Lewis acids on a number of types of organic compounds. Two examples are:

$$R\text{-OH} + H^{\oplus} \rightleftharpoons R\text{-}\overset{\oplus}{O}\overset{H}{\underset{H}{}} \rightleftharpoons R^{\oplus} + H_2O$$

$$R\text{-Cl} + AlCl_3 \rightleftharpoons R^{\oplus} + AlCl_4^{\ominus}$$

and we shall encounter other methods in future chapters. We should recall that such reactions generally occur in polar solvents, and understand that the **solvation** of the resulting ions (Section 2-3) provides a large part of the *driving force* for their formation. That is, the energy liberated when the polar solvent molecules **solvate** the ions (associate with them by electrostatic attraction) provides much of the energy required to promote the heterolytic bond fission.

Carbonium ions are classified as primary, secondary, or tertiary depending upon the number of hydrogen atoms attached to the carbonium ion center. Again, as with free radicals, the stabilities of alkyl carbonium ions,

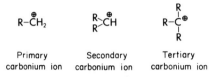

| Primary | Secondary | Tertiary |
| carbonium ion | carbonium ion | carbonium ion |

as well as their relative ease of formation, are found to be in the order: tertiary > secondary > primary. Thus in the generation of a carbonium ion, when there is a choice among primary, secondary, and tertiary carbonium ions, the most stable tertiary ion is preferentially formed. The action of a Lewis acid on a carbon-carbon double bond, for example, produces the more stable carbonium ion in considerable preponderance over the less stable.

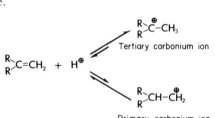

As with alkyl radicals, the order of stability of primary, secondary, and tertiary alkyl carbonium ions is explainable in terms of **hyperconjugation** or **no-bond resonance**. For example, the least stable primary ethyl carbonium ion may delocalize its positive charge only through the four canonical structures shown in Figure 6-10, while the more stable secondary isopropyl carbonium ion has seven analogous canonical structures in its hybrid, and the most stable tertiary *t*-butyl carbonium ion has ten such canonical structures. Again, the more canonical structures which may be written, the more stable the carbonium ion proves to be. Benzyl carbonium ions and allyl carbonium ions, which we shall encounter in more detail later, are considerably more stable and easily formed than simple

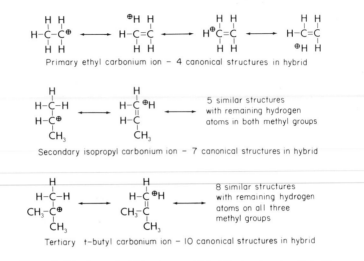

Figure 6-10. Canonical Structures of Alkyl Carbonium Ion Hybrids

alkyl carbonium ions because of the more effective stabilization of their resonance hybrids through the canonical structures shown in Figures 6-11 and 6-12.

Figure 6-11. Canonical Structures of the Benzyl Carbonium Ion Hybrid

$$CH_2=CH-\overset{\oplus}{C}H_2 \longleftrightarrow \overset{\oplus}{C}H_2-CH=CH_2$$

Figure 6-12. Canonical Structures of the Allyl Carbonium Ion Hybrid

c. The Configuration of Carbonium Ions. There is a considerable body of evidence, some of which we shall consider in detail in later chapters, that the configurations of carbonium ions involve flat, planar structures, as illustrated below. Such planar structures, with their 120° geometry and

sp^2 hybridization, are a prerequisite for stabilization of the carbonium ion through resonance or hyperconjugation. When the structure of a molecule is such as to preclude 120° geometry and sp^2 hybridization in the corresponding carbonium ion, the ion fails to form. Thus, while triphenylchloromethane ionizes spontaneously in liquid SO_2 to form the triphenylmethyl carbonium ion (see Section 6-6a), the bridged analog, 1-bromotriptycene, does not. Similarly, while ordinary tertiary alkyl chlorides of

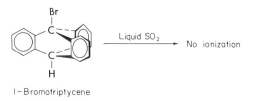

1–Bromotriptycene

the type R_3C—Cl react rapidly with silver nitrate solution to form silver chloride and a transient carbonium ion, the bridged chloride, 1-chloroapocamphane, is highly unreactive. The reason such bridged structures

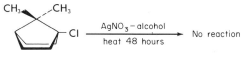

1– Chloroapocamphane

fail to generate carbonium ions is that the rigid structural constraint of their rings makes it geometrically impossible for a resulting carbonium ion to have the planar structure required for its stabilization.

6-7. Some Aspects of Carbanions

When certain organic compounds are treated with strong Lewis bases, a hydrogen atom attached to carbon may be removed as a proton, yielding a carbanion.

$$\mathbf{B:} \ + \ \underset{\underset{R_3}{|}}{\overset{\overset{R_1}{|}}{H:C}}\text{-}R_2 \ \rightleftharpoons \ \mathbf{B:}\overset{\oplus}{H} \ + \ \overset{\ominus}{:}\underset{\underset{R_3}{|}}{\overset{\overset{R_1}{|}}{C}}\text{-}R_2$$

Lewis base

The extent of carbanion formation—that is, the equilibrium point of the equation shown—depends upon both the strength of the base B: and the nature of the organic compound. The bases commonly employed to generate carbanions, and their relative base strengths, are: R—$O:^{\ominus}$ (alkoxide ion) > H—$O:^{\ominus}$ (hydroxide ion) > $R_3N:$ (amines). As was the case with free radicals and carbonium ions, carbanion formation and stability are enhanced when the carbanion has the possibility of spreading its negative charge over a large resonance hybrid structure. Thus certain hydrocarbons such as triphenylmethane, cyclopentadiene, and indene are capable of forming stable sodium or potassium salts, as illustrated below.

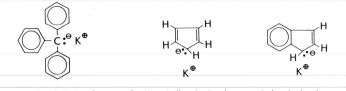

Triphenylmethylpotassium   Cyclopentadienylpotassium   Indenylpotassium

The equivalent canonical structures making up the cyclopentadienyl carbanion hybrid are shown in Figure 6-13.

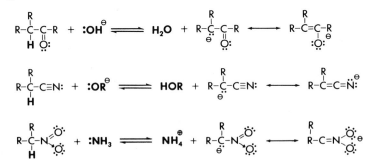

Figure 6-13. Canonical Structures of the Cyclopentadienyl Carbanion Hybrid

One type of *transient* carbanion extremely important in a wide variety of organic reactions is that formed at a carbon atom adjacent to a group having multiple linkages. The formation of such carbanions, plus the canonical forms of their hybrids, is shown in the following typical general examples.

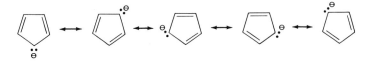

We see that in each case a proton on the carbon atom adjacent to the multiply bonded (**unsaturated**) group is removed by the Lewis base, and that the resulting carbanion is able to distribute its negative charge over a three-atom hybrid. The hydrogen atoms on carbon atoms adjacent to

unsaturated groups are thus considerably more acidic than those of ordinary C—H bonds. These hydrogen atoms on α-carbon atoms are designated as **α-hydrogen atoms** and are readily removed as protons by strong bases. The resulting transient carbanions can then engage in a variety of product-forming reactions, a number of which will be discussed in detail in subsequent chapters.

The configurations of simple carbanions are believed to be tetrahedral, like that of carbon. The configurations appear to be unstable, however, and such carbanions are thought to undergo rapid spontaneous **inversion of configuration** during their lifetime, as shown in Figure 6-14. Car-

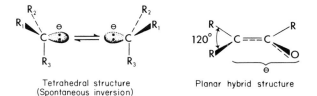

Tetrahedral structure
(Spontaneous inversion)

Planar hybrid structure

Figure 6-14. Configurations of Carbanions

banions which are significantly stabilized by resonance, such as those discussed above, on the other hand, are thought to have a planar configuration and 120° geometry to accommodate the sp^2 hybridization necessary for their resonance hybrid structures (Figure 6-14).

6-8. Energy Relations During Chemical Reactions

Let us consider a general reaction of the type:

$$A-X + B-Y \rightleftharpoons A-Y + B-X$$

It is of considerable practical importance to chemists to know whether the equilibrium point of such a reaction lies far to the right, far to the left, or somewhere in between. How can the equilibrium positions of such reactions be estimated, and what are the factors determining them? Let us examine some of these questions in a general qualitative manner, emphasizing that a more rigorous treatment lies beyond our present scope and, indeed, beyond the needs of most practicing organic chemists.

A rough estimate of the overall direction of many organic reactions can be made on the basis of the heat liberated or required during the reaction. This in turn can be estimated from known bond energies. Consider, for example, the reaction between methane and chlorine to form chloro-methane and hydrogen chloride. In the overall reaction one C–H and one Cl–Cl bond are broken, requiring (Table 2-7) a total energy of 157 kcal/mole, while one C–Cl bond and one H–Cl bond are formed, liberating a total energy of 184 kcal/mole. The overall reaction thus occurs with a net *liberation* of 27 kcal/mole, and is therefore said to be **exothermic** (gives off heat energy). Since the reaction liberates energy, we would expect it—

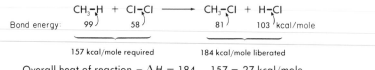

$$\text{Bond energy:}\qquad \underset{99}{CH_3\text{–}H} \ + \ \underset{58}{Cl\text{–}Cl} \ \longrightarrow \ \underset{81}{CH_3\text{–}Cl} \ + \ \underset{103}{H\text{–}Cl} \ \text{kcal/mole}$$

$$\underbrace{\phantom{157 \text{ kcal/mole required}}}_{157 \text{ kcal/mole required}} \qquad \underbrace{\phantom{184 \text{ kcal/mole liberated}}}_{184 \text{ kcal/mole liberated}}$$

Overall heat of reaction $= \Delta H = 184 - 157 = 27$ kcal/mole

like a ball rolling downhill—to occur of its own accord. Conversely, the reverse reaction would require the *consumption* of 27 kcal/mole (it is **endothermic**, that is, absorbs heat energy) and, like a ball rolling uphill, would not be expected to occur spontaneously.

Whether or not a spontaneous reaction will occur at a practical rate, however, depends upon another factor, namely, the **activation energy** of the reaction. Again, the ball and hill analogy is instructive. Given a slight push, a ball resting on a high plateau will roll spontaneously downhill into a valley below. This spontaneous process will be hindered, however, if an additional hill intervenes between the plateau and the valley (Figure 6-15). The chemical analogy to this is illustrated in Figure 6-16, where the energy relationships during an exothermic chemical reaction are indicated.

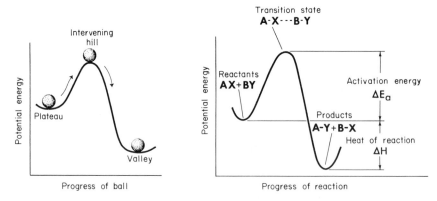

Figure 6-15. Activation Energy Analogy

Figure 6-16. An Exothermic Reaction

Generally, an **activation energy barrier** to the reaction must be sur-
mounted before the system reaches the midpoint of the reaction (the
transition state or **activated complex**) and before the "downhill plunge"
to products can occur. In Figure 6-15, the higher the intervening hill, the
more energy must be put into the push before the ball can reach the hilltop
and begin its spontaneous downhill path. In Figure 6-16 we see that,
analogously, the higher the activation energy barrier, the more potential
energy the system must gain before the transition state is reached. Therefore, reactions with high activation energies occur more slowly than those
with low activation energies, since at ordinary temperatures the kinetic
energies of only a small fraction of the reactant molecules will be great
enough to provide sufficient energy on collision to reach the transition state
(Figure 6-17). Thus we see that it is the activation energy and not the heat

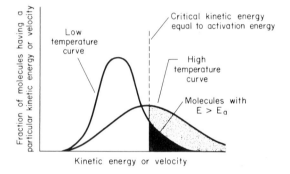

Figure 6-17. Distribution of Molecular Kinetic Energies

of reaction which determines the reaction rate. The mathematics applying
to such rates show, for example, that for activation energies of 5, 10, and 15
kcal/mole, the relative reaction rates will be in a ratio of 10,000:100:1. At
higher temperatures, however, the kinetic energies of the reactant molecules are greater and a larger fraction of them will have the requisite energy
on collision to reach the transition state (Figure 6-17). Thus the rate of the
reaction will increase with increasing temperature. The higher its activation energy, the more a reaction will be accelerated at higher temperatures.
A 50° temperature rise, for example, will increase the rate of a reaction
whose activation energy is 5 kcal/mole by only 50 per cent, but will
increase by threefold the rate of a reaction whose activation energy is
15 kcal/mole.

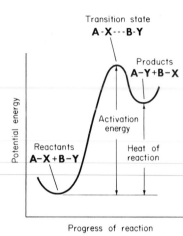

Figure 6-18. An Endothermic Reaction

An endothermic reaction similarly has a specific activation energy required to reach its transition state (Figure 6-18). The activation energy here must always be at least as great as the heat of reaction. For reactions involving carbonium ions or carbanions where there is a discrete reaction intermediate, there are actually two (or more) activation energies involved —one leading to a transition state for formation of the intermediate, and a second leading to a transition state between the intermediate and the final product, as shown in Figure 6-19. The portion of the overall reaction having the highest activation energy barrier is the slowest step in the sequence, and is called the **rate-determining step** of the reaction. Many of the steps in free radical reactions, on the other hand, are believed to occur with zero or negligible activation energies.

The student may be left with the impression that exothermic reactions occur spontaneously and endothermic reactions do not. This is not generally true, however, and a number of spontaneous endothermic reactions are in fact known. More accurately, a chemical reaction will proceed in the right-hand direction if the so-called **free energy change** (ΔG) of the reaction is negative, and will go in the reverse direction if ΔG is positive. Moreover, the equilibrium constant (K) for such reactions is quantitatively related to the free energy change by the equation:

$$\Delta G = -2.3RT \times \log_{10} K$$

where R = the so-called **gas constant** (1.98 cal/mole × degree)
       T = the absolute temperature

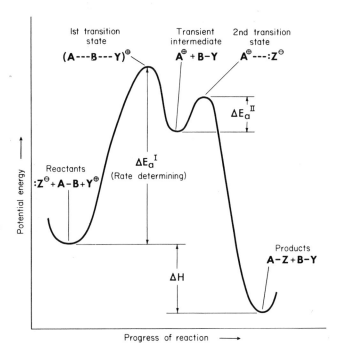

Figure 6-19. An Exothermic Reaction with a Transient Intermediate

The above discussion can be made more correct by substituting ΔG where ΔH was used, and is strictly applicable as given only to those (theoretical) reactions for which $\Delta G = \Delta H$. For fuller and more rigorous treatments of the energetics of chemical reactions the student is referred to the Supplementary Reading list.

SUPPLEMENTARY READING

Mechanisms

1. "The Reactive Intermediates of Organic Chemistry," R. Stewart, *J. Chem. Educ.*, **38,** 308 (1961).
2. "Models Illustrating the Lewis Theory of Acids and Bases," F. Y. Herron, *J. Chem. Educ.*, **30,** 199 (1953).
3. "Proton-Donors in the Electronic Theory of Acids and Bases," W. F. Luder, *J. Chem. Educ.*, **22,** 301 (1945).
4. "Hyperconjugation: An Elementary Approach," R. C. Ferreira, *J. Chem. Educ.*, **29,** 554 (1952).
5. "Organic Chemical Reactions," J. D. Roberts, *Scientific American*, November, 1957.

Free Radicals

1. "Electron Paramagnetic Resonance in Free Radicals," J. A. MacMillan, *J. Chem. Educ.*, **38,** 438 (1961).
2. "Free Radical Chemistry in Solution," R. J. Gritter, *J. Chem. Educ.*, **35,** 475 (1958).
3. "Chemistry of Organic Free Radicals in the Vapor Phase," H. E. De La Mer and W. E. Vaughan, *J. Chem. Educ.*, **34,** 10, 64 (1957).
4. "Frozen Free Radicals," C. M. Herzfeld and A. M. Bass, *Scientific American*, March, 1957.

Energetics of Reactions

1. "How Can You Tell Whether a Reaction Will Occur?" G. E. MacWood and F. H. Verhoek, *J. Chem. Educ.*, **38,** 334 (1961).
2. "The Uses and Abuses of Bond Energies," B. E. Knox and H. B. Palmer, *J. Chem. Educ.*, **38,** 292 (1961).
3. "Entropy and Free Energy," W. F. Luder, *J. Chem. Educ.*, **21,** 265 (1944).

CHAPTER 7

Hydrocarbons—Alkanes

WE RECALL THAT compounds made up only of carbon and hydrogen are called **hydrocarbons.** Among organic compounds, the hydrocarbons form the basic *parent* carbon skeletons to which other functional groups (Section 2–5) are attached or in which such groups occur. In this and the next three chapters we shall examine briefly the chemical and physical aspects of these important types of compounds.

7-1. Classes of Hydrocarbons

There are two principal series of hydrocarbons, the aliphatic series and the aromatic series, and several classes of hydrocarbons within each series. As we have seen, methane, CH_4, is the parent hydrocarbon of the aliphatic series, and benzene, C_6H_6, that of the aromatic series. The classes within the aliphatic series are the **alkanes** (paraffins), **alkenes** (olefins), **alkynes** (acetylenes), and **cycloalkanes.** The classes within the aromatic series are the **monocyclic** (mononuclear) aromatics, which contain a single benzene nucleus, and the **polycyclic** (polynuclear) aromatics, which contain two or more benzene nuclei. **Hydroaromatics** (cycloalkenes) bridge the two series, so to speak, and **alkylaromatics** have structural units derived from both series. These various classes of hydrocarbons are summarized in Figure 7-1.

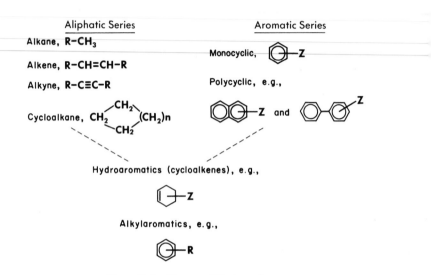

Figure 7-1. Classes of Hydrocarbons

7-2. Nomenclature

How are the million or so existing organic compounds named? Historically, as organic compounds were discovered, they were named rather haphazardly, the name often suggesting the source. Thus formic acid, H—COOH, was so named because it was found as a constituent of ants (Latin, *formica*), while lactic acid, CH_3—CH(OH)—COOH, was found in milk (Latin, *lactis*). Such names are now referred to as **trivial** or **common names.** As the number of known organic compounds increased, however, trivial nomenclature became burdensome and impractical, and chemists attempted to develop more rational naming systems. The system in use today is based on logical rules formulated at meetings of the International Union of Pure and Applied Chemistry (Liège, 1930; Amsterdam, 1949), and is known as the IUPAC system. To apply the IUPAC system, the structure of the compound to be named must be known. The nomenclature rules are applied to the structure, and a name is developed which is completely unique for that structure alone. Similarly, for every proper IUPAC name, there is one, and only one, corresponding Kekulé structure. IUPAC nomenclature is almost invariably used for more complex molecules, but trivial names are quite often employed in practice for simpler substances. It is therefore necessary not only to learn IUPAC nomenclature rules, but also to memorize a certain minimum number of trivial names. We shall employ IUPAC nomenclature except in cases where common practice involves extensive use of the trivial name, and shall develop nomenclature rules for each class of compounds as we first encounter it.

Alkanes are the homologous series of hydrocarbons having the empirical formula C_nH_{2n+2}. Their earlier designation as **paraffins** (Latin, little affinity) comes from their chemical inertness, while the alternative name **saturated hydrocarbons** arises from the fact that all of the carbon valences in these hydrocarbons are *saturated* with hydrogen. Straight-chain alkanes (**normal** alkanes) form the basis of IUPAC nomenclature. A number of normal alkanes and their structures are listed in Table 7-1. Also used in IUPAC nomenclature are all of the alkyl groups containing up to four carbon atoms. These are shown in Table 7-2. It is necessary to memorize these tables, as they constitute the foundation not only of alkane nomenclature but of nomenclature throughout the aliphatic series as well.

Table 7-1. Some Normal Alkanes

Name	Number of Carbons	Structure
Methane	1	CH_4
Ethane	2	CH_3—CH_3
Propane	3	CH_3—CH_2—CH_3
Butane	4	CH_3—$(CH_2)_2$—CH_3
Pentane	5	CH_3—$(CH_2)_3$—CH_3
Hexane	6	CH_3—$(CH_2)_4$—CH_3
Heptane	7	CH_3—$(CH_2)_5$—CH_3
Octane	8	CH_3—$(CH_2)_6$—CH_3
Nonane	9	CH_3—$(CH_2)_7$—CH_3
Decane	10	CH_3—$(CH_2)_8$—CH_3
Undecane	11	CH_3—$(CH_2)_9$—CH_3
Dodecane	12	CH_3—$(CH_2)_{10}$—CH_3
Tridecane	13	CH_3—$(CH_2)_{11}$—CH_3
Tetradecane	14	CH_3—$(CH_2)_{12}$—CH_3
Pentadecane	15	CH_3—$(CH_2)_{13}$—CH_3
Eicosane	20	CH_3—$(CH_2)_{18}$—CH_3

Table 7-2. The Common Alkyl Groups

Name	Structure	Abbreviation
Methyl	CH_3-	Me
Ethyl	CH_3CH_2-	Et
Propyl	$CH_3CH_2CH_2-$	Pr
Isopropyl (*i*-propyl)	CH_3 $CH-$ CH_3	*i*-Pr
Butyl	$CH_3CH_2CH_2CH_2-$	Bu
Secondary butyl (*s*-butyl)	CH_3 $CH-$ CH_3CH_2	*s*-Bu
Isobutyl (*i*-butyl)	CH_3 $CHCH_2-$ CH_3	*i*-Bu
Tertiary butyl (*t*-butyl)	CH_3 $\mid$ CH_3-C- $\mid$ CH_3	*t*-Bu

Nomenclature note: The names of the groups corresponding to the normal alkanes in Table 7-1 are obtained by replacing the -*ane* ending of the alkane with -*yl*. Thus $CH_3-(CH_2)_6-CH_2-$ is the octyl group, $CH_3-(CH_2)_{10}-CH_2-$ the dodecyl group, etc.

To name a complicated alkane by the IUPAC system, we apply the following rules and procedures to its structure:

1. The suffix designating an alkane is -*ane*.
2. Select the longest sequence (chain) of carbon atoms in the molecule. This constitutes the "parent" alkane on which the structure is named. If there are two or more long chains of equal length, select the one containing the greatest number of substituents as the parent.
3. Number the consecutive carbon atoms on the parent chain from whichever end puts the substituents on carbons having the lowest numbers.
4. Name each group as a substituent of the parent chain, indicating by a preceding number the carbon atom to which it is attached. If two groups are on the same carbon, the number is repeated before the second group. Numbers are separated from the rest of the name by hyphens. If the same substituent appears on the chain more than once, the position numbers are separated by commas and the prefixes *di-*, *tri-*, *tetra-*, etc., are used to indicate the number of times it appears.

Examples: Give IUPAC names for the following alkanes.

$$\overset{1}{CH_3}-\overset{2}{CH_2}-\overset{3}{CH}-\overset{4}{CH_2}-\overset{5}{CH_2}-\overset{6}{CH_2}-\overset{7}{CH}-\overset{8}{CH_2}-\overset{9}{CH_2}-\overset{10}{CH_3}$$

with lower numbering: 10 9 8 7 6 5 4 3 2 1

$\underset{8}{\mid}$ CH_3 $\underset{4}{\mid}$ CH_2-CH_3

(a) The longest consecutive chain is C_{10}. The alkane is therefore a substituted decane.

(b) Numbering the chain from the left puts the substituents at C3 and C7, from the right at C4 and C8. Therefore, number from the left.

(c) The substituents are methyl at C3 and ethyl at C7.

(d) The name is accordingly: 3-methyl-7-ethyldecane.

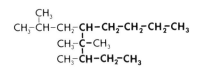

(a) The longest chain is C_9, and the alkane is therefore a substituted nonane. Note that here we must "cut around corners" to locate the longest chain.

(b) Numbering from the bottom up assigns lowest numbers to the substituents.

(c) Substituents are: three methyls at C3, C4, C4; isobutyl at C5.

(d) The name is therefore: 3,4,4-trimethyl-5-isobutylnonane.

5. In cases where a substituent on the longest chain is more complex than one of the eight alkyl groups in Table 7-2. the substituent is named as a *substituted* alkyl group whose carbon atoms are numbered *out* from the parent chain. Parentheses are employed to avoid confusion with the numbering of the parent chain.

Example:

$$CH_3-CH_2-CH_2-CH_2-\overset{\overset{\displaystyle C5}{|}}{CH}-CH_2-CH_2-CH_2-CH_2-CH_2-CH_2-CH_2-CH_3$$

$$CH_3-\underset{\underset{\displaystyle CH_3-\underset{\underset{\displaystyle CH_3}{|}}{CH}}{|}}{\overset{|}{C}}-CH_3 \longleftarrow (C1) \qquad \diagdown\!\!-Tridecane$$

$$(C2)$$

Propyl

There is a propyl group at C5 of the tridecane chain. On the propyl group there are in turn three methyl groups at (C1), (C1), and (C2). In short, there is a (1,1,2-trimethylpropyl) substituent at C5 of the tridecane chain. The name is accordingly: 5-(1,1,2-trimethylpropyl)tridecane. Note in all of the above examples that the entire name is written as a single word.

7-3. Physical Properties of Alkanes

The physical properties of organic compounds depend upon both the number and the kinds of atoms in the molecule and on the structure of the molecule. The physical properties of the alkanes illustrate certain patterns which we shall encounter in other homologous series as well. Figure 7-2 shows a molecular model of a long-chain, normal alkane. We must appre-

Figure 7-2. Hirschfelder Model of Dodecane

ciate, however, that such molecules are not rigid structures, but—as gases or liquids at least—are in a state of constant, snake-like motion (see Section 2-8f), a factor which influences their physical properties.

a. Boiling Points. The boiling points of normal alkanes increase smoothly with increasing molecular weight, as shown in Figure 7-3. Notice

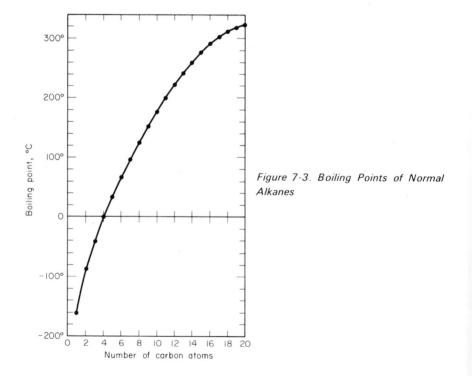

Figure 7-3. Boiling Points of Normal Alkanes

that C_1 to C_4 alkanes are gases at room temperature and that pentane is the first liquid alkane. While it is a general phenomenon that boiling points increase with increasing molecular weight, they are also influenced by molecular structure. Thus the three isomeric pentanes have decreasing boiling points as indicated, dimethylpropane being a gas at room tempera-

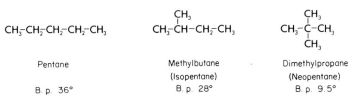

CH₃–CH₂–CH₂–CH₂–CH₃	CH₃–CH–CH₂–CH₃ (with CH₃ above)	CH₃–C–CH₃ (with CH₃ above and below)
Pentane	Methylbutane (Isopentane)	Dimethylpropane (Neopentane)
B. p. 36°	B. p. 28°	B. p. 9.5°

ture. The pattern of decreasing boiling point with increasing branching of the molecular structure is a general one, and the most highly branched isomers are found to have the lowest boiling points.

b. Melting Points. The normal alkanes are liquids from pentane through heptadecane, $C_{17}H_{36}$ (m.p. 22.5°); beginning at octadecane, $C_{18}H_{38}$ (m.p. 28°), they are solids at room temperature. Ordinary household paraffin wax is a typical solid paraffin, consisting mainly of normal alkanes in the C_{20} to C_{30} range. The melting points of normal alkanes, plotted against the number of carbon atoms, do not fall on a smooth curve, as do the boiling points. Rather, we find two curves gradually converging at high molecular weights (Figure 7-4)—an upper curve for alkanes having an even number of carbon atoms, and a lower curve for those with an odd number. Moreover, melting points do not vary with molecular structure in the regular way that boiling points do, nor does increased branching have a uniform effect on melting point. Since melting points generally reflect the

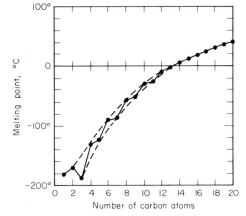

Figure 7-4. Melting Points of Normal Alkanes

stability of a crystal lattice, however, symmetrical, compact molecules which can fit together tightly in a lattice are invariably higher melting than are isomers having unsymmetrical molecular structures. This generalization is illustrated dramatically with the two isomeric octanes, 2-methylheptane and the highly symmetrical tetramethylbutane.

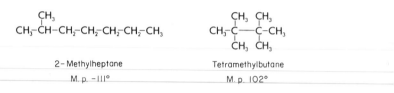

2-Methylheptane	Tetramethylbutane
M. p. −111°	M. p. 102°

c. Solubility and Other Properties. Alkanes are almost completely insoluble in water. Methane, the most soluble, has a solubility of 0.00002 gram/ml at 25°—about the same as that of nitrogen. Water solubility decreases with increasing molecular weight, and we find that solid paraffins are not even *wetted* by water. Decreasing water solubility with increasing molecular weight proves to be a general pattern, found in other homologous series as well. The lack of solubility of alkanes in water is due to the low polarity of the carbon-hydrogen bond, and its consequent failure to partake in hydrogen bonding with water molecules (see Section 11-3). On the other hand, alkanes are quite soluble in organic solvents, particularly other hydrocarbons. This illustrates the principle of "like dissolves like," a generalization stating that structurally similar substances are mutually miscible, while structurally dissimilar substances are not.

The densities of liquid alkanes are less than one, and even paraffin wax ($d \sim 0.9$) will float on water. Aliphatic C—H bonds show characteristic infrared stretching frequencies at 2850 to 2970 cm^{-1}, while —CH$_2$— bending vibrations give rise to absorption around 1465 cm^{-1}, and the CH$_3$— group itself shows a characteristic infrared maximum at 1375 cm^{-1}.

7-4. Sources and Uses of Alkanes—The Petroleum Industry

a. Petroleum. Throughout millions of years, animal, vegetable, and marine residues from prehistoric times have been subjected to geological conditions which have converted them into a complex mixture of organic substances called petroleum. Subterranean pools of petroleum and their accompanying pockets of natural gas are distributed widely throughout the world, and surface seepages of oil have been known for thousands of years. The first commercial production of petroleum in Rumania in 1857 was followed shortly by Colonel Edwin L. Drake's celebrated well near

Titusville, Pennsylvania, in 1859, and during the ensuing century the world's production of petroleum has exceeded 150 billion gallons. In 1962 the United States alone produced over 112 million gallons of crude petroleum, more than 40 per cent of the world output. Petroleum and its accompanying natural gas constitute the principal source of alkanes up to C_{40}, as well as of many aromatic, alicyclic, and heterocyclic substances.

   b. Natural Gas. This raw material contains the volatile, low molecular weight alkanes from C_1 to about C_8. Its composition varies widely with its source, but a typical percentage distribution might be: methane, 80; ethane, 13; propane, 3; butanes, 1; C_5 to C_8 alkanes, 0.5; nitrogen, 2.5. After removal of its propane and butane constituents by liquefaction, natural gas is used mainly as a fuel; it is carried in pipelines directly from the oil fields to all heavily populated sections of the United States. The propane–butane fraction is compressed into cylinders and sold as **bottled gas** for fuel in rural areas. Large quantities of natural gas are also converted by incomplete combustion or by thermal decomposition into finely divided **carbon black:**

$$CH_4 + O_2 \text{ (air)} \longrightarrow C + 2H_2O$$

$$CH_4 \xrightarrow{1200°} C + 2H_2$$

This product is used as a filler in compounding rubber and as a pigment in inks and paints. By methods to be discussed later, natural gas is also converted into industrially important alcohols, aldehydes, ketones, carboxylic acids, and halogenated alkanes.

   Methane is also formed in nature by the decay of more recent plant and animal matter. From peat bogs and stagnant pools, for example, it rises as bubbles called **marsh gas.** Like other alkanes, methane is highly flammable, and its spontaneous ignition in marshy areas causes the ghostly blue flames called **will-o'-the-wisps.** The methane occurring in coal mines is called **fire damp.**

   c. Petroleum Refining. Raw petroleum is commercially useless. It may be **refined,** or separated into useful products, however, by fractional distillation (Section 3-2) into a series of fractions of increasing boiling point and molecular weight. This fractionation is carried out either near the oil fields or—after shipment of the crude oil by pipeline, rail, or boat—at refineries (Figure 7-5) located near large urban centers. A typical fractionation of California petroleum is illustrated in Table 7-3. Such fractions satisfy a large bulk of the fuel requirements of our economy. Gasoline, of course, is used as the fuel in all of our automobile engines, and lower frac-

Figure 7-5. A Large Oil Refinery at Catlettsburg, Kentucky—Crude Oil Capacity in Excess of 80,000 Barrels per Day (courtesy Ashland Oil and Refining Company)

tions are blended with it. Kerosene is used as tractor and jet engine fuel, while gas oil is burned as diesel fuel and for domestic heating. From the higher fractions of certain types of petroleum, paraffin wax and petroleum jelly (Vaseline) may be obtained by chilling. Chemical purification, as

Table 7-3. Fractionation of Petroleum

Fraction	Boiling Range, °C	Carbon Content
Gas	Below 20	C_1-C_4
Petroleum ether	20–60	C_5-C_6
Light naphtha	60–100	C_6-C_7
Straight-run gasoline	40–200	C_5-C_{10}
Kerosene	175–325	$C_{11}-C_{18}$
Gas oil	300–500	$C_{15}-C_{40}$
Lubricating oil	Above 400 (vacuum)	
Asphalt, petroleum coke	Nonvolatile	

well as distillation, is used to remove undesirable constituents of each fraction, and additives may be put in to improve specific fuel or lubricant characteristics. The asphalt residues are widely used for roofing and road construction.

d. *Cracking.*   The rapid expansion in production of automobiles early threatened to outstrip known supplies of available fuel, since a 42 gallon barrel of crude oil yields only 5 or 6 gallons of straight-run gasoline on distillation. This threat has been countered not only by continued exploration and discovery of new oil fields but also by the development of the art of cracking, whereby higher molecular weight fractions of petroleum distillate are broken down into the C_5 to C_{10} hydrocarbons characteristic of the gasoline range. **Thermal cracking** involves heating higher petroleum fractions for short periods at 400° to 450° and 175 to 250 psi (pounds per square inch), and yields smaller alkane molecules as well as alkenes and aromatics. **Catalytic cracking** increases the efficiency of the process by utilizing natural or synthetic clays as cracking catalysts which promote the desired reactions and hinder carbonization, while allowing the use of lower operating pressures (10 to 50 psi). Such cracking methods have more than doubled the yield of gasoline hydrocarbons from crude petroleum.

e. *Octane Number—Reforming.*   We are all familiar with the **knock** which an automobile engine develops under strain on a long pull. This knock, caused by premature and uneven combustion of the fuel, decreases engine power and increases wear, and is especially prone to occur in modern, high-compression engines. Not all C_5 to C_{10} alkanes have equal fuel performance with respect to knocking properties. To describe the knocking characteristics of fuels two pure alkanes have been selected as standards: normal heptane (octane number 0), which knocks more, and 2,2,4-trimethylpentane (octane number 100), which knocks less than the usual gasoline alkanes. These two pure fuels are blended, and the knock performance of the various blends is compared in a standard test engine with the performance of the gasoline being rated. The **octane number** of the gasoline is defined as that percentage of 2,2,4-trimethylpentane mixed with heptane which gives a blend having the same knocking characteristics in the test engine as does the gasoline in question. Tests with pure hydrocarbons show that straight-chain alkanes knock badly (have low octane numbers), while highly branched alkanes, alkenes, and aromatic hydrocarbons have high octane numbers. Gasolines produced by thermal or catalytic cracking have high octane numbers, since branched molecules as well as alkenes and aromatics are formed in the process. Straight-run gasolines with low octane numbers may be improved by **reforming,** a process somewhat similar to cracking, which again brings about the rearrangement of straight-chain alkanes into branched alkanes and aromatic hydrocarbons. The octane number of gasolines may also be increased by adding **knock inhibitors** such as tetraethyllead, $Pb(C_2H_5)_4$, which moderate the explosions in the cylinders of the engine. Octane numbers of regular gasolines have increased from about 60 to 90 during the past 30 years, and high-test aviation fuels can be tailored to have octane ratings over 100.

f. Polymerization and Alkylation. Both the fractionation of petroleum and the subsequent cracking and reforming operations produce highly volatile C_3 and C_4 hydrocarbons as well as gasoline. Gasoline yields may be further increased by converting these lower hydrocarbons into the desired C_5 to C_{10} range by **polymerization** and **alkylation**, processes which are formally the reverse of cracking. In polymerization, gaseous

Polymerization: $2\,C_3H_6 \xrightarrow[\text{200°, 500 psi}]{H_3PO_4} C_6H_{12}$

                                         Propylene C_6 alkenes

alkenes are combined with each other in the presence of phosphoric acid catalyst, under heat and pressure, to yield branched alkenes in the gasoline fraction range—with octane numbers around 80. Alkylation involves the addition of an isoalkane to an alkene at temperatures below 20° in the presence of sulfuric acid or hydrogen fluoride catalysts, and results in the formation of branched alkanes of proper molecular weight and high octane number. The alkylation of ethylene with isobutane to form 2,2-dimethylbutane, along with other products, is illustrative.

Alkylation:

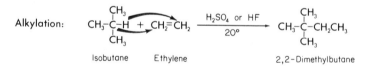

Isobutane   Ethylene   2,2-Dimethylbutane

g. Synthetic Fuels. Lacking in significant petroleum deposits, Germany since World War I has pioneered in the production of liquid fuels from other sources. The original **Bergius process** involves the destructive hy-

Bergius Process

$$n\,C + (n + 1)\,H_2 \xrightarrow[\text{450°, }10^4\text{ psi}]{FeO} C_nH_{2n+2}$$

drogenation of coal into liquid hydrocarbons. One ton of gasoline is obtainable from about 2 tons of coal. Powdered coal is mixed with small amounts of metal oxide catalysts and heated at 450° with hydrogen at pressures of 10,000 psi. The resulting oil is vaporized and passed with more hydrogen over additional catalyst, after which it is fractionated into gasoline (octane number 75 to 80), gas oil, and a residue which is recycled. The **Fischer-Tropsch process** (1933) makes use of carbon monoxide obtained from coke by the **water-gas** reaction. The carbon monoxide is enriched with ad-

Water-gas Reaction

$$C \text{ (coke)} + H_2O \text{ (steam)} \xrightarrow{\text{High temp.}} CO + H_2$$

Fischer-Tropsch Process

$$2n\,CO + (4n + 1)\,H_2 \xrightarrow[250°]{\text{Co-Th}} C_nH_{2n} + C_nH_{2n+2} + 2n\,H_2O$$

ditional hydrogen and passed over a cobalt-thorium catalyst at 200° to 250°, to yield a complex mixture of aliphatic hydrocarbons. The octane rating of the product is low, so that reforming is required. Such synthetic fuels have not yet been widely developed in this country owing to our abundant oil reserves.

7-5. Synthesis of Alkanes

The smaller alkanes from C_1 to C_5 may be obtained in pure form by fractional distillation of petroleum or natural gas. Above the pentanes, however, the number of isomers becomes so large, and the boiling point differences between the isomers so small, that it is impractical to isolate pure higher alkanes from petroleum fractions. Individual alkanes of higher molecular weights must therefore be prepared synthetically. The synthetic methods presented here are applicable to alkanes of any size, and are illustrated as general equations with R representing any alkyl group (see Section 2-5).

a. Catalytic Hydrogenation of Alkenes. The double bond of an alkene will add hydrogen quantitatively in the presence of platinum, palladium, or nickel catalysts to form an alkane having the same carbon skeleton:

$$R-CH=CH-R + H_2 \xrightarrow{\text{Pt, Pd, or Ni}} R-CH_2-CH_2-R$$

With the more active platinum or palladium catalysts, the reaction may be conducted at room temperature and with an atmospheric pressure of hydrogen. With less active but less expensive nickel catalysts, higher temperatures (100° to 150°) and hydrogen pressures (1000 to 2000 psi) are usually employed to increase the reaction rate. Alkene **hydrogenation** (**reduction**) is the most important alkane synthesis, since the reaction is a perfectly general one and is limited only by the availability of the alkene. Alkenes, in turn, are readily available from alcohols (see Section 8-3a). By conducting such hydrogenations quantitatively it is possible to tell how

Figure 7-6. Apparatus for Hydrogenation at Atmospheric Pressure

many double bonds are present in an alkene molecule, since each double bond is hydrogenated in the same fashion. Figures 7-6, 7-7, and 7-8 illustrate laboratory apparatus for atmospheric, medium, and high pressure hydrogenations.

b. Reduction of Alkyl Halides. Alkyl halides may be reduced directly to alkanes as shown in the following general equation:

$$R-X + 2 (H) \longrightarrow R-H + H-X$$

The hydrogen for the reduction may be obtained by the action of hydrochloric acid on zinc, alcohol on sodium, or water on sodium amalgam ($Na \cdot Hg$). Hydrogen gas and platinum or palladium catalyst may also be used. Alkyl halides may be prepared in turn from alcohols as described in Section 11-7e.

Figure 7-7. Apparatus for Medium Pressure Hydrogenation

Figure 7-8. Apparatus for High Pressure Hydrogenation
(courtesy American Instrument Company)

c. Reduction of Tosyl Esters with Lithium Aluminum Hydride. The reaction of many types of alcohols with the reagent *p*-toluenesulfonyl chloride (tosyl chloride) yields a class of compounds known as *p*-toluenesulfonic esters (*p*-toluenesulfonates), commonly called tosylates. Reduction of such esters

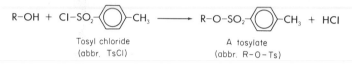

R–OH + Cl–SO$_2$–⟨ ⟩–CH$_3$ ⟶ R–O–SO$_2$–⟨ ⟩–CH$_3$ + HCl

Tosyl chloride   A tosylate
(abbr. TsCl)   (abbr. R–O–Ts)

in ether solution with the versatile reducing agent lithium aluminum hydride, LiAlH$_4$, affords in good yield the alkane corresponding to the

$$4 \text{ R–OTs} + \text{LiAlH}_4 \longrightarrow 4 \text{ R–H} + \text{LiOTs} + \text{Al (OTs)}_3$$

Example:

$$4 \text{ CH}_3\text{CH}_2\text{–OTs} + \text{LiAlH}_4 \longrightarrow 4 \text{ CH}_3\text{CH}_3 + \text{LiOTs} + \text{Al (OTs)}_3$$
Ethyl tosylate   Ethane

original alcohol. It should be noted that this reagent will also reduce alkyl halides, and forms an alternative reducing agent to those mentioned in the

$$4 \text{ R–X} + \text{LiAlH}_4 \longrightarrow 4 \text{ R–H} + \text{LiX} + \text{AlX}_3$$

previous paragraph. Since its introduction in 1947, lithium aluminum hydride has substantially replaced many older reducing agents.

d. Hydrolysis of Grignard Reagents. When a solution of an alkyl halide in anhydrous (moisture-free) ethyl ether, C_2H_5—O—C_2H_5, is stirred with magnesium shavings, a vigorous reaction takes place. The ether boils and the magnesium dissolves, forming a solution known as a **Grignard reagent.** The exact structure of the Grignard reagent is still open to considerable question, but its formulation as R—Mg—X is convenient and suitable for most purposes. The Grignard reagent is one of the most

$$\text{R–X} + \text{Mg} \xrightarrow{\text{Anhydrous ether}} \text{R–Mg–X}$$
Alkylmagnesium halide
A Grignard reagent

Example: $\text{CH}_3\text{CH}_2\text{–I} + \text{Mg} \xrightarrow{\text{Anhydrous ether}} \text{CH}_3\text{CH}_2\text{–Mg–I}$
          Ethyl iodide   Ethylmagnesium iodide

powerful synthetic tools of the organic chemist, reacting avidly with most classes of organic compounds as well as with a wide variety of inorganic substances. The discovery of this versatile reagent merited the Nobel Prize in 1912 for Victor Grignard of the University of Lyons (France). Compounds such as R—MgX, which have a direct carbon to metal bond in their structure, are called **organometallic compounds.**

One reaction of Grignard reagents is **hydrolysis,** or decomposition by

$$R-MgX + HO-H \longrightarrow R-H + HO-Mg-X$$

Example:

$$\begin{matrix} CH_3 \\ {} \\ CH_3 \end{matrix}\!\!\!>\!\!CHCH_2MgBr + H_2O \longrightarrow \begin{matrix} CH_3 \\ {} \\ CH_3 \end{matrix}\!\!\!>\!\!CH-CH_3 + Mg(OH)Br$$

Isobutylmagnesium   Isobutane
bromide

the action of water, to form an alkane having the same carbon skeleton as the original alkyl halide. Thus the reaction sequence $R{-}X \rightarrow R{-}MgX \rightarrow R{-}H$ provides an alternative path for converting alkyl halides into alkanes. Similar rapid reactions occur between Grignard reagents and both alcohols, ROH, and amines, RNH_2. We should therefore emphasize here that Grignard reagents cannot be prepared from halides whose structures also contain —OH or —NH_2 functions. Figure 7-9 shows the type of ap-

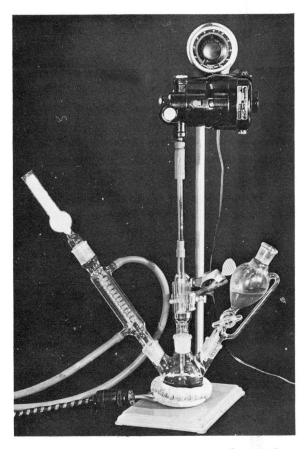

Figure 7-9. Apparatus for Preparing and Reacting Grignard Reagents

paratus which organic chemists typically employ for the preparation and reaction of Grignard reagents.

e. Total Reduction of Carbonyl Groups. The carbonyl groups of aldehydes and ketones may be reduced to methyl, CH_3—, and methylene, —CH_2—, groups, respectively,

$$R-CH=O + 4 \text{ (H)} \longrightarrow R-CH_3 + H_2O$$

$$R-\underset{\underset{O}{\|}}{C}-R' + 4 \text{ (H)} \longrightarrow R-CH_2-R' + H_2O$$

by two general methods. The **Clemmenson reduction**, illustrated with acetone, employs hydrochloric acid and zinc amalgam as the reducing agent. The **Wolff-Kishner reduction**, shown with acetaldehyde, utilizes hydrazine as the reducing agent and sodium ethoxide, C_2H_5—O—Na, as a catalyst. Both techniques are widely used for converting aldehydes and ketones to hydrocarbons, the latter being preferable for aldehydes and the former for ketones.

Clemmenson Reduction

$$CH_3-\underset{\underset{O}{\|}}{C}CH_3 + 4 \text{ HCl} + Zn\cdot Hg \longrightarrow CH_3CH_2CH_3 + ZnCl_2 + H_2O + 2Hg$$

     Acetone   Propane

Wolff-Kishner Reduction

$$CH_3-CH=O + H_2N-NH_2 \xrightarrow{C_2H_5ONa} CH_3CH_3 + H_2O + N_2$$

  Acetaldehyde   Hydrazine   Ethane

7-6. Reactions of Alkanes

As mentioned earlier, the historic name "paraffins" for the alkanes derives from the chemical inertness of this class of hydrocarbons. Alkanes do, however, undergo several types of reactions which are of commercial and practical importance.

a. Oxidation. At high temperatures all alkanes combine with oxygen (burn) to form carbon dioxide and water, liberating energy:

$$H-(CH_2)_nH + (3n + 1)[O] \longrightarrow n CO_2 + (n + 1) H_2O + Heat$$

This reaction is the basis of *all* uses of hydrocarbons as fuels, and our economy, health, and comfort are largely grounded upon it. The heat liberated per mole of hydrocarbon during its combustion is called its **heat of combustion.** This increases regularly as we go up the homologous series of alkanes, the increment per —CH_2— group being about 158 kcal/mole. Thus methane has a heat of combustion of about 212 kcal/mole, ethane 373, propane 531, and so on to decane, 1620. The detailed mechanism of combustion is complicated and not completely understood, but appears definitely to involve free radicals. The incomplete combustion of natural gas with insufficient oxygen to produce carbon black has been discussed above. Partial air oxidation of alkane fractions from petroleum also provides a commercial source of various oxygenated compounds such as alcohols and carboxylic acids.

b. Pyrolysis. The decomposition of a compound by heat is called **pyrolysis** (Greek: *pyro*, fire + *lysis*, loosening). When an alkane is passed through a hot metal tube at 500° to 700°, it breaks down (**pyrolyzes**) into a mixture of lower molecular weight alkanes, alkenes, and hydrogen, as illustrated with propane and butane below. Larger alkanes yield even

$$CH_3-CH_2-CH_3 \xrightarrow{600°} \begin{cases} CH_3-CH=CH_2 \ + \ H_2 \\ \text{Propylene} \\ \\ CH_2=CH_2 \ + \ CH_4 \\ \text{Ethylene} \end{cases}$$

Propane

$$CH_3-CH_2-CH_2-CH_3 \xrightarrow{600°} \begin{cases} H_2 \ + \ \text{Mixture of } C_4H_8 \text{ alkenes} \\ CH_4 \ + \ CH_3-CH=CH_2 \\ CH_3-CH_3 \ + \ CH_2=CH_2 \end{cases}$$

Butane

more complex mixtures, since the initial products are also subject to pyrolysis. Note that both C–H and C–C bonds rupture and that the carbon chain may break at any point. The mechanism of pyrolysis involves free radicals, which presumably fragment as follows:

$$R\!:\!CH_2\!-\!CH_2\!\cdot \longrightarrow R\cdot \ + \ CH_2=CH_2 \text{ etc.}$$

Such free radical fragmentation is frequently encountered during free radical reactions. The importance of this reaction as a cracking technique in petroleum technology has been discussed above.

c. Isomerization. The molecular rearrangement of one isomer into a mixture containing one or more other isomers is called **isomerization**. Alkanes are readily isomerized by strong Lewis acid catalysts. Thus butane is converted into an equilibrated mixture containing 80 per cent isobutane by the action of aluminum chloride or bromide at 25°:

$$CH_3-CH_2-CH_2-CH_3 \underset{}{\overset{AlCl_3 \text{ or } AlBr_3}{\rightleftharpoons}} \begin{matrix} CH_3 \\ | \\ CH_3-CH-CH_3 \end{matrix}$$

20%   80%

The mechanism of such isomerizations is known to involve carbonium ions, and may be formulated as a sequence of four steps. The process is initiated by traces of alcohols, alkyl halides or alkenes, called **promotors**, which form a carbonium ion, $R^\oplus$, as in step 1. $R^\oplus$ then abstracts a hydride ion, $:H^\ominus$, from butane in step 2, forming a secondary butyl carbonium ion (7-**1**).

1. $\quad R-Cl + AlCl_3 \rightleftharpoons R^\oplus + AlCl_4^\ominus$

2. $\quad CH_3-CH_2-CH_2-CH_3 + R^\oplus \rightleftharpoons CH_3-\overset{\oplus}{C}H-CH_2-CH_3 + R-H$

$\qquad\qquad\qquad\qquad\qquad\qquad\qquad\qquad 7\text{-}1$

3. $\quad CH_3-\overset{\oplus}{C}H-\underset{\underset{\displaystyle CH_3}{\diagdown}}{CH_2} \xrightleftharpoons{\;:CH_3\sim\;} CH_3-\underset{\underset{\displaystyle CH_3}{|}}{\overset{\overset{\displaystyle H\searrow}{|}}{C}}-\overset{\oplus}{C}H_2 \xrightleftharpoons{\;:H\sim\;} CH_3-\underset{\underset{\displaystyle CH_3}{|}}{\overset{\oplus}{C}}-CH_3$

$\qquad\qquad 7\text{-}1 \qquad\qquad\qquad\qquad\qquad\qquad\qquad 7\text{-}2$

4. $\quad CH_3-\underset{\underset{\displaystyle CH_3}{|}}{\overset{\oplus}{C}}-CH_3 + CH_3-CH_2-CH_2-CH_3 \rightleftharpoons CH_3-\underset{\underset{\displaystyle CH_3}{|}}{CH}-CH_3 + CH_3-\overset{\oplus}{C}H-CH_2-CH_3$

$\qquad 7\text{-}2 \qquad\qquad\qquad\qquad\qquad\qquad\qquad\qquad\qquad\qquad 7\text{-}1$

Next a methyl group and then a hydrogen atom migrate ($\sim$) as in step 3, *each taking its bonding pair of electrons with it during the migration.* Notice that the net result of these migrations is the formation of the more stable tertiary butyl carbonium ion (7-**2**) from the less stable secondary ion 7-**1**. The final step (4) involves abstraction of a hydride ion from butane by the tertiary butyl carbonium ion, forming the isobutane product and regenerating a secondary butyl carbonium ion, which then repeats the process of step 3. The migration of an atom or group with its bonding electrons from one carbon atom to an adjacent carbonium ion center is called a **cationic 1,2 shift**. The driving energy for such 1,2 shifts is the formation of a more stable carbonium ion from a less stable one (see Section 6-6b). 1,2 shifts are very commonly observed in reactions proceeding by carbonium ion mechanisms, and frequently lead—as in the present example—to products with a *rearranged* carbon skeleton. The importance of such isomerizations in the reforming of straight-run gasoline to increase its molecular branching and octane number has been described above.

   d. Halogenation. A mixture of chlorine and methane is perfectly stable if kept in the dark. On exposure to sunlight, however, reaction proceeds with explosive violence, and the hydrogen atoms of methane are replaced (substituted) by chlorine atoms. This **photochemical** (light-induced) chlorination cannot be controlled, and more than one hydrogen atom on each methane molecule is replaced. Thus, the final reaction mixture also contains di-, tri-, and tetrachloromethanes. Chlorine reacts photochemically or at high temperatures in the same manner with other alkanes, as described below. Bromine reacts similarly, though less vigorously, while

$$CH_4 + Cl_2 \xrightarrow{\text{Ultraviolet light}} CH_3Cl + HCl$$

Chloromethane
(Methyl chloride)

$$CH_3Cl + Cl_2 \xrightarrow{\text{Ultraviolet light}} CH_2Cl_2 + HCl$$

Dichloromethane
(Methylene chloride)

$$CH_2Cl_2 + Cl_2 \xrightarrow{\text{Ultraviolet light}} CHCl_3 + HCl$$

Trichloromethane
(Chloroform)

$$CHCl_3 + Cl_2 \xrightarrow{\text{Ultraviolet light}} CCl_4 + HCl$$

Tetrachloromethane
(Carbon tetrachloride)

iodine is too inert to effect such substitutions. Fluorine reacts explosively with most organic compounds.

Halogenation of homologs of methane is complicated by the fact that more than one position isomer may result, depending upon which hydrogen in the alkane chain is replaced. Thus propane can give two monochlorinated products, pentane can give three. In practice it is usually im-

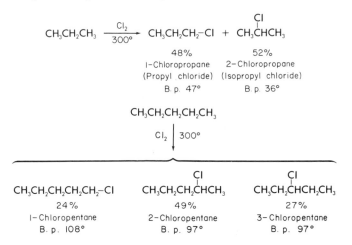

$$CH_3CH_2CH_3 \xrightarrow[300°]{Cl_2} CH_3CH_2CH_2-Cl + CH_3\overset{\text{Cl}}{\underset{|}{C}}HCH_3$$

48%	52%
1-Chloropropane	2-Chloropropane
(Propyl chloride)	(Isopropyl chloride)
B.p. 47°	B.p. 36°

$$CH_3CH_2CH_2CH_2CH_3$$

$$\downarrow Cl_2 \quad 300°$$

$CH_3CH_2CH_2CH_2CH_2-Cl$	$CH_3CH_2CH_2\overset{\text{Cl}}{\underset{|}{C}}HCH_3$	$CH_3CH_2\overset{\text{Cl}}{\underset{|}{C}}HCH_2CH_3$
24%	49%	27%
1-Chloropentane	2-Chloropentane	3-Chloropentane
B.p. 108°	B.p. 97°	B.p. 97°

possible to control the positions of such substitutions and, as indicated, mixtures of products are invariably obtained. The close boiling points of the isomers make their separation by fractional distillation difficult or impossible, and polyhalogenated products complicate the mixtures still further. Therefore the direct halogenation of alkanes is never used as a laboratory preparation for individual alkyl halides, although the reaction is of some importance on an industrial scale. Thus C_5-alkane mixtures from petroleum are chlorinated to give a mixture of chloropentanes, which in turn is hydrolyzed to give C_5-alcohol mixtures useful as solvents. For such purposes chemical homogeneity is unimportant.

The mechanism of alkane halogenation is well studied and known to involve a **free radical chain reaction**. This type of process, which we shall encounter frequently in later chapters, may be illustrated by the above photochlorination of methane. The reaction is initiated by the photochemical dissociation of a chlorine molecule into two chlorine atoms (step 1). The chlorine atom then attacks a methane molecule (step 2), forming HCl and a methyl radical. The latter attacks a chlorine molecule (step 3) to form methyl chloride and another chlorine atom, which then repeats the sequence of step 2. The **chain propagation** steps (2 and 3) are thus repeated indefinitely, with $CH_3\cdot$ and $Cl\cdot$ acting as the **chain carriers**.

Chain initiation:

1. $Cl:Cl \xrightarrow{\text{Ultraviolet light}} 2\ Cl\cdot$

Chain propagation:

2. $Cl\cdot + CH_4 \longrightarrow H:Cl + CH_3\cdot$

3. $CH_3\cdot + Cl:Cl \longrightarrow CH_3:Cl + Cl\cdot$

Chain termination:

4. $2\ CH_3\cdot + M \longrightarrow CH_3:CH_3 + M$

5. $2\ Cl\cdot + M \longrightarrow Cl:Cl + M$

In principle, one chlorine atom could thus initiate a chain which would result in reaction of an indefinite amount of methane and chlorine. Chains may be **terminated**, however, by several processes, such as the combination of two methyl radicals to form ethane (step 4), the combination of two chlorine atoms to form a chlorine molecule (step 5), or reaction of the chain carriers with traces of impurities. Note in steps 4 and 5 a **third body** (symbolized by M), usually another molecule or the wall of the reaction vessel, must participate to absorb the kinetic energy of the two radicals. Without the third body the fragments would merely "bounce apart" again. Such termination steps do not generate new free radicals, and the chain is broken. In practice the **chain length** of such reactions (number of chain-propagating steps in sequence prior to termination) may be quite long, and in some cases may be controlled by addition of **inhibitors** such as hydroquinone. Inhibitors act as radical traps which selectively scavenge

Hydroquinone

the chain carriers and terminate the chain. The methyl chloride product itself is then subject to further chlorination by a similar mechanism, producing CH_2Cl_2, $CHCl_3$, and CCl_4.

   e. Nitration.   When a mixture of an alkane and nitric acid vapors is passed rapidly through a narrow metal tube at 400° to 450°, one hydrogen atom on the alkane is substituted by a nitro group, $-NO_2$. The process is called **vapor phase nitration,** and yields a class of compounds called

Vapor Phase Nitration

$$R-H \ + \ HO-NO_2 \ \xrightarrow{450°} \ R-NO_2 \ + \ H-OH$$
$$\text{A nitroalkane}$$

nitroalkanes. The reaction is more complicated than suggested in the general equation, however, since cracking of the alkane chain occurs at the high temperatures involved. Thus ethane yields a mixture of both nitroethane and nitromethane, while propane affords four nitroalkanes. The conversion of each alkane is only 20 to 40 per cent, but may be increased by recycling the unreacted alkane after condensing the nitrated products.

$$CH_3CH_3 \ \xrightarrow[450°]{HNO_3} \ CH_3CH_2NO_2 \ + \ CH_3NO_2$$

73%	27%
Nitroethane	Nitromethane
B. p. 115°	B. p. 101°

$$CH_3CH_2CH_3 \ \xrightarrow[450°]{HNO_3} \ CH_3CH_2CH_2NO_2 \ + \ CH_3\overset{\overset{\displaystyle NO_2}{|}}{C}HCH_3 \ + \ CH_3CH_2NO_2 \ + \ CH_3NO_2$$

32%	33%	26%	9%
1-Nitropropane	2-Nitropropane		
B. p. 132°	B. p. 120°		

The mechanism of the reaction is believed also to involve free radical intermediates. Nitroalkanes are stable, nontoxic, and noncorrosive, and are used as solvents, fuels, and starting materials for the synthesis of other types of aliphatic compounds.

   f. Carbene Insertion.   Just as the alkane chain is susceptible to attack by free radical intermediates (see "Halogenation" and "Nitration"), so also is it attacked by the reactive intermediate carbene (see Section 6-2). In the process C—H bonds are converted into C—CH_3 bonds, and the reaction is known as **carbene insertion.** Notice in the example given that

Generation of carbene:

$$CH_2=C=O \ \xrightarrow[\text{decomposition}]{\text{Gas phase photochemical}} \ :CH_2 \ + \ CO$$
$$\text{Ketene} \qquad\qquad\qquad\qquad \text{Carbene}$$

Carbene insertion:

$$CH_3CH_2CH_3 \ + \ :CH_2 \ \xrightarrow{\text{Gas phase}} \ CH_3CH_2CH_2{-}CH_3 \ + \ CH_3\overset{\overset{\displaystyle CH_3}{|}}{C}HCH_3$$

64%	36%

secondary hydrogens (the two on —CH$_2$—) are attacked by carbene in slight preference to primary hydrogens (the six on —CH$_3$'s). If the insertion attack occurred purely statistically, the ratio of products would be 6:2 (that is, 75 per cent butane and 25 per cent isobutane).

SUPPLEMENTARY READING

Nomenclature
1. "The General Philosophy of Organic Nomenclature," C. D. Hurd, *J. Chem. Educ.*, **38,** 43 (1961).
2. "The Geneva Congress on Organic Nomenclature, 1892," E. A. Evieux, *J. Chem. Educ.*, **31,** 326 (1954).

Alkanes
1. "The Mechanisms of the Reactions of Aliphatic Hydrocarbons," L. Schmerling, *J. Chem. Educ.*, **28,** 562 (1951).
2. "The Reactive Paraffins," E. E. Gilbert, *J. Chem. Educ.*, **18,** 435 (1941).

Petroleum and Petroleum Refining
1. "Hydrocarbons in Petroleum," F. D. Rossini, *J. Chem. Educ.*, **37,** 554 (1960).
2. "Chemistry in the Manufacture of Modern Gasoline," C. N. Kimberlin, *J. Chem. Educ.*, **34,** 569 (1957).
3. "The Chemistry of Lubricating Oil Additives," A. Miller, *J. Chem. Educ.*, **33,** 308 (1956).
4. "Recent Advances in Petroleum Refining," R. H. Shoemaker, E. L. d'Ouville, and R. F. Marscher, *J. Chem. Educ.*, **32,** 30 (1955).
5. "The Origin of Petroleum," T. W. Nelson, *J. Chem. Educ.*, **31,** 399 (1954).
6. "Tetraethyl Lead: A Product of American Research," S. P. Nickerson, *J. Chem. Educ.*, **31,** 560 (1954).

The Grignard Reagent
1. "Fifty Years of the Grignard Reaction," H. Rheinboldt, *J. Chem. Educ.*, **27,** 476 (1950).

Nitroalkanes
1. "The Discovery of the Nitroparaffins by Victor Meyer," G. Schmidt, *J. Chem. Educ.*, **27,** 557 (1950).

CHAPTER 8

Hydrocarbons—Alkenes

THE NAME **alkene** is the IUPAC designation for compounds containing the carbon-carbon double bond, $>C=C<$. These compounds are also called (1) **ethylenes** (after *ethylene*, $CH_2=CH_2$, the simplest member of the series), (2) **olefins** (after *olefiant gas*, an early name for ethylene), and (3) **unsaturated compounds** (since they are not "saturated" with all of the hydrogen possible for their structures). Alkenes have the general empirical formula C_nH_{2n}, each having two less hydrogen atoms than the corresponding alkane, C_nH_{2n+2}. As introduced in Sections 2-8 and 5-3, the geometric aspects of the flat ethylene molecule are revealed by electron diffraction and spectroscopic studies to be as shown below. Figure 8-1 shows ball-and-stick and Hirschfelder models of the ethylene molecule.

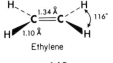

Ethylene

143

Figure 8-1. Molecular Models of Ethylene

Table 8-1. Nomenclature of Alkenes

Structural Formula	IUPAC Name
$CH_2{=}CH_2$	Ethene (ethylene)
$CH_3CH{=}CH_2$	Propene (propylene)
$CH_3CH_2CH{=}CH_2$	1-Butene
$CH_3CH{=}CHCH_3$	2-Butene
$CH_3\underset{\underset{CH_3}{\mid}}{C}{=}CH_2$	Isobutene (isobutylene)
$CH_3CH_2CH_2CH{=}CH_2$	1-Pentene
$CH_3CH_2CH{=}CHCH_3$	2-Pentene
$\overset{1}{CH_2}{=}\overset{2}{\underset{\underset{CH_3}{\mid}}{C}}\overset{3}{CH_2}\overset{4}{CH_3}$	2-Methyl-1-butene
$CH_3\underset{\underset{CH_3}{\mid}}{C}{=}CHCH_3$	2-Methyl-2-butene
$\overset{4}{CH_3}\overset{3}{\underset{\underset{CH_3}{\mid}}{CH}}\overset{2}{CH}{=}\overset{1}{CH_2}$	3-Methyl-1-butene
$CH_3CH_2CHCH_2CH_2{-}\underset{\underset{NO_2}{\mid}}{\overset{\overset{CH_2CH_2CH_2CH_3}{\mid}}{C}}{-}CH{=}CHCH_3$ with $\underset{\mid}{Cl}$ below first CHCH₂	7-Chloro-4-nitro-4-butyl-2-nonene
$CH_3CH{=}CHCH{=}CH_2$	1,3-Pentadiene
$CH_3CH{=}CHCH{=}CHCH{=}CHCHCH_2CH_3$ with $\underset{\mid}{Cl}$	8-Chloro-2,4,6-decatriene

8-1. Nomenclature

The IUPAC name for a specific alkene is obtained by selecting the longest chain containing the double bond, then deleting the -*ane* suffix from the name of the corresponding alkane and adding the suffix -*ene*. The position of the double bond in the alkene chain is indicated by a number, counted from that end of the chain which will make it the lowest possible. When more than one double bond occurs in a molecule we have a **polyunsaturated alkene**, and the suffixes -*diene* (two double bonds), -*triene* (three), etc., replace the alkane -*ane* ending. The principles of alkene nomenclature are exemplified in Table 8-1, with commonly used trivial names given in parentheses.

8-2. Sources and Physical Properties of Alkenes

The commercial source of the lower alkenes is the gas obtained by cracking petroleum (Section 7-4). To obtain pure alkenes above C_4, however, we must resort to synthetic methods, since the boiling points of higher alkenes obtained from cracking gases are too close to permit efficient fractional distillation. The boiling points and melting points of individual alkenes (Table 8-2) are not markedly different from those of the corre-

Table 8-2. Boiling and Melting Points of Some Alkenes

Structure	B.p., °C	M.p., °C
$CH_2=CH_2$	−102	−169
$CH_3CH=CH_2$	−48	−185
$CH_3CH_2CH=CH_2$	−5	−130
$CH_3CH=CHCH_3$ (*cis*)	+4	−139
$CH_3CH=CHCH_3$ (*trans*)	+1	−106
$(CH_3)_2C=CH_2$	−7	−141

sponding alkanes (see Figures 7-3 and 7-4; also Table 9-2). Note the differences in the physical properties of the geometrical isomers *cis*- and *trans*-2-butenes. Olefinic unsaturation in a molecule may readily be detected both chemically (Section 8-4b) and by infrared spectrometry, where absorption bands in the 1650 cm^{-1} region ($C=C$ stretching) are characteristic. The types of alkyl substituents on a double bond and even the configurations of *cis* and *trans* isomers can also be revealed by the infrared spectra of alkenes.

8-3. Synthesis of Alkenes

Alkenes are prepared in the laboratory by one of three general methods: (1) the **dehydration** of alcohols, (2) the **dehydrohalogenation** of alkyl halides, and (3) the **dehalogenation** of vicinal dihalides. Each reaction involves the removal of two atoms or groups located on adjacent carbon atoms in the molecule, with accompanying formation of the carbon-carbon double bond. Such reactions are called **elimination reactions**. We shall

Elimination Reaction

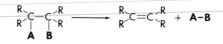

also encounter several additional elimination reactions yielding alkenes in later chapters.

a. Dehydration of Alcohols. On warming with an acid catalyst (such as H_2SO_4, H_3PO_4, or P_2O_5), or on heating at higher temperatures ($>350°$) with aluminum oxide, alcohols undergo **dehydration** (elimination of

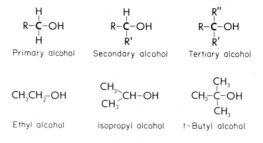

H—OH) to form alkenes. The reaction is a perfectly general one, but the ease of dehydration varies for different types of alcohols. Alcohols are classified as **primary, secondary,** or **tertiary** depending upon whether the OH-bearing carbon atom is also attached to one (or no), two, or three other carbon atoms (that is, alkyl or aryl groups). The general structures of primary, secondary, and tertiary alcohols, with a specific example of each, are shown below. Tertiary alcohols dehydrate most easily, secondary

H	H	R″
R–C–OH	R–C–OH	R–C–OH
H	R′	R′
Primary alcohol	Secondary alcohol	Tertiary alcohol

CH_3CH_2-OH $\overset{CH_3}{\underset{CH_3}{>}}CH-OH$ $CH_3-\overset{CH_3}{\underset{CH_3}{\overset{|}{\underset{|}{C}}}}-OH$

Ethyl alcohol   Isopropyl alcohol   t-Butyl alcohol

next, and primary least readily. Tertiary alcohols will often dehydrate on mere heating, as during distillation, while primary alcohols may require dehydrating conditions as drastic as concentrated H_2SO_4 at $150°$.

The commonly accepted mechanism for the acid-catalyzed dehydration of alcohols can be represented in three steps. In step 1 the acid catalyst **protonates** (transfers one of its acid protons to) an unshared pair of electrons on the OH oxygen atom, whereupon (step 2) the C—O bond of the protonated alcohol ruptures to form a carbonium ion. This ion then loses a proton (step 3) to another alcohol molecule, forming the olefin and regenerating the protonated intermediate of step 1. The relative stabilities

1. $R-CH_2-CH_2-\overset{..}{\underset{..}{O}}H + H_2SO_4 \xrightleftharpoons[]{Protonation} R-CH_2-CH_2-\overset{\oplus}{\underset{H}{O}}H + HSO_4^{\ominus}$

2. $R-CH_2-CH_2 \overset{\oplus}{\underset{H}{O}}{:}H \rightleftharpoons R-CH_2-CH_2^{\oplus} + H-\overset{..}{\underset{..}{O}}-H$

3. $R-\overset{H}{\underset{(H)}{C}}{\rightharpoonup}CH_2 + R-CH_2-CH_2-\overset{..}{\underset{..}{O}}-H \longrightarrow R-\overset{H}{\underset{}{C}}=CH_2 + R-CH_2-CH_2-\overset{\oplus}{\underset{H}{O}}{:}H$

of carbonium ions have already been discussed (Section 6-6b), and we recall that the order of stability was tertiary > secondary > primary. This order of stability and the accompanying ease of formation of the carbonium ion intermediates explain the parallel sequence for the ease of dehydration of alcohols; that is, tertiary > secondary > primary. Elimination reactions which proceed through prior ionization to a carbonium ion intermediate, as in the example above, are referred to as **E1 eliminations**, which are discussed more fully in Section 8-3b.

The Saytzeff Rule. With unsymmetrical secondary (or tertiary) alcohols, of the type R—CH(OH)—R', for example, the question arises as to which group (R or R') will lose its proton during dehydration. Thus with 2-butanol, we see that 1-butene or 2-butene could result from dehydration, depending upon whether the adjacent hydrogen atom on the methyl or

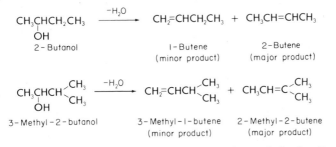

$$CH_3CHCH_2CH_3 \xrightarrow{-H_2O} CH_2{=}CHCH_2CH_3 + CH_3CH{=}CHCH_3$$
$$\underset{OH}{|}$$

2-Butanol   I-Butene   2-Butene
                    (minor product)   (major product)

$$\underset{\underset{OH}{|}}{CH_3CHCH}{\overset{CH_3}{\underset{CH_3}{\big<}}} \xrightarrow{-H_2O} CH_2{=}CHCH{\overset{CH_3}{\underset{CH_3}{\big<}}} + CH_3CH{=}C{\overset{CH_3}{\underset{CH_3}{\big<}}}$$

3-Methyl-2-butanol   3-Methyl-l-butene   2-Methyl-2-butene
                       (minor product)   (major product)

ethyl group, respectively, is lost. Actually, as indicated, both alkenes are formed, with 2-butene predominating. Similarly, with 3-methyl-2-butanol the more highly substituted alkene, 2-methyl-2-butene, is the major product.

Hydrogen atoms in a structure are also classified as primary, secondary, or tertiary according to the number of alkyl substituents present on the carbon atom to which they are attached. The **Saytzeff rule** states that in

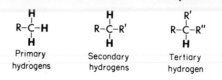

dehydration and dehydrohalogenation (Section 8-3b) reactions, the ease of removal of hydrogen atoms in forming alkenes is tertiary > secondary > primary. The net result is that the *double bond of the alkene is formed predominantly toward the carbon atom having the most alkyl substituents*. One accepted explanation for this generalization involves relief of **steric** (bulk) **strain** during olefin formation. The *crowding* of groups on a carbon atom attached to a tertiary hydrogen (bond angles 109.5°) is greater, for example, than on a carbon attached to two secondary hydrogens, putting the former carbon atom under greater steric strain. This compressional strain is called **B strain**, since the steric repulsions are at the *back* of the carbon. Now, as shown in Figure 8-2, there is greater *relief* of B strain in going from the intermediate carbonium ion to that alkene (bond angles 120°) formed by elimination of the tertiary hydrogen than to that formed by elimination of a secondary (or primary) hydrogen; therefore the former alkene is produced preferentially.

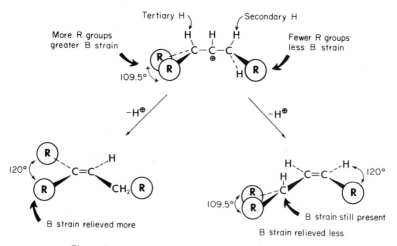

Figure 8-2. *B–Strain Rationalization of Saytzeff Rule*

In certain catalytic dehydrations, the Saytzeff rule does not apply. Thus the vapor phase dehydration of secondary alcohols of the type $RCH(OH)CH_3$ over thorium oxide catalyst at 350° to 450° has been found to yield exclusively 1-alkenes of the type $RCH{=}CH_2$.

The Wagner-Meerwein Rearrangement. One limitation to the synthesis of alkenes by alcohol dehydration is the fact that this reaction is often attended by a molecular rearrangement. Thus, the acid-catalyzed dehydration of 3,3-dimethyl-2-butanol (8-1) affords very little of the anticipated 3,3-methyl-1-butene (8-2), yields mainly the *skelatally rearranged* isomers 2,3-dimethyl-2-butene (8-3) (the major product) and 2,3-dimethyl-1-butene.

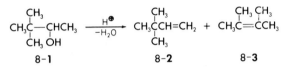

8-1   8-2   8-3

The cause of such rearrangements is the tendency for less stable primary and secondary (for example, 8-4) carbonium ions to rearrange (*by migration of an alkyl group with its pair of bonding electrons*) into more stable tertiary carbonium ions such as 8-5 before losing a proton to produce the alkene.

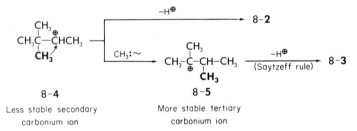

8-4   8-5

Less stable secondary   More stable tertiary
carbonium ion   carbonium ion

Such rearrangements occurring during reactions which proceed via carbonium ion intermediates are called **Wagner-Meerwein rearrangements,** after the two chemists who first investigated them systematically around 1915. The effect of alcohol structure on rearrangement tendency during dehydration may be summarized as follows:

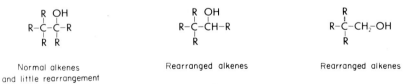

Normal alkenes   Rearranged alkenes   Rearranged alkenes
and little rearrangement

To produce unrearranged alkenes from primary and secondary alcohols which have a strong tendency to rearrange during dehydration, several alternative synthetic methods are available. The alcohol 8-1 may be dehydrated without rearrangement by passing its vapors over alumina at 400° under slightly alkaline conditions. It may be converted to its **S-methyl xanthate**, pyrolysis of which (**Chugaeff reaction**) affords unrearranged alkene 8-2. Pyrolysis of **acetate esters** also gives unrearranged alkenes. These methods, summarized in the accompanying equations, will be discussed in more detail in later chapters.

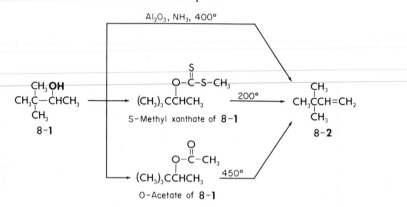

b. Dehydrohalogenation of Alkyl Halides. Alkyl halides may be converted to alkenes by heating with potassium hydroxide in ethanol, C_2H_5OH, solvent, a reaction referred to as **dehydrohalogenation** (that is, elimination of the elements of hydrogen halide). As with the dehydration of alco-

$$\underset{\substack{\text{Alkyl halide}}}{R-\overset{\overset{\displaystyle R}{|}}{\underset{\underset{\displaystyle H}{|}}{C}}-\overset{\overset{\displaystyle R}{|}}{\underset{\underset{\displaystyle X}{|}}{C}}-R} + KOH \xrightarrow{C_2H_5OH} R-\overset{\overset{\displaystyle R}{|}}{C}=\overset{\overset{\displaystyle R}{|}}{C}-R + KX + HOH$$

hols, tertiary alkyl halides react most readily, then secondary, and finally primary. The ease of dehydrohalogenation is thus:

$$\underset{\text{Tertiary alkyl halide}}{R_3C-X} \quad > \quad \underset{\text{Secondary alkyl halide}}{R_2CH-X} \quad > \quad \underset{\text{Primary alkyl halide}}{RCH_2-X}$$

With respect to the ease of dehydrohalogenation as a function of the halogen substituent, the order of reactivity is: alkyl iodides (R—I) > alkyl bromides (R—Br) > alkyl chlorides (R—Cl). Again, as with alcohol dehydration, unsymmetrical secondary or tertiary alkyl halides lead to mixtures of alkenes on dehydrohalogenation, and the **Saytzeff rule** again applies to the elimination; that is, the double bond of the alkene forms predominantly toward the adjacent carbon atom having the fewer hydrogen atoms. This may be illustrated by the reactions of 2-bromobutane and 2-bromo-2-methylbutane.

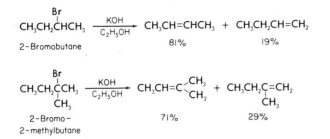

E1 and E2 Mechanisms. The mechanism of dehydrohalogenation for tertiary and many secondary alkyl halides is similar to that of alcohol dehydration; that is, the reaction is an **E1 elimination** involving prior formation of a carbonium ion intermediate:

$$RCH_2\overset{R}{\underset{R}{C}}X \xrightarrow[\text{Slow}]{-:X^\ominus} RCH_2\overset{R}{\underset{R}{C}}^\oplus \xrightarrow[\text{Fast}]{-H^\oplus} RCH=C\overset{R}{\underset{R}{\diagup}}$$

As with other *E*1 eliminations, dehydrohalogenation is subject to the Wagner-Meerwein rearrangement if the initially formed carbonium ion may rearrange to a more stable carbonium species prior to its final loss of a proton:

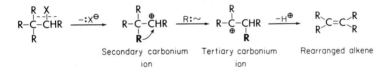

With primary alkyl halides containing a β-hydrogen atom, however, the so-called **E2 elimination** mechanism is operative. Here the basic reagent ($:OH^\ominus$) *directly abstracts* a β-hydrogen atom at the same time that the double bond is forming and the halide ion is leaving. Such a mechanism,

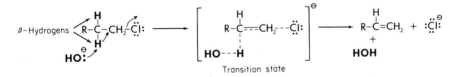

which leads in one continuous step (that is, through a single transition state) to the product, is referred to as a **synchronous** or **concerted mechanism**. We shall encounter other examples of *E*2 eliminations in later chapters. The designations *E*1 and *E*2 are based on reaction rate studies.

$E1$ eliminations are **monomolecular** reactions. In the present examples, this means that the rate of the dehydrohalogenation reaction is dependent only upon the concentration of the alkyl halide, and is independent of the concentration of the base. $E2$ eliminations, on the other hand, are **bimolecular** reactions; that is, the rate at which they proceed is proportional to the product of the concentrations of both the alkyl halide and the base.

$E1$ Dehydrohalogenation:

$$\text{Rate} = k[\text{RX}]$$

$E2$ Dehydrohalogenation:

$$\text{Rate} = k[\text{RX}][\text{OH}^{\ominus}]$$

Most $E2$ reactions appear to be **stereospecific** and to involve what is called **trans elimination**. That is, the atoms or groups being eliminated from adjacent carbon atoms occupy a *trans*-like spatial arrangement (are as far apart as possible) at the onset of elimination. The following general picture of the geometry of $E2$ elimination reactions is typical of specific examples which we shall encounter later. We see that one isomer of the starting alkyl halide yields exclusively one geometrical isomer of the alkene product, whereas the other isomeric halide yields exclusively the other

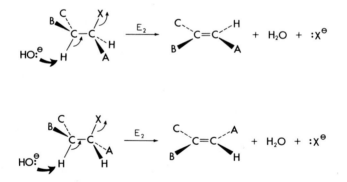

isomeric alkene (*stereospecificity*). Note that the term *trans* elimination refers to the positions of the leaving groups (H and X) at the time of the elimination, and not to the geometrical configurations (*cis* or *trans*) of the alkene product.

c. Dehalogenation of Vicinal Dihalides. A compound having two halogen atoms on adjacent carbon atoms is called a **vicinal dihalide** (Latin: *vicinalis*, neighboring). Treatment of such compounds (usually *vic*-dibromides) with zinc metal or with sodium iodide affords unrearranged alkenes. The reaction is of limited applicability because the dihalides them-

$$R-\underset{\underset{Br}{|}}{\overset{\overset{R}{|}}{C}}-\underset{\underset{Br}{|}}{\overset{\overset{R}{|}}{C}}-R + Zn \longrightarrow \underset{R}{\overset{R}{>}}C=C\underset{R}{\overset{R}{<}} + ZnBr_2$$

$$R-\underset{\underset{Br}{|}}{\overset{\overset{R}{|}}{C}}-\underset{\underset{Br}{|}}{\overset{\overset{R}{|}}{C}}-R + 2NaI \longrightarrow \underset{R}{\overset{R}{>}}C=C\underset{R}{\overset{R}{<}} + 2NaBr + I_2$$

selves are ordinarily obtained from alkenes in the first place (Section 8-4b). However, it is often useful to convert an alkene temporarily to a *vic*-dibromide in order to *protect* the double bond while a reaction is being performed at another part of the molecule, after which the alkene is regenerated by debromination. Similarly, mixtures of alkanes and alkenes having close boiling points may be separated by converting the alkene component to a high-boiling dibromide, separating by distillation, and then regenerating the alkene.

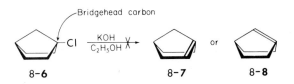

Bredt's Rule. Interestingly, it has been generally found that elimination reactions which might lead to double bonds at the **bridgehead atoms** of small bicyclic systems fail to occur. Thus 1-chlorobicyclo[2.2.1]heptane (**8-6**), although a tertiary halide, fails to dehydrohalogenate to either of the two possible bridgehead alkenes, **8-7** or **8-8**. **Bredt's rule** generalizes such

Bridgehead carbon

$$\text{8-6} \xrightarrow[\text{C}_2\text{H}_5\text{OH}]{\text{KOH}} \text{8-7} \quad \text{or} \quad \text{8-8}$$

8-6   8-7   8-8

observations by stating that double bonds to bridgehead atoms in bicyclic systems do not form. The validity of Bredt's rule arises from the severe distortion which the normally planar, 120°-angled double bond would suffer if it were constrained to the bridgehead atoms of such structures. The related failure of carbonium ions to form at bridgehead atoms in bicyclic systems has already been noted (Section 6-6c). In bridged molecules possessing larger ring systems, however, Bredt's rule does not apply, since distortions of the usual double bond geometry can be less severe. Thus the bicyclo[4.3.1]decene (8-**9**) is a known compound.

8-9

8-4. Reactions of Alkenes

In contrast to the chemically inert alkanes, alkenes are extremely reactive toward a wide variety of reagents. Alkenes react principally by a direct **addition reaction**, where the reacting reagent (**addendum**) merely *adds across* the carbon-carbon double bond to yield a product which contains all of the atoms of both reactants.

Addition Reaction

Alkene   Addendum   Addition product

The total energy of the $\geq C = C \leq$ bond is 146 kcal/mole, of which the π bond makes up about 63 and the σ bond 83 kcal (Section 2-9). In addition reactions the peripheral electrons of the weaker π bond attract the electrophilic (electron-seeking, δ^+) end of the addendum ($A^{\delta+} : B^{\delta-}$) to form a loose π **complex**, wherein the electrophilic end of the addendum is "buried" in the π-electron cloud. The π complex may next rearrange to a carbonium ion, which ultimately reacts with the nucleophilic remainder ($:B^\ominus$) of the addendum. Two new σ bonds result from the rupture of the π bond and reaction with the addendum, and energy is released in the

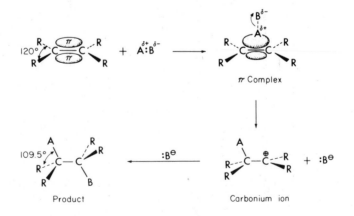

overall process. The original σ bond of the $\diagup C = C \diagdown$ is not involved in the addition reaction, and remains intact. We shall see later that other multiple bonds (for example, $\diagup C = O$, $-C \equiv N$) also undergo similar characteristic addition reactions. Note how the molecular geometry changes during the addition.

Semistable π complexes of alkenes with strong Lewis acids of both inorganic and organic types are known, analogous to those postulated during addition reactions. Some of these can be studied as individual chemical entities, and will be discussed in greater detail later. Silver nitrate, for example, will complex with alkenes, as will also tetranitromethane.

$$R_2C{=}CR_2 \;+\; Ag^\oplus NO_3^\ominus \;\rightleftharpoons\; \left[\begin{array}{c} Ag^\oplus \\[-2pt] | \\[-2pt] R_2C{+}CR_2 \end{array} \right] NO_3^\ominus$$

$$Ag^\oplus \; \pi \; \text{complex}$$

a. Addition of Hydrogen. The catalytic hydrogenation of alkenes has already been discussed (Section 7-5a) as the principal synthesis for alkanes. We shall now consider this reaction in greater detail. During hydrogenation we break the π bond of the alkene (which requires 63 kcal/mole) and the σ bond of a hydrogen molecule (104 kcal/mole; see Table 2-7), then form two C—H σ bonds (liberating 99 kcal/mole each). The overall energy liberated during hydrogenation (**heat of hydrogenation**) can therefore be calculated:

$$\begin{array}{ccccc} & & & & \overset{\text{H H}}{\underset{| \;\;|}{}} \\ R_2C{=}CR_2 & + & H{-}H & \longrightarrow & R_2C{-}CR_2 \; + \; \text{Energy} \end{array}$$

π bond: 63 σ bond: 104   Two σ bonds: 99 each

Total energy required: 167 kcal/mole   Total energy liberated: 198 kcal/mole

Net energy liberated: $198 - 167 = 31$ kcal/mole

Hydrogenation is thus a potentially spontaneous process, since energy is liberated. It does not occur without a specific metal catalyst, however, because the *activation energy* (energy of the transition state; Section 6-8) *is too high.* The function of the catalyst is to lower the activation energy sufficiently so that the reaction will proceed rapidly at reasonable temperatures (25° to 150°). The catalyst functions by **adsorbing** (loosely binding) the two reactants onto its surface, a process which itself liberates energy and "partially breaks" the $\diagup C = C \diagdown$ π bond and the H—H σ bond. The addition reaction then proceeds, whereupon the product becomes **desorbed** from the catalyst surface, freeing it to absorb new reactant mole-

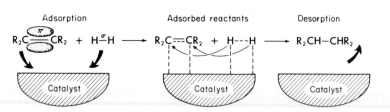

Figure 8-3. *Schematic Course of Catalytic Hydrogenation*

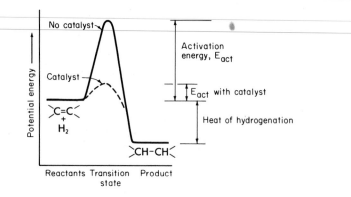

Figure 8-4. *Energy Relationships during Catalytic Hydrogenation*

cules. These functions of the hydrogenation catalyst are shown schematically in Figures 8-3 and 8-4.

The heats of hydrogenation of alkenes vary somewhat depending upon their structure. Thus the three branched alkenes 8-**10,** 8-**11,** and 8-**12** liberate 30.3, 28.5, and 26.9 kcal/mole, respectively, on hydrogenation to their common 2-methylbutane (8-**13**) product. Alkenes having lower heats of hydrogenation are said to be *more stable* than those with higher heats of hydrogenation; that is, they are closer in energy to the correspond-

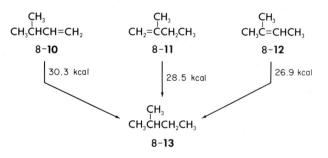

ing alkane (Figure 8-4). Thus alkene **8-12** is more stable than **8-10** by 3.4 kcal/mole, and more stable than **8-11** by 1.6 kcal/mole. In this manner the relative stabilities of alkenes can be estimated as a function of their structures. These stabilities prove to be in the following order:

$$R_2C{=}CR_2 > R_2C{=}CHR > R_2C{=}CH_2 > RCH{=}CHR > RCH{=}CH_2 > CH_2{=}CH_2$$

We thus see that the more highly substituted is the alkene, the greater is its stability. In the same way, *trans* alkenes are found to be more stable than the isomeric *cis* alkenes by about 1 kcal/mole.

b. Addition of Halogen. When an alkene is treated at room temperature with chlorine or bromine (usually in an inert solvent such as carbon tetrachloride), the halogen adds rapidly to the double bond of the alkene to produce a *vicinal* dihalide. The process is called **halogen addition,** and

$$\underset{R}{\overset{R}{>}}C{=}C\underset{R}{\overset{R}{<}} + X_2 \longrightarrow R{-}\underset{\underset{X}{|}}{\overset{\overset{R}{|}}{C}}{-}\underset{\underset{X}{|}}{\overset{\overset{R}{|}}{C}}{-}R \quad (X = Cl,\ Br)$$

Alkene   vic–Dibromoalkane

should be clearly distinguished from the term *halogenation*, which applies to substitution reactions involving halogen (Section 7-6d). Iodine is too unreactive to undergo a similar addition reaction. A quick diagnostic test for carbon-carbon double bonds involves the dropwise addition of a red solution of bromine in carbon tetrachloride to the alkene, whereupon immediate decolorization occurs as the colorless *vic*-dibromoalkane is formed without the evolution of hydrogen bromide.

The mechanism of halogen addition to alkenes is thought to be a two-step ionic process. The π electrons of the alkene **polarize** the halogen by repelling its electrons, whereupon the electrophilic δ^+ end of the resulting halogen dipole forms a π complex (**8-14**) with the double bond, which ultimately yields a carbonium ion (**8-15**) and a halide anion (step 1). The

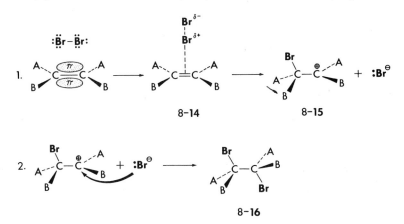

8-14   8-15

8-16

halide anion then attacks the carbonium ion from the *other side* of the original plane of the double bond (step 2), forming the product 8-16. Evidence that halogen addition occurs in two steps involving an intermediate carbonium ion comes from the fact that when such additions are conducted in the presence of inorganic salts (NaCl, NaNO$_3$, etc.), the nucleophilic anion of the added salt finds its way into the final product. Since such salts are

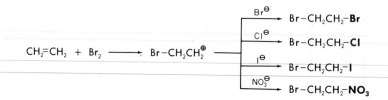

without action on alkenes in the absence of halogens, the indicated mechanism is clearly corroborated. Further confirmation of such a two-step mechanism comes from the chlorination at 0° of isobutene labeled at its methylene group ($=CH_2$) with radioactive carbon. Degradation of the radioactive methallyl chloride product (8-18) with ozone (Sections 4-5 and 8-4h) yields unlabeled formaldehyde (8-19), suggesting that at low temperatures the initially formed tertiary carbonium ion (8-17) loses a proton as indicated to yield discretely labeled methallyl-*1*-C^{14} chloride (8-18) rather than adding :Cl$^\ominus$. In the overall process, the original 1,2 double bond of the starting alkene has rearranged to the 2,3 position.

$$CH_3\overset{CH_3}{\underset{|}{C}}=C^{14}H_2 \xrightarrow{Cl_2} CH_3\overset{CH_3}{\underset{\oplus}{\underset{|}{C}}}-C^{14}H_2Cl \xrightarrow{-H^\oplus} CH_2\overset{CH_3}{\underset{|}{=C}}-C^{14}H_2Cl \xrightarrow{O_3} CH_2=O + O=\overset{CH_3}{\underset{|}{C}}-C^{14}H_2Cl$$

Isobutene–1–C^{14} 8-17   8-18   8-19

Evidence for the stereochemical course of halogen addition comes, among other sources, from the stereochemical configurations of the products obtained from halogen addition to cyclic olefins (**cycloalkenes**). Cyclopentene, for example, adds bromine to give *trans*-1,2-dibromocyclopentane, and not the corresponding *cis* isomer which would result if the bromine molecule added in one step from the same side of the double bond.

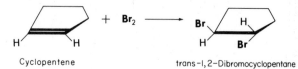

Cyclopentene   *trans*–1,2–Dibromocyclopentane

In analogy with the above equation leading to 8-16, similar **trans addition** of halogen also occurs in acyclic alkenes. Thus the carbonium ion (8-**15**) in step 1 must be *incapable of free rotation* around its central C—C bond during the period of its existence; otherwise the stereoisomer 8-**20** should be formed in addition to the observed 8-**16**. To explain this apparent lack

8-20

of free rotation it has been postulated that the carbonium ion 8-**15** is actually a **cyclic bromonium ion**, whose rigid cyclic structure prevents free rotation. Attack on the bromonium ion by anions in the environment then explains not only the products formed during halogenation but also the observed stereoselectivity (*trans* addition) of such reactions.

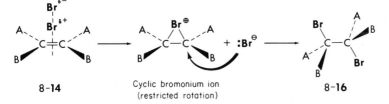

8-14   Cyclic bromonium ion   8-16
               (restricted rotation)

c. *Addition of Hydrogen Halide.* Alkenes react with hydrogen chloride, hydrogen bromide, and hydrogen iodide to form alkyl halides, a reaction called **hydrohalogenation**. The reaction is conducted by passing the

$$\underset{R}{\overset{R}{\diagdown}}C=C\underset{R}{\overset{R}{\diagup}} + HX \longrightarrow R-\underset{\underset{H}{|}}{\overset{\overset{R}{|}}{C}}-\underset{\underset{X}{|}}{\overset{\overset{R}{|}}{C}}-R \quad (X = Cl, Br, I)$$

Example: $CH_3CH=CHCH_3$ + HBr $\longrightarrow$ $CH_3\overset{\overset{Br}{|}}{C}HCH_2CH_3$

               2 - Butene   2 - Bromobutane
        (a symmetrical alkene)

anhydrous hydrogen halide gas directly into the alkene, which may be dissolved in an inert solvent. The order of reactivity for the addition of hydrogen halides to alkenes is: HI > HBr > HCl.

When an alkene is unsymmetrical, such as the type R—CH=CH$_2$, there is the possibility of obtaining two isomeric products during hydrohalogenation. Thus the addition of HBr to propene could yield 1-bromo-

propane, 2-bromopropane, or both, while isobutene might give 1-bromo-
2-methylpropane, 2-bromo-2-methylpropane, or both. Note that only a

$$\underset{\text{Propene}}{CH_3CH=CH_2} + HBr \longrightarrow \underset{\text{1-Bromopropane}}{CH_3CH_2CH_2Br} \text{ and/or } \underset{\underline{\text{2-Bromopropane}}}{CH_3\overset{\overset{\displaystyle Br}{|}}{C}HCH_3}$$

$$\underset{\substack{\text{Isobutene}\\ \text{(unsymmetrical alkenes)}}}{\overset{\overset{\displaystyle CH_3}{|}}{CH_3}C=CH_2} + HBr \longrightarrow \underset{\substack{\underline{\text{1-Bromo-}}\\ \underline{\text{2-methylpropane}}}}{\overset{\overset{\displaystyle CH_3}{|}}{CH_3}CHCH_2Br} \text{ and/or } \underset{\substack{\underline{\text{2-Bromo-}}\\ \underline{\text{2-methylpropane}}}}{\overset{\overset{\displaystyle CH_3}{|}}{CH_3}\underset{\underset{\displaystyle Br}{|}}{C}CH_3}$$

single product forms on addition of a symmetrical addendum (for example,
Br_2) to an unsymmetrical alkene, or on addition of an unsymmetrical
addendum (for example, HX) to a symmetrical alkene. Only if we have
both unsymmetrical addenda *and* unsymmetrical alkenes is there the possibility of obtaining more than one product. The situation is fortunately
simplified, however, by the fact that in such cases only one of the two possible products is found to predominate. In the above illustrations, for
example, 2-bromopropane and 2-bromo-2-methylpropane prove to be the
major products. In 1869 the Russian chemist V. Markownikoff summarized the observed course of such additions in the statement (**Markownikoff's rule**) that: *In ionic additions of unsymmetrical addenda to alkenes,
the hydrogen or positive end of the addendum attaches to the carbon atom of the double
bond which bears the greater number of hydrogen atoms.* **Markownikoff addition**
can thus be summarized as follows:

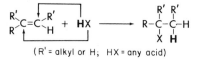

(R′ = alkyl or H; HX = any acid)

In unsymmetrical alkenes of the type R—CH=CH—R′ (2-pentene, for
example) an approximately equimolar mixture of the two addition products is obtained, however, since each carbon atom of the double bond contains the *same* number of hydrogen atoms.

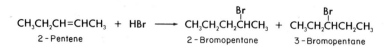

The mechanism of the addition of acids to alkenes is believed to be an
ionic process which may be summarized as follows. The proton of the acid

becomes loosely associated with the π electrons of the alkene, forming a π complex (8-**21**) which reverts to a carbonium ion (step 1). With unsymmetrical alkenes two possible carbonium ions may form, and the more stable one, as usual, will predominate. In the example shown, the more stable secondary carbonium ion (8-**22**) predominates, and ultimately reacts rapidly with the :X$^\ominus$ anion to form the final product (step 2). Note

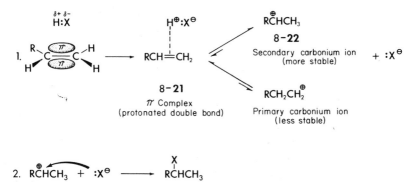

that the preferential formation of the most stable carbonium ion intermediate (tertiary > secondary > primary) explains the orientation during addition which is summarized in Markownikoff's rule.

The Peroxide Effect. In 1933 M. Kharasch and F. Mayo at the University of Chicago discovered that the presence of organic peroxides (compounds of the type R—O—O—R) during the reaction of hydrogen bromide with alkenes reverses the ordinary Markownikoff mode of addition. This phenomenon, called the **peroxide effect**, does not apply to additions in-

$$RCH=CH_2 + HBr \quad \underset{\text{Peroxides absent}}{\overset{\text{Peroxides present}}{\Bigg\{}} \quad \begin{array}{ll} RCH_2CH_2Br & \text{Anti-Markownikoff addition} \\[1em] \overset{\text{Br}}{\underset{|}{RCHCH_3}} & \text{Markownikoff addition} \end{array}$$

volving hydrogen chloride or hydrogen iodide. A variety of evidence supports the theory that the peroxide effect (**anti-Markownikoff addition**) is due to a different reaction mechanism, namely, the intervention of free radical rather than carbonium ion intermediates. The free radical chain mechanism explaining the anti-Markownikoff addition of hydrogen bromide to alkenes is believed to be as shown below. In the chain-initiating steps the thermal or photochemical dissociation of the peroxide produces a free alkoxy radical (RO·), which then attacks HBr to form a bromine atom. In the chain-propagating steps the bromine atom attacks the alkene, converting it preferentially into its most stable (tertiary > secondary >

Chain initiation:

$$RO:OR \longrightarrow 2\ RO\cdot$$

$$RO\cdot + H:Br \longrightarrow RO:H + Br\cdot$$

Chain propagation:

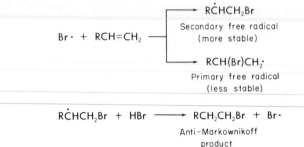

Secondary free radical
(more stable)

Primary free radical
(less stable)

$$R\overset{\cdot}{C}HCH_2Br + HBr \longrightarrow RCH_2CH_2Br + Br\cdot$$

Anti-Markownikoff
product

primary) bromoalkyl free radical. The latter then reacts with more HBr, forming the anti-Markownikoff product and another bromine atom, which is free to continue the chain.

d. Addition of Sulfuric Acid. On thorough mixing with an alkene at room temperature, sulfuric acid will add across the double bond to form an **alkyl hydrogen sulfate.** The product is soluble in the sulfuric acid, so that as reaction proceeds the alkene dissolves. The mechanism of the

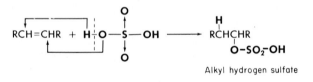

Alkyl hydrogen sulfate

Example: $CH_2=CH_2 + H_2SO_4 \longrightarrow CH_3CH_2OSO_3H$
             Ethylene   Ethyl hydrogen sulfate

addition is exactly analogous to the ionic addition of hydrogen halides, and Markownikoff's rule accordingly applies in the case of unsymmetrical alkenes. When alkyl hydrogen sulfates are heated with water they are **hydrolyzed** (decomposed by the water) into sulfuric acid and an alcohol of analogous structure. The overall process of addition of sulfuric acid to an alkene, followed by hydrolysis of the alkyl hydrogen sulfate product,

$$CH_3CH=CH_2 \xrightarrow{H_2SO_4} CH_3\overset{OSO_3H}{\underset{|}{C}HCH_3} \xrightarrow{H_2O,\,heat} CH_3\overset{OH}{\underset{|}{C}HCH_3} + H_2SO_4$$

Propene   2-Propyl hydrogen   2-Propanol
                        sulfate

constitutes an important commercial method for preparing secondary and tertiary alcohols from the alkene fractions obtained on petroleum cracking. This two step process is referred to as **hydration** of the alkene, since its overall result is the addition of the elements of H—OH across the double bond. Highly reactive alkenes, in fact, can be hydrated directly by merely heating them with water in the presence of an acid catalyst. The solubility of alkenes in sulfuric acid makes it a useful commercial and laboratory reagent for separating alkenes from alkanes, which are unaffected by it at room temperature and hence are insoluble.

e. *Formation of Halohydrins.* When a solution of sodium hypochlorite, $NaOCl$ (obtained by bubbling Cl_2 into $NaOH$ solution), is acidified, hypochlorous acid, $HOCl$, is liberated. Treatment of an alkene with such a cold, acid solution results in addition of the hypochlorous acid across the double bond. A similar addition to alkenes occurs with hypobromous acid,

$$CH_2{=}CH_2\ +\ HO{-}Cl\ \longrightarrow\ \overset{\displaystyle OH}{C}H_2\overset{\displaystyle Cl}{C}H_2$$

Ethylene   2 - Chloroethanol
(ethylene chlorohydrin)

$$CH_3CH{=}CH_2\ +\ HO{-}Br\ \longrightarrow\ CH_3\overset{\displaystyle OH}{C}H\overset{\displaystyle Br}{C}H_2$$

Propene   I - Bromo - 2 - propanol
(propylene bromohydrin)

$HOBr$. The compounds obtained from such reactions are called **halohydrins**, and their systematic and trivial nomenclatures are illustrated in the examples shown. Note that the addition follows Markownikoff's rule if the HO—X is assumed to add ionically as $X^{\oplus}$ and $:OH^{\ominus}$.

f. *Hydroxylation.* The hypothetical addition of the elements of hydrogen peroxide, HO—OH, to the double bond of an alkene is called **hydroxylation.** The products of such addition are simple dihydroxy alcohols

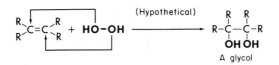

A glycol

called **glycols** (Greek: *glycys*, sweet). Glycols, which will be discussed in greater detail later, are commercially important as solvents, antifreeze compounds, and sources of other commercial chemicals. Hydrogen peroxide itself does not add directly to the alkene as shown, but the overall process may be accomplished by one of three commonly employed reagents: potassium permanganate, $KMnO_4$; performic acid, H—CO—OOH; and osmium tetroxide, OsO_4. Osmium tetroxide is an expensive

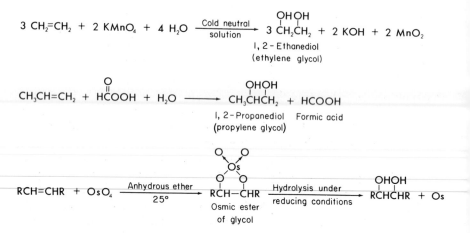

$$3 \ CH_2{=}CH_2 \ + \ 2 \ KMnO_4 \ + \ 4 \ H_2O \xrightarrow[\text{solution}]{\text{Cold neutral}} \ 3 \ \overset{OH}{C}H_2\overset{OH}{C}H_2 \ + \ 2 \ KOH \ + \ 2 \ MnO_2$$

1, 2 - Ethanediol
(ethylene glycol)

$$CH_3CH{=}CH_2 \ + \ H\overset{O}{\overset{\|}{C}}OOH \ + \ H_2O \longrightarrow \ CH_3\overset{OH}{C}H\overset{OH}{C}H_2 \ + \ HCOOH$$

1, 2 - Propanediol   Formic acid
(propylene glycol)

$$RCH{=}CHR \ + \ OsO_4 \xrightarrow[25°]{\text{Anhydrous ether}} \ RCH{-}CHR \xrightarrow[\text{reducing conditions}]{\text{Hydrolysis under}} \ R\overset{OH}{C}H\overset{OH}{C}HR \ + \ Os$$

Osmic ester
of glycol

and very toxic reagent, and is ordinarily employed only for laboratory scale hydroxylations of rare or expensive alkenes. With cycloalkenes the three reagents result in different stereochemical courses of hydroxylation, and they may be employed individually to prepare cyclic glycols of particular stereochemical configurations. The results shown for cyclopentene are typical.

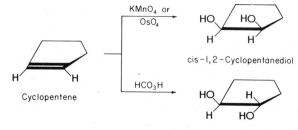

KMnO$_4$ or
OsO$_4$

cis-1,2-Cyclopentanediol

HCO$_3$H

trans-1,2-Cyclopentanediol

Cyclopentene

g. Oxidation. In contrast to alkanes, which are stable to chemical oxidizing agents, alkenes are rapidly oxidized. With such reagents as potassium permanganate, KMnO$_4$, or chromium trioxide, CrO$_3$, for example, alkenes are cleaved by oxidation into products which themselves are stable to further oxidation. The nature of these oxidation products depends upon the structure of the alkene undergoing oxidation, as seen in the following general examples.

$$RCH{=}CH_2 \xrightarrow{(O)} RCOOH \ + \ CO_2$$

Carboxylic acid

$$\overset{R}{\underset{R}{>}}C{=}CH_2 \xrightarrow{(O)} \overset{R}{\underset{R}{>}}C{=}O \ + \ CO_2$$

Ketone

$$RCH=C\underset{R}{\overset{R}{\diagdown}} \xrightarrow{(O)} RCOOH + \underset{R}{\overset{R}{\diagdown}}C=O$$

Carboxylic acid   Ketone

These reactions take place by further oxidation (resulting in C—C cleavage) of the initially produced glycols described above (Section 8-4f), and glycols are obtainable only under carefully controlled reaction conditions if potassium permanganate is the oxidizing agent.   The oxidation of alkenes is useful as (1) a synthetic means of preparing ketones and carboxylic acids, (2) a degradative reaction helpful in determining the structures of alkenes (see Section 4-5), and (3) a diagnostic test for the presence of the carbon-carbon double (or triple) bond.   This test (**Baeyer test** for carbon-carbon unsaturation) involves the use of a purple solution of potassium permanganate. If the substance being tested is an alkene, the purple permanganate color disappears and a precipitate of brown manganese dioxide, MnO_2, is formed.   The Baeyer test must be used with caution, however, since other readily oxidizable groups (for example, —CH=O) in a molecule will also result in a positive test.

h. Ozonization.   Ozone, which exists as a resonance hybrid structure,

$$:\overset{\oplus}{\underset{..}{O}}=\overset{..}{\underset{..}{O}}-\overset{..\ominus}{\underset{..}{O}}: \longleftrightarrow :\overset{\oplus}{\underset{..}{O}}-\overset{..}{\underset{..}{O}}-\overset{..\ominus}{\underset{..}{O}}: \longleftrightarrow :\overset{..\ominus}{\underset{..}{O}}-\overset{\oplus}{\underset{..}{O}}=\overset{..}{\underset{..}{O}}: \longleftrightarrow :\overset{..\ominus}{\underset{..}{O}}-\overset{..}{\underset{..}{O}}-\overset{\oplus}{\underset{..}{O}}:$$

Ozone resonance hybrid

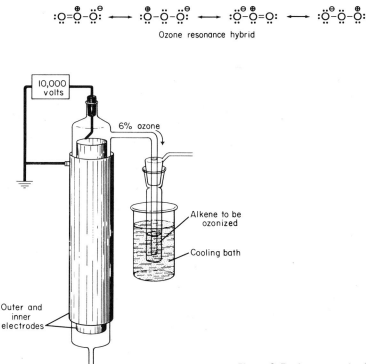

Figure 8-5. Apparatus for Ozonization

may be prepared in 6 to 8 per cent concentration by passing a stream of oxygen through a silent electric discharge (Figure 8-5). When a stream of ozone-rich oxygen is bubbled into a solution of an alkene in an inert solvent, the ozone molecule adds to the double bond of the alkene, forming an alkene **molozonide**. The initially formed molozonide is unstable and

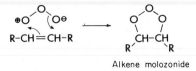

Alkene molozonide

undergoes an interesting rearrangement to a more stable isomer, the alkene **ozonide**. The molozonide apparently spontaneously cleaves into

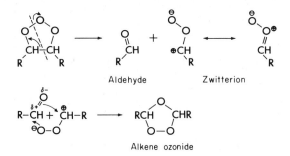

Aldehyde   Zwitterion

Alkene ozonide

an aldehyde (or ketone) and a resonance hybrid **zwitterion** (an ion bearing both ⊕ and ⊖ charges), which then "flips over" and adds to the carbonyl group of the aldehyde (or ketone) to form the more stable ozonide. Evidence for this dissociation-recombination mechanism comes from the fact that ozonization of an alkene in the presence of an *extraneous* aldehyde or ketone leads to a mixture of ozonides. Under these conditions the zwitterion fragment has the choice of adding either to the aldehyde (or ketone) produced by dissociation of the molozonide or to the extraneous aldehyde or ketone. As further evidence, diperoxides are formed as by-products during ozonization. These arise from reaction of the zwitterion fragment with itself.

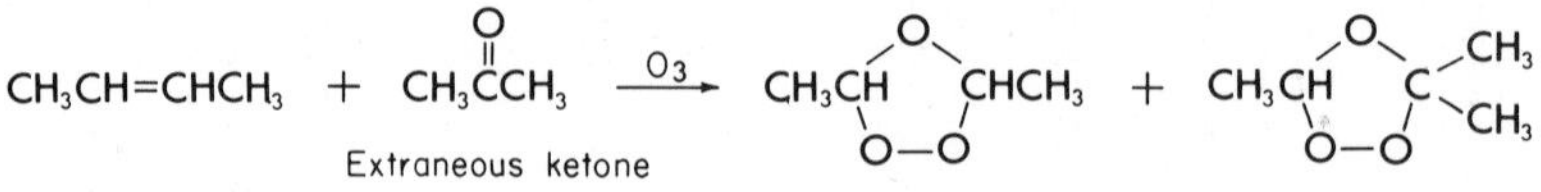

CH₃CH=CHCH₃ + CH₃CCH₃ —O₃→ CH₃CH   CHCH₃ + CH₃CH   C CH₃

Extraneous ketone

Zwitterion   Diperoxide

Ozonides, like other compounds containing the peroxide group, —O—O—, often explode violently and unpredictably. They are therefore seldom isolated as such, but are rather decomposed *in situ* by reduction with zinc metal or other reducing agents. The overall cleavage of alkenes into aldehydes and ketones by the action of ozone is called **ozonolysis.**

$$\underset{\underset{O-O}{}}{\overset{\overset{O}{}}{RCH\ CHR}} + Zn + 2H^{\oplus} \xrightarrow{H_2O,\ CH_3COOH} 2\ RCH=O + H_2O + Zn^{2+}$$

The use of ozonolysis as a means of determining the structure of alkenes has already been discussed (Section 4-5).

i. Hydroboration. In 1956 H. C. Brown of Purdue University discovered that diborane, B_2H_6, readily adds at 0° to 25° to the double bond of alkenes. This **hydroboration** reaction proves to be quite general and has

$$6\ CH_2=CH_2 + B_2H_6 \xrightarrow{0°} 2\ \underset{\text{Triethylborane}}{CH_3CH_2\overset{\overset{CH_2CH_3}{|}}{B}CH_2CH_3}$$

opened new synthetic vistas for organic chemists, since the trialkylborane products may readily be converted into other useful substances. For example, oxidation of tri-*n*-alkylboranes with alkaline hydrogen peroxide provides a general synthesis for primary alcohols. Note that the boron atom adds to the least substituted end of the double bond and that the

$$\underset{\text{1-Butene}}{6\ CH_3CH_2CH=CH_2} + B_2H_6 \longrightarrow \underset{\text{Tri-n-butylborane}}{2\ (CH_3CH_2CH_2CH_2)_3B} \xrightarrow[H_2O_2,\ NaOH]{(O)} \underset{\text{1-Butanol}}{6\ CH_3CH_2CH_2CH_2OH}$$

overall process amounts to the **anti-Markownikoff hydration** of the alkene. This contrasts to the sulfuric acid hydration of alkenes described above, which involved predominately Markownikoff addition. The stereochemistry of the hydroboration reaction has been extensively studied, and the process proves to involve exclusively *cis* addition. Thus hydroboration of 1-methylcyclopentene, followed by oxidation, affords only *trans*-2-methylcyclopentanol, indicating that the overall anti-Markownikoff addition of H—OH has occurred in a *cis* fashion. Hydrolysis of trialkylboranes

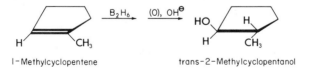

1-Methylcyclopentene   *trans*-2-Methylcyclopentanol

with aqueous acids yields alkanes, providing an alternative procedure for the conversion of alkenes into alkanes. Treatment of trialkylboranes with

$$6 \ (CH_3)_2C=CH_2 \ + \ B_2H_6 \ \longrightarrow \ 2 \ [(CH_3)_2CHCH_2]_3B \ \xrightarrow{H_2O, \ H^{\oplus}} \ 6 \ CH_3\overset{\overset{\displaystyle CH_3}{|}}{C}CH_3$$

Isobutene   Triisobutylborane   Isobutane

alkaline silver nitrate solution induces a **coupling** reaction, affording a route to higher alkanes. New synthetic applications of the hydroboration reaction are being reported with great frequency.

$$2 \left(\overset{\displaystyle CH_3}{\underset{\displaystyle CH_3}{}} CHCH_2 \right)_3 B \ \xrightarrow[0°]{AgNO_3, \ NaOH} \ 3 \ CH_3\overset{\overset{\displaystyle CH_3}{|}}{C}HCH_2CH_2\overset{\overset{\displaystyle CH_3}{|}}{C}HCH_3$$

Triisobutylborane   2,5 – Dimethylhexane

j. Allylic Halogenation. A carbon atom adjacent to a double bond is called an **allylic** carbon after the name of the allyl group, and substituents on an allylic carbon are called allylic substituents. At high temperatures

Allylic hydrogen → **H**
Allylic carbon ↗R–C–CH=CH–R CH_2=CH–CH$_2^-$
Allylic halogen → **X**   Allyl group

or under the influence of ultraviolet light, conditions which favor the halogenation of alkanes by substitution (Section 7-6d), alkenes may undergo **allylic halogenation**, that is, substitution of one of their allylic hydrogens by halogen. The allylic chlorination of propene is important

$$CH_2=CHCH_3 \ + \ Cl_2 \ \xrightarrow{500°-600°} \ CH_2=CHCH_2Cl$$

Propene   3 – Chloro -1- propene
                                                         (allyl chloride)

since the product, allyl chloride, serves as the starting material for the manufacture of glycerine and other commercially important products. Allylic halogenation occurs by a free radical mechanism analogous to that of alkane halogenation (Section 7-6d), in contrast to the ionic mechanism of halogen addition to alkenes (Section 8-4b). At the high temperatures and vapor phase conditions involved during allylic halogenation, halogen addition to the alkene does not occur. Substitution takes place at the allylic position rather than at some alternate position, since the intermediate allyl radical, stabilized by resonance, is more stable and more readily formed than alternative radicals.

$$R-\overset{\displaystyle \cdot}{C}H-CH=CH_2 \ \longleftrightarrow \ R-CH=CH-CH_2\cdot$$

Resonance hybrid of substitued allyl radical

On a laboratory scale, allylic bromination reactions are conveniently and quantitatively carried out using *N*-bromosuccinimide ("NBS") in an inert solvent. The reactivity and synthetic usefulness of allylic bromides make this reaction quite important to the synthetic organic chemist.

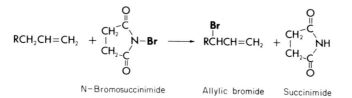

N–Bromosuccinimide   Allylic bromide   Succinimide

k. Alkylation. 2,2,4-Trimethylpentane ("isooctane"), which is used as an aviation fuel and as a standard fuel for determining octane numbers (Section 7-4e), is made commercially by the acid-catalyzed addition of isobutane to isobutene. Such a reaction is referred to as **alkylation** of the

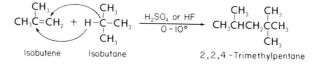

Isobutene   Isobutane   2,2,4-Trimethylpentane

alkene by the alkane. The process is believed to proceed through the following carbonium ion chain mechanism. In step 1 a proton adds to the

1. $(CH_3)_2C=CH_2 + H^\oplus \rightleftharpoons (CH_3)_3C^\oplus$

2. $(CH_3)_3C^\oplus + CH_2=C(CH_3)_2 \longrightarrow (CH_3)_3CCH_2\overset{\oplus}{C}(CH_3)_2$

3. $(CH_3)_3CCH_2\overset{\oplus}{C}(CH_3)_2 + (CH_3)_3CH \longrightarrow (CH_3)_3CCH_2CH(CH_3)_2 + (CH_3)_3C^\oplus$

double bond of isobutene, producing the more stable t-butyl carbonium ion. This in turn adds to isobutene (step 2) to produce a tertiary C_8 carbonium ion. The latter finally abstracts a hydride ion ($:H^\ominus$) from isobutane (step 3), forming the product and regenerating the t-butyl carbonium ion.

l. Polymerization of Alkenes. A **polymer** is a high molecular weight molecule made up of many identical smaller structural units (Greek: *poly*, many + *meros*, part). Polymers are formed by a process called **polymerization** of the basic small unit, called the **monomer**. Under the influence of various catalysts, alkene monomers undergo **addition polymerization** (add one to another indefinitely), forming polymers called **polyalkenes**. Alkene polymerization occurs by four principal pathways.

Free Radical Polymerization. When ethylene is heated at 100° under 15,000 psi pressure in the presence of traces (0.01 per cent) of oxygen, it polymerizes into a waxy polymer of high molecular weight called **poly-ethylene** or polythene.

$$nCH_2=CH_2 \xrightarrow[0.01\% \ O_2]{100°, \ 15,000 \ psi} \ (CH_2-CH_2)_n \quad (n = 600-1000)$$

This polymer, chemically similar to paraffin wax (Section 7-4c), is widely used for wire insulation, bottles, toys, packaging, and wearing apparel. Substituted ethylene molecules may also be readily polymerized, giving a wide variety of polymers which provide the raw materials for the modern plastic fabrication industry. These are called **vinyl polymers**, on the basis of the **vinyl group**, $CH_2=CH-$, present in the monomers from which they are made. In Table 8-3 we see some of the structural variations and uses of such vinyl polymers. Similar polymerization of tetrafluoro-ethene, $F_2C=CF_2$, produces the tough plastic Teflon, which is one of the most chemically inert substances known and even finds use as a metal coating in "greaseless" cooking utensils.

Table 8-3. Some Plastics from Vinyl Polymerization

$$nCH_2=\overset{\overset{R}{|}}{\underset{\underset{X}{|}}{C}} \xrightarrow{\text{Peroxide catalyst}} (CH_2-\overset{\overset{R}{|}}{\underset{\underset{X}{|}}{C}})_n$$

R	X	Polymer	Use
—H	—Cl	Polyvinyl chloride (Koroseal)	Rubber substitute, raincoats, lacquers
—H	—C≡N	Polyvinyl cyanide, poly-acrylonitrile (Orlon)	Fabrics, clothing
—H	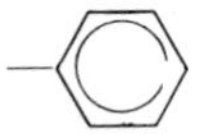 —⬡	Polystyrene	Electrical insulators, foamed plastic fabrication
—H	—O—CO—CH₃	Polyvinyl acetate (Vinylite)	Plastic sheets, films, fibers
—CH₃	—CO—OCH₃	Polymethylmethacrylate (Lucite, Plexiglass)	Transparent sheets, tubes and molded objects
—Cl	—Cl	Polyvinylidene chloride (Saran)	Sheeting, packag-ing, seat covers

Vinyl polymerization of the above type has been found to proceed through a free radical mechanism, as illustrated below. In step 1 the **initiator** (a peroxide or other free radical source) decomposes to produce

1. RO-OR $\longrightarrow$ 2 RO·

2. RO· + CH$_2$=CH $\longrightarrow$ RO-CH$_2$CH·
            | |
            X   X

3. RO-CH$_2$CH· + CH$_2$=CH $\longrightarrow$ RO-CH$_2$CH-CH$_2$CH· $\xrightarrow{\text{Etc.}}$ Polymer
       | | | |
       X   X   X   X

a free radical. The radical then attacks the vinyl monomer, adding to it and forming a new radical (step 2). This radical then adds to a new vinyl monomer molecule forming a **dimer** radical, which in turn adds to another monomer unit to form a **trimer** radical, and so on indefinitely (step 3). Eventually the growing chain is terminated by some process which does not produce a new radical site on the chain. By careful control of polymerization conditions, polymer chains of differing average chain lengths can be produced. Another means of controlling the properties of vinyl polymers is the process of **copolymerization**, whereby a mixture of two (or more) monomers is polymerized. In this case the final polymer will have both monomer units *randomly* distributed along its chain. The Vinylite listed in Table 8-3 is actually a copolymer of vinyl acetate and vinyl chloride.

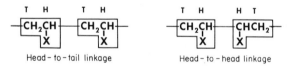

CH$_2$=CH + CH$_2$=CH $\xrightarrow{\text{Peroxide catalyst}}$ $\left(\text{CH}_2\text{CH-CH}_2\text{CH-CH}_2\text{CH-CH}_2\text{CH}\right)_n$
     | | | | | |
     X   Y   X   Y   X   X

Vinyl copolymer

Vinyl polymers prove to involve *head-to-tail* monomer linkages rather than head-to-head. One reason for this structural preference is the greater

Head-to-tail linkage   Head-to-head linkage

stability of the secondary free radicals involved in head-to-tail addition over the stability of the primary free radicals which would be involved in head-to-head addition. Another reason involves the steric repulsions between the vinyl substituents (X) which would prevail during head-to-head addition.

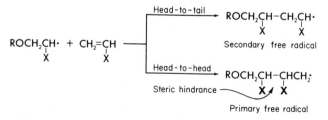

Cationic Polymerization. Alkenes will polymerize in the presence of acid catalysts via a carbonium ion mechanism. One important application of this reaction is the controlled conversion (60 per cent sulfuric acid) of isobutene from petroleum cracking into a mixture of two C_8 alkenes ("diisobutylene"), a process called **dimerization.** Catalytic hydrogena-

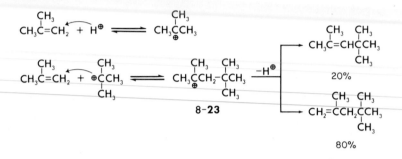

tion of the octene mixture obtained provides another commercial source of 2,2,4-trimethylpentane ("isooctane"). Under other controlled conditions the dimeric carbonium ion **8-23** can add to another isobutene molecule to form a trimeric carbonium ion, which adds again to isobutene, and so on, to produce a high polymer. Thus with boron fluoride, BF_3, at $-100°$ isobutene is converted into a rubber-like solid, **polyisobutylene,** $+CH_2C(CH_3)_2+_n$, which may have molecular weights up to 400,000.

Anionic Polymerization. This type of polymerization proceeds by way of a carbanion mechanism, which is initiated (step 1) by the action of a strong electron donor. The initial carbanion produced attacks another molecule

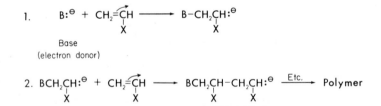

of the alkene, and so on (step 2), producing a growing anionic chain which becomes the polymer.

Coordination Polymerization. Control over the polymerization of alkenes has been revolutionized by the technique of **coordination polymerization** pioneered by K. Ziegler in Germany and G. Natta in Italy, who were awarded the Nobel prize in 1963 for their discoveries. The so-called **Ziegler catalysts** for such polymerizations consist of mixtures of triethylaluminum, $(C_2H_5)_3Al$, and titanium tetrachloride, $TiCl_4$, or of other organometallic compounds and salts, containing suspended inert solids.

The mechanistic details of this elegant process have yet to be elucidated, and the following equation represents an oversimplified, provisional expression.

$$-CH_2CH_2 \underset{Ti}{\diagdown} \quad \xrightarrow{CH_2 = CH_2} \quad -CH_2CH_2 \underset{Ti}{\diagdown}\overset{\displaystyle CH_2}{\diagdown}_{CH_2} \quad \longrightarrow \quad -CH_2CH_2-CH_2CH_2 \underset{Ti}{\diagdown} \quad \xrightarrow{CH_2 = CH_2, \text{ Etc.}} \quad \text{Polymer}$$

The coordination polymerization of ethylene occurs under much milder conditions than does its free radical polymerization, and produces a much more uniform and regular polymer chain having no branching. The resulting polyethylene is stronger and higher melting than that obtained by free radical polymerization. The Ziegler catalysts in conjunction with proper inert supports, moreover, permit for the first time the *stereochemical control* of alkene polymerization. Polypropylene, for example, can have three stereochemical arrangements (Figure 8-6): **isotactic** (all CH$_3$ groups on the same side of the extended polymer chain), **syndiotactic** (CH$_3$ groups alternating on each side of the chain), and **atactic** (CH$_3$ groups

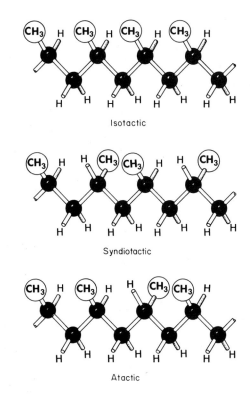

Figure 8-6. Stereoisomeric Forms of Polypropylene

Isotactic

Syndiotactic

Atactic

randomly oriented). With Ziegler catalysts on crystalline supports, iso-tactic polypropylene results, from which high-melting, strong fibers can be made. With amorphous supports, soft, rubbery atactic polypropylene is formed.

8-5. Dienes and Polyenes

Dienes, alkenes containing two double bonds, fall into three classes depending on the relative positions of their double bonds. Dienes with iso-

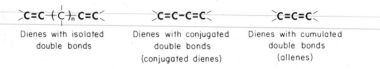

| Dienes with isolated double bonds | Dienes with conjugated double bonds (conjugated dienes) | Dienes with cumulated double bonds (allenes) |

lated double bonds separated by one or more carbon atoms are not novel, for their chemical behavior parallels exactly that of the simple alkenes described above. Allenes are a rather unimportant class of dienes which will be discussed briefly later. Conjugated dienes, on the other hand, are an important class of compounds with several unique chemical properties not shared by simple alkenes.

Dienes may be prepared by applying any alkene synthesis to a molecule having two of the requisite functional groups in the proper position. Thus 1,3-butadiene, CH_2=$CHCH$=CH_2, may be made, as it is in Germany, by the dehydration of the 1,4-glycol, 1,4-butanediol, HO—$CH_2CH_2CH_2$-CH_2—OH. In this country 1,3-butadiene is made by the dehydrogenation of butane using special catalysts (Cr_2O_3–Al_2O_3).

As measured by heats of hydrogenation (Table 8-4), the stability of conjugated dienes is *greater* than that of isolated dienes. We see that the nonconjugated 1,4-pentadiene (no. 2) has the expected heat of hydrogenation, about twice that of the simple alkene 1-pentene (no. 1), but that the

Table 8-4. Heats of Hydrogenation of Some Alkenes and Dienes

No.	Compound	Heat of Hydrogenation, kcal/mole
1	$CH_3CH_2CH_2CH$=CH_2	30.1
2	CH_2=$CHCH_2CH$=CH_2	60.8
3	CH_3CH=$CHCH$=CH_2	54.1
4	CH_3CH_2CH=CH_2	30.3
5	CH_2=$CHCH$=CH_2	57.1

conjugated 1,3-pentadiene (no. 3) has a heat of hydrogenation some 6.7 kcal/mole *lower* than no. 2. Similarly, 1,3-butadiene (no. 5) has a heat of hydrogenation some 3.5 kcal/mole lower than twice the value for 1-butene (no. 4). This *extra stability* of conjugated dienes as well as the *shortened C–C bond distance* between the two double bonds (1.46 Å, 0.08 Å shorter than the normal C–C bond distance of 1.54 Å) is explained by ascribing a certain amount of **double bond character** to the central single bond between the two conjugated double bonds. In order to rationalize these peculiarities, resonance and molecular orbital theories symbolize the structure of 1,3-butadiene, for example, as shown below. The resonance energy or delocalization energy of conjugated dienes is thus about 3 to 6 kcal/mole.

$$CH_2=CH-CH=CH_2 \longleftrightarrow \cdot CH_2-CH=CH-CH_2 \cdot \longleftrightarrow \overset{\oplus}{CH_2}-CH=CH-\overset{..}{\overset{\ominus}{CH_2}} \longleftrightarrow \overset{..}{\overset{\ominus}{CH_2}}-CH=CH-\overset{\oplus}{CH_2}$$

|←—→|
|1.46|
| Å |

Canonical structures of 1,3–butadiene

One molecular orbital representation of 1,3–butadiene
(π orbital encompasses all four carbon atoms)

   a. 1,4 Addition to Conjugated Dienes.   When *one mole* of a reagent capable of adding to an alkene reacts with a conjugated diene, two products are formed, a normal 1,2-addition product and a 1,4-addition product. The

	1,2 Product	1,4 Product
Br_2	$CH_2-CHCH=CH_2$ $\;\;\;\vert\;\;\;\;\vert$ $\;\;\;Br\;\;Br$	$+\;CH_2CH=CHCH_2$ $\;\;\;\;\;\vert\;\;\;\;\;\;\;\;\;\;\;\vert$ $\;\;\;\;\;Br\;\;\;\;\;\;\;\;\;\;Br$
HCl	$CH_2-CHCH=CH_2$ $\;\;\;\vert\;\;\;\;\vert$ $\;\;\;H\;\;Cl$	$+\;CH_2CH=CHCH_2$ $\;\;\;\;\;\vert\;\;\;\;\;\;\;\;\;\;\;\vert$ $\;\;\;\;\;H\;\;\;\;\;\;\;\;\;\;Cl$
H_2 catalyst	$CH_2-CHCH=CH_2$ $\;\;\;\vert\;\;\;\;\vert$ $\;\;\;H\;\;H$	$+\;CH_2CH=CHCH_2$ $\;\;\;\;\;\vert\;\;\;\;\;\;\;\;\;\;\;\vert$ $\;\;\;\;\;H\;\;\;\;\;\;\;\;\;\;H$

$CH_2=CH-CH=CH_2$ at left.

latter product, which is often the major one, is said to arise by **conjugate addition** to the diene. A second mole of the reagent adds in the normal fashion to the remaining double bond of either product. With dienes having isolated double bonds, only normal 1,2 addition is observed. Conjugate addition is explained in terms of resonance theory as illustrated in the following two-step bromination mechanism. The allyl type of carbonium ion intermediate initially formed is actually a resonance hybrid of

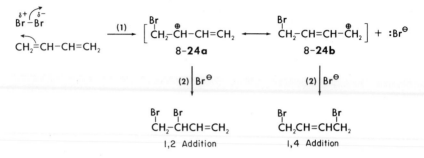

canonical structures 8-**24a** and 8-**24b**. The hybrid may then be attacked by :Br$^\ominus$ at either of its centers of maximum electron deficiency, leading thus to products of both normal (from 8-**24a**) and conjugate addition (from 8-**24b**).

b. Polymerization of Conjugated Dienes. The polymerization of conjugated dienes is of commercial importance since it affords various types of synthetic rubber. Polymerization of 1,3-butadiene, for example, is initiated by free radicals and proceeds by 1,4 addition, producing a soft, rubbery polymer. Butadiene polymers, which can be vulcanized as

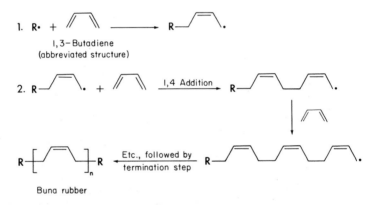

described below, have been produced since 1927 under the name of **Buna rubber.** The similar polymerization of 2-chloro-1,3-butadiene (chloroprene) leads to a rubber substitute called **Neoprene**, which is superior to

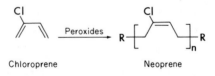

Chloroprene   Neoprene

natural rubber in its resistance to oil, gasoline, and organic solvents. Conjugated dienes may also be copolymerized with vinyl monomers to

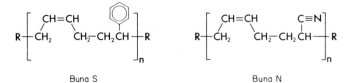

Buna S   Buna N

produce other "synthetic rubber" polymers. Thus copolymerization of 1,3-butadiene with styrene, C_6H_5—CH=CH$_2$, affords **Buna S** rubber, while copolymerization with acrylonitrile, CH_2=CH—C≡N, yields **Buna N** rubber.

Natural Rubber. Natural rubber itself occurs in a milky suspension (**latex**) in many plants. The principal source is the rubber tree, from which the latex is tapped by making incisions in the bark. Crude rubber is precipitated from the latex by addition of acetic acid, and the coagulated material is rolled into sheets of **crepe** rubber. Extensive physical and chemical investigations of rubber over a number of years have revealed it to be a *cis* polymer of 2-methyl-1,3-butadiene (isoprene) having head-to-tail linkages. By using stereoselective polymerization catalysts such as the Ziegler catalysts (Section 8-41), natural rubber with its *cis* configurations has recently been synthesized from isoprene.

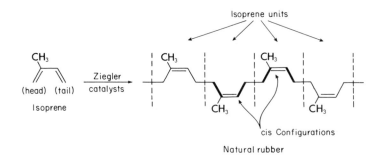

Natural rubber

The hardness and durability of both natural and synthetic rubbers are improved by the technique of **vulcanization**, accidentally discovered by Charles Goodyear in 1834. When rubber is heated with sulfur (**vul-**

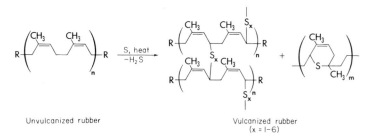

Unvulcanized rubber   Vulcanized rubber
                                                    (x = 1-6)

canized), it undergoes a free radical reaction whereby groups of sulfur atoms substitute into adjacent polymer, and cyclic sulfide units are formed within each chain. The resulting cross-linked polymer is tougher than the original unvulcanized rubber.

Natural Polyenes. Many polyunsaturated compounds occur in nature, and the polyunsaturated fats will be discussed in a later chapter. *Conjugated* polyene compounds are also found in many natural sources. Vitamin A, for example, is a fat-soluble vitamin present in fish liver oils. Medically, it proves necessary for resisting infections and for proper vision. Its earlier source in cod liver oil has been supplemented by commercial synthesis since 1950. β-Carotene is one of the several structurally related reddish pigments of tomatoes, carrots, and other fruits and vegetables, and is believed to be a precursor of vitamin A in the body. The isoprene units from which these structures are built are indicated by broken lines in the accompanying formulas.

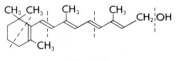

Vitamin A

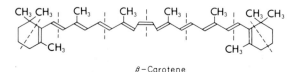

β–Carotene

c. The Color of Conjugated Polyenes. The bright colors of the above natural polyenes are noteworthy. Crystalline vitamin A, for example, is yellowish in color, while β-carotene is deep orange. What is the basis for such colors in conjugated polyenes?

The ultraviolet absorption (Section 4-9) of the isolated carbon-carbon double bond occurs in the difficultly accessible spectral region of 1625 Å. Conjugated double bonds, on the other hand, constitute chromophores which show absorption at longer wavelengths, and the greater the number of conjugated double bonds, the longer the wavelength at which absorption occurs. The effect of increasingly extended conjugation on the absorption spectra of some diphenylpolyenes is shown in Table 8-5. Such **batho-chromic shifts** (shifts of absorption maxima to longer wavelengths) are interpreted in terms of the more extensive π-electron system which long conjugated systems offer for resonance stabilization of the *photoexcited* molecule, making the energy of the *photoexcited state* of the molecule closer

Table 8-5. Effect of Increasing Conjugation on Light Absorption

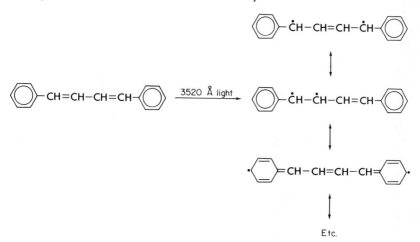

n	First Absorption Band, Å
1	3190
2	3520
3	3770
4	4040
5	4240
11	5300
15	5700

to that of the *ground* (unexcited) *state*. In the illustration below we note that the conjugated polyene is able to accommodate the photoexcited electrons over its entire π-electron system. The greater the number of conjugated double bonds, the greater the number of canonical structures which can be visualized for the photoexcited polyene. When polyunsaturated compounds lack conjugation, however—that is, if their double bonds are *isolated*—such bathochromic shifts do not occur and the positions of the absorption maxima are characteristic of simple alkenes.

Resonance-stabilized photoexcited polyene

d. Isomerizations of Alkenes and Polyenes. Under certain conditions the double bonds of alkenes and polyenes prove unstable with respect to both their geometry and their position. Under heat or ultraviolet radiation, for example, *cis* and *trans* isomers equilibrate as shown below. The ease of

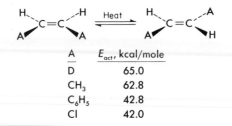

A	E_{act}, kcal/mole
D	65.0
CH_3	62.8
C_6H_5	42.8
Cl	42.0

equilibration, as reflected in the activation energy, appears to increase with bulkier substituents, and the *trans* isomers generally predominate in such equilibria.

In the presence of alkali, isolated double bonds frequently migrate into conjugation with other unsaturated groupings. The rearrangement of safrole, the essence of sassafras oil, into isosafrole is typical of such isomerizations. We note that the isolated double bond moves into conjugation

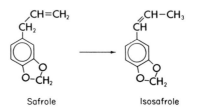

Safrole	Isosafrole

with the π electrons of the benzene ring and that a hydrogen atom migrates simultaneously in the process.

When heated at 200° to 300°, 1,5-dienes undergo an interesting isomerization called the **Cope rearrangement,** which is illustrated in the equilibration of 2,6-octadiene with 3,4-dimethyl-1,5-hexadiene. Such reactions

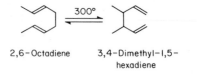

2,6-Octadiene	3,4-Dimethyl-1,5- hexadiene

are referred to as **valence bond isomerizations**, since they occur by a mere reshuffling of the valence bonds of the components, and not by migrations of atoms or groups within the molecule. Valence bond isomerizations may also involve interchanges of both rings and double bonds, as illustrated in the following examples recently investigated by nuclear magnetic resonance techniques. The case of "bullvalene" is particularly in-

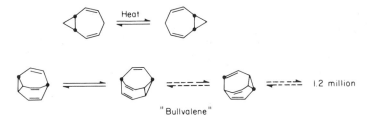

"Bullvalene"

teresting, since over 1.2 million valence bond isomers are possible for this structure. NMR data suggest that the Cope rearrangement of this hydrocarbon has the result that no two carbon atoms are permanently bonded to each other, and the ten carbon atoms of the rings effectively "wander" over the surface of a sphere.

SUPPLEMENTARY READING

Markownikoff
1. "The Markovnikov Rule," G. Jones, *J. Chem. Educ.*, **38,** 297 (1961).
2. "Vladimer Vasilevich Markovnikov," H. M. Leicaster, *J. Chem. Educ.*, **18,** 53 (1941).

Hydroboration and Metal Hydrides
1. "Hydroboration," H. C. Brown, W. A. Benjamin, Inc., New York, 1962.
2. "New Selective Reducing Agents," H. C. Brown, *J. Chem. Educ.*, **38,** 173 (1961).
3. "Reduction with Complex Metal Hydrides," N. G. Gaylord, *J. Chem. Educ.*, **34,** 367 (1957).
4. "The Boron Hydrides," B. Siegel and J. L. Mack, *J. Chem. Educ.*, **34,** 314 (1957).

Synthetic Polymers
1. "New Horizons in Elastic Polymers," H. L. Fisher, *J. Chem. Educ.*, **37,** 369 (1960).
2. "Contributions of Vinyl Polymerization to Organic Chemistry," F. R. Mayo, *J. Chem. Educ.*, **36,** 157 (1959).
3. "The Geometry of Giant Molecules," C. C. Price, *J. Chem. Educ.*, **36,** 160 (1959).
4. "Anionic Polymerization of Vinyl Monomers," A. Zilkha, M. Albeck, and M. Frankel, *J. Chem. Educ.*, **35,** 345 (1958).
5. "Polymerization of Ethylene at Atmospheric Pressure. A Demonstration Using a 'Ziegler' Type Catalyst," A. Zilkha, N. Calderon, J. Rabini, and M. Frankel, *J. Chem. Educ.*, **35,** 344 (1958).
6. "Structure of Synthetic High Polymers," F. C. McGrew, *J. Chem. Educ.*, **35,** 178 (1958).
7. "Polymerization," G. Natta, *Scientific American*, Sept. (1957).
8. "Vinyl Ester Resins," C. Benton, *J. Chem. Educ.*, **21,** 144 (1944).

9. "Synthetic Rubber and Plastics," E. A. Hauser, *J. Chem. Educ.*, **21,** 15 (1944).

10. "Synthetic Resin Design," A. G. Chenicek, *J. Chem. Educ.*, **21,** 495 (1944).

11. "Structure of Synthetic Chain Polymers as shown by X-Rays," C. S. Fuller and W. B. Baker, *J. Chem. Educ.*, **20,** 3 (1943).

12. "Plexiglas and Other Acrylic Resins," C. B. Wooster, *J. Chem. Educ.*, **19,** 430 (1942).

13. "Synthetic Resins and Plastics," H. A. Neville, *J. Chem. Educ.*, **19,** 9 (1942).

Rubber

1. "Building a Natural Rubber Latex Compound," D. W. Button, *J. Chem. Educ.*, **34,** 255 (1957).

2. "Rubber Plus Chemistry," H. L. Fisher, *J. Chem. Educ.*, **28,** 328 (1951).

3. "Cold Rubber," W. B. Reynolds, *J. Chem. Educ.*, **27,** 494 (1950).

4. "Natural and Synthetic Rubbers," H. L. Fisher, *J. Chem. Educ.*, **19,** 522 (1942).

Addition of Halogen

1. "The Bromonium Ion," J. G. Traynham, *J. Chem. Educ.*, **40,** 392 (1963).

Polyenes

1. "Color and Chemical Constitution," N. J. Juster, *J. Chem. Educ.*, **39,** 596 (1962).

CHAPTER 9

Hydrocarbons—Alkynes and Cycloalkanes

ALKYNES

THE TERM **alkyne** is the systematic designation for the class of unsaturated aliphatic hydrocarbons containing the carbon-carbon triple bond, —C≡C—. The type formula of the simple alkynes is C_nH_{2n-2}. This homologous series is also referred to as **acetylenes,** after its simplest member, acetylene, HC≡CH, a gaseous compound whose Kekulé structure, molecular dimensions, and molecular models are shown below. We have seen (Section 5-3) that acetylene is a *linear* molecule. The same is true for

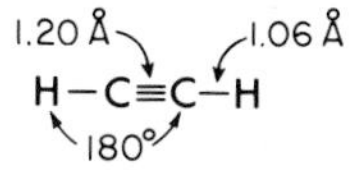

$$1.20\ \text{Å} \qquad 1.06\ \text{Å}$$
$$\text{H}-\text{C}{\equiv}\text{C}-\text{H}$$
$$180°$$

substituted acetylenes, R—C≡C—R, and for this reason *cis-trans* isomerism is impossible in this class of compounds. The carbon-carbon triple bond, made up of one σ bond and two π bonds, is both shorter (1.20 Å) and stronger (200 kcal/mole) than the carbon-carbon double bond (1.35 Å; 146 kcal/mole) or single bond (1.54 Å; 83 kcal/mole).

Figure 9-1. Molecular Models of Acetylene

9-1. Nomenclature and Physical Properties of Alkynes

The IUPAC names for alkynes are constructed by deleting the *-ane* ending from the name of the corresponding alkane and adding the suffix *-yne*, with numbers again indicating the position of the triple bond in the longest carbon chain containing it. Examples of the nomenclature of representative alkynes are given in Table 9-1.

Table 9-1. Nomenclature of Alkynes

Structure	IUPAC Name
HC≡CH	Ethyne
CH₃C≡CH	Propyne
CH₃CH₂C≡CH	1-Butyne
CH₃C≡CCH₃	2-Butyne
CH₃CHC≡CH | CH₃	3-Methyl-1-butyne
CH₃CHCH₂C≡CCHCH₂CH₃ | | Cl CH₃	2-Chloro-6-methyl-4-octyne

The alkynes have physical properties roughly similar to those of the alkenes and alkanes, as seen in Table 9-2. Note that the boiling points, melting points, and specific gravities of the alkynes, however, are all slightly *higher* than those of the corresponding alkenes and alkanes. Simple monosubstituted acetylenes of the type R—C≡C—H have characteristic infrared absorption bands at 2105 to 2150 cm^{-1} due to stretching of the C≡C triple bond, and at 3300 cm^{-1} due to stretching of the C—H single bond.

Table 9-2. Comparative Physical Properties of Some Hydrocarbons

Hydrocarbon	B.p., °C	M.p., °C	Specific Gravity (as liquid)
HC≡CH	−84*	−82	0.618
CH_2=CH_2	−102	−169	0.610
CH_3CH_3	−89	−172	0.546
CH_3C≡CH	−23	−102	0.671
CH_3CH=CH_2	−48	−185	0.610
$CH_3CH_2CH_3$	−42	−187	0.582
CH_3CH_2C≡CH	+9	−122	0.668
CH_3CH_2CH=CH_2	−5	−130	0.626
$CH_3CH_2CH_2CH_3$	−0.5	−135	0.579
CH_3C≡CCH_3	+27	−24	0.694
CH_3CH=$CHCH_3$ (trans)	+1	−106	
$CH_3CH_2CH_2C$≡CH	+48	−95	0.695
$CH_3CH_2CH_2CH$=CH_2	+30	−138	0.643
$CH_3CH_2CH_2CH_2CH_3$	+36	−130	0.626

*Sublimes.

9-2. Acetylene and Naturally Occurring Alkynes

Acetylene, the simplest member of the alkyne series, is the only alkyne of significant industrial importance. It is prepared by the action of water on calcium carbide, which in turn is cheaply available by fusing coke and calcium oxide ("quicklime"; made from limestone) in an electric furnace.

$$CaCO_3 \xrightarrow{\text{Heat}} CaO + CO_2$$
Limestone　　　　　Quicklime

$$CaO + 3C \xrightarrow{3000°} CaC_2 + CO$$
Calcium carbide

$$CaC_2 + 2H_2O \longrightarrow Ca(OH)_2 + C_2H_2$$
Acetylene

Pure acetylene is practically odorless. That prepared from calcium carbide has a characteristic, unpleasant odor owing to traces of sulfur and phosphorus compounds. These impurities may be removed by passing the gas through a solution of mercuric chloride in dilute hydrochloric acid. Other methods for the commercial production of acetylene (used mainly in Germany) include the pyrolysis of methane in an electric arc and the partial combustion of methane with oxygen at high temperature.

Acetylene burns with a bright, white flame, and the acetylene or "carbide" lamp was used widely as a source of illumination prior to the development of the electric light. A major use of acetylene is in the welding and cutting of metals, since the temperature of the flame of an oxyacetylene torch is as high as 2700°. Because of its low cost and high chemical reactivity, acetylene is also employed as a starting material for the commercial synthesis of a wide variety of important organic compounds, including acetic acid and monomers which are polymerized to make plastics and synthetic rubber. Acetylene is a rather unstable substance. Under pressure, particularly when liquefied, it is liable to explode violently when subjected to heat or shock. For commercial purposes acetylene may be safely stored and transported in pressure cylinders packed with porous briquettes impregnated with acetone, in which acetylene is highly soluble.

Naturally occurring alkynes in plant products have been known since 1892, when Arnaud isolated tariric acid from the seed oil of the tariri plant (*Tariri antidesma*). Since 1941, particularly in Norway and England,

$$CH_3-(CH_2)_{10}-C{\equiv}C-(CH_2)_4-COOH$$
Tariric acid

vigorous research programs have uncovered a large number of other natural acetylenic derivatives in natural fats and oils, in higher plants, and in fungi. The structures and sources of a few of these are shown below. Two of these possess *conjugated* acetylenic bonds.

$$CH_3CH{=}CH-(C{\equiv}C)_4-CH{=}CH_2 \qquad HC{\equiv}C-C{\equiv}C-CH{=}C{=}CH-(CH{=}CH)_2-CH_2COOH$$

1,11-Tridecadiene-3,5,7,9-tetrayne   Mycomycin
(common garden Calliopsis plant)   (cultures of Norcardia acidophilus fungi)

$$CH_3-(CH_2)_5-CH{=}CH-C{\equiv}C-(CH_2)_7-COOH$$
Ximenynic acid
(kernel oils of Ximenia plants)

9-3. Synthesis of Alkynes

In contrast to acetylene itself, mono- and disubstituted acetylenes of the type R—C≡C—H and R—C≡C—R′ cannot be made directly. Several general indirect methods are available, however, for the synthesis of such substituted alkynes.

a. Dehydrohalogenation of 1,2-Dihalides. The action of potassium hydroxide in alcohol solution on compounds containing halogen atoms on adjacent carbon atoms (1,2-dihalides) results in the elimination of two molecules of hydrogen halide and the formation of a carbon-carbon triple bond. Since 1,2-dihalides are readily available by the action of halogens

$$\underset{\substack{|\ \ |\\ X\ \ X}}{RCH-CH_2} + 2KOH \xrightarrow{\text{Alcohol}} R-C{\equiv}CH + 2KX + 2H_2O$$

on alkenes (Section 8-4b), this reaction provides a general method for the conversion of alkenes into alkynes. Side reactions limit the utility of this conversion, however. For example, an alternative dehydrohalogenation path yields allenes as by-products to the desired alkyne. In addition, the

$$\underset{\substack{|\ \ |\\ X\ \ X}}{\overset{3\quad 2\quad 1}{RCH_2-CH-CH_2}} \xrightarrow{\text{Alcoholic KOH}} RCH_2-C{\equiv}CH + \underset{\text{An allene}}{RCH=C=CH_2}$$

HX removal from: C1−C2; C2−C1 C2−C1; C3−C2

alcoholic KOH reagent tends to promote migration of the triple bond from the 1 position toward the middle of the carbon chain (Section 9-4f). The use of sodium amide, $NaNH_2$, as a dehydrohalogenating agent, however, eliminates the latter difficulty, since this reagent promotes the migration of triple bonds toward the *end* of the carbon chain and affords pure 1-alkynes.

$$\underset{\substack{|\ \ |\\ X\ \ X}}{RCH-CH_2} + 2NaNH_2 \longrightarrow RC{\equiv}CH + 2NaX + 2NH_3$$

b. Dehydrohalogenation of 1,1-Dihalides. 1,1-Dibromides and 1,1-dichlorides may be prepared by the action of phosphorus tribromide and trichloride, respectively, on aldehydes. Treatment of such 1,1-dihalides with alcoholic KOH or with sodium amide again brings about a double dehydrohalogenation yielding a 1-alkyne. The same reaction sequence may be applied to ketones to produce disubstituted alkynes.

$$\underset{\text{Aldehyde}}{RCH_2-CH{=}O} \xrightarrow{PX_5} \underset{\substack{|\\ X}}{RCH_2-CH-X} \xrightarrow[\text{Liquid } NH_3]{NaNH_2} RC{\equiv}CH$$

$$\underset{\text{Ketone}}{\overset{\overset{\displaystyle O}{\overset{\displaystyle \|}{}}}{RCH_2-C-R'}} \xrightarrow{PX_5} RCH_2-CX_2-R' \xrightarrow[\text{Liquid } NH_3]{NaNH_2} RC{\equiv}CR'$$

c. Alkylation of Alkynes. Acetylene itself and monosubstituted acetylenes, $RC{\equiv}CH$, contain a hydrogen atom attached to a triply bonded carbon atom. Such **acetylenic hydrogens** are slightly acidic in nature (cf. hydrogen cyanide, $H—C{\equiv}N$, a weak acid) and may be replaced by certain metals to form salts known as **metal acetylides**. Thus acetylene may be converted to sodium acetylide as shown. The acidity of the

$$HC \equiv CH \ + \ Na \ \xrightarrow{\text{Liquid NH}_3} \ HC \equiv \overset{\ominus}{C} \colon \overset{\oplus}{Na} \ + \ \tfrac{1}{2} H_2$$

Sodium acetylide

$\equiv$C—H hydrogen in acetylene follows the general rule that hydrogens linked to atoms by sp bonds (Section 5-3) are more acidic than those linked by sp^2 bonds (e.g., $=CH_2$) or by sp^3 bonds (e.g., $—CH_3$).

Reaction of sodium acetylide with methyl iodide yields propyne. Disubstituted alkynes may be made from monosubstituted derivatives by a similar reaction sequence. This **alkylation** reaction, however, is limited

$$HC \equiv \overset{\ominus}{C} \colon \overset{\oplus}{Na} \ + \ CH_3 I \ \longrightarrow \ HC \equiv CCH_3 \ + \ NaI$$

Propyne

$$RC \equiv CH \ \xrightarrow[\text{Liquid NH}_3]{Na} \ RC \equiv \overset{\ominus}{C} \colon \overset{\oplus}{Na} \ \xrightarrow{CH_3 I} \ RC \equiv CCH_3$$

in practice to the introduction only of primary alkyl groups of the type $RCH_2CH_2—$ onto a triply bonded carbon atom. Sodium acetylides are *strong bases*, and with secondary and tertiary alkyl halides they generally bring about dehydrohalogenation rather than yielding the desired alkylation product. Note that disubstituted alkynes of the type $RC \equiv CR'$ do not

$$HC \equiv \overset{\ominus}{C} \colon \overset{\oplus}{Na} \ + \ \underset{\underset{Br}{|}}{CH_3 CHCH_3}$$

Dehydrohalogenation $\longrightarrow HC \equiv CH \ + \ NaBr \ + \ CH_3 CH = CH_2$

Alkylation $\xrightarrow{\ \ X\ \ } HC \equiv CCH\overset{\diagup CH_3}{\diagdown CH_3} \ + \ NaBr$

contain an acetylenic hydrogen, and are accordingly incapable of forming salts with sodium or other metals.

9-4. Reactions of Alkynes

Like alkenes, alkynes are a very reactive class of compounds chemically, contrasting again to the unreactive alkanes. Let us next examine several important types of reaction characteristic of alkynes.

a. Formation of Metal Derivatives. The formation of sodium acetylides by the action of sodium in liquid ammonia on alkynes containing an acetylenic hydrogen has been discussed above. Similar salts will form with lithium and potassium. Such **alkali metal acetylides** are stable when dry, but are readily hydrolyzed (decomposed) by water, regenerating the

$$RC \equiv \overset{\ominus}{C} \colon \overset{\oplus}{Na} \ + \ H_2 O \ \longrightarrow \ RC \equiv CH \ + \ NaOH$$

original alkyne. **Heavy metal acetylides**, however, notably those of copper and silver, have different properties. These may be prepared by passing acetylene or a monosubstituted alkyne into ammoniacal solutions of cuprous or silver hydroxides. With each reagent, all available acetylenic hydrogen atoms are replaced by the heavy metal, and the salt precipitates as a dark solid. These heavy metal acetylides are decomposed back to the

$$2Cu(NH_3)_2OH \ + \ HC\equiv CH \ \longrightarrow \ CuC\equiv CCu \ + \ 2H_2O \ + \ 4NH_3$$

Cuprous acetylide

$$Ag(NH_3)_2OH \ + \ CH_3C\equiv CH \ \longrightarrow \ CH_3C\equiv CAg \ + \ H_2O \ + \ 2NH_3$$

Silver methylacetylide

alkyne precursor by dilute acid, but are stable in water. In the dry state they are highly sensitive to shock and are violently explosive, although they may be handled safely when moist. Sodium acetylide, by contrast, does not explode even on heating. Since disubstituted alkynes, as well as alkenes and alkanes, fail to give precipitates with ammoniacal solutions of silver or cuprous ions, these reagents may be used diagnostically as a test for the —C≡CH function.

The acetylenic hydrogen on acetylene or a monosubstituted alkyne will react **metathetically** (by double decomposition) with a Grignard reagent, yielding an **acetylene Grignard reagent** and the alkane corresponding to the original Grignard reagent. Such acetylene Grignard reagents react as do saturated Grignard reagents, and are important synthetically for introducing alkyne functions into other molecules.

$$CH_3MgI \ + \ CH_3CH_2C\equiv CH \ \longrightarrow \ CH_4 \ + \ CH_3CH_2C\equiv CMgI$$

Methylmagnesium   1-Butyne   1-Butynylmagnesium
iodide   iodide

b. Hydrogenation. Just as with alkenes (Section 8-4a), alkynes are capable of adding hydrogen in the presence of hydrogenation catalysts such as platinum, palladium, or nickel. With alkynes, however, *two* moles of hydrogen may add, the first mole yielding an alkene and the second an alkane. By proper selection of reaction conditions, it is possible to inter-

$$RC\equiv CR \ + \ H_2 \ \xrightarrow{Pt} \ RCH=CHR \ \xrightarrow{H_2, \ Pt} \ RCH_2CH_2R$$

rupt the hydrogenation at the intermediate stage and to isolate the alkene.

An important stereochemical generalization regarding catalytic hydrogenation is illustrated in the hydrogenation of alkynes to alkenes. The catalytic hydrogenation of the linear alkyne 2-butyne, for example, yields *cis*-2-butene, but none of the *trans* isomer. This and similar results indicate

$$CH_3C\equiv CCH_3 \ + \ H_2 \ \xrightarrow{Pt} \ \begin{matrix} CH_3 & CH_3 \\ C=C \\ H & H \end{matrix} \ + \ \left(No \ \begin{matrix} CH_3 & H \\ C=C \\ H & CH_3 \end{matrix} \right)$$

2-Butyne   cis-2-Butene   trans-2-Butene

that the hydrogen molecule adds to the triple bond in a *cis* fashion; that is, both hydrogen atoms add to the *same side* of the alkyne molecule. We hypothesize that this stereochemical course is the consequence of a **cyclic transition state** for catalytic hydrogenation, which may be symbolized as follows.

Similar stereochemistry is observed during the catalytic hydrogenation of substituted cycloalkenes, whenever the substituted cycloalkane products are capable of geometric isomerism. Thus 1,2-dimethylcyclohexene (9-1) yields *cis*-1,2-dimethylcyclohexane (9-3), again as a consequence of a cyclic transition state (9-2).

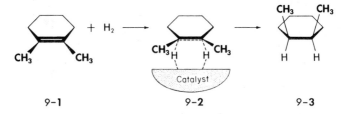

9-1   9-2   9-3

c. Addition of Halogen. A mixture of chlorine and acetylene reacts explosively when exposed to light. The reaction may be controlled by diluting the reactants with an inert gas or by employing inert solvents such as carbon tetrachloride. Two moles of chlorine will add to acetylene, and

$$HC{\equiv}CH + Cl_2 \longrightarrow \underset{\underset{\text{Dichloroethene}}{1,2-}}{HC{=}CH} \overset{Cl_2}{\longrightarrow} \underset{\underset{\text{Tetrachloroethane}}{1,1,2,2-}}{Cl_2CHCHCl_2}$$

under proper experimental conditions the intermediate olefinic product may be isolated. Bromine adds to alkynes in the same fashion, but iodine adds less readily, only one mole reacting with each mole of acetylene.

d. Addition of Hydrogen Halides. Two moles of hydrogen iodide or hydrogen bromide add to one mole of acetylene as illustrated. Hydrogen

$$HC{\equiv}CH + HX \longrightarrow \underset{\text{Vinyl halide}}{CH_2{=}CHX} \overset{HX}{\longrightarrow} CH_3CHX_2$$

chloride adds only very sluggishly to acetylene. Note that the addition of the second mole of HX to the intermediate vinyl halide *follows Markown-ikoff's rule* (Section 8-4c). The vinyl halide may be isolated under proper experimental conditions. With hydrogen bromide the second stage of the addition is subject to the *peroxide effect* (Section 8-4c).

   e. Hydration. Acetylene undergoes addition of water under the influence of dilute sulfuric acid and mercuric sulfate catalyst. The initially formed product, vinyl alcohol, is unstable (see below) and immediately

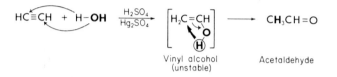

Vinyl alcohol (unstable)   Acetaldehyde

isomerizes as shown to form acetaldehyde. The overall process is commercially important since the acetaldehyde product may be catalytically oxidized by air to acetic acid. With substituted acetylenes a similar hydration takes place, proceeding via Markownikoff addition to yield ketones, as illustrated by the conversion of propyne to acetone.

$$CH_3CH{=}O \xrightarrow[\text{Mn salts}]{\text{Air}} CH_3COOH$$

Acetaldehyde   Acetic acid

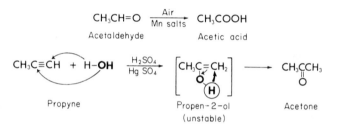

Propyne   Propen-2-ol   Acetone
                          (unstable)

   Keto-Enol Tautomerization. Compounds containing the $-C{=}C-OH$ grouping—that is, vinyl alcohol and its homologs—are called **enols**. The name derives from the presence of the *ene* function, $-C{=}C-$, and the *ol* function, $-OH$, on the same carbon atom. Generally, enols are not stable as such, but, as in the examples above, undergo spontaneous conversion into an isomeric **keto** form. This isomerization, referred to as

Enol form of ketone   Enolate anion   Keto form of ketone

keto-enol tautomerization, occurs by ionization of the hydroxylic proton of the enol, followed by a bond shift in the resulting **enolate anion** and recombination with a proton (not necessarily the original one) at the adjacent carbon atom. The system exists in a mobile equilibrium, and generally the keto constituent vastly predominates in the equilibrium mixture. This important type of isomerization will be discussed in greater detail in Section 12-7a.

While enols are generally unstable with respect to their isomeric keto form, certain O-substituted derivatives of enols, such as enol esters, $R—CH=CH—O—CO—R'$, and enol ethers, $R—CH=CH—OR'$, are perfectly stable compounds and often constitute industrially important derivatives (see Section 9-4g).

f. Alkyne Rearrangements. The action of strong alkali on 1-alkynes results in their conversion into allenes, as shown in the following general equation. In 1951 T. L. Jacobs of the University of California at Los

$$RCH_2C\equiv CH \xrightarrow[\text{heat}]{\text{Solid KOH}} RCH=C=CH_2$$

1-Alkyne   Allene

Angeles made an extensive study of such rearrangements, found that the allene product was in equilibrium with both unrearranged and re-arranged alkyne, and offered the following mechanistic explanation of the rearrangement.

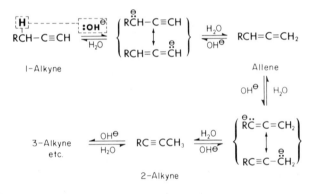

We see that reversible proton abstraction from the starting 1-alkyne, the allene, or the rearranged 2-alkyne leads to resonance-stabilized car-banions which may reversibly recapture protons in alternate ways. A mobile equilibrium thus results, in which the most stable component predominates. When sodium amide, suspended in a hydrocarbon solvent, is the base catalyzing such rearrangements, the 1-alkyne component of the equilibrium mixture forms preferentially, since it is removed irre-versibly from the mixture by formation of its sodium salt:

$$RC\equiv CCH_3 \underset{}{\overset{NaNH_2}{\rightleftharpoons}} RCH=C=CH_2 \underset{}{\overset{NaNH_2}{\rightleftharpoons}} RCH_2C\equiv \overset{\text{Acetylenic H}}{CH} \xrightarrow{NaNH_2} RCH_2C\equiv \overset{\ominus}{C} \colon \overset{\oplus}{Na} + NH_3$$

g. Vinylation. Under appropriate reaction conditions and with proper catalysts, a wide variety of compounds containing slightly acidic hydrogen atoms will add to the triple bond of acetylene to form so-called vinyl derivatives, according to the general equation shown below. It is apparent that the previously discussed hydration and hydrogen halide addition

$$HC{\equiv}CH + H{-}A \xrightarrow{\text{Catalyst}} CH_2{=}CH{-}A$$

H—A	Product
H—OCOCH$_3$	CH$_2$=CH—OCOCH$_3$, vinyl acetate
H—OR	CH$_2$=CH—OR, alkyl vinyl ethers
H—C≡N	CH$_2$=CH—C≡N, vinyl cyanide (acrylonitrile)
H—SR	CH$_2$=CH—SR, alkyl vinyl sulfides

reactions are special cases of this more general process. Many reactions of this type were developed by J. W. Reppe and his collaborators in Germany prior to and during World War II, and a number of the resulting vinyl derivatives have proved important as monomers for polymerization into various types of plastics and synthetic rubbers (see Table 8-3).

h. Polymerization. Depending upon the experimental conditions, acetylene may be caused to polymerize in several different ways. Thermal treatment of acetylene at 400°, or at lower temperatures with certain metallic catalysts, induces its conversion into benzene and smaller quantities of other aromatic hydrocarbons. The first *linear* polymerization of

$$3CH{\equiv}CH \xrightarrow{400°} \bigcirc$$

acetylene was accomplished by J. A. Nieuwland in 1929, who found that acetylene could be dimerized into vinylacetylene or trimerized into divinylacetylene under the influence of cuprous chloride and ammonium chloride.

$$2HC{\equiv}CH \xrightarrow[\text{NH}_4\text{Cl}]{\text{Cu}_2\text{Cl}_2} CH_2{=}CHC{\equiv}CH \xrightarrow[\text{Cu}_2\text{Cl}_2,\text{NH}_4\text{Cl}]{\text{HC}{\equiv}\text{CH}} CH_2{=}CHC{\equiv}CCH{=}CH_2$$

Vinylacetylene   Divinylacetylene

On careful addition of hydrogen chloride to vinylacetylene the important conjugated diene 2-chloro-1,3-butadiene (chloroprene) is formed. We

$$CH_2{=}CHC{\equiv}CH \xrightarrow{\text{HCl}} \begin{array}{c} \text{Cl} \\ | \\ \text{CH-C} \\ \diagup\quad\diagdown \\ \text{CH}_2\quad\text{CH}_2 \end{array}$$

Chloroprene

recall that the peroxide-catalyzed polymerization of this diene monomer affords the commercially important synthetic rubber Neoprene (Section 8-5b). In 1940 Reppe and his co-workers made the noteworthy discovery that acetylene could be polymerized in the presence of nickel cyanide into the previously rare and theoretically important hydrocarbon 1,3,5,7-cyclooctatetraene. Ever since its original preparation by R. Willstätter at the

University of Munich in 1911 during the course of his investigations on the pomegranate alkaloid *pseudo*-pelletierine, the cyclooctatetraene molecule has fascinated organic chemists. We notice that cyclooctatetraene is a

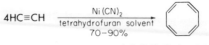

$$4HC\equiv CH \xrightarrow[\substack{\text{tetrahydrofuran solvent}\\70-90\%}]{Ni(CN)_2}$$

1, 3, 5, 7–Cyclooctatetraene

vinylog of benzene; that is, it has *one extra* **vinyl group**, —CH=CH—, interposed between two of the carbon atoms of the benzene ring. In particular, it has been of interest to establish whether cyclooctatetraene exists as a resonance hybrid, analogous to the hybrid structure of benzene

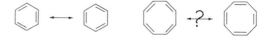

Figure 9-2. Resonance Hybrids of Benzene and Cyclooctatetraene

(Figure 9-2). Heat of combustion data, however, indicate that cyclooctatetraene has a resonance energy (Chapter 5) of only some 4 to 5 kcal/mole, in contrast to 36 kcal/mole for benzene. Cyclooctatetraene also shows the chemical properties of a simple, conjugated alkene, rather than an aromatic hydrocarbon. Furthermore, Raman and infrared spectral analyses show that cyclooctatetraene has a puckered structure of either the "crown" or "tub" type, rather than the flat, planar structure which would

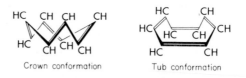

Crown conformation   Tub conformation

Figure 9-3. Geometrical Configurations of Cyclooctatetraene

be required by the resonance hybrid of Figure 9-2. Accordingly, it is concluded that cyclooctatetraene is simply a cyclic, conjugated diene, and not a resonance hybrid analogous to benzene. The absence of resonance in cyclooctatetraene may be interpreted in terms of bond angle strain (Section 9-6). However, Hucel's rule for aromaticity (Section 10-9) is also violated.

CYCLOALKANES

CYCLOALKANES or cycloparaffins, sometimes referred to as alicyclic compounds, are saturated aliphatic hydrocarbons whose molecular structures contain one or more rings. The monocyclic cycloalkanes have a type formula C_nH_{2n}, and are thus isomeric with simple alkenes. Table 9-3 shows the structures and names of some simple cycloalkanes, and gives a comparison of the boiling and melting points of each with those of its straight-chain analog.

Table 9-3. Structures and Physical Properties of Cycloalkanes

Name	Molecular Formula	Structure[a]	B.p., °C	M.p., °C
Cyclopropane	C_3H_6		$-33\,(-42)$[b]	$-127\,(-187)$[b]
Cyclobutane	C_4H_8		$13\,(-0.5)$	$-80\,(-135)$
Cyclopentane	C_5H_{10}		$49\,(36)$	$-94\,(-130)$
Cyclohexane	C_6H_{12}		$81\,(69)$	$6\,(-94)$
Cycloheptane	C_7H_{14}		$118\,(98)$	$-12\,(-91)$
Cyclooctane	C_8H_{16}		$149\,(126)$	$14\,(-57)$

[a] Structures of cycloalkanes are usually represented as regular polygons. Each apex represents a carbon atom bonded to two hydrogen atoms.
[b] Parenthetical figures indicate values for the corresponding normal alkane.

We see that the cycloalkanes boil some 10° to 20° higher and melt far higher (36° to 100°) than the straight-chain alkanes of similar carbon content. Densities of cycloalkanes are also some 20 per cent higher than densities of comparable normal alkanes, indicating that the cycloalkanes are more *compact* molecules. Like open-chain analogs, cycloalkanes are soluble in typical organic solvents, but increasingly insoluble in water as their molecular weights increase.

Cycloalkanes are named, as seen in Table 9-3, by simply placing the prefix *cyclo-* before the name of the corresponding normal alkane. Poly-substituted cycloalkanes are named by numbering the several substituents consecutively around the ring, as shown.

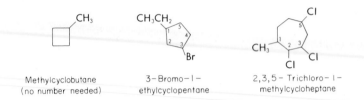

Methylcyclobutane
(no number needed)

3-Bromo-1-
ethylcyclopentane

2,3,5-Trichloro-1-
methylcycloheptane

9-5. Sources, Occurrence, and Uses of Cycloalkanes

The principal source of C_5 and C_6 cycloalkanes and their alkyl-sub-stituted homologs is petroleum. In the petroleum industry these compounds are called **naphthenes**, as they are isolable from the "naphtha fraction" obtained on distilling petroleum. Such crude naphthenes make good fuels which have high octane ratings. Cycloalkane derivatives having various ring sizes occur widely in the plant kingdom, and several groups of these constitute the important class of natural products called **terpenes**. A few examples of simple monocyclic cycloalkane derivatives from plant sources are shown below. Among plant products, however, we more

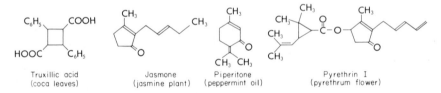

Truxillic acid
(coca leaves)

Jasmone
(jasmine plant)

Piperitone
(peppermint oil)

Pyrethrin I
(pyrethrum flower)

frequently encounter cycloalkane derivatives whose structures involve several rings of different sizes fused to one another, the rings sharing several carbon atoms in common. A few such naturally occurring fused-ring cycloalkane derivatives are illustrated below.

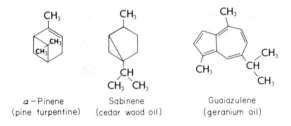

α-Pinene
(pine turpentine)

Sabinene
(cedar wood oil)

Guaiazulene
(geranium oil)

Alkylcyclohexanes from petroleum, and methylcyclohexane in particu-lar, constitute an important industrial source of aromatic compounds. Their conversion is accomplished by the **hydroforming process**, which involves the catalytic removal of hydrogen from the alkylcyclohexane. This

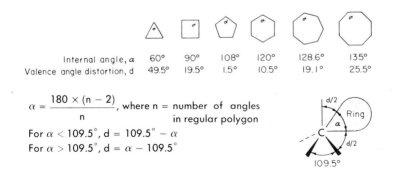

Methylcyclohexane $\xrightarrow[\text{300 psi}]{\text{Mo}_2\text{O}_3-\text{Al}_2\text{O}_3,\ 560°}$ Toluene + 3H$_2$

process proved particularly important during World War II when, along with related processes (such as the dehydrocyclization of heptane) it permitted an expansion in the production of toluene (for TNT manufacture) from less than 40 million gallons per year in 1940 to over 250 million gallons per year in 1944. Cyclopropane is used in medicine as a general inhalation anesthetic. It is one of the most potent anesthetics, and in low concentrations can even produce insensitiveness to pain without loss of consciousness. Its use is somewhat limited, however, both by its expense and by the explosion hazard attending its administration with oxygen.

9-6. Ring Strain and Geometry of Cycloalkanes

Before 1879 no cyclic compounds were known either naturally or synthetically containing other than a five or six-membered ring. It was therefore then generally believed that larger or smaller rings were incapable of existence. Between 1880 and 1885, however, William H. Perkin, Jr., succeeded in synthesizing cyclopropane, cyclobutane, and cyclobutane derivatives, although with difficulty and in low yield. Furthermore, cyclopropane and cyclobutane derivatives were found in certain respects to be more reactive chemically than cyclopentane and cyclohexane derivatives— that is, to be less stable. Such observations led Adolf von Baeyer in 1885 to propose a theory of **ring strain** which purported to explain these differences in stability. Consider the internal angles of regular polygons of different sizes (Figure 9-4). Baeyer assumed the normal tetrahedral angle

Internal angle, α	60°	90°	108°	120°	128.6°	135°
Valence angle distortion, d	49.5°	19.5°	1.5°	10.5°	19.1°	25.5°

$\alpha = \dfrac{180 \times (n-2)}{n}$, where n = number of angles in regular polygon

For $\alpha < 109.5°$, d = $109.5° - \alpha$
For $\alpha > 109.5°$, d = $\alpha - 109.5°$

Figure 9-4. Internal Angles of Regular Polygons and "Valence Angle Distortion"

(109.5°) for carbon, and noted that this angle must suffer *distortion* from its normal value when carbon atoms are constrained to cyclic structures. The total **valence angle distortion** (Figure 9-4), he argued, was at a minimum with cyclopentane and not too large with cyclohexane. Baeyer thus concluded that **ring strain** (instability due to valence angle distortion) was at a minimum in these compounds, making for their greater stability and prevalence in nature. The basic error in Baeyer's thinking, which will be immediately apparent if we construct a molecular model of cyclohexane, was the assumption that such cycloalkane rings above C_5 must be flat. H. Sachse first pointed out this error in 1890, but his suggestions commanded no attention until championed by E. Mohr in 1918. These workers pointed out the now obvious fact that rings larger than C_5 might exist without valence angle distortion if only they be visualized as *puckered*. Thus cyclohexane may exist in two puckered conformations which are strain free because they retain the normal tetrahedral angle of 109.5° about each carbon atom. These puckered structures are referred to as **chair** and **boat conformations**, and are represented as shown in Figure 9-5.

Chair conformation   Boat conformation

Figure 9-5. Strain-free Conformations of Cyclohexane

Dreiding models (Section 2-8c) show the chair conformation to be quite rigid, while the boat conformation is rather flexible—that is, it is readily converted into equivalent boat conformations by simple twists along the carbon-carbon bond axes. These two conformational isomers exist in dynamic equilibrium and have not yet been isolated individually. Theoretical calculations and experimental evidence indicate that the *chair form is considerably more stable than the boat form* and that at room temperature the ratio of chair to boat conformation populations at equilibrium is about 1000:1. By adopting analogous puckered conformations, larger cycloalkane rings may also exist with no bond angle distortion. Thus cycloheptane exists also in chair and boat conformations (Figure 9-6), the chair form again predominating at equilibrium. Cyclooctane has a number of strain-free conformations (Figure 9-7), of which the **crown** and **saddle**

Chair conformation   Boat conformation

Figure 9-6. Strain-free Conformations of Cycloheptane

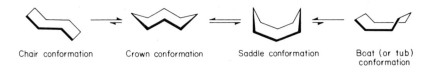

Chair conformation   Crown conformation   Saddle conformation   Boat (or tub) conformation

Figure 9-7. Strain-free Conformations of Cyclooctane

forms are apparently the most prevalent at equilibrium. If we build molecular models of C_5 through C_8 cycloalkanes, we find that the conformations for each cycloalkane in Figures 9-5, 9-6, and 9-7 are readily interconvertible by small twisting motions, and that such interconversions involve additional intermediate conformations, or **conformational transition states**. In molecular terms, this implies dynamic equilibrium among all such conformations for each cycloalkane, strictly analogous to the previously described equilibria among various conformations of open-chain derivatives which arise through rotations about single bonds (Section 2-8f). Rings of still larger sizes have even more analogous, interconvertible, strain-free conformational isomers.

The heats of combustion of cycloalkanes provide direct experimental evidence that ring strain is actually present only in small ring compounds (below C_5). In Table 9-4 we see that the heat liberated per $-CH_2-$ unit during combustion of cycloalkanes is anomalously high for cyclopropane and cyclobutane and that after cyclopentane it approaches a lower, constant value which is about equal to that characteristic of open-chain compounds, which are clearly incapable of ring strain. These data show that cyclopropane and cyclobutane contain *more energy* per $-CH_2-$ unit—that is, they are *less stable*—than the larger cycloalkanes from C_5 up.

Table 9-4. Heats of Combustion of Cycloalkanes

Ring Size	Heat of Combustion, kcal/mole	Heat of Combustion per $-CH_2-$ Unit, kcal/mole
3	505.5	168.5
4	662.2	165.6
5	793.6	158.7
6	944.5	157.4
7	1108	158.3
8	1269	158.6
10	1586	158.6
15	2362	157.5
Open chain	—	157.4

What determines the preferred conformation of a cycloalkane derivative? Again, as with open-chain derivatives, the major factor is steric **non-bonded repulsions** of the substituents on the rings, due to the *bulk* of these substituents (Section 2-8f). Consider, for example, the positions of the hydrogen atoms in cyclohexane (Figure 9-8). We see that in the boat con-

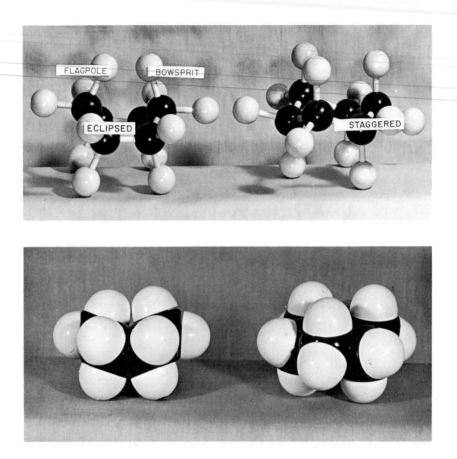

Figure 9-8. Positions of Hydrogen Atoms in Cyclohexane Conformations

formation the eight hydrogen atoms on the four central carbons are *eclipsed*, four on each side of the ring, and therefore are in a position of maximum steric repulsion. In addition, there is steric repulsion between the **bowsprit** and **flagpole hydrogens** pointing toward the center of the ring above the two *bow* and *stern* carbon atoms. In the chair conformation, on the other hand, all of the hydrogen atoms around the ring are in *staggered* positions of minimum steric repulsion, and this conformation, being therefore of lower energy, is vastly preferred. Only in the case of certain bicyclic derivatives, as well as in a few other special cases, does the boat conformation in cyclohexane prevail. Two such bicyclic derivatives are shown in Figure 9-9, where we see that the ordinary carbon-carbon bond lengths of

Bicyclo [2.2.1] heptane   Bicyclo [2.2.2] octane

Figure 9-9. Constrained Boat Conformations

Nomenclature note: Name on the basis of the total number of carbon atoms. Indicate the size of each "bridging arm" between the carbon atoms common to all rings by counting the number of carbon atoms in each bridging arm, arranging the numbers in decreasing order in the name.

the *bridging* carbon atoms above the cyclohexane ring require that this ring be constrained exclusively to the boat conformation. The chair conformation would require too great a stretching of these carbon-carbon bonds.

Repulsion forces between hydrogen atoms likewise dictate that cyclopentane (Figure 9-10) preferentially assumes a puckered conformation

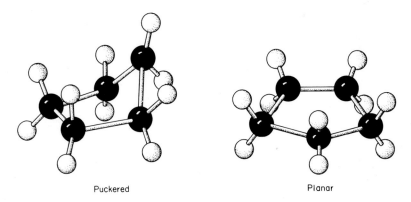

Puckered   Planar

Figure 9-10. Conformations of Cyclopentane

permitting some staggering of adjacent hydrogen atoms, rather than the planar conformation which eclipses all hydrogens—in spite of the neg-

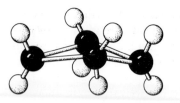

Figure 9-11. Conformation of Cyclobutane

ligible ring strain of the planar structure. Even in cyclobutane (Figure 9-11) there is evidence that some puckering exists, relieving the eclipsed hydrogen interactions inherent in the planar conformation—despite the fact that such puckering actually increases the already considerable ring strain in this molecule. Present evidence thus indicates that of all the cycloalkanes only cyclopropane, which has no conformational alternative, exists as a true planar molecule.

The crown or tub structure and lack of resonance in the cyclooctate-traene molecule (Figure 9-3) are also understandable in terms of hydrogen eclipsing and bond angle strain. For the planar structure required of the resonance hybrid suggested in Figure 9-2, cyclooctatetraene would need strained internal bond angles of 135° and eclipsed hydrogen atoms. Such requirements would "cost" more energy (over 100 kcal/mole) than would be gained by existence as a resonance hybrid, and cyclooctatetraene there-fore adopts the lower-energy crown or tub conformation illustrated in Figure 9-3.

Polycyclic cycloalkanes, when not constrained to boat conformations as in Figure 9-9, may also have the possibility of conformational isomerism. The *cis* and *trans* isomers of decahydronaphthalene (decalin), for example, whose preparation by W. Hückel in 1925 first convinced chemists of the

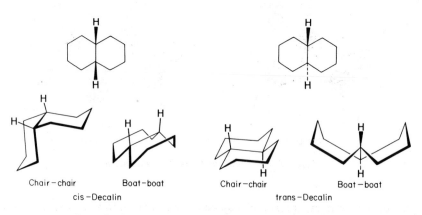

Figure 9-12. Chair and Boat Conformations of the Decalins

validity of the puckered rings postulated by Sachse and Mohr, each have the alternative **chair-chair** and **boat-boat** conformations shown in Figure 9-12, as well as additional **chair-boat** conformations. The *trans* form of decalin proves to be the more stable of the two, and each geometrical isomer again appears to adopt the *more stable chair-chair conformation*, dictated, as before, by minimum steric repulsions between hydrogen atoms about the ring. Another example of the presence of chair conformations in fused-ring systems is the $C_{10}H_{16}$ hydrocarbon adamantane, first isolated

Adamantane

in 1933 by the Czechoslovakian chemist S. Landa from a high-boiling petroleum fraction, and later (1941) synthesized by V. Prelog. The beautiful molecular symmetry of this high-melting (270°) and remarkably stable hydrocarbon, whose structure consists of four mutually fused cyclo-hexane chair conformations, is carried to full fruition in the diamond, the "most perfect" form of carbon. We see that the adamantane structure literally comprises a small portion of the diamond crystal lattice, which is an "infinite jungle-gym" structure of mutually fused cyclohexane chair conformations (Figure 9-13).

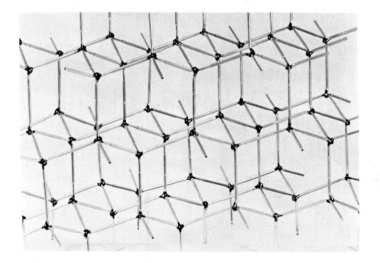

Figure 9-13. The Diamond Crystal Lattice

Axial and Equatorial Substituents. An important point of conformational nomenclature should be made here. In the preferred chair conformation of cyclohexane (Figure 9-14) we see that six bonds are *perpendicular* to the "average plane" of the cyclohexane ring and six bonds lie *in plane* with the ring. The perpendicular bonds are referred to as **axial bonds**, and the

Figure 9-14. Axial and Equatorial Positions in Cyclohexane

in-plane bonds are **equatorial**. Substituents (including hydrogen) on cyclohexane are called axial or equatorial depending on which type of position they occupy.

A monosubstituted cyclohexane can exist as two stereoisomeric chair conformations with the substituent either axially or equatorially oriented. These forms are interconvertible via the small amount of boat conformation in equilibrium with them, each interconversion occurring by a *flipping* (simultaneous rotation about two bonds) of the ends of the cyclohexane ring (Figure 9-15). Which chair form is preferred, that with the axial or

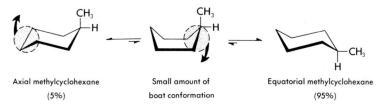

| Axial methylcyclohexane | Small amount of | Equatorial methylcyclohexane |
| (5%) | boat conformation | (95%) |

Figure 9-15. Interconversion of Axial and Equatorial Substituents

with the equatorial substituent? Theoretical calculations involving an estimate of the nonbonded steric repulsions between the substituent and nearby hydrogen atoms on the ring indicate that *equatorially substituted cyclohexane derivatives are preferred over axial derivatives.* In methylcyclohexane (Figure 9-15), for example, the rapid equilibrium involves a final ratio of equatorial to axial substituent (chair conformation) of about 95:5. With the larger *t*-butyl group in *t*-butylcyclohexane, only the equatorial chair conformation appears to exist. In polysubstituted cyclohexanes the situation is slightly more complicated. With *trans*-1,4-dimethylcyclohexane,

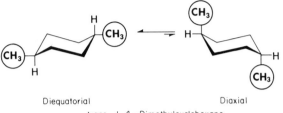

Diequatorial   Diaxial

trans − 1,4 − Dimethylcyclohexane

the **diequatorial** form vastly predominates over the **diaxial** form of the chair conformation. In *cis*-1,4-dimethylcyclohexane, however, the two

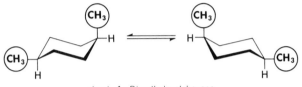

cis − 1,4 − Dimethylcyclohexane

chair conformations are equivalent, each of necessity having one axial and one equatorial methyl group.

One aspect of modern conformational analysis in ring systems is the interpretation of physical and chemical properties in terms of theoretically preferred ring conformations involving axial and equatorial substituents. In general, it is found in cyclic systems that chair conformations are more stable than boat conformations, and that the most stable chair conformations are those which have the largest groups or the largest number of groups in equatorial positions.

9-7. Synthesis of Cycloalkanes

The synthesis of cycloalkane derivatives follows two general paths: (1) the preparation of the desired derivative from a compound already containing a ring of the desired size and (2) synthesis of the desired ring by **cyclization** (ring closure) reactions involving one or more molecules of an open-chain compound. Let us consider several representative examples of each of these general approaches.

a. Hydrogenation of Aromatic Compounds. Benzene may be catalytically hydrogenated at elevated temperature and pressure to yield cyclohexane.

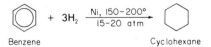

Benzene   Cyclohexane

We recognize this reaction as the reverse of the previously discussed hydroforming reaction (Section 9-5). Another important example is the hydrogenation of phenol to cyclohexanol, a cyclic alcohol important as a starting

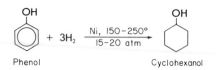

Phenol   Cyclohexanol

material for the preparation of a wide variety of cyclohexane derivatives.
The hydrogenation of naphthalene or naphthalene derivatives may be controlled so as to proceed *partially* to produce tetrahydronaphthalene (tetralin) derivatives or *fully* to produce decahydronaphthalene (decalin) derivatives—examples of bicyclic cyclohexane compounds. It is apparent that
the hydrogenation of aromatic compounds themselves limits us to the
preparation of cyclohexane derivatives.

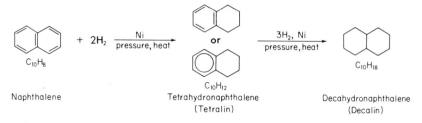

Naphthalene   Tetrahydronaphthalene   Decahydronaphthalene
                                (Tetralin)   (Decalin)

b. Ring Closure Reactions. Let us consider some type of reaction capable
of producing a new carbon-carbon bond. Such a reaction might be generalized as

$$R-Y \ + \ Y-R \ \longrightarrow \ R-R \ + \ Y_2$$

where Y represents a functional group which may be removed as the alkyl
groups **couple** together. If such a **coupling reaction** is conducted with a
molecule having the two functional groups, Y, *in the same molecule*, it may
occur in an *intramolecular* manner, forming the new carbon-carbon bond
between the "head" and "tail" ends of the original difunctional molecule;

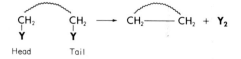

Head   Tail

in other words, **cyclization** may take place. This technique provides a
general approach to the synthesis of cycloalkane derivatives, and many
reactions of open-chain compounds are adaptable to it. Cyclopropane, for

example, was prepared in 1907 by Willstätter, by the action of zinc dust on 1,3-dibromopropane. Another example is the preparation of cyclo-

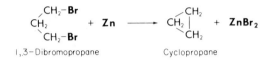

butanecarboxylic acid by Perkin in 1883. Analogous reactions have been used to synthesize rings up to C_6 or C_7, and we shall encounter other

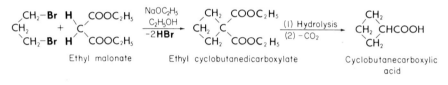

specific examples in future chapters. Product yields become small or negligible, however, in attempts to synthesize larger rings (C_8 and up) by such cyclization reactions. We note that there is always an alternative *intermolecular* path available to such cyclization reactions, namely, the formation of a linear polymer. This intermolecular polymerization path

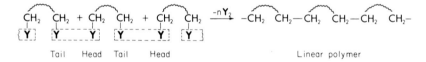

predominates over the desired intramolecular cyclization path in long-chain difunctional molecules because the *probability* of the "head" of a given molecule finding and reacting with its own "tail" before it reacts with the "tail" of another molecule diminishes with increasing chain length. In 1933 K. Ziegler observed that if cyclization reactions involving long-chain molecules were conducted in solvents under conditions of *very high dilution*, this probability factor could be reversed, and the "head" of an individual molecule would again have the opportunity of reacting with its own "tail" before reacting with a second molecule. Modifications of Ziegler's **high dilution technique** have since been widely used to synthesize in acceptable yields cycloalkane derivatives with ring sizes up to C_{25} or higher.

 c. *Cycloaddition Reactions.* Another type of ring-forming reaction involves the interaction of two reactants, rather than the intramolecular reaction of a single reactant, as above. Such reactions are referred to as **cycloaddition reactions**. The most important type reaction in this category is the **Diels-Alder reaction** (1928), which is probably the most general method for the preparation of cyclohexane derivatives and which won for its German discoverers, O. Diels and K. Alder, the Nobel Prize for chemistry in 1950. The Diels-Alder **diene synthesis**, as it is sometimes called, consists in the 1,4 addition of the activated double bond of a suitable vinyl derivative (called the **dienophile**) to the two ends of a conjugated diene system (Section 8-5). The reaction, which may be generalized as shown below, proves to be highly stereospecific. Thus, addition

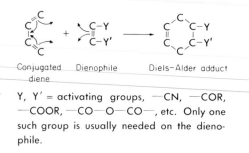

Conjugated   Dienophile   Diels-Alder adduct
diene

Y, Y′ = activating groups, —CN, —COR, —COOR, —CO—O—CO—, etc. Only one such group is usually needed on the dienophile.

of the diene to the dienophile occurs exclusively in a *cis* fashion—that is, to one side of the dienophile—and the geometrical configuration present in the original dienophile is found to be preserved in the adduct, as seen in the following examples.

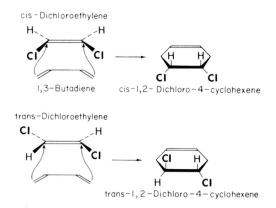

cis–Dichloroethylene

1,3–Butadiene   cis–1,2– Dichloro–4–cyclohexene

trans–Dichloroethylene

trans–1,2–Dichloro–4–cyclohexene

The versatility of the Diels-Alder diene synthesis in preparing complex cyclohexane derivatives is illustrated with several specific examples in the equations below.

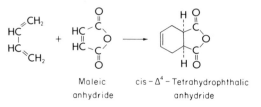

Maleic   cis–Δ⁴–Tetrahydrophthalic
anhydride   anhydride

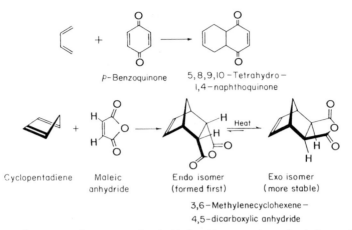

p-Benzoquinone 5,8,9,10-Tetrahydro-1,4-naphthoquinone

Cyclopentadiene Maleic anhydride Endo isomer (formed first) Exo isomer (more stable)

3,6-Methylenecyclohexene-4,5-dicarboxylic anhydride

Nomenclature note: The presence of a double bond in a complex molecule is sometimes indicated by the symbol Δ with a numerical superscript to designate the carbon atom involved in the double bond (p. 208). The designations endo (inside) and exo (outside) refer to the orientation of the substituents (here the cyclic anhydride grouping) as being directed to the inside or the outside of the cyclohexene ring in the adduct.

We note especially the applicability of this reaction to the preparation of bicyclic ring systems.

For obvious reasons, the Diels-Alder reaction is often referred to as a **1,4 cycloaddition** reaction. Another type of cycloaddition process, leading however to cyclobutane derivatives, is the so-called **1,2 cycloaddition** of substituted alkenes to themselves (dimerization), to other alkenes, or to dienes. These reactions occur with alkenes containing halogen atoms or other electron-attracting substituents, and may be initiated either by heat or by ultraviolet radiation. The examples shown are typical.

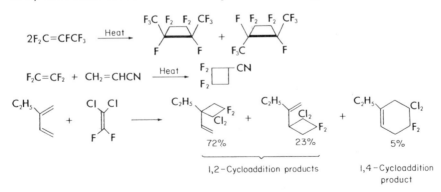

1,2-Cycloaddition products   1,4-Cycloaddition product

A recent elegant general synthesis of cyclopropane derivatives, the **Simmons-Smith reaction** (1959), involves the interaction of an alkene with diiodomethane in the presence of a zinc-copper alloy. The reaction is thought to involve the initial formation of a carbene (Section 6-2) complex with ZnI_2, followed by addition of the carbene to the alkene double bond.

$$CH_2I_2 + Zn(Cu) \longrightarrow CH_2\text{---}ZnI_2$$
Carbene complex

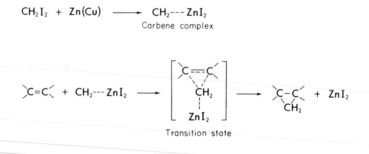

Transition state

9-8. Reactions of Cycloalkanes

With a few notable exceptions involving small-ring compounds and large-ring compounds, the reactions of the cycloalkanes parallel closely those of open-chain alkanes (Section 7-6). Thus photochemical halogenations, for example, will occur under similar conditions.

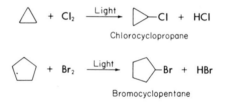

a. Ring-Opening Reactions of Small Rings. Cyclopropane and cyclobutane, because of their lower stability due to ring strain (see Table 9-4), frequently react with ring opening, thereby *relieving* the ring strain. Catalytic hydrogenation, for example, opens the rings of these compounds to give

$$\triangle + H_2 \xrightarrow{\text{Ni, 80°}} CH_3CH_2CH_3$$

$$\square + H_2 \xrightarrow{\text{Ni, 180°}} CH_3CH_2CH_2CH_3$$

saturated straight-chain alkanes. Cyclopentane, which is strain-free, proves to be stable under similar conditions even at 300°. Lower cycloalkanes may be isomerized into alkenes either thermally or catalytically, as shown, and cyclopropane brominates with ring opening, in contrast to the simple substitution observed with cyclopentane. With hydrogen

$$\triangle \xrightarrow{\text{Heat}} CH_3CH=CH_2$$

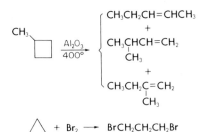

$$\triangle \ + \ Br_2 \ \longrightarrow \ BrCH_2CH_2CH_2Br$$

halides, methylcyclopropane undergoes ring opening with the equivalent
of Markownikoff additions (Section 8-4c). These and similar ring-opening

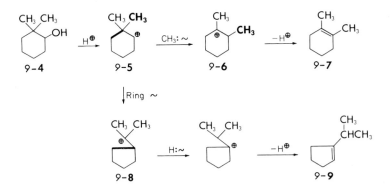

Methylcyclopropane

reactions of cyclopropane and cyclobutane compounds are thought to
occur because they relieve the strain present in these small ring structures.
In C_5 and higher cycloalkanes, where ring strain is absent, analogous ring-
opening reactions are not observed and the reactions parallel those of the
open-chain alkanes. It is noteworthy that cyclopropane, in contrast to
propylene, gives a negative Baeyer test with potassium permanganate
(Section 8-4g).

   b. Ring Expansions and Contractions.   During a number of reactions of
cycloalkane derivatives, molecular rearrangements may take place. These
rearrangements, which are of the Wagner-Meerwein type (Section 8-3a)
and involve carbonium ion intermediates, may lead to expansion or contraction of the cycloalkane ring. It is beyond our scope to examine such
ring-size changes in detail, but a few examples may be cited.

   Dehydration of the cyclic secondary alcohol 2,2-dimethylcyclohexanol
(9-4) with acidic reagents affords a mixture of 1,2-dimethylcyclohexene
(9-7) and 1-isopropylcyclopentene (9-9).   Note that *both* dehydration

products have rearranged carbon skeletons, and that the driving force for the 1,2 shifts of both the methyl group and the ring bond is the tendency for the secondary carbonium ion 9-**5** to rearrange to the more stable tertiary carbonium ions 9-**6** and 9-**8**.

Alkylcycloalkanes become isomerized into equilibrated mixtures of products under the influence of Lewis acid catalysts such as aluminum chloride in the presence of traces of alcohols or alkenes, the reaction of ethylcyclopentane being typical. Such isomerizations again involve the

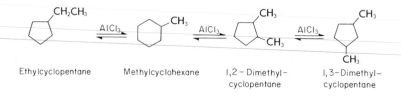

| Ethylcyclopentane | Methylcyclohexane | 1,2 – Dimethyl–cyclopentane | 1,3–Dimethyl–cyclopentane |

formation of carbonium ion intermediates which undergo 1,2 shifts of alkyl groups or ring bonds. Reactions of cycloalkane derivatives which involve carbonium ion intermediates are thus often of limited synthetic utility because of the mixtures of products which may result.

c. Transannular Effects in Medium-Large Rings. With cycloalkane derivatives in the C_8 to C_{11} ring-size range, a number of anomalies in physical and chemical properties become evident. These are currently interpreted and classified as **transannular effects**—that is, effects produced by the interaction of two groups located *across* the ring from each other. Again we must content ourselves with only a few representative examples.

In certain chemical reactions of C_8 to C_{11} cycloalkane derivatives, transannular participation may lead to stable products containing a new ring system. Thus the catalytic reduction of 1,6-cyclodecanedione (9-**10**) yields not only the anticipated 1,6-cyclodecanediol (9-**11**) but also 9,10-dihydroxydecalin (9-**12**), the latter product arising by transannular ring

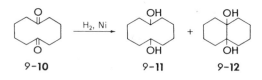

9-10   9-11   9-12

closure. Another transannular ring closure is illustrated in the conversion of 5-cyclodecene-1-ol *p*-toluenesulfonate (9-**13**) into the two octalin (octahydronaphthalene) derivatives $\Delta^{1,2}$-octalin (9-**14**) and $\Delta^{1,9}$-octalin (9-**15**),

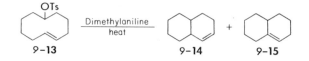

9-13   9-14   9-15

on heating with dimethylaniline. In other reactions, transannular participation may involve a molecular rearrangement in which an atom or group
migrates across the ring. V. Prelog at the Technische Hochschule in
Zurich and A. C. Cope at the Massachusetts Institute of Technology have
provided a number of examples of such rearrangements, one of which is
shown below. We notice that there has been a transannular 1,6-hydride
shift (shown, as indicated, by deuterium labeling) during the acid-
catalyzed dehydration of the 1-methyl-6-deutero-1,6-cyclodecanediol.

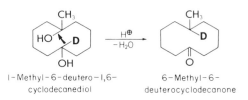

1-Methyl-6-deutero-1,6- cyclodecanediol	6-Methyl-6- deuterocyclodecanone

Such transannular effects are fairly common in cyclic derivatives in the
C_8 to C_{11} ring-size range, but are found only rarely in rings below C_8 and
above C_{11} or C_{12}. If we build molecular models of the "medium-large
rings" which show these transannular effects, we see that the natural conformations of the rings place groups located on opposite sides of the rings
very close to one another in space (Figure 9-16). Thus, in actuality, trans-

Figure 9-16. Transannular Proximity in the Cyclooctane Ring
(Crown Conformation)

annular participation during reactions involving medium size ring compounds occurs over rather short spatial distances. It is limited to medium
size rings because only in these are the optimum spatial distances probable
within the available conformations of the ring.

SUPPLEMENTARY READING

1. "Adolf von Baeyer (1835–1917)," F. Henrich, *J. Chem. Educ.*, **7**, 1231 (1930).
2. "Karl Friedrich Mohr," R. E. Oesper, *J. Chem. Educ.*, **4**, 1357 (1927).

3. "Cyclobutane Chemistry.   I. Structure and Strain Energy," A. Wilson and
   D. Goldhamer, *J. Chem. Educ.*, **40,** 504 (1963).
4. "Cyclobutane Chemistry.   II. Reactions and Mechanisms," A. Wilson and
   D. Goldhamer, *J. Chem. Educ.*, **40,** 599 (1963).
5. "Conformational Analysis in Mobile Systems," E. Eliel, *J. Chem. Educ.*, **37,**
   126 (1960).
6. "Recent Advances in Stereochemistry," D. J. Cram, *J. Chem. Educ.*, **37,** 317
   (1960).
7. "The Synthesis of Diamond," H. T. Hall, *J. Chem. Educ.*, **38,** 484 (1961).

CHAPTER 10

Aromatic Hydrocarbons

THE **aromatic series** of compounds (see Section 2-4) has benzene, the simplest aromatic hydrocarbon, as its "parent molecule"—analogous to methane in the aliphatic series. The name "aromatic" came originally from the fact that the members of this series generally have pronounced and frequently pleasant odors. The aromatic series is built upon the structure of benzene in two ways: (1) by simple replacement of hydrogen atoms on the benzene nucleus with other substituents (**substituted benzenes**) and (2) by attachment of one or more additional rings (with or without substituents) at one or more of the positions in the parent benzene ring (**polynuclear aromatic derivatives**).

10-1. Structure, Nomenclature, and Physical Properties of Aromatic Hydrocarbons

Table 10-1 shows the structures, names, and some physical properties of a number of the more important aromatic hydrocarbons which, as a class,

Table 10-1. Some Important Aromatic Hydrocarbons

Name	Structure	M.p., °C	B.p., °C
Benzene		5	80
Toluene		−93	110
o-Xylene		−28	144
m-Xylene		−54	139
p-Xylene		13	138
Naphthalene		80	218
α-Methylnaphthalene		−19	244
β-Methylnaphthalene		35	241
Biphenyl		71	254
Fluorene		114	295
Anthracene		216	354
Phenanthrene		101	340
Pyrene		151	>360
Coronene		440	−

are also referred to as **arenes**. It is seen that arenes are either liquids or solids at room temperature, as is also true of functionally substituted arenes. Aromatic derivatives burn with a characteristic smoky flame, and many of them are quite toxic.

In Table 10-1 we note the usual regular increase in boiling point with increasing molecular weight, discernible in all series. Notice also that isomeric compounds (the three xylenes; α- and β-methylnaphthalenes; phenanthrene and anthracene) have quite similar boiling points. The effect of molecular symmetry on melting point is strikingly apparent on comparing the melting points of p-xylene, for example, with the other isomeric xylenes, or of anthracene with phenanthrene. Again we see that greater molecular symmetry, giving rise to more stable crystal lattices, leads generally to higher melting points (Section 7-3b). Notice the unusually high melting point of the very highly symmetrical compound, coronene.

Polynuclear arenes with rings attached at more than one position (naphthalene, anthracene, etc.) are referred to as **fused-ring hydrocarbons**. In Table 10-1 simple benzene derivatives have been written with circles in their rings, to emphasize the fact that their π bond structures represent resonance hybrids (Chapter 5). Fused-ring arenes, on the other hand, are generally written with "frozen" Kekulé bond structures, as shown. This is a matter of convenience, and does not imply that these hydrocarbons do not also have resonance hybrid structures. Naphthalene, for example, has a resonance energy of 74 kcal/mole, anthracene 105, and phenanthrene 110. The amusing question "Does coronene have a hole in the middle?" is meaningless in terms of a resonance hybrid, and arises only because of the "frozen" bond structure usually written for it.

It is interesting to examine some of the alternative suggestions for the structure of benzene, which historically "competed" with Kekulé's suggested structure. Several of these are shown in Figure 10-1. Clearly, these representations were attempts to symbolize the chemical inertness of benzene, which we now rationalize in terms of a resonance hybrid or π bond

Kekulé (1864)   Claus (1867)   Dewar (1867)   Armstrong–Baeyer (1887)   Thiele (1899)

Figure 10-1. Early Suggestions for the Structure of Benzene

delocalization (Chapter 5). "Dewar benzene" (bicyclo[2.2.0]hexadiene) has recently been synthesized by E. E. Van Tamelen at Stanford University. On standing, the substance undergoes a valence bond isomerization (Section 8-5d) into benzene.

In 1964, at a meeting in Ghent, Belgium, celebrating the 100th anniversary of Kekulé's original paper on the structure of benzene, Dr. H. G. Viehe of Union Carbide Corporation's European Research Associates reported the isolation of additional valence bond isomers of substituted benzenes. These were obtained by the trimerization of *t*-butylfluoroacetylene, *t*-BuC≡CF, below 0°, and consisted of a "prismane" structure, a "benzvalene" structure, and a "Dewar" structure. The prismane form (analogous to the prism structure for benzene proposed by A. Ladenburg in 1869) is a stable solid, but the other isomers undergo valence bond isomerization to Kekulé structures on heating or standing.

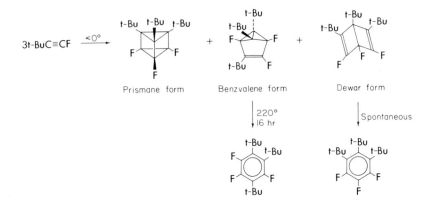

Benzene was discovered in 1825 by the English experimentalist Michael Faraday, who first isolated the hydrocarbon during studies on the liquefaction of illuminating gas. The name "benzene" originated from J. Liebig's suggestion, *benzol*, while Faraday's discovery is commemorated in the name of the **phenyl group** (C_6H_5-) (Greek: *pheno*, I bear light) derived from benzene. The phenyl group is usually abbreviated by chemists as Ph–, or sometimes ϕ–. It will be advantageous for us here to consider briefly a few of the underlying principles of aromatic nomenclature, although this subject will be further developed in subsequent chapters.

Derivatives having single substituents on the benzene ring are named, as shown, in the customary manner (commonly employed names are shown in parentheses).

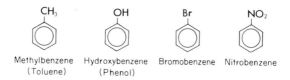

Methylbenzene   Hydroxybenzene   Bromobenzene   Nitrobenzene
(Toluene)   (Phenol)

More than one substituent on the benzene ring gives rise to position isomerism. With two substituents, isomers are distinguished either by the use of the prefixes *ortho* (*o*-), *meta* (*m*-) and *para* (*p*-), or by using numbers, as shown below. With two different substituents, two names are possible, and either is acceptable (for example, *o*-hydroxytoluene ≡ *o*-methyl-phenol).

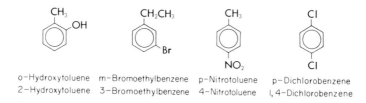

o-Hydroxytoluene   m-Bromoethylbenzene   p-Nitrotoluene   p-Dichlorobenzene
2-Hydroxytoluene   3-Bromoethylbenzene   4-Nitrotoluene   1,4-Dichlorobenzene

With three or more substituents on the ring, numbers are customarily used, counting being done in such a way as to utilize the smallest numbers:

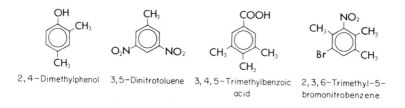

2,4-Dimethylphenol   3,5-Dinitrotoluene   3,4,5-Trimethylbenzoic   2,3,6-Trimethyl-5-
                                          acid   bromonitrobenzene

In naphthalene derivatives, Greek letters or numbers are used for mono-substitution products, while numbers are employed for polysubstituted naphthalenes:

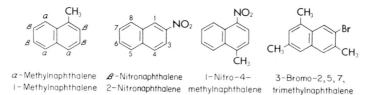

α-Methylnaphthalene   β-Nitronaphthalene   1-Nitro-4-   3-Bromo-2,5,7,
1-Methylnaphthalene   2-Nitronaphthalene   methylnaphthalene   trimethylnaphthalene

Phenanthrene and anthracene are numbered as follows to indicate the positions of their substituents:

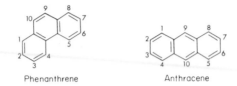

Phenanthrene   Anthracene

Aryl groups derived from aromatic hydrocarbons are named typically as illustrated in the following examples:

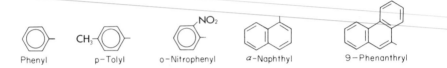

Phenyl   p-Tolyl   o-Nitrophenyl   α-Naphthyl   9-Phenanthryl

Such aryl groups, in turn, may be named as simple or complex substituents in aliphatic derivatives. The customary numbering of the aliphatic chain is then employed, as in the following illustrations:

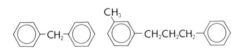

Diphenylmethane   1-(m-Tolyl)-3-phenylpropane   2-(2,4-Dinitrophenyl)-   1-Bromo-3-
                                                       1-butene   (α-naphthyl)-
                                                                             cyclopentane

10-2. Sources of Aromatic Compounds

The principal source of aromatic derivatives is the tar obtained on the **destructive distillation (carbonization, coking)** of coal. When coal is heated in the absence of air, it decomposes into three main products, **coke oven gas, coal tar,** and **coke.** Coke oven gas, consisting primarily of methane and hydrogen (32 and 52 per cent, respectively), is purified by passing through "scrubbers," then is used as an industrial and domestic fuel. Coke, which is almost pure carbon, is used for the reduction of iron ore in the blast furnace (Figure 10-2). The coal tar is subjected to fractional distillation (Figure 10-3) and chemical separations to recover the valuable aromatic and heterocyclic constituents it contains. These include most of the hydrocarbons listed in Table 10-1, plus many more, as well as numerous oxygenated aromatic derivatives (for example, phenol, p-cresol,

Figure 10-2. Metallurgical Coke from Destructively Distilling Coal Being Ejected from a Coke Oven (courtesy United States Steel Corporation)

Figure 10-3. Distillation Units for the Fractionation of Coal Tar (courtesy United States Steel Corporation)

and α-naphthol) and heterocyclic nitrogen compounds (for example, pyridine, quinoline, and acridine). Over 150 individual aromatic compounds have been isolated from coal tar, naphthalene (11 per cent) being the most abundant.

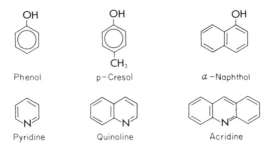

A second important source of aromatic hydrocarbons is petroleum. The **hydroforming reaction** for the conversion of methylcyclohexane from petroleum into industrially important toluene has already been discussed (Section 9-5). Petroleum itself from most parts of the world contains varying quantities of aromatic hydrocarbons, and that from Borneo contains up to 39 per cent.

Lastly, both simple and fused-ring aromatic compounds occur in a wide variety of plant materials, and these are frequently important as sources for specific aromatic derivatives. A few examples of naturally occurring aromatic compounds, along with their sources and uses, are shown here. We shall encounter many additional examples in future chapters.

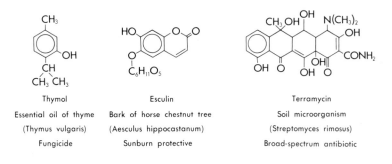

Thymol	Esculin	Terramycin
Essential oil of thyme	Bark of horse chestnut tree	Soil microorganism
(Thymus vulgaris)	(Aesculus hippocastanum)	(Streptomyces rimosus)
Fungicide	Sunburn protective	Broad-spectrum antibiotic

10-3. Syntheses of Aromatic Compounds

Probably the first synthesis of benzene was accomplished in 1868 by M. Berthelot, who obtained this hydrocarbon in low yield by passing acetylene through a red hot porcelain tube (Section 9-4h). A recent modification of this synthesis affords hexadeuterobenzene, C_6D_6, by circulating dideuteroacetylene, $DC{\equiv}CD$, through a bed of silica–alumina catalyst.

When chemists speak of synthesis as a source of aromatic compounds, however, they almost invariably refer to the preparation of homologs or derivatives of arenes. Except in cases of particular complex ring systems, it is seldom necessary to synthesize the ring system itself in an aromatic derivative, since this can usually be obtained intact in aromatic or cyclo-aliphatic precursors of the types mentioned above. An important laboratory synthesis of aromatic rings, somewhat related to the industrial hydro-forming process, is the **dehydrogenation** of cyclohexane derivatives (often called **hydroaromatic** compounds). This is accomplished by heating the hydroaromatic derivative with sulfur, selenium, or 10 per cent palladium–charcoal catalyst, as illustrated in the equations below. Since specifically

Cyclohexane   Benzene

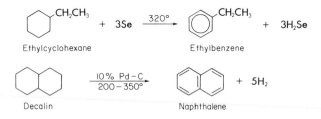

substituted cyclohexane derivatives can usually be obtained synthetically, the dehydrogenation reaction thus provides a convenient method for preparing specifically substituted aromatics. The synthesis of other derivatives of arenes will be discussed where pertinent throughout the remainder of the book.

10-4. Reactions of Aromatic Hydrocarbons

The chemical inertness of the benzene ring limits the number of reactions exhibited by the ring systems of aromatic compounds. These reactions, however, while relatively few in number, are of paramount importance, since they lead to functional derivatives which are key starting materials for the synthesis of a wide variety of aromatic substances.

a. Addition Reactions. In contrast to alkenes and alkynes, which readily react by addition, benzene and other arenes undergo addition reactions to only a limited extent. Hydrogen may be added catalytically under conditions of heat and pressure, forming industrially important hydroaromatic derivatives (Section 9-7a). A recent technique for partially reducing aromatic rings is the so-called **Birch reduction**, which employs sodium or lithium metal as a reducing agent in nonaqueous solvents such as liquid ammonia, amines, and ethyl ether. Note in the examples shown that one or more double bonds remain intact in the reduction product. The re-

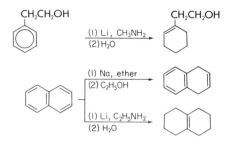

action is believed to involve organosodium or organolithium anionic intermediates, such as 10-1, which are converted to hydroaromatic compounds, such as 10-2, on subsequent treatment with hydroxylic solvents.

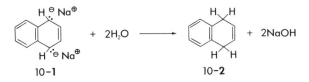

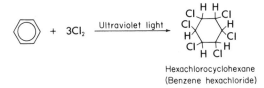

Under the influence of ultraviolet irradiation, chlorine and bromine will *add* to benzene, rather than reacting (Section 10-4b) by substitution. On

Hexachlorocyclohexane
(Benzene hexachloride)

chlorine addition, nine noninterconvertible stereoisomers of the hexachlorocyclohexane product are possible, of which eight have been characterized. The crude chlorinated mixture is commercially important, since one of its isomeric constituents (γ-hexachlorocyclohexane) is a potent insecticide. The mixture is marketed under the names of *Lindane, Gammexane,* and *666.* The pure γ isomer is also used medicinally in treatment of scabies.

A final type of addition reaction involving aromatic systems might be mentioned, that involving carbene (Section 6-2). When carbene is generated in the presence of benzene, for example, addition occurs with the formation of the bicyclic diene norcaradiene, bicyclo[4.1.0]heptadiene, which in turn undergoes valence bond isomerization to produce 1,3,5-cycloheptatriene (tropilidene).

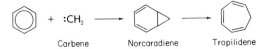

Carbene   Norcaradiene   Tropilidene

b. Substitution Reactions. The most important reactions of aromatic hydrocarbons are *substitution reactions*, that is, reactions in which a functional group replaces one of the hydrogen atoms on the aromatic ring. The more important of these are discussed below, each reaction being illustrated with benzene itself.

$$Ar \underset{\llcorner}{\overset{\ulcorner}{-}} H \underset{\ }{\overset{\ }{+}} X \underset{\lrcorner}{\overset{\urcorner}{-}} Y \longrightarrow Ar{-}Y + H{-}X$$

General substitution reaction of an arene

Nitration. The action of nitric acid (in the presence of sulfuric acid) on benzene leads to **nitration** of the benzene ring, and formation of nitrobenzene. Depending on the intrinsic reactivity of the aromatic compound

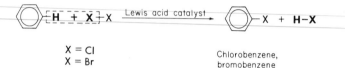

$$\text{Nitrobenzene}$$

being nitrated, nitration conditions may vary from "gentle" (dilute HNO_3, low temperatures) to "drastic" (fuming HNO_3 plus concentrated H_2SO_4, high temperatures) in order to accomplish the desired nitration.

Halogenation. In the presence of catalysts such as $FeCl_3$, $AlCl_3$, or I_2 (Lewis acids), benzene will react with chlorine or bromine, forming chloro- or bromobenzene and hydrogen halide. In the absence of catalyst, how-

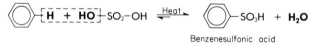

$$X = Cl$$
$$X = Br$$

Chlorobenzene,
bromobenzene

ever, such substitution reactions do not occur. Chlorobenzene finds commercial use in the production of aniline, phenol, and DDT and as a solvent. The direct **iodination** of arenes requires a special technique, since the equilibrium position of the reaction lies far to the left. Iodoben-

$$Ar\text{--}H + I_2 \quad \rightleftharpoons \quad Ar\text{--}I + H\text{--}I$$

zene may be prepared in good yield, however, if the hydrogen iodide by-product is simultaneously removed by oxidation to iodine with nitric acid or mercuric oxide.

$$\bigcirc + I_2 \xrightarrow[\text{86\% yield}]{HNO_3} \bigcirc\!\!-\!I + HI$$

Iodobenzene

Sulfonation. When aromatic hydrocarbons are heated with concentrated sulfuric acid, **sulfonation** occurs. The resulting **arenesulfonic acids** are

$$\bigcirc\!\overline{[H + HO]}\!-\!SO_2\text{--}OH \xrightleftharpoons{\text{Heat}} \bigcirc\!\!-\!SO_3H + H_2O$$

Benzenesulfonic acid

strong acids (Sections 13–21) and are quite hygroscopic. Benzenesulfonic acid is used in the manufacture of phenol and as an intermediate in organic syntheses.

Friedel-Crafts Reactions. In 1877 the French chemist Charles Friedel and his American collaborator, James M. Crafts, discovered that alkyl halides, R—X, and acyl halides, R—CO—X, react vigorously with aromatic hydrocarbons in the presence of anhydrous aluminum chloride catalyst. The products from alkyl halides proved to be alkylated arenes, while those from acyl halides were ketones, as shown in the following examples:

Friedel-Crafts Hydrocarbon Synthesis

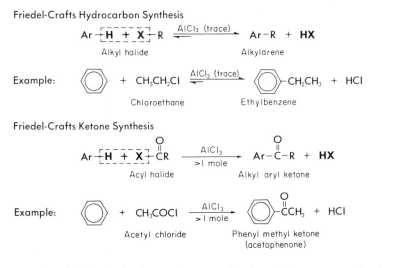

The Friedel-Crafts **hydrocarbon synthesis** and **ketone synthesis** constitute important methods for the preparation of substituted aromatic derivatives, and will be referred to frequently in some of their variations in future chapters. Notice that the hydrocarbon synthesis requires only a catalytic amount of aluminum chloride, while the ketone synthesis requires a slight excess over one full molar equivalent. This is because in the latter case the ketone product binds the aluminum chloride as a 1:1 complex or adduct, and a full molar equivalent is required to permit this reaction.

$$\underset{Ar}{\overset{R}{\diagdown}}C=\overset{..}{O}: \ + \ AlCl_3 \longrightarrow \underset{Ar}{\overset{R}{\diagdown}}C=\overset{\delta+}{O}\overset{\delta-}{:} \ AlCl_3$$

Ketone—aluminum chloride complex

Other metal halides, as well as mineral acids, will serve in the same catalytic capacity as aluminum chloride, which is the most vigorous and effective of such "Friedel-Crafts catalysts." Alternative Lewis acid catalysts, in decreasing order of potency are: $AlCl_3 > FeCl_3 > SnCl_4 > BF_3 > ZnCl_2$ and $HF > H_2SO_4 > P_2O_5 > H_3PO_4$. Other functional groups, particularly hydroxyl, will also participate in Friedel-Crafts reactions if sufficient catalyst is employed.

$$Ar-[H + HO]-R \xrightarrow{\text{Excess } AlCl_3} Ar-R \ + \ H_2O$$
Alcohol

$$Ar-[H + HO]-\overset{O}{\overset{\|}{C}}-R \xrightarrow{\text{Excess } AlCl_3} Ar-\overset{O}{\overset{\|}{C}}-R \ + \ H_2O$$
Carboxylic acid

c. π-Complex Formation.   An interesting and frequently useful type reaction of arenes is **complex formation** between polynitroaromatic compounds and polynuclear aromatic hydrocarbons.   Naphthalene, for example, interacts with 1,3,5-trinitrobenzene to form a crystalline, yellow,
1:1 complex (10-**3**; m.p. 153°).   The equilibrium for such a reaction in-

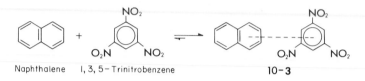

Naphthalene   l, 3, 5 – Trinitrobenzene   10-**3**

volving benzene lies far to the left, but with polynuclear hydrocarbons the
crystalline complexes are stable and may be recrystallized, thereby affording a means of purifying polynuclear arenes.   Such complexes may be decomposed chemically or by passing their solutions through a column of
aluminum oxide, whereupon the complex is broken up and the polynitro
component is preferentially adsorbed (see Section 3-5a).   It is thought that
the attraction forces binding the components of such complexes are electrostatic ones, arising by polarization of the π electrons of the polynuclear
hydrocarbon under the influence of the permanent dipoles (Section 2-2d)
of the polynitro compound.   This situation is shown schematically in
Figure 10-4, and such complexes are accordingly called π **complexes**
(see also Section 8-4).

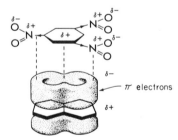

*Figure 10-4. Electrostatic Attraction in Aromatic
π Complexes.*

The structure of π complexes is reminiscent of the structure of the allo-
tropic form of carbon called **graphite**, which is revealed by X-ray diffraction measurements to consist of endless sheets of planar benzene rings,
honeycombed in a chicken-wire structure.   Layers of such sheets are in
turn "connected" by weaker and longer bonding forces, as shown in Figure
10-5.   An interesting consequence of the graphite structure is that, under
mechanical stress, one plane of benzene rings may readily slip laterally

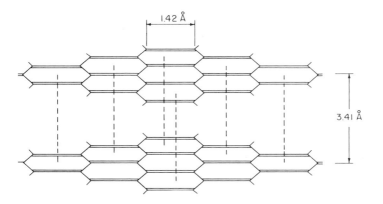

Figure 10-5. Crystal Lattice Structure of Graphite

over an adjacent plane. This permits the extensive practical use of graphite as a lubricant. The "loose" structure of graphite also reflects in its low density (2.22), which contrasts to the high density (3.51) of the diamond crystal (Figure 9-13). The electrical conductivity of graphite is interpreted in terms of its vast system of delocalized π electrons.

d. Side-Chain Oxidation. While not a reaction of the aromatic ring as such, the important **side-chain oxidation** of alkylated aromatic hydrocarbons may profitably be considered at this point. Vigorous oxidizing agents such as potassium permanganate, chromic oxide, or sodium dichromate (in H_2SO_4) do not readily attack the benzene nucleus, because of its inherent stability. With alkyl-substituted arenes, however, such oxidizing agents readily oxidize the alkyl substituents, "chewing them down" to carboxyl (or other oxidized) groups. Since the oxidant first

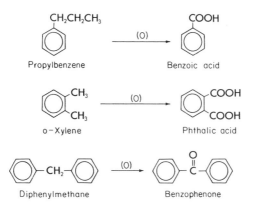

attacks the carbon atom adjacent to the aromatic ring, a carboxyl group results regardless of the chain length of the alkyl substituent. Several typical examples of side-chain oxidations are shown in the preceding equations. Note the last example, where the ketone benzophenone is the stable oxidation product.

10-5. Mechanism of Electrophilic Aromatic Substitution

A variety of experimental evidence indicates that the above **electrophilic substitution** reactions of aromatic hydrocarbons (Section 10-4b) occur by a common mechanism. We shall consider this first in general terms, then with reference to specific substitution reactions. The first step of the reaction is known to involve attack on the π electrons of the aromatic ring by an **electrophilic reagent** (Section 6-5). Notice that the initial adduct of the reagent to the ring is a cationic species in which the π-electron

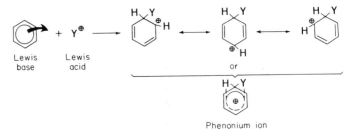

Phenonium ion

system of the ring has been destroyed. Such intermediates are stabilized as resonance hybrids, and are referred to as aronium ions (for example, phenonium ion), or as σ complexes, since a discrete σ bond has been formed. Notice also that the positive charge on this hybrid ion tends to be concentrated at the *ortho* and *para* positions of the ring. The second step of the substitution reaction involves abstraction of a proton from the σ complex by an anionic species in the environment, yielding the substitution product and regenerating the aromatic π-electron system:

Now, what are the specific Lewis acids, $Y^{\oplus}$, which intervene in each of the substitution reactions described in Section 10-4b? These form and are named as shown in the following equations:

Nitration: $HO-NO_2 + 2H_2SO_4 \longrightarrow (NO_2^{\oplus}) + H_3O^{\oplus} + 2HSO_4^{\ominus}$

Nitronium ion

Chlorination: $Cl_2 + FeCl_3 \longrightarrow \left(Cl^{\oplus}\right) + FeCl_4^{\ominus}$

Chloronium ion

Sulfonation: $2H_2SO_4 \longrightarrow \left(SO_3\right) + H_3O^{\oplus} + HSO_4^{\ominus}$

Note here that the neutral molecule sulfur trioxide constitutes the electrophilic Lewis acid. Its electrophilic character arises as a consequence of the incomplete octet of electrons around its sulfur atom:

:Ö:
S:Ö:
:Ö:

Friedel-Crafts alkylation: $R{-}Cl + AlCl_3 \longrightarrow \left(R^{\oplus}\right) + AlCl_4^{\ominus}$

Alkyl carbonium ion

Friedel-Crafts acylation: $R{-}\overset{\overset{\textstyle O}{\|}}{C}{-}Cl + AlCl_3 \longrightarrow \left(R{-}\overset{\overset{\textstyle O}{\|}}{C}\oplus\right) + AlCl_4^{\ominus}$

Acylium ion

Thus the electrophilic species, $NO_2^{\oplus}$, $Cl^{\oplus}$, $Br^{\oplus}$, SO_3, $R^{\oplus}$, and $RCO^{\oplus}$, may each act as the Lewis acid $Y^{\oplus}$ in the general equation above. The completely formulated mechanism for the bromination of benzene, for example, would therefore involve the steps shown in Figure 10-6. The corresponding steps in other electrophilic substitution reactions of benzene are analogous.

(1) $Br_2 + FeBr_3 \longrightarrow Br^{\oplus} + FeBr_4^{\ominus}$

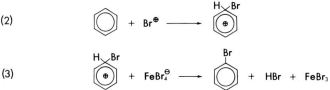

(2)

(3)

Figure 10-6. Mechanism for the Bromination of Benzene

In Friedel-Crafts alkylations it is noteworthy that *isomerization* of the alkyl group frequently accompanies the reaction. The alkylation of benzene with 1-chloropropane, for example, affords *i*-propylbenzene rather than propylbenzene. This occurs because the initially formed primary propyl carbonium ion (10-4) rearranges to the more stable secondary *i*-propyl carbonium ion (10-5) prior to its attack on the benzene ring. Such

$$CH_3CH_2CH_2Cl + AlCl_3 \rightleftharpoons CH_3CH_2CH_2^{\oplus} + AlCl_4^{\ominus}$$
$$10\text{-}4$$

$$CH_3CH_2CH_2^{\oplus} \xrightleftharpoons{H:\sim} CH_3\overset{\oplus}{C}HCH_3$$
$$10\text{-}5$$

isomerizations of alkyl groups during alkylations will occur any time the initially formed carbonium ion can rearrange to a more stable carbonium ion by migration of a hydride ion or alkyl group (see Section 8-3a). Since Friedel-Crafts alkylation is a *reversible* reaction, 1-propylbenzene itself may therefore be isomerized into 2-propylbenzene by the action of aluminum chloride.

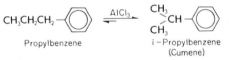

Propylbenzene   *i*-Propylbenzene
                                   (Cumene)

10-6. Polysubstitution; Orientation Effects in Electrophilic Substitutions

Not all of the substitution reactions discussed in Section 10-4b give exclusively the monosubstitution products shown in the equations. The bromination of benzene in the presence of FeCl₃ catalyst, for example, affords not only bromobenzene, but small amounts of *o*-, *m*-, and *p*-dibromobenzenes as well, while the bromination of phenol yields 2,4,6-tribromophenol. Similarly, in Friedel-Crafts alkylations, the reaction does not stop at the monoalkylated stage, since the alkylbenzene product is more readily alkylated than is benzene itself. As shown in the accompany-

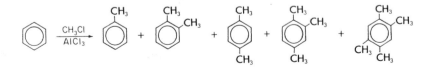

ing example, mixtures result, and purification must be undertaken to obtain a pure, individual product.

In other reactions such as nitration, sulfonation, and Friedel-Crafts acylation, on the other hand, polysubstitution tends *not* to occur, and can be accomplished only by going to reaction conditions more drastic than those prevailing during the initial substitution. The progressive nitration of benzene is a good illustration of this latter class of substitution reactions.

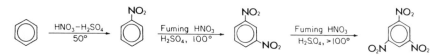

Notice that the introduction of the first nitro groups is easy, while the introduction of the second nitro group is harder, and that of the third harder still. In the above two equations we find another major difference in the behavior of methyl and nitro substituents. Notice in the alkylation case that each new methyl group enters the ring in a position *ortho* or *para* to an existing methyl group, whereas in nitration each new nitro group enters into a position *meta* to an existing nitro group. Extensive observations of a similar sort reveal that there are two classes of substituents in aromatic rings: (1) those which enhance further electrophilic substitution (*activate the ring*) and direct the incoming substituent primarily to positions *ortho* and *para* to themselves, and (2) those which hinder further electrophilic substitution (*deactivate the ring*) and direct new substituents primarily to positions *meta* to themselves. The members of each of these classes of substituents, as well as their relative directive potencies, are summarized in Figure 10-7.

Examination of Figure 10-7 and the foregoing discussion leads to two important generalizations:

1. If the substituent (X) bonded to the ring is a single atom, has a negative charge, or is singly bonded to other atoms, *ortho-para* substitution and ring activation occur. An exception is the halogens, which are *ortho-para* directing, but actually ring deactivating.

2. If the substituent (X) on the ring bears a positive charge or is multiply bonded to other atoms, *meta* substitution and ring deactivation occur.

These generalizations permit us to predict the major products which will be formed in substitution reactions involving a large number of aromatic derivatives. It is found, however, that we do not obtain exclusively *ortho-para* or *meta* products under the influence of these *ortho-para-* or *meta-*directing substituents. Rather, mixtures of products are almost invariably obtained, and Figure 10-7 summarizes only the principal types of products which will be formed. Moreover, the amounts of "unpredicted" substitu-

Ortho-para Directors (Promote Polysubstitution)

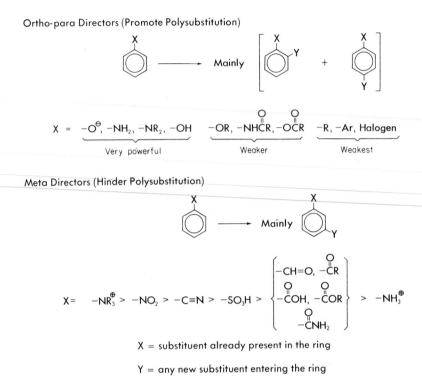

$$X = \quad -O^{\ominus}, -NH_2, -NR_2, -OH \qquad -OR, -NHCR, -OCR \qquad -R, -Ar, Halogen$$

Very powerful   Weaker   Weakest

Meta Directors (Hinder Polysubstitution)

X = substituent already present in the ring

Y = any new substituent entering the ring

Figure 10-7. Directive Abilities of Substituents

tion products as well as the isomer distribution among the products depend not only on the directive strength of the substituent (X) on the ring, but also on the nature of the incoming substituent (Y) and the experimental conditions (such as temperature) employed in conducting the substitution reaction. Some of these effects are seen in Figure 10-8, which shows the isomer distributions among products obtained during nitrations of various

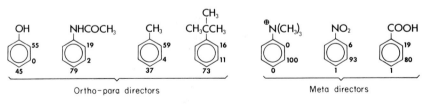

Ortho-para directors   Meta directors

Figure 10-8. Isomer Distribution in Nitration Reactions

substituted benzenes. The figure at each ring position indicates the percentage of the total nitration which occurs at that ring position. The isomer distribution in a purely statistical substitution would be *o:m:p/* 40:40:20. We see that the stronger *ortho-para* directors allow the least *meta* substitution and that the stronger *meta* directors permit the least *ortho-para* substitution. These generalizations hold as well for other reactions besides nitration. Notice also that the bulky *ortho-para*-directing *t*-butyl group, because it effectively "shields" its adjacent *ortho* positions by its size (**steric hindrance**), allows less *ortho* substitution than does the smaller methyl group.

The data in Figure 10-7 permit the prediction of the principal products from substitution reactions involving polysubstituted and polynuclear aromatic derivatives as well as simple ones. In making such predictions we need only to observe (1) whether the nature and positions of the existing substituents are such as to lead to directive effects which tend to reinforce or to compete with each other, (2) which of the directing substituents is the more powerful, and (3) what sort of steric interactions are pertinent. The several examples in Figure 10-9 illustrate the application of these prin-

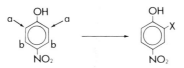

(a) Combined directive effect; ortho to OH, meta to NO₂.
(b) Position not activated.

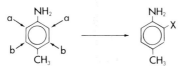

(a) Activated more; ortho to strong o,p-director; p-position blocked.
(b) Activated less; ortho to weak o,p-director; p-position blocked.

(a) Ring deactivated by NO₂ group.
(b) Activated o-position, but hindered by bulk of O₂N—⬡—CH₂— group.
(c) Activated p-position, not sterically hindered.

Figure 10-9. Multiple Directive Effects

ciples. Again, the products shown will in most cases not be the exclusive product, but rather the major one.

The reason for the *ortho-para-* or *meta*-directing effects of various substituents is readily understandable in terms of the mechanism of electrophilic aromatic substitution (Section 10-5). Let us first examine the effects of the substituents on the distributions of the π electrons of the aromatic ring. Consider the case of the formyl group, —CH=O, a typical *meta* director. The —CH=O group, like other *meta*-directors, is *electron-withdrawing* from the ring, giving rise to a resonance hybrid such as that in Figure 10-10. Notice that the hybrid has *centers of positive charge* at the *ortho*

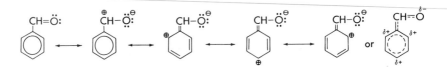

Figure 10-10. Resonance Hybrid of Benzaldehyde

and *para* positions. The electron-withdrawing nature of other *meta*-directing groups likewise leads generally to hybrids having higher positive charge densities at the *ortho* and *para* positions of the ring, as shown in Figure 10-11.

The resonance hybrids describing the electron distribution in benzene derivatives bearing *ortho-para*-directing substituents, on the other hand, have centers of *negative* charge at the *ortho* and *para* positions, as illustrated

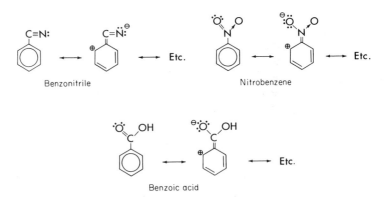

Figure 10-11. Resonance Hybrids of Benzene Derivatives with Meta-Directing Substituents

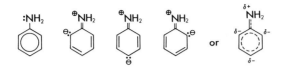

Figure 10-12. Resonance Hybrid of Aniline

with aniline (Figure 10-12). *Ortho-para*-directing substituents, in general, are *electron injecting* into the ring, and the *ortho* and *para* positions of the ring thus become centers of higher negative charge density. Further examples appear in Figure 10-13.

The directive influence of substituents is now understandable if we recall that the attacking species in electrophilic aromatic substitution is an electron-seeking Lewis acid. Clearly this electrophile will seek out positions of highest electron density in the ring as points to attack. With *ortho-para* directors present, these points of maximum negative charge density are (Figures 10-12 and 10-13) the *ortho* and *para* positions—and, indeed, attack will be *facilitated* at these positions (compared to benzene itself) because of the excess negative charge residing there. With *meta* directors present, on the other hand, the electrophile will be *repelled* by the excess of positive charge density at the *ortho* and *para* positions (Figures 10-10 and 10-11) and hence will attack instead at the *meta* position, so to speak, by default. Furthermore, the positively charged nature of the ring will generally *hinder* substitution, so that it occurs less readily than in the case of benzene itself. These simple electronic considerations thus explain not only the directive influence of various substituents but also their acti-

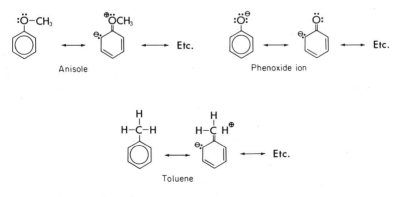

Figure 10-13. Resonance Hybrids of Benzene Derivatives with Ortho-para-Directing Substituents

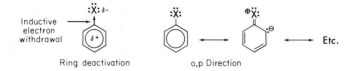

Figure 10-14. Inductive and Resonance Effects in Halobenzenes

vating or deactivating effects during the course of electrophilic aromatic substitution.

The halogen atom in halobenzenes, C_6H_5—X falls on the borderline between the two classes of substituents listed in Figure 10-7. Owing to the relatively high electronegativity of halogen atoms (Section 2-2d), which results in general electron withdrawal from the ring, the halobenzenes are deactivated toward electrophilic substitution. At the same time, the presence of unshared p electrons on the halogen atoms permits resonance interaction with the ring resulting in *ortho-para* substitution. These conflicting effects are summarized in Figure 10-14.

10-7. Nucleophilic and Free Radical Aromatic Substitution

Although electrophilic attack is the usual mechanism of aromatic substitution, in a few rare instances substitution reactions on the benzene ring are observed to occur by nucleophilic or free radical mechanisms. *m*-Dinitrobenzene and 1,3,5-trinitrobenzene are **hydroxylated** by alkaline potassium ferricyanide, for example, nucleophilic attack by $OH^\ominus$ occurring

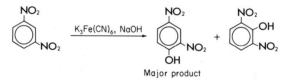

Major product

at the *ortho* and *para* positions. The presence of strongly electron-withdrawing NO_2 groups induces positive charges at these positions (Figure 10-15), which are then subject to attack by the nucleophilic $OH^\ominus$ ion.

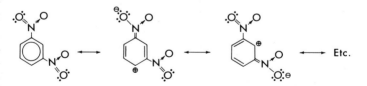

Figure 10-15. Resonance Hybrid of m-Dinitrobenzene

Aromatic substitution reactions effected by free radicals are known, but are of only limited preparative value. One typical example is the methylation of aromatic compounds using *t*-butyl peroxide. *t*-Butyl peroxide is heated in the presence of the aromatic compound, decomposing into a *t*-butoxy radical, which in turn decomposes into acetone and a methyl radical. The latter attacks the aromatic ring, inserting a methyl group at the *ortho*, *meta*, and *para* positions. We notice that free radical substitutions are not nearly as position selective as are electrophilic substitutions and that attack by the radical at the *ortho* position tends to predominate.

$(CH_3)_3CO\!\!-\!\!OC(CH_3)_3$ $\xrightarrow{\text{Heat}}$ $(CH_3)_3CO\cdot$ $\longrightarrow$ $(CH_3)_2C\!=\!O$ $+$ $CH_3\cdot$

t-Butyl peroxide   t-Butoxy radical   Acetone   Methyl radical

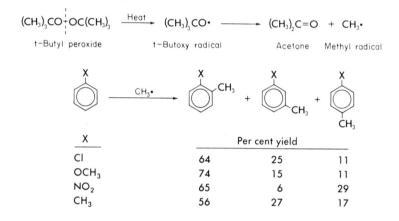

X	Per cent yield		
Cl	64	25	11
OCH₃	74	15	11
NO₂	65	6	29
CH₃	56	27	17

10-8. Structure Determination of Benzene Derivatives

Let us digress for a moment and examine the question of how we know the structures of the various isomers of polysubstituted aromatic hydrocarbons. Given samples of the three xylenes, for example, how do we know which is the *ortho*, the *meta*, and the *para* isomer? Historically, such information was gained largely by *interconversions* of compounds of unknown structure into derivatives of known structure. One of the xylenes, for instance, could be oxidized to phthalic acid, a dibasic acid known to have its two carboxyl groups *ortho* to one another because it, alone of the three phthalic acids, was capable of forming a cyclic anhydride on heating. *Assuming no molecular rearrangements*, this conversion meant that the xylene in question must also have been the *ortho* isomer. Similarly, with knowledge

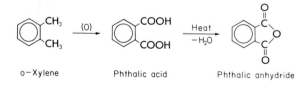

o-Xylene   Phthalic acid   Phthalic anhydride

of the structures of isophthalic and terephthalic acids, the structures of
m-xylene and *p*-xylene could be determined by analogous oxidations.

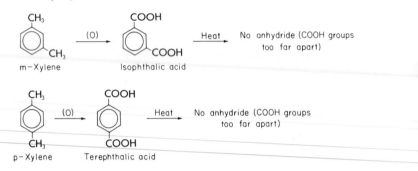

A second method of structure establishment is by *synthesis*, relating the
isomer in question to an analogous cyclohexane derivative. In 1892, for
example, W. Perkin, Jr., confirmed the structure of terephthalic acid by its
conversion into *cis*- and *trans*-cyclohexane-1,4-dicarboxylic acids, which
were in turn synthesized independently as shown. Assuming no molecular
rearrangements in the conversions involved, the structure of terephthalic
acid (and hence *p*-xylene) was thus established.

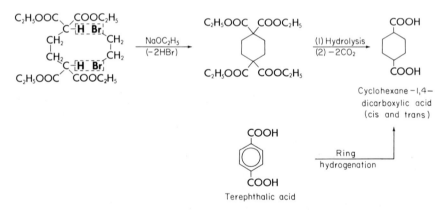

The difficulties inherent in such methods, and their lack of generality,
led W. G. Körner of Milan in 1874 to propose an "absolute method" for
the structure determination of polysubstituted benzene derivatives. This
method involved determining the *total number* of isomers produced during
further substitution reactions on each of the polysubstituted benzene derivatives in question. The application of Körner's method to the structure
establishment of the three xylenes is shown in Figure 10-16. We see that,
on nitration, *o*-xylene can produce two isomeric mononitroxylenes, *m*-

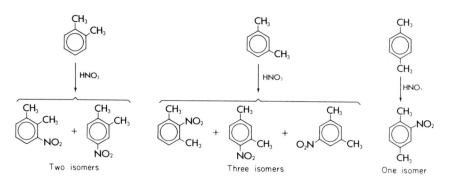

Figure 10-16. Application of Körner's "Absolute Method" to the Structure Determination of the Isomeric Xylenes

xylene can produce three, while *p*-xylene will yield only one. By separating and counting the number of nitration (or other substitution) products from each xylene, the structure of each xylene isomer could thus be determined. While Körner's method was infallible in principle, it was limited in practice by the difficulties inherent in separating the isomeric substitution products formed (chromatography in its different forms was unavailable at the time), and by the fact that certain of the isomers might be formed only in very low yield, thus occurring to but trivial extents in the crude product mixtures.

The most convenient method today for establishing the positions of substituents on the benzene ring is by infrared spectroscopy. Aromatic rings in general have characteristic C—H stretching frequencies near 3030 cm^{-1} and C=C vibrations in the 1600 to 1500 cm^{-1} region. In addition, characteristic **infrared absorption patterns** (groups and intensities of bands) in the 2000 to 1600 cm^{-1} region have been found to be indicative of and diagnostic for monosubstituted, disubstituted (1,2-, 1,3-, and 1,4-), trisubstituted (1,3,5-, 1,2,4-, and 1,2,3-), and tetrasubstituted (1,2,4,5- and 1,2,3,5-) benzene derivatives. The recent developments of such structural shortcuts, of course, rests on the examination of countless compounds whose structures are known through the above classical techniques.

10-9. Non-Benzenoid Aromatic Derivatives

In 1938 E. Hückel observed that the number of π electrons in benzene (six) conformed to the pattern $4n + 2$ (where n is an integer), and suggested that other conjugated cyclic polyenes whose number of π electrons conformed to this pattern should also show aromatic properties. We note that 1,3,5,7-cyclooctatetraene (Section 9-4h) contains eight π electrons, does not conform to this pattern, and is not aromatic, whereas naphthalene with ten π electrons (4 × 2 + 2) is aromatic.

Hückel's rule has stimulated organic chemists to synthesize a number of **non-benzenoid** ring systems conforming to the $4n + 2$ pattern of π electrons, to see if this simple generalization correctly predicts aromatic character. The resonance stabilization of the tropylium cation (Figure 6-9) and the cyclopentadienyl carbanion (Figure 6-13) have already been discussed. These stable ionic species, each with six π electrons, conform to Hückel's rule and are generally represented as shown here to emphasize their aromatic character. The aromatic nature of the cyclopentadienyl

Tropylium   Cyclopentadienyl   Ferrocene
cation   anion

anion is strikingly apparent in its "sandwich structure" iron derivative, ferrocene, which actually undergoes electrophilic substitution reactions (Friedel-Crafts acylation, sulfonation, etc.) more readily than does benzene itself. Another bicyclic polyene conforming to Hückel's rule is the crystalline blue hydrocarbon azulene, which is isomeric with naphthalene ($C_{10}H_8$). Azulene has a resonance energy (Section 5-1) of 49 kcal/mole, forms a π complex with 1,3,5-trinitrobenzene (Section 10-4c), and undergoes typical electrophilic substitution reactions. It occurs as a structural unit in certain natural products, and its structure is represented as the resonance hybrid shown in Figure 10-17.

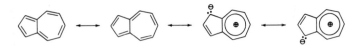

Figure 10-17. Resonance Hybrid of Azulene

The simplest cyclic system conforming to Hückel's rule is the cyclopropenyl cation (4 × 0 + 2). While unknown itself, its triphenyl derivative has been prepared, and found to give stable, high melting salts.

Cyclopropenyl cation

Triphenylcyclopropenyl bromide
(M. p. 271°)

Higher conjugated cyclopolyenes (**annulenes**) have also been synthesized to test Hückel's rule. [14]-Annulene (4 × 3 + 2) is quite unstable. [18]-Annulene (4 × 4 + 2) is highly reactive, but its NMR spectrum is suggestive of some aromatic character. Below a certain ring size (about C_{30}), however, such annulenes cannot meet the requirement for aromaticity of being planar, since their "interior" hydrogen atoms interfere with one another sterically when the molecule adopts a planar conformation.

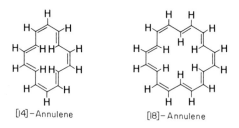

[14]–Annulene   [18]–Annulene

10-10. Heterocyclic Compounds

We have learned (Section 2-4) that heterocyclic compounds consist of cyclic structures whose rings contain one or more atoms other than carbon. Such structures may be monocyclic, bicyclic, or polycyclic, and the **hetero atoms** which they contain are most usually nitrogen, oxygen, or sulfur. Heterocyclic compounds occur widely throughout nature; indeed, probably the majority of known organic compounds are heterocyclic in structure. The heterocyclic series is thus an extremely important one, and one which has been actively studied by organic chemists since the beginning of their science. Our examination of this series must unfortunately be very brief. However, the chemistry of the heterocyclic series, while unique in some respects, is not vastly different than that of the aromatic and cycloaliphatic series previously considered, so that an introduction to a few basic principles in the present section will permit us to include heterocyclic compounds in future discussion.

Some of the more important parent ring systems of heterocyclic compounds containing one hetero atom are shown in Figure 10-18. As mentioned, heterocyclic compounds may have more than one hetero atom, and

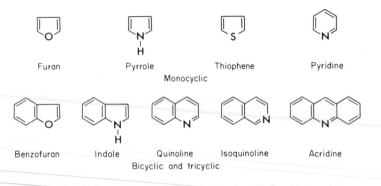

Furan   Pyrrole   Thiophene   Pyridine

Monocyclic

Benzofuran   Indole   Quinoline   Isoquinoline   Acridine

Bicyclic and tricyclic

Figure 10-18. Some Heterocyclic Compounds with One Hetero Atom

a few representative examples of these ring systems are shown in Figure 10-19. Many unsaturated heterocyclics of the sort shown in Figures 10-18 and 10-19 are found in coal tar (Section 10-2). The ring systems may also be produced synthetically.

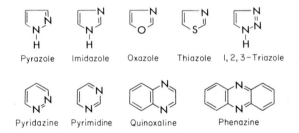

Pyrazole   Imidazole   Oxazole   Thiazole   1, 2, 3−Triazole

Pyridazine   Pyrimidine   Quinoxaline   Phenazine

Figure 10-19. Some Heterocyclic Compounds with Two or More Hetero Atoms

Unsaturated heterocyclic compounds such as those in Figures 10-18 and 10-19 show distinct aromatic properties. In particular, they tend to react by electrophilic substitution (as does benzene), rather than by addition (as do alkenes). The following substitution reactions of several heterocyclic compounds are typical.

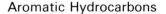

2−Furansulfonic acid

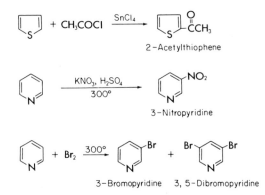

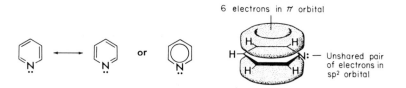

The aromatic properties of unsaturated heterocyclic compounds are understandable in terms of their electronic structures. We see immediately, for example, that pyridine may exist as a resonance hybrid, which may be represented as shown in Figure 10-20. Notice that pyridine is

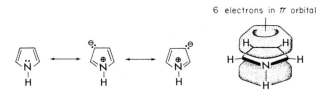

Figure 10-20. Resonance and Molecular Orbital Representations of Pyridine

electronically exactly like benzene (Figure 5-7), except that the pair of sp^2 electrons on the nitrogen atom is not shared with another atom, and pyridine obeys Hückel's rule ($4 \times 1 + 2 = 6 \ \pi$ electrons). Similarly, pyrrole is electronically equivalent to the cyclopentadienyl carbanion (Figure 6-13). Its resonance hybrid and molecular orbital representation are shown in Figure 10-21. Heat of combustion data show the following

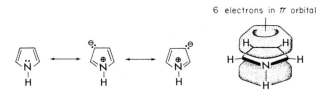

Figure 10-21. Resonance and Molecular Orbital Representations of Pyrrole

resonance energies for typical unsaturated heterocyclic compounds: furan, 24; thiophene, 29; pyrrole, 24; pyridine, 43; and quinoline, 75 kcal/mole.

The positions at which heterocyclic rings are attacked during electrophilic substitutions can also be rationalized by resonance theory, in terms similar to the theory of benzene substitution (Section 10-5). The preference for attack on the furan and thiophene rings at the 2 position, and on the pyridine ring at the 3 position, for example, is explained in terms of similar resonance stabilization for the intermediate σ complexes involved, as shown in Figure 10-22.

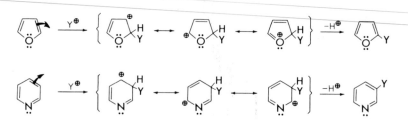

Figure 10-22. Mechanism of Electrophilic Substitution in Furan and Pyridine

Analogously to benzene, unsaturated heterocyclic compounds may be reduced catalytically or chemically to produce saturated heterocycles. The following examples are typical.

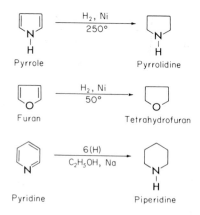

Like cycloalkanes, reduced heterocyclic rings have no aromatic properties. Rather, they behave chemically in accord with the typical behavior of the disubstituted hetero atoms they contain. Thus tetrahydrofuran behaves like an alkyl ether, ROR; tetrahydrothiophene like an alkyl sulfide, RSR; and pyrrolidine and piperidine like aliphatic secondary amines, RNHR.

As mentioned above, both unsaturated and saturated mono- and poly-nuclear heterocycles are abundant throughout the plant and animal kingdoms. Many such naturally occurring heterocyclic compounds are both physiologically important and chemically interesting. The alkaloids (Chapter 16), for example, comprise a large group of both simple and complex nitrogen heterocyclics, some of which have been used since antiquity (and still are used) in medicine. Two such structures, with their sources and uses, are illustrated below.

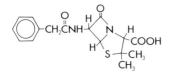

Penicillin G

Penicillium chrysogenum fermentation

Antibiotic drug

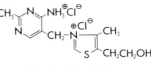

Thiamine hydrochloride

Plant and animal tissues

Vitamin B₁ hydrochloride

SUPPLEMENTARY READING

1. "Faraday's Discovery of Benzene," L. C. Newell, *J. Chem. Educ.*, **3,** 1248 (1926).
2. "Kekulé's Theory of Aromaticity," A. Gero, *J. Chem. Educ.*, **31,** 201 (1954).
3. "Charles Friedel (1832–1899) " A. Willemart, *J. Chem. Educ.*, **26,** 2 (1949).
4. "The Orientation and Mechanism of Electrophilic Aromatic Substitution," L. N. Ferguson, *J. Chem. Educ.*, **32,** 42 (1955).
5. "Directive Influence of Substituents in the Benzene Ring," Y. P. Varshni, *J. Chem. Educ.*, **30,** 465 (1953).
6. "Substituent Effects in the Benzene Ring. A Demonstration," F. L. Lambert, *J. Chem. Educ.*, **35,** 342 (1958).
7. "Nucleophilic Substitution in Aromatic Systems," R. G. Gillis, *J. Chem. Educ.*, **32,** 296 (1955).
8. "Aromatic Substitution by Free Radicals," P. F. Nelson, *J. Chem. Educ.*, **32,** 606 (1955).
9. "Three of Benzene's Valence Isomers Isolated, *Chem. Eng. News*, **42,** 38 (Dec. 7, 1964).

CHAPTER 11

Alcohols, Alkyl Halides, and Ethers

ALCOHOLS, ALKYL HALIDES, AND ETHERS are important classes of organic compounds both because of their uses in the laboratory, theoretically, and commercially and because alcohols and ethers, at least, are found widely throughout nature. Again, the functional groups involved ($-OH$, $-X$, and $-OR$; Section 2-5) in these classes are found among aliphatic, cyclo-aliphatic, aromatic, and heterocyclic representatives of the classes. The three classes may be conveniently examined in a single chapter, since ordinarily each class may be readily converted into the others. We shall begin our survey with the alcohols.

ALCOHOLS

11-1. Nomenclature of Alcohols

Alcohols comprise the class of compounds whose structures contain the hydroxyl group attached to a carbon atom bonded in turn only to hydrogen or another carbon. Thus the type formula for aliphatic alcohols is R—OH, and that of aromatic alcohols (**phenols**) is Ar—OH. Aliphatic alcohols are frequently named as "alcohols" on the basis of the aliphatic groups from which they are derived, for example:

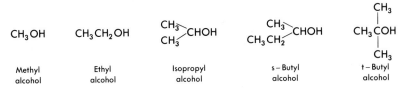

| Methyl alcohol | Ethyl alcohol | Isopropyl alcohol | s–Butyl alcohol | t–Butyl alcohol |

Alcohols, particularly more complex ones, are also named by the IUPAC system, whose systematic designation for the —OH function is *-ol*. This is added as a suffix to the root name (name minus *-e*) of the parent hydrocarbon:

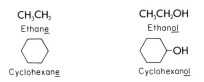

The position of the —OH function in higher alcohols is indicated by an appropriate number on the longest straight chain, selected again to be as small as possible and usually occurring just before the final part of the name:

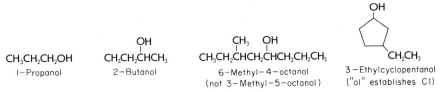

Monocyclic and bicyclic aromatic alcohols are called **phenols** and **naphthols**, respectively, and are ordinarily named on this basis (see Section 10-1).

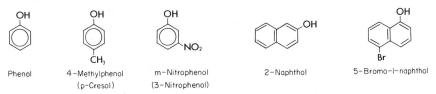

Alcohols, particularly in the aromatic and heterocyclic series, are often also named as hydroxy derivatives, a number indicating the position of the

—OH function.   Note that the hetero atom is assigned the number 1.

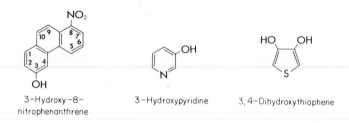

3—Hydroxy—8—
nitrophenanthrene

3—Hydroxypyridine

3,4—Dihydroxythiophene

Aliphatic alcohols are classed as **primary, secondary,** or **tertiary** according to the number of groups on the OH-bearing carbon atom, as already described (Section 8-3a).   Thus ethanol, CH_3CH_2OH, benzyl alcohol, $C_6H_5CH_2OH$, and allyl alcohol, $CH_2{=}CHCH_2OH$, are primary alcohols; 2-butanol and cyclohexanol are secondary; and *t*-butyl alcohol is tertiary.   Note in cyclohexanol that the "two alkyl groups" are involved in a carbocyclic ring.   Phenols, which have distinctly different chemical properties, are *not* classified as secondary alcohols.   Long (C_{12} up), straight-chain primary alcohols are commonly named on the basis of corresponding carboxylic acids which occur naturally as esters in fats and oils (see Sec-

$CH_3(CH_2)_{10}CH_2OH$ $CH_3(CH_2)_{12}CH_2OH$ $CH_3(CH_2)_{14}CH_2OH$ $CH_3(CH_2)_{16}CH_2OH$

Lauryl alcohol   Myristyl alcohol   Cetyl alcohol   Stearyl alcohol
(1—Dodecanol)   (1—Tetradecanol)   (1—Hexadecanol)   (1—Octadecanol)

tion 13-8).   Straight-chain primary alcohols are frequently referred to as *normal* alcohols.   Thus an alternative name for 1-butanol is *n*-butyl alcohol, and for 1-dodecanol, *n*-dodecyl alcohol.

11-2. Physical Properties and Characterization of Alcohols

The boiling points of alcohols show the same characteristic increase with increasing molecular weight which we found to be characteristic among the hydrocarbons (Figure 7-3 and Table 9-2).   The boiling points of alcohols, however, are much higher than those of hydrocarbons of comparable molecular weight, for reasons discussed in Section 11-3.   Increased branching in the alkyl group of the alcohol leads to lower boiling points, as seen in the following C_5 primary alcohols.   Similarly among isomeric

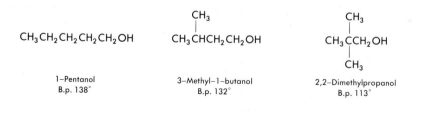

1—Pentanol
B.p. 138°

3—Methyl—1—butanol
B.p. 132°

2,2—Dimethylpropanol
B.p. 113°

alcohols of different types, primary have the highest boiling points, secondary next, and tertiary the lowest. This generalization is illustrated by the following boiling point comparisons: 1-propanol (97°) and 2-propanol (82°); *n*-butyl (117°), *s*-butyl (99.5°), and *t*-butyl (83°) alcohols. Analogous effects of branching and functional group position on boiling points are found in other classes of organic compounds as well.

Melting points of normal alcohols above 1-propanol (m.p. $-126°$) increase with increasing molecular weight. Up to about $C_{12}H_{25}OH$ (1-dodecanol, m.p. 24°) such alcohols are liquids at room temperature, while those above C_{12} are solids. As far as structural effects on the melting points of alcohols is concerned, our previously encountered generalization (Sections 7-3b and 10-1) again operates, that greater molecular symmetry, producing more stable crystal lattices, is reflected in higher melting points. This effect is illustrated in the following structures.

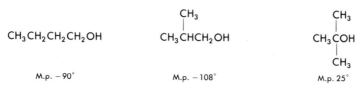

$$CH_3CH_2CH_2CH_2OH \qquad CH_3\underset{|}{\overset{CH_3}{C}}HCH_2OH \qquad CH_3\underset{|}{\overset{CH_3}{\underset{CH_3}{C}}}OH$$

M.p. $-90°$ \qquad M.p. $-108°$ \qquad M.p. 25°

Methyl, ethyl, and the propyl alcohols are soluble in water in all proportions (see Section 11-3). Above C_4, however, the alcohols become increasingly insoluble in water with increasing molecular weight. Branching in the structure of the alcohol makes generally for greater water solubility, as illustrated by the fact that *t*-butyl alcohol is infinitely miscible with water, whereas *n*-butyl alcohol is soluble to the extent of only about 9 per cent at 15°.

The OH function in alcohols may be identified by both chemical and spectroscopic means. Infrared absorption frequencies in the 3100 to 3600 cm^{-1} region are characteristic of the OH group, while chemically alcohols can often be identified by the fact that, like water, they react with sodium metal with liberation of hydrogen. Primary, secondary, and tertiary alco-

$$HOH + Na \longrightarrow Na^{\oplus}OH^{\ominus} + \tfrac{1}{2}H_2$$

$$ROH + Na \longrightarrow Na^{\oplus}OR^{\ominus} + \tfrac{1}{2}H_2$$

hols may be distinguished chemically by the Lucas test, as described in Section 11-7e.

11-3. Hydrogen Bonding

Comparison of the boiling points of alcohols with those of hydrocarbons having comparable molecular weights indicates that alcohols boil at "abnormally" high temperatures. The several examples given in Table 11-1

**Table 11-1. Boiling Points and Molecular Weights
of Some Hydrocarbons and Alcohols**

Compound	Molecular Weight	B.p., °C
CH_3CH_3	30	-88.6
CH_3OH	32	$+64.7$
$CH_3CH_2CH_3$	44	-42.2
CH_3CH_2OH	46	$+78.3$
$CH_3CH_2CH_2CH_3$	58	-0.5
$CH_3CH_2CH_2OH$	60	$+97.2$
$C_6H_5CH_3$ (toluene)	92	110.8
C_6H_5OH (phenol)	94	181.4

are typical. Similarly, the boiling point of water is anomalously high. This is seen in Table 11-2, which compares the boiling points and molecular weights of water and other pertinent compounds. We note that not only does water boil about 262° higher than methane, the hydrocarbon of comparable molecular weight, but also that the boiling point of water drops dramatically as we replace the hydrogen atoms of water with methyl groups, even though the molecular weight is thereby increased. Such peculiarities were first generally clarified by W. M. Latimer and W. H. Rodebush in 1920, in terms of the concept of **hydrogen bonding**.

**Table 11-2. Boiling Points of Some Low Molecular
Weight Compounds**

Compound	Molecular Weight	B.p., °C
CH_4	16	-161.7
HOH	18	$+100.0$
CH_3OH	32	$+64.7$
CH_3OCH_3	46	-23.7

Let us recall (Section 2-2d) that the H–O bond in the hydroxyl group is *partially ionic* in character, and therefore has a permanent dipole moment (Figure 2-4). The positively charged end of this dipole is attracted to the negatively charged end of the dipole in an adjacent water or alcohol molecule. This attraction repeats itself indefinitely, leading to **dipole-dipole association** of all of the molecules in the sample (Figure 11-1). The attrac-

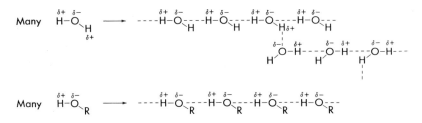

Figure 11-1. Hydrogen Bonding.   Dipole-Dipole Attraction in Water and Alcohol Molecules

tion forces between the positive H end of a dipole and a center of negative charge is called a **hydrogen bond**, and is symbolized by a dotted line. Liquids whose molecules are held together in bulk by dipole-dipole attraction are called **associated liquids**, and generally have markedly higher boiling points than do nonassociated liquids where such attractions are absent. Extra energy (heat) must be put into the bulk of an associated liquid to disrupt its dipole-dipole attractions prior to vaporization, thus leading to "abnormally" high boiling points. Hydrogen bonding is also evident in the infrared spectra of alcohols. With alcohol *vapors* (molecules too far apart for hydrogen bonding), the O—H stretching frequency is about 3700 cm^{-1}. In associated liquid alcohols, however, this absorption band broadens and shifts to lower frequencies (longer wavelengths) as a result of hydrogen bonding. The bond strength (Section 2-9) of the hydrogen bond appears to be in the range of 5 to 10 kcal/mole, some 5 to 10 per cent of the strength of an ordinary covalent bond. It should be emphasized that hydrogen bonding is merely a particularly effective case of ordinary dipole-dipole attraction and that it occurs primarily when the hydrogen atom may be flanked by either oxygen, nitrogen, or fluorine (Figure 11-2). Elements below the first row of the periodic table are not sufficiently electronegative for molecules containing them to associate through hydrogen bonding.

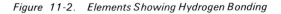

Figure 11-2.   Elements Showing Hydrogen Bonding

The solubility of the lower alcohols in water is also a consequence of hydrogen bonding, mutual miscibility being permitted by hydrogen bonding *between* the two species of molecules (Figure 11-3). This accords with the chemists' dictum that "like dissolves like"; that is, that structurally similar compounds tend to be mutually miscible. With higher alcohols water solubility decreases because the large hydrocarbon-like R group "gets in the way," preventing proper alignment and proximity of the OH groups of the water and alcohol molecules. The decreasing effectiveness of hydrogen bonding in higher alcohols is also apparent in Table 11-1, where we see that the boiling points of the higher alcohols are closer to those of hydrocarbons of comparable weight than is the case with the lower alcohols.

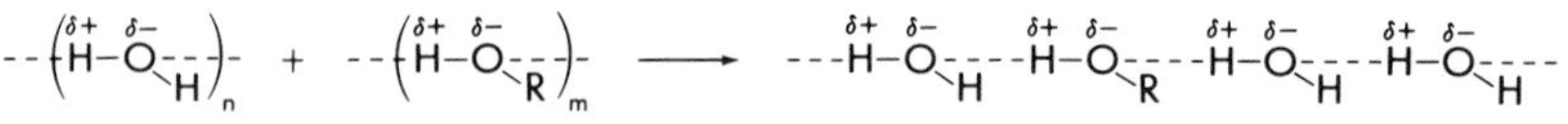

$$--\left(\overset{\delta+}{H}-\overset{\delta-}{O}\overset{-}{\underset{H}{-}}\right)_{n} + --\left(\overset{\delta+}{H}-\overset{\delta-}{O}\overset{-}{\underset{R}{-}}\right)_{m} \longrightarrow ---\overset{\delta+}{H}-\overset{\delta-}{\underset{H}{O}}---\overset{\delta+}{H}-\overset{\delta-}{\underset{R}{O}}---\overset{\delta+}{H}-\overset{\delta-}{\underset{H}{O}}---\overset{\delta+}{H}-\overset{\delta-}{\underset{H}{O}}---$$

Figure 11-3.   Mutual Miscibility of Water and Alcohols

In the proper structural situation *intramolecular* hydrogen bonding may occur, giving rise to cyclic **chelate rings** (Greek: *chele*, claw). This condition contrasts to the above examples of intermolecular hydrogen bonding, and leads to boiling points and solubilities, for example, which are closer to those found for nonassociated molecules of similar molecular weight. In the intramolecular case, the attraction forces of hydrogen bonding are mainly "spent" within the individual molecule, and extend much less effectively to neighboring molecules. Intramolecular hydrogen bonding is particularly prone to prevail when five- or six-membered chelate ring structures are possible. These factors are illustrated in the examples of Figure 11-4.

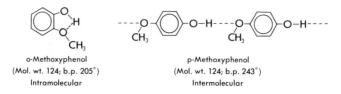

o-Methoxyphenol   p-Methoxyphenol
(Mol. wt. 124; b.p. 205°)   (Mol. wt. 124; b.p. 243°)
Intramolecular   Intermolecular

Figure 11-4.   Intramolecular and Intermolecular Hydrogen Bonding

11-4. Sources and Uses of Alcohols

a. *Methanol (Wood Alcohol).* Methanol was originally obtained from the distillate obtained during the destructive distillation (charcoaling) of wood, a cord of wood yielding some 15 gallons of methanol, 8 to 25 gallons of acetic acid, and small amounts of acetone and other compounds. Since 1923 methanol has been increasingly produced by the catalytic reduction of carbon monoxide in the presence of chromium and zinc oxides, an inno-

$$2\,H_2 \;+\; CO \xrightarrow[350-400°]{Cr_2O_3 - ZnO} CH_3OH$$

vation which has cut the cost of commercial methanol more than half. In 1961 over 1 million tons of methanol were produced synthetically, as against only 5300 tons obtained by the destructive distillation of wood. More recently methanol has been obtained industrially by the controlled air oxidation of natural gas. Its main uses are as a solvent, a denaturant for ethyl alcohol, and a radiator antifreeze and in the manufacture of form-aldehyde. Methanol is acutely poisonous; injury or death results from in-gestion, inhalation of its vapors, or absorption through the skin. Numerous cases of blindness and death have been reported due to the thoughtless consumption of wood alcohol as a beverage.

b. *Ethanol (Grain Alcohol).* Ethanol for beverage purposes has been pro-duced since antiquity by the **fermentation** (degradation by action of en-zymes in yeast or other microorganisms) of sugars in fruit juices or starches in grains. **Enzymes** are complex organic "catalysts" which are secreted by living cells and which are capable of bringing about *specific* biochemical reactions characteristic of the enzyme. The enzymes of yeast and certain other cells are capable of fermenting sugars or starches into ethanol as shown in the following equations. Note how each enzyme promotes a specific reaction.

$$2\,(C_6H_{10}O_5)_n \;+\; n\,H_2O \xrightarrow[\text{(enzyme in malt)}]{\text{Diastase}} n\,C_{12}H_{22}O_{11}$$

Starch   Maltose (A sugar)

$$C_{12}H_{22}O_{11} \;+\; H_2O \xrightarrow[\text{(enzyme in yeast)}]{\text{Maltase}} 2\,C_6H_{12}O_6$$

Maltose   Glucose (A simpler sugar)

$$C_6H_{12}O_6 \xrightarrow[\text{(enzyme in yeast)}]{\text{Zymase}} 2\,CO_2 \;+\; 2\,CH_3CH_2OH$$

Glucose   Ethanol

Fermentation continues until the solution contains about 12 per cent ethanol, whereupon the enzyme becomes **denatured** (irreversibly destroyed) and fermentation stops. The resulting alcohol concentration is typical of undistilled wines. Higher ethanol concentrations (up to 95 per cent, or "190 proof") are obtainable by fractional distillation of the fermented solution, and mixtures of intermediate concentration (40 to 50 per cent; 80 to 100 proof) constitute the "distilled spirits" (brandy, whiskey, etc.) of commerce. Minor by-products of fermentation (higher alcohols, ketones, and esters) constitute a contaminant known as **fusel oil**; although it is largely removed by distillation, the small residual quantities provide the distinctive flavors of various distilled beverages. Fermentation in closed containers traps the carbon dioxide produced, and affords the "sparkling" (carbonated) wines so popular on the Continent. The term **proof** or **proof spirit** originated in the early method of testing whiskey by pouring it onto gunpowder and lighting it. If the gunpowder ignited after the alcohol had burned, proof was at hand that the whiskey had not been excessively diluted with water. 100 proof whiskey, which would pass such a test, contains 50 per cent ethanol.

The synthesis of ethanol was reported by Hennel in England as early as 1828 (the same year in which Wöhler synthesized urea), but the first continuous commercial production of synthetic ethanol in the United States was not achieved until 1931. Ethylene gas from hydrocarbon cracking (Section 7-4d) is absorbed in concentrated sulfuric acid to yield a mixture of ethyl hydrogen sulfate and ethyl sulfate. Addition of water brings about hydrolysis to ethanol, which is recovered by distillation. In 1960 the syn-

$$CH_2{=}CH_2 \;+\; HO{-}SO_2{-}OH \;\xrightarrow{100°}\; CH_3CH_2O{-}SO_2{-}OH$$
$$\text{Ethyl hydrogen sulfate}$$

$$CH_3CH_2O{-}SO_2{-}OH \;+\; CH_2{=}CH_2 \;\xrightarrow{100°}\; CH_3CH_2O{-}SO_2{-}OCH_2CH_3$$
$$\text{Ethyl sulfate}$$

$$CH_3CH_2O{-}SO_2{-}OH \;+\; H_2O \;\longrightarrow\; CH_3CH_2OH \;+\; HO{-}SO_2{-}OH$$

$$CH_3CH_2O{-}SO_2{-}OCH_2CH_3 \;+\; 2\,H_2O \;\longrightarrow\; 2\,CH_3CH_2OH \;+\; HO{-}SO_2{-}OH$$

thetic process accounted for 91 per cent of the total ethanol produced in the United States (273 million gallons). The principal raw material for the fermentation process is blackstrap molasses, the syrupy residue from the refining of cane sugar (sucrose). Ethanol produced either synthetically or by molasses fermentation is referred to as nonbeverage alcohol.

Purification of ethanol by distillation from aqueous solution proceeds only to 95 per cent, since the resulting mixture ($C_2H_5OH{:}H_2O/95{:}5$) has a constant boiling point (78.15°) lower than that of pure ethanol (78.3°). Such a *constant boiling mixture* is called an **azeotrope**. To obtain **absolute alcohol** (100 per cent; 200 proof), the 5 per cent water in the azeotrope must be removed. This is done either by chemical means (such as heating with calcium oxide) or by further distillation in the presence of a third component (for example, benzene) which will form a lower-boiling azeotrope containing water. With benzene, two azeotropes with ethanol and water are known, as follows:

Ethanol–benzene–water (18.5:74.1:7.4), ternary azeotrope, b.p. 64.8°
Ethanol–benzene (19.8:80.2), binary azeotrope, b.p. 68.2°

By adding sufficient benzene and distilling, water is removed first as the lower-boiling ternary azeotrope (b.p. 64.8°), then benzene is removed as the higher-boiling binary azeotrope (b.p. 68.2°), and finally absolute ethanol (b.p. 78.3°) distills. Absolute ethanol is used in certain chemical applications where traces of water have a deleterious effect. Water cannot be effectively removed from ethanol or other alcohols by the common drying agent calcium chloride because alcoholates, $CaCl_2 \cdot xROH$, analogous to hydrates, are formed.

Ethanol which is employed for beverage purposes is taxed for revenue in all countries. In 1965, for example, 190 proof ethanol costs $6.35 per gallon tax-free in the United States, but $30.50 per gallon with federal tax. For almost all tax-free, nonbeverage purposes the law requires that ethanol be rendered unfit for drinking by **denaturing**, that is, by addition of contaminants which will render it unpalatable or toxic. In 1960 almost 97 per cent of the ethanol produced in the United States was denatured. Nonbeverage ethanol is widely used as a solvent and cleaning agent and as a raw material for the production of acetaldehyde, acetic acid, ethyl chloride, butadiene, and other industrially important chemicals.

c. Higher Alcohols. Higher alcohols in the C_3 to C_5 range are used mainly as solvents and plasticizers and as raw materials for the production of other compounds. They are commercially available from a variety of sources. The fractional distillation of fusel oil provided an early source of propyl, isobutyl, and several amyl, $C_5H_{11}OH$, alcohols. 1-Butanol, along with acetone and ethanol, is obtained by the anaerobic bacterial fermentation of corn mash or blackstrap molasses. Addition of sulfuric acid to the alkene, followed by hydrolysis (Section 8-4d), provides a source of secondary and tertiary alcohols from the C_3 to C_5 alkene fractions from petroleum cracking. Vapor phase chlorination of pentanes produces mixtures of amyl chlorides, $C_5H_{11}Cl$ isomers (Section 7-6d), from which amyl alcohols are produced by alkaline hydrolysis. Some higher alcohols are obtained as by-products during the above-discussed catalytic synthesis of methanol, the Fischer-Tropsch synthesis (Section 7-4g), and the partial air oxidation of alkanes.

Straight-chain, saturated primary alcohols in the C_{12} to C_{18} range, important in the manufacture of detergents, are prepared by the catalytic hydrogenation of natural fats (see Section 13-8). In 1954 K. Ziegler in Germany discovered that straight-chain primary alcohols could be obtained via aluminum alkyls, and since 1962 commercial production of long-chain homologs has been undertaken in this country. This procedure, the **Alfol process**, utilizes purified aluminum, ethylene, hydrogen, and air as raw materials, as illustrated in Figure 11-5.

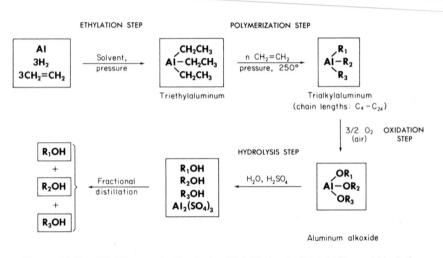

Figure 11-5.   Alfol Process for Producing High Molecular Weight Normal Alcohols

11-5. Synthesis of Alcohols

The following syntheses constitute the most important general methods for the preparation of alcohols on a laboratory scale. In contrast to the industrial methods discussed above, these syntheses almost invariably yield a single product, such that purification problems are minimized. Certain methods have been discussed previously, and will be cited only briefly.

a. Reduction of Carbonyl Compounds.   Lithium aluminum hydride provides the most convenient laboratory reagent for the quantitative reduction of aldehydes and ketones to alcohols. The carbonyl group of carboxylic acids and carboxylic esters is also reduced by this reagent, giving primary

Figure 11-6. Chemists in Protective Clothing Charge a High Pressure Bomb Reactor in the Course of Research in Developing the Alfol Process (courtesy Continental Oil Company)

alcohols from the $R\overset{|}{-}C\!\!=\!\!O$ function in each case. Notice also that the carboxylic ester is cleaved into two alcohol fragments. The initial product in

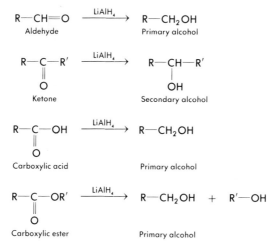

the reduction is a lithium tetraalkoxyaluminum derivative (11-**1**), formed by transfer of a hydride ion ($H:^{\ominus}$) from the reagent to the positive end of the carbonyl group. This intermediate is subsequently hydrolyzed to the desired alcohol by treatment with water. The above carbonyl reductions

$$4 \, \overset{\delta+}{R}CH\overset{\delta-}{=\!\!=}O \; + \; Li^{\oplus}AlH_4^{\ominus} \longrightarrow$$

$$(RCH_2O)_4Al^{\ominus}Li^{\oplus} \xrightarrow{\; 4\,H_2O \;} 4\,RCH_2OH \; + \; Al(OH)_3 \; + \; LiOH$$
$$\mathbf{11\text{-}1}$$

may also be achieved catalytically with hydrogen or by means of sodium in ethanol, but the more convenient lithium aluminum hydride (dissolved in ethyl ether or tetrahydrofuran) has largely replaced the latter technique.

b. Hydrolysis of Alkyl Halides.   A procedure sometimes useful for the preparation of alcohols is the hydrolysis of alkyl halides, a reaction which occurs in the presence of base catalysts in accord with the following equation.

$$R{-\!\!-}X \; + \; KOH \xrightarrow{\; H_2O{-}EtOH \;} R{-\!\!-}OH \; + \; KX$$

The process is reversible, and the base functions to drive the reaction to the right by neutralizing the acid, HX, produced. The ease of hydrolysis of alkyl halides is in the order tertiary > secondary > primary; in fact, tertiary alkyl halides may often be hydrolyzed by merely heating with water. Since alkyl halides are water insoluble, however, the reaction is usually conducted in aqueous ethanol, in which the reactants form a homogeneous solution. Alkyl halide hydrolysis is a typical nucleophilic substitution reaction, and will be discussed in greater detail in Section 11-12d.

c. Hydration of Alkenes.   This important industrial method for the preparation of alcohols has been discussed in Sections 11-4b and 8-4d.

d. Hydroboration of Alkenes.   This new technique for the preparation of primary alcohols has been discussed in Section 8-4i.

e. Syntheses Employing the Grignard Reagent.   The most versatile technique for the synthesis of alcohols involves the addition of the Grignard reagent (in ethyl ether solution; Section 7-5d) to the carbonyl group of an aldehyde, ketone, or ester.   The reaction type is shown below.   We see

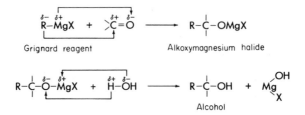

that the alkyl group of the Grignard reagent adds to the more positive end (carbon) of the carbonyl group to form an **alkoxymagnesium halide,** which is then hydrolyzed with ice water to form the desired alcohol. Hydrolysis is ordinarily carried out under acidic conditions to prevent the formation of gelatinous magnesium hydroxide, which would interfere with the isolation of the product. Let us illustrate the application of this reaction to the preparation of primary, secondary, and tertiary alcohols.

Primary Alcohols from RMgX and Formaldehyde

$$R-MgX + CH_2=O \longrightarrow R-CH_2-OMgX \xrightarrow{H_2O} R-CH_2OH$$

Formaldehyde   Primary alcohol

Example: $CH_3CH_2CH_2MgBr + CH_2{=}O \longrightarrow CH_3CH_2CH_2CH_2OMgBr \xrightarrow{H_2O}$
Propylmagnesium bromide

$$CH_3CH_2CH_2CH_2OH$$
1-Butanol

The resulting primary alcohol has one more carbon atom than the original alkyl halide from which the Grignard reagent was derived.

Secondary Alcohols from RMgX and Aldehydes

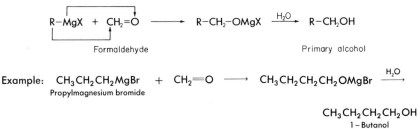

Example:

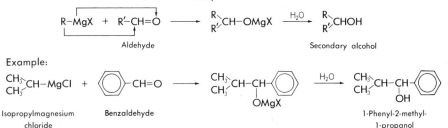

Isopropylmagnesium   Benzaldehyde   1-Phenyl-2-methyl-
chloride   1-propanol

Note that secondary alcohols may be prepared with two identical or two different R groups.

Tertiary Alcohols from RMgX and Ketones

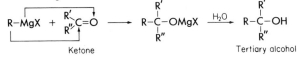

Ketone   Tertiary alcohol

Example:

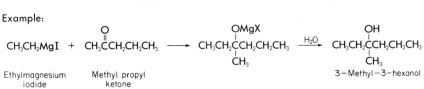

Ethylmagnesium   Methyl propyl   3-Methyl-3-hexanol
iodide   ketone

In this manner tertiary alcohols may be prepared which have any desired number of the three R groups the same or different.

Tertiary Alcohols from RMgX and Esters

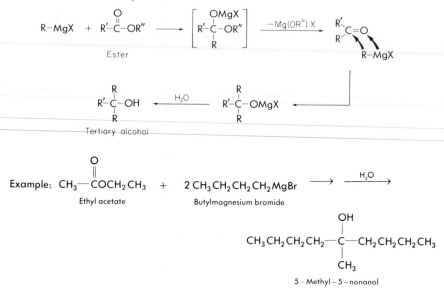

Example: CH₃—COCH₂CH₃ + 2 CH₃CH₂CH₂CH₂MgBr → H₂O →

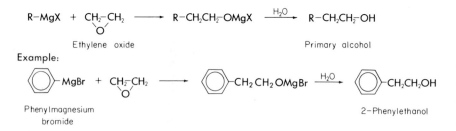

Notice that in this case the initial adduct of the Grignard reagent to the ester spontaneously loses the elements of X—Mg—OR″ to form an intermediate ketone, which then reacts in the ordinary way with a second molecule of the Grignard reagent. Subsequent hydrolysis finally affords a tertiary alcohol in which at least two of the three R groups are identical.

Finally, primary alcohols may be prepared by addition of Grignard reagents to the heterocyclic ether ethylene oxide (p. 341). The primary

R—MgX + CH₂–CH₂ → R–CH₂CH₂–OMgX —H₂O→ R–CH₂CH₂–OH
                  \O/
              Ethylene oxide   Primary alcohol

Example:

alcohol resulting from this reaction has a chain of two carbon atoms more than the alkyl halide from which the Grignard reagent is derived.

It should be emphasized that under ordinary conditions Grignard reagents *do not add* to the carbonyl group of carboxylic acids. Rather, an

$$R-\overset{\overset{\displaystyle O}{\parallel}}{C}-O-H \ + \ R'-MgX \longrightarrow R-\overset{\overset{\displaystyle O}{\parallel}}{C}-OMgX \ + \ R'H$$

$$11\text{-}2 \qquad 11\text{-}3$$

insoluble halomagnesium salt (11-**2**) of the acid forms, along with the alkane (11-**3**) or arene corresponding to the original Grignard reagent.

11-6. Polyhydric Alcohols

Alcohols containing more than one OH function are called **polyhydric alcohols** or **polyols**. They are classed in several categories according to the number of OH groups present in the molecule.

  a. Diols. Diols, which contain two OH groups per molecule, are usually termed **glycols** (Greek: *glykys*, sweet). So-called 1,1-glycols (11-**4** and 11-**5**), having both OH groups on the same carbon atom, are nonexistent except in a few special circumstances. They are ordinarily unstable with respect to an aldehyde or ketone and water (**Erlenmeyer's rule**); that is, the following equilibria lie far to the right. The simplest 1,2-gylcol is

$$R-CH\!\!\begin{array}{c}\diagup OH \\ \diagdown OH\end{array} \ \rightleftarrows \ R-CH{=}O \ + \ H_2O$$

$$11\text{-}4$$

$$\begin{array}{c}R\diagdown \\ R\diagup\end{array}\!C\!\!\begin{array}{c}\diagup OH \\ \diagdown OH\end{array} \ \rightleftarrows \ \begin{array}{c}R\diagdown \\ R\diagup\end{array}\!C{=}O \ + \ H_2O$$

$$11\text{-}5$$

ethylene glycol (1,2-ethanediol), which is prepared commercially from ethylene by several routes, one of which is shown in the following equation. It is widely employed (1961 production: 591,650 tons) as a radiator anti-

$$CH_2{=}CH_2 \ + \ Air \ \xrightarrow[250°]{Ag} \ CH_2\!\!\begin{array}{c}\diagdown \\ \diagup\end{array}\!\!CH_2 \ \xrightarrow{H_2O,\,H^{\oplus}} \ HO-CH_2CH_2-OH$$

Ethylene oxide   Ethylene glycol

freeze (for example, Prestone), hydraulic brake fluid, humectant, and industrial solvent, as well as in the synthesis and formulation of plastics and fibers. Propylene glycol and trimethylene glycol (a 1,3-diol) are industrially important diols used for similar purposes. 1,2-Glycols are often called **α-glycols**, and tetrasubstituted α-glycols of the type shown below are given

CH₃—CH —CH₂   CH₂ CH₂ CH₂   R—C—C—R
  | | | | | |
 OH   OH   OH   OH   OH OH

Propylene glycol   Trimethylene glycol   A pinacol

(1,2-Propanediol)   (1,3-Propanediol)

the special term **pinacols.** We should recall that the general method for the preparation of α-glycols involves the hydroxylation of alkenes by means of $KMnO_4$, OsO_4, or HCO_3H (Section 8-4f).

b. Triols. The most important triol is **glycerol** (glycerin, 1,2,3-propanetriol), a thick, sweet syrup obtained as a by-product in the manufacture of soap (see Section 13-9). It is widely utilized (1961 production: 139,600 tons) as a solvent, lubricant, plasticizer, sweetening agent, antifreeze, and deicing agent and in the manufacture of nitroglycerine and dynamite. Since 1938 it has also been prepared synthetically from propylene by the sequence of reactions shown below.

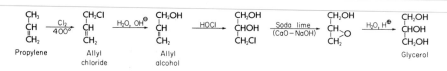

c. Higher Polyols. Higher polyols such as tetrols **(tetritols)**, pentols **(pentitols)**, and hexols **(hexitols)** are also known, and may be prepared by reduction of certain types of sugars (see Section 16-8d) or by other methods. A few representative examples are shown. Several are commercially important. Glucitol, for example, is used in medicine, as a sweetening agent, and in the manufacture of vitamin C; while pentaerythritol is employed in the manufacture of the explosive PETN (pentaerythritol tetranitrate). Higher polyols, as well as ethylene glycol and glycerol, are extremely soluble in water (recall "like dissolves like"; Section 11-3).

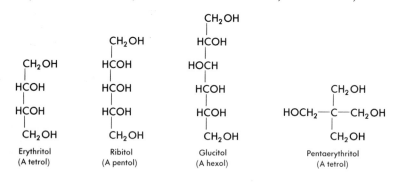

11-7. Reactions of Alcohols

Alcohols are quite reactive substances chemically, undergoing a variety of transformations which involve either the retention or the loss of their oxygen atoms. The most important types of reactions shown by alcohols are illustrated below.

a. *Oxonium Salt Formation.*   Alcohols in general, as well as other oxy-genated compounds, are soluble in sulfuric acid and other concentrated mineral acids as a result of **oxonium salt formation** (Section 6-5). Notice that the oxygen atom of the alcohol, acting as a Lewis base, is **protonated** through interaction of a pair of its unshared electrons with the proton of the acid. The resulting oxonium salt is soluble in the acidic medium by

$$R\!-\!\overset{..}{\underset{..}{O}}\!-\!H \; + \; H_2SO_4 \;\; \rightleftharpoons \;\; R\!-\!\overset{\overset{H}{|}}{\underset{..}{O}}\!-\!H^{\oplus} \; + \; HSO_4{}^{\ominus}$$

Protonated alcohol
(An oxonium cation)

virtue of the solvation of its ions (Section 2-3). Such a reaction is strictly analogous to the familiar formation of hydronium ions in water, a typical Lewis acid–Lewis base interaction. The addition of water to such oxonium salt solutions regenerates the original alcohol by a simple mass action effect.

$$H\!-\!O\!-\!H \; + \; H\!-\!Cl \;\; \rightleftharpoons \;\; H\!-\!\overset{\overset{H}{|}}{O}\!-\!H^{\oplus} \; + \; :Cl^{\ominus}$$

Hydronium ion

$$R\!-\!\overset{\overset{H}{|}}{O}\!-\!H^{\oplus} \; + \; \text{Excess } H\!-\!O\!-\!H \;\; \rightleftharpoons \;\; R\!-\!O\!-\!H \; + H\!-\!\overset{\overset{H}{|}}{O}\!-\!H^{\oplus}$$

b. *Reaction with Metals.*   Just as water reacts with sodium, alcohols react with alkali or alkaline earth metals to yield hydrogen and a **metal alkoxide**, as shown in the following typical examples. Reaction with

$$Na \; + \; CH_3CH_2OH \;\; \longrightarrow \;\; CH_3CH_2O^{\ominus}\,Na^{\oplus} \; + \; \tfrac{1}{2}H_2$$

Sodium ethoxide

$$Mg \; + \; 2\,(CH_3)_2CHOH \;\; \longrightarrow \;\; 2\,(CH_3)_2CHO^{\ominus}\,Mg^{2+} \; + \; H_2$$

Magnesium isopropoxide

alcohols is gentler than with water (explosion hazard!), and alcohols are frequently employed to destroy residual sodium after its use in certain or-ganic reactions. Primary alcohols react most readily, secondary next, and tertiary least readily with such metals. The metal salts of several alco-hols (such as sodium methoxide, NaOMe; aluminum isopropoxide, $Al(O\!-\!i\text{-}Pr)_3$; and aluminum t-butoxide, $Al(O\!-\!t\text{-}Bu)_3$) are commerci-ally available and are widely used as catalysts or reagents in organic syn-theses. Such metal salts are hydrolyzed almost completely to the original alcohol on treatment with water, since water is a stronger acid than the alcohol.

$$Na^{\oplus}\;{}^{\ominus}OR \; + \; HOH \;\; \rightleftharpoons \;\; HOR \; + \; Na^{\oplus}\;{}^{\ominus}OH$$

c. Ester Formation.   Esters are oxygen-containing products formed by the reaction of alcohols with inorganic acids, organic acids, or the corresponding acid halides. **Inorganic esters** result by *intermolecular dehydration* on merely warming an alcohol with a mineral acid, excess sulfuric acid sometimes being added to combine with the water formed. Commercially important examples of this reaction are shown in the following equations, using sulfuric, nitrous, and nitric acids, respectively. Methyl sulfate is used

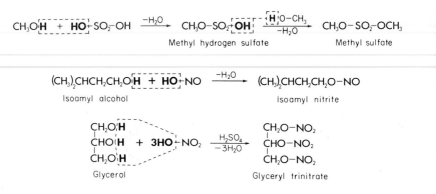

as a methylating agent in organic syntheses. Isoamyl nitrite finds application in medicine as a vasodilator in the treatment of angina pectoris. Glyceryl trinitrate ("nitroglycerin") is an important explosive, both alone and when blended with inert *diatomaceous earth* to produce **dynamite**, and it is used medicinally in the treatment of coronary attacks. Inorganic esters may also be prepared by the action of inorganic acid halides on alcohols or phenols, as in the commercially important preparation of the mixture of cresyl phosphates, which is used as a plasticizer in lacquers, hydraulic system fluid, and a lead scavenger in gasoline ("TCP").

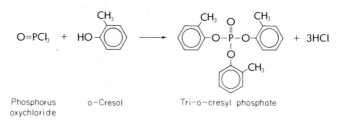

Organic esters are formed in much the same way from organic acids or acid halides, as shown in the following equations. The process is referred to as **O-acylation**, since the **acyl group**, $R—\overset{|}{C}\!\!=\!\!O$, replaces the hydrogen of the —OH function of the alcohol. These reactions will be discussed in more detail in Section 13-10.

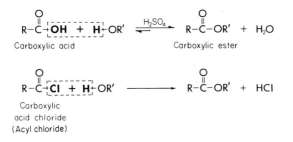

Carboxylic acid   Carboxylic ester

Carboxylic
acid chloride
(Acyl chloride)

d. Dehydrogenation and Oxidation. Primary and secondary alcohols may be **dehydrogenated** to aldehydes and ketones, respectively, if their vapors are passed over certain metal catalysts at high temperatures. Notice

$$R-CH_2-OH \underset{320°}{\overset{Cu-Ni}{\rightleftarrows}} R-CH{=}O + H_2$$

Primary alcohol   Aldehyde

$$\begin{matrix}R \\ R\end{matrix}{>}CH-OH \underset{320°}{\overset{Cu-Ni}{\rightleftarrows}} \begin{matrix}R \\ R\end{matrix}{>}C{=}O + H_2$$

Secondary alcohol   Ketone

that these reactions constitute a reversal of the previously discussed catalytic hydrogenation of aldehydes and ketones (Section 11-5a). If the dehydrogenation is conducted in the presence of air, the hydrogen produced is oxidized to water and the reaction can be caused to go to completion.

$$\begin{matrix}\\ \end{matrix}{>}CH-OH + (O) \xrightarrow[320°]{Cu-Ni} \begin{matrix}\\ \end{matrix}{>}C{=}O + H_2O$$

Tertiary alcohols, having no hydrogen atom on the carbon bearing the OH group, do not undergo dehydrogenation, but may alternatively suffer *dehydration* at sufficiently high temperatures, forming alkenes.

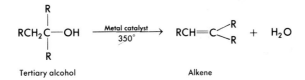

Tertiary alcohol   Alkene

The above catalytic dehydrogenations may be duplicated by the use of chemical oxidizing agents such as chromic anhydride in acetic acid, CrO_3-CH_3COOH; sodium dichromate in sulfuric acid, $Na_2Cr_2O_7-H_2SO_4$; or alkaline potassium permanganate, $KMnO_4-KOH$. Secondary alcohols produce ketones, as above. The aldehydes produced by oxidizing primary alcohols, however, are subject to further oxidation under these reaction conditions, and carboxylic acids ultimately result. By special techniques (Section 12-3a) it is often possible to isolate the intermediate aldehyde, if desired.

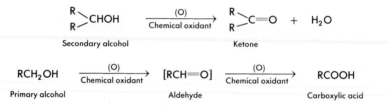

Tertiary alcohols are resistant to chemical oxidizing agents in alkaline or neutral media. With acidic oxidants (for example, $Na_2Cr_2O_7–H_2SO_4$) or under drastic conditions, however, they tend to dehydrate. The resulting alkene is then oxidized to smaller fragments, as in the following general example.

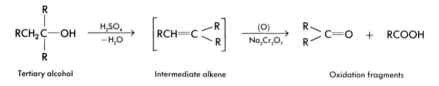

e. Conversion to Alkyl Halides. The action of HCl, HBr, and HI on alcohols results in the **replacement** of their OH function by halogen.

$$ROH + HX \longrightarrow RX + H_2O$$

We recognize this process as the reversal of the hydrolysis of an alkyl halide (Section 11-5b). The reactivities of the hydrogen halides in this reaction are in the order: HI > HBr > HCl, while the reactivities of alcohols are: allyl and benzyl > tertiary > secondary > primary. The **Lucas test** for distinguishing primary, secondary, and tertiary alcohols is based on this reaction. The alcohol is treated with $HCl–ZnCl_2$ reagent, in which it is soluble owing to oxonium salt formation (Section 11-7a). Tertiary alcohols react almost instantly, rapidly forming an insoluble layer of tertiary alkyl chloride. Secondary alcohols form an insoluble secondary chloride in 5 to 10 minutes, while primary alcohols remain in solution unreacted, and form a primary alkyl chloride only on heating.

The mechanism of this acid-catalyzed replacement reaction involves initial protonation of the alcohol, forming an oxonium salt (11-**6**). This may then be attacked directly by the nucleophilic $:X^{\ominus}$ to form water and the alkyl halide product (S_N2 mechanism; see Section 11-12d), or may undergo prior ionization to a carbonium ion (11-**7**), which then reacts with the halide ion to form the product (S_N1 mechanism; Section 11-12d). Those replacements following the latter path frequently afford rearranged prod-

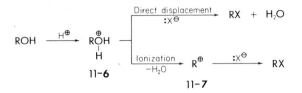

ucts, if less stable primary or secondary carbonium ions can rearrange to more stable tertiary carbonium ions before the final step involving the halide ion. Two examples of the **Wagner-Meerwein rearrangement** (Section 8-3a) attending this reaction are illustrated below.

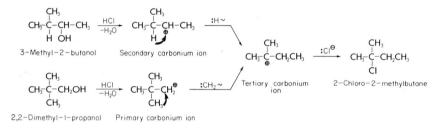

Alcohols may also be converted to alkyl halides by heating with certain inorganic acid halides, reagents less prone to induce molecular rearrangement during the replacement. General examples of this technique are shown in the following equations.

$$3\,ROH \;+\; PBr_3 \longrightarrow 3\,RBr \;+\; P(OH)_3$$

Phosphorus tribromide   Phosphorous acid

$$5\,ROH \;+\; PCl_5 \longrightarrow 5\,RCl \;+\; O{=}P(OH)_3 \;+\; H_2O$$

Phosphorus pentachloride   Phosphoric acid

$$ROH \;+\; SOCl_2 \xrightarrow{\text{1 Mole pyridine}} RCl \;+\; HCl \;+\; SO_2$$

Thionyl chloride

f. Dehydration. This important elimination reaction of alcohols, which has been discussed as a method for synthesizing alkenes (Section 8-3a), should be systematically reviewed at this point.

11-8. Reactions of Glycols

Glycols and higher polyols undergo most of the reactions characteristic also of monohydric alcohols. In particular, such higher alcohols will (under proper reaction conditions) (a) form oxonium salts, (b) react with alkali metals, (c) afford inorganic and organic esters, (d) undergo oxidation or dehydrogenation at one or more of their OH functions, and (e) suffer replacement of one or more of their OH groups by halogen atoms.

These reactions are illustrated with ethylene glycol. In addition, α-glycols

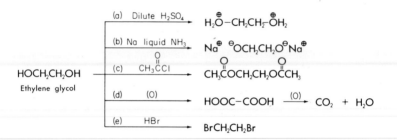

undergo the following important reactions, characteristic of this class.

a. Cleavage of α-Glycols. The inorganic oxidants periodic acid, HIO_4, and lead tetraacetate, $Pb(OCOCH_3)_4$, possess the property of cleaving α-glycols into aldehydes or ketones, with rupture of the C–C bond between the two adjacent OH-bearing carbon atoms. Note that the type of product obtained depends upon the number of groups on each OH-bearing carbon.

$$R-CH+C{\overset{R}{\underset{R}{\diagup}}} \quad \xrightarrow[HIO_4 \text{ or } Pb(OCOCH_3)_4]{(O)} \quad RCH=O \quad + \quad O=C{\overset{R}{\underset{R}{\diagup}}}$$

$$\underset{OH\ \ OH}{}$$

$\quad\quad a-Glycol \quad\quad\quad\quad\quad\quad\quad\quad\quad\quad\quad Aldehyde \quad\quad Ketone$

In cyclic α-glycols having five- and six-membered rings, *cis* isomers are cleaved more rapidly than *trans* isomers, and lead tetraacetate in acetic acid solution may be used to distinguish *cis* and *trans* cyclic α-glycols by

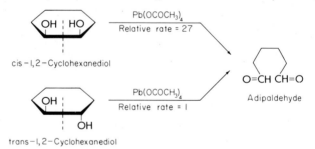

their different cleavage rates. In larger rings, conformational factors bring about a reversal in these relative cleavage rates; that is, *trans* α-glycols are cleaved more rapidly. It has been suggested that cyclic inorganic esters such as 11-**8** and 11-**9** play intermediate roles in such cleavage reactions.

$$\begin{matrix} R-CH-O \diagdown \quad \diagup OCOCH_3 \\ \quad\quad\quad Pb \\ R-CH-O \diagup \quad \diagdown OCOCH_3 \end{matrix} \quad\quad\quad \begin{matrix} \overset{OH}{} \\ R-CH-O \diagdown | \diagup O \\ \quad\quad\quad I \\ R-CH-O \diagup \diagdown O \end{matrix}$$

$$\quad\quad\quad 11-\textbf{8} \quad\quad\quad\quad\quad\quad\quad\quad\quad 11-\textbf{9}$$

Such cyclic esters would explain the greater reactivity of α-glycols having *cis*-like configurations. More recently a concerted mechanism has been proposed for the lead tetraacetate cleavage.

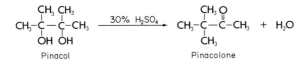

b. The Pinacol Rearrangement. In 1860 the German chemist R. Fittig discovered that hot 30 per cent sulfuric acid converted the α-glycol 2,3-dimethyl-2,3-butanediol (pinacol; Greek: *pinax*, plate; large, plate-like crystals; m.p. 41° to 43°) into the ketone pinacolone—a dehydration reaction involving molecular rearrangement. This **pinacol rearrangement**

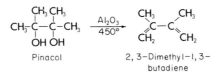

proves to be a general acid-catalyzed reaction for α-glycols, and its mechanism is believed to follow the carbonium ion path illustrated below. The

$$\underset{\underset{HO\ OH}{|}\ \underset{}{|}}{R-\overset{R}{\underset{}{C}}-\overset{R}{\underset{}{C}}-R} \xrightarrow{H^\oplus} \underset{\underset{HO\ OH_2}{\oplus}}{R-C-C-R} \xrightarrow{-H_2O} \underset{HO}{R-C-C-R} \xrightarrow{R:\sim} R-C-C-R \xrightarrow{-H^\oplus} R-C-C-R$$

sequence is to be visualized as a smooth *concerted* process, with the alkyl (or aryl) group migrating simultaneously as the OH is abstracted by the proton catalyst. We notice the fundamental similarity of this 1,2 shift with that of the Wagner-Meerwein rearrangement (Sections 8-3a and 11-7e). Pinacols may be dehydrated without rearrangement by passing their vapors over alumina (alkaline conditions) at high temperature.

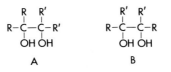

Extensive, theoretically important studies have been made on the rearrangements of *unsymmetrical* pinacols of the general structures shown below.

$$\underset{\underset{OH\ OH}{|}\ \underset{}{|}}{R-\overset{R}{\underset{}{C}}-\overset{R'}{\underset{}{C}}-R'} \qquad \underset{\underset{OH\ OH}{|}\ \underset{}{|}}{R-\overset{R'}{\underset{}{C}}-\overset{R'}{\underset{}{C}}-R}$$

A   B

Those of Type A, where there is a choice as to which hydroxyl group will be preferentially removed, prove to follow primarily that path which initially produces the *more stable* of the two possible carbonium ions, as in the following example. Those of Type B, which have two equivalent hy-

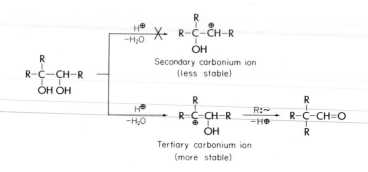

Secondary carbonium ion
(less stable)

Tertiary carbonium ion
(more stable)

droxyl groups and yield a single carbonium ion, prove ordinarily to follow that path wherein the more nucleophilic (potentially electron-rich) group preferentially migrates. Thus in the following example, the phenyl group has a greater intrinsic **migratory aptitude** than does the methyl group.

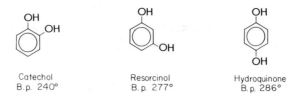

11-9. Phenols

We have seen that phenol (PhOH, m.p. 42°, b.p. 181°) is the prototype alcohol in the aromatic series. It has many chemical properties in common with aliphatic alcohols, but more important ones not shared by alcohols. For the latter reason, phenols as a class must be considered separately. The nomenclature of substituted phenols has been discussed previously (Section 11-1). Simple dihydric phenols are usually named trivially as follows. Note the lower boiling point of catechol as compared to resorcinol

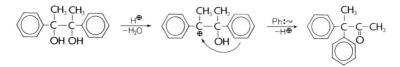

Catechol
B.p. 240°

Resorcinol
B.p. 277°

Hydroquinone
B.p. 286°

and hydroquinone, a consequence of intramolecular as opposed to intermolecular hydrogen bonding (Section 11-3). Phenols may be identified qualitatively by the characteristic color reactions they show with ferric chloride solution (**ferric chloride test**).

a. Synthesis, Sources, and Uses of Phenols. Phenol is obtained commercially both from coal tar (Section 10-2) and, synthetically, by the alkaline hydrolysis of chlorobenzene (Dow process) and the acid-catalyzed decomposition of cumene hydroperoxide. A convenient laboratory synthesis of phenols involves the fusion of arenesulfonic acids with molten alkali. Other laboratory methods will be discussed later.

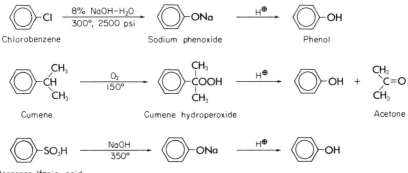

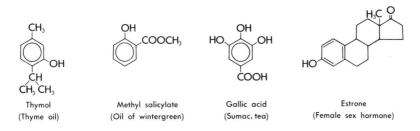

Phenols and polyhydroxybenzene compounds occur widely throughout the plant and animal kingdom, and may be derived from both monocyclic and polycyclic aromatic hydrocarbons. The following examples are representative.

Commercially phenol is extremely important, and the United States production in 1961 was some 731.3 million pounds. Phenol and its derivatives are used as disinfectants, in topical anesthetics, and as germicides. Hydroquinone and related compounds are used in photographic developers. The principal use of phenol itself is in the manufacture of phenol–formaldehyde resins and plastics, of which more than 500 million pounds are produced annually. Bakelite, an example of such a **cross-linked,** infusible polymer, has been produced commercially since 1909 (Figure 11-7).

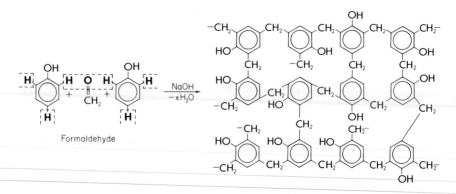

Formaldehyde

Figure 11-7.   Formation of a Phenol–Formaldehyde Polymer

b. Acidity of Phenols.   Phenols, in contrast to aliphatic alcohols, are weakly acidic. They react with sodium hydroxide, for example, to form sodium salts which are stable in water solution, as indicated in the following equation. We recall that the equilibrium point for the corresponding

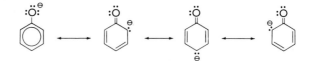

Sodium phenoxide

reaction of aliphatic alcohols lies far to the left (Section 11-7b). The enhanced acidity of phenols over alcohols is explained in terms of the resonance stabilization which is possible for the phenoxide ion (Figure 11-8), a feature not possible for alkoxide ions. When a phenol possesses electron-

Figure 11-8.   Canonical Structures for the Phenoxide Ion Hybrid

withdrawing nuclear substituents which may themselves partake in the resonance hybrid, the acidity of the phenol proves to be even greater. Thus p-nitrophenol is some 600 times stronger as an acid than is phenol because of the greater resonance stabilization of the p-nitrophenoxide anion (Figure 11-9), while 2,4,6-trinitrophenol (picric acid) is almost as strong an acid as the mineral acids.

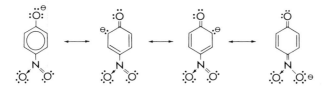

Figure 11-9.   Canonical Structures of the p-Nitrophenoxide Ion Hybrid

c. Reactions of Phenols.   The reactions of phenols fall into two classes, those involving the phenolic hydroxyl group and those involving the benzene nucleus. Many of the reactions involving the hydroxyl group are similar to analogous reactions of aliphatic alcohols, as seen in the following equations. The last reaction, **zinc dust distillation,** is often used in de-

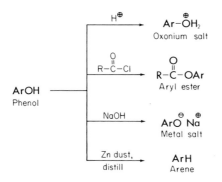

grading complex phenols into hydrocarbons for characterization purposes.

Reactions involving the aromatic nucleus of phenols are the typical substitution reactions of the benzene ring (Section 10-4b), as in the following examples of halogenation, nitration, and sulfonation. The *ortho-para-*

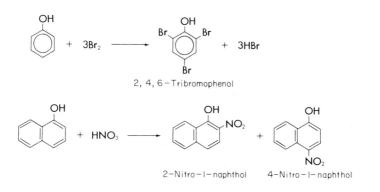

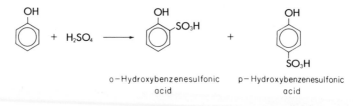

o-Hydroxybenzenesulfonic   p-Hydroxybenzenesulfonic
acid   acid

directing ability and the powerful activating effect of the phenolic hydroxyl group on the benzene ring have already been discussed in terms of the mechanism of electrophilic aromatic substitution (Section 10-5). We recall that this activation permits such substitution reactions to take place much more readily with phenols than with benzene itself. Bromination of phenol with excess bromine, for example, affords the tribromo derivative directly and instantly, whereas bromination of benzene yields only a monobromo derivative unless more vigorous reaction conditions are employed. Another illustration of the activating effect of the phenolic hydroxyl group is the **mercuration** of phenols with mercuric acetate, a reaction not shown by benzene.

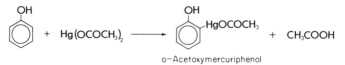

o-Acetoxymercuriphenol

Friedel-Crafts reactions are not usually undertaken with phenols as such, since the unprotected hydroxyl group reacts with aluminum chloride to form a salt

$$PhOH \ + \ AlCl_3 \ \longrightarrow \ PhOAlCl_2 \ + \ HCl$$

Derivatives of phenols such as ethers or esters, however, allow the Friedel-Crafts reaction to be applied. Thus anisole may be smoothly alkylated or acylated.

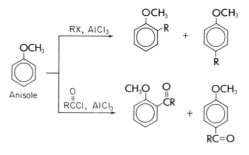

ORGANIC HALIDES

ALKYL HALIDES, RX; aryl halides, ArX; and their polyhalogen analogs are important classes of compounds from both practical and theoretical view-points. They are widely used in organic syntheses, their transformations have provided much general information on organic reaction mechanisms, and they are commercially and industrially important. Ethyl chloride, C_2H_5Cl, is widely used in the preparation of the antiknock compound tetraethyllead (Section 7-4e), while methyl bromide, CH_3Br, is used as a fumigant and gopher poison, and carbon tetrachloride, CCl_4, as a solvent, cleaning agent, and fire extinguisher. Higher alkyl chlorides (for example, amyl chlorides, $C_5H_{11}Cl$ isomers) and polychloroalkanes are employed industrially as solvents. Organic fluorides such as dichlorodifluorometh-ane, CCl_2F_2 (Freon 12), find use as nontoxic, nonflammable refrigerants and as propellants in spray-can containers. Halogen compounds comprise many of the modern pesticides such as DDT, lindane (page 225), and

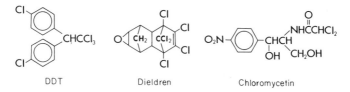

DDT   Dieldren   Chloromycetin

Dieldren; and chloromycetin, from cultures of the soil bacterium *Strepto-myces venezuelae*, is an important halogen-containing antibiotic.

11-10. Nomenclature, Physical Properties, and Characterization of Halides

Alkyl halides are named either (1) with two words, as halides of the alkyl groups to which the halogen atom is attached, or (2) as one word, following the IUPAC system. Aryl halides are named similarly. The IUPAC system is ordinarily used in the case of more complex alkyl or aryl halides. The following representative examples of mono- and polyhalides illustrate these principles, the less common name being shown paren-thetically in each case.

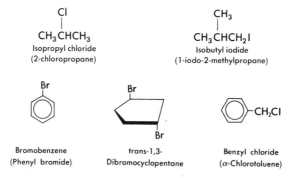

The lower alkyl chlorides are gases at room temperature, while higher alkyl and aryl halides are generally liquids. Boiling points of these compounds show the usual increase with increasing molecular weight, whether the weight increase is due to larger organic groups or to heavier halogen atoms. Thus *n*-butyl chloride, bromide, and iodide boil, respectively, at 77°, 102°, and 130°. The boiling points of alkyl chlorides are about the same as those of alkanes of comparable molecular weight (Figure 7-3), while boiling points of alkyl bromides and iodides are even lower than those of alkanes of similar molecular weight. Thus alkyl halides are *normal liquids*, and not associated like alcohols. For this reason organic halides are typically insoluble in water, but soluble in common organic solvents (like dissolves like). Alkyl halides are colorless when pure, and have a pleasant, sweetish odor. Alkyl chlorides are less dense than water, while alkyl bromides and iodides are denser than water. With the exception of polyfluoroalkanes, alkyl and aryl halides are generally quite toxic. Alkyl fluorides, RF, have chemical properties rather different from those of other alkyl halides, and are usually not considered as typical members of this class of compounds.

Alkyl halides may be recognized by their infrared spectra (RCl has characteristic absorption bands in the 750 to 700, RBr in the 600 to 500, and RI in the 500 cm^{-1} regions of the spectrum), or by way of qualitative analysis for halogen after fusion with sodium metal (Section 4-1). Formation of an insoluble silver halide precipitate on heating with alcoholic silver nitrate solution is also diagnostic for many organic halides.

11-11. Syntheses of Organic Halides

Simple organic halides may be prepared by several general methods, the more important of which are summarized below.

a. From Alcohols. We recall that HCl, HBr, and HI, as well as phosphorus halides and thionyl halides, are reagents capable of converting alcohols into alkyl halides (Section 11-7e). Alkenes are formed as minor by-products in such reactions. Tertiary alcohols tend to give the most alkene by-product, and primary alcohols the least.

b. From Alkenes. The conversion of alkenes into alkyl halides may be accomplished by addition of the appropriate hydrogen halide to the alkene (Section 8-4c).

c. From Alkanes and Arenes. The direct halogenation of alkanes is of limited synthetic value since it produces *mixtures* of alkyl halides as well as polyhalogenated alkanes (Section 7-6d). This reaction (chlorination) is conducted on an industrial scale, however, to produce chloroalkane solvents. Aryl halides may be conveniently prepared from aromatic hydrocarbons by means of direct halogenation, a typical electrophilic substitution reaction (Sections 10-4b, 10-5). Other syntheses of aryl halides will be discussed later.

d. *From Other Alkyl Halides.* The action of inorganic halides on alkyl halides frequently brings about replacement of the halogen atom of the alkyl halide. Thus alkyl iodides may be prepared by the action of sodium iodide (dissolved in acetone) on alkyl chlorides or bromides (**Finkelstein reaction**). The by-product sodium chloride or bromide is insoluble in

$$\text{RX} + \text{NaI} \xrightarrow{\text{Acetone}} \text{RI} + \text{NaX} \quad (\text{X} = \text{Cl, Br})$$

acetone and precipitates, thus driving the reaction to the right.

e. *Organic Fluorine Derivatives.* Alkyl fluorides and polyfluoroalkanes, which cannot generally be prepared by the methods in Sections 11-11a,b,c, are prepared industrially and in the laboratory by halogen replacement reactions using certain metal fluorides. The following examples are typical.

$$2\,\text{RBr} + \text{Hg}_2\text{F}_2 \longrightarrow 2\,\text{RF} + \text{Hg}_2\text{Br}_2$$

$$\text{CHCl}_3 \xrightarrow{\text{SbF}_3} \text{CHCl}_2\text{F} \xrightarrow{\text{SbF}_3} \text{CHClF}_2 \xrightarrow{\text{SbF}_3} \text{CHF}_3$$

Perfluoroalkanes (**fluorocarbons**), wherein all hydrogen atoms of an alkane have been replaced by fluorine, may be prepared by direct replacement of the hydrogens of the alkane by means of inorganic fluorides, as in the following example. Fluorocarbons, useful as inert lubricants and fabricatable polymers (see Teflon, Section 8-41), are valuable because of their extreme chemical inertness.

$$\text{CH}_3(\text{CH}_2)_4\text{CH}_3 + 28\,\text{CoF}_3 \longrightarrow \underset{\text{Perfluorohexane}}{\text{CF}_3(\text{CF}_2)_4\text{CF}_3} + 14\,\text{HF} + 28\,\text{CoF}_2$$

11-12. Reactions of Organic Halides

The principal reactions of alkyl and aryl halides are the following.

a. *Dehydrohalogenation.* We recall that the action of basic reagents such as alcoholic KOH on alkyl halides results in the formation of alkenes (Section 8-3b).

b. *Reduction.* The reduction of alkyl halides by chemical means or catalytically with hydrogen results in the formation of alkanes (Section 7-5b).

c. *Formation of Organometallic Compounds.* The formation of the synthetically important Grignard reagent, RMgX, from alkyl halides has already been discussed (Section 7-5d), and the applications of alkylmagnesium and arylmagnesium halides to the synthesis of alcohols are treated in Section 11-5e. Organometallic compounds may also be formed by the action of other metals on alkyl halides, or by the interaction of Grignard reagents on inorganic halides. The following examples are typical of such syntheses:

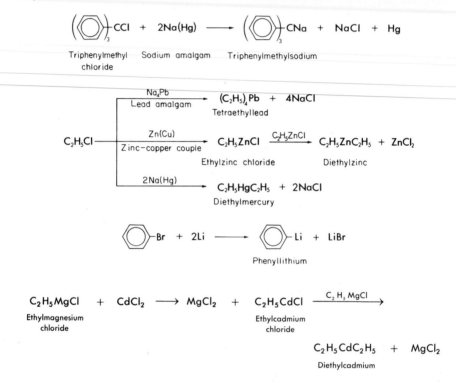

$$(\text{C}_6\text{H}_5)_3\text{CCl} + 2\text{Na(Hg)} \longrightarrow (\text{C}_6\text{H}_5)_3\text{CNa} + \text{NaCl} + \text{Hg}$$

Triphenylmethyl chloride · Sodium amalgam · Triphenylmethylsodium

$$\text{C}_2\text{H}_5\text{Cl} \xrightarrow{\begin{array}{c}\text{Na}_4\text{Pb}\\ \text{Lead amalgam}\end{array}} (\text{C}_2\text{H}_5)_4\text{Pb} + 4\text{NaCl}$$

Tetraethyllead

$$\xrightarrow{\begin{array}{c}\text{Zn(Cu)}\\ \text{Zinc-copper couple}\end{array}} \text{C}_2\text{H}_5\text{ZnCl} \xrightarrow{\text{C}_2\text{H}_5\text{ZnCl}} \text{C}_2\text{H}_5\text{ZnC}_2\text{H}_5 + \text{ZnCl}_2$$

Ethylzinc chloride · Diethylzinc

$$\xrightarrow{2\text{Na(Hg)}} \text{C}_2\text{H}_5\text{HgC}_2\text{H}_5 + 2\text{NaCl}$$

Diethylmercury

$$\text{C}_6\text{H}_5\text{-Br} + 2\text{Li} \longrightarrow \text{C}_6\text{H}_5\text{-Li} + \text{LiBr}$$

Phenyllithium

$$\text{C}_2\text{H}_5\text{MgCl} + \text{CdCl}_2 \longrightarrow \text{MgCl}_2 + \text{C}_2\text{H}_5\text{CdCl} \xrightarrow{\text{C}_2\text{H}_5\text{MgCl}}$$

Ethylmagnesium chloride · Ethylcadmium chloride

$$\text{C}_2\text{H}_5\text{CdC}_2\text{H}_5 + \text{MgCl}_2$$

Diethylcadmium

Dialkylzinc compounds are spontaneously flammable and are of little synthetic use. Organomercury compounds are used medicinally and in agriculture as fungicides. Organolithium and organocadmium compounds are frequently used in organic synthesis, and show reactions generally similar to those of the Grignard reagent, for example:

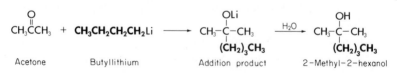

$$\underset{\text{Acetone}}{\text{CH}_3\overset{\text{O}}{\overset{\|}{\text{C}}}\text{CH}_3} + \underset{\text{Butyllithium}}{\text{CH}_3\text{CH}_2\text{CH}_2\text{CH}_2\text{Li}} \longrightarrow \underset{\text{Addition product}}{\text{CH}_3\underset{(\text{CH}_2)_3\text{CH}_3}{\overset{\text{OLi}}{\underset{|}{\overset{|}{\text{C}}}}}\text{CH}_3} \xrightarrow{\text{H}_2\text{O}} \underset{\text{2-Methyl-2-hexanol}}{\text{CH}_3\underset{(\text{CH}_2)_3\text{CH}_3}{\overset{\text{OH}}{\underset{|}{\overset{|}{\text{C}}}}}\text{CH}_3}$$

Like the Grignard reagent, many organometallic compounds are hydrolyzed by water into the corresponding hydrocarbon. Heavy metal organo-

$$R\text{—}Metal\text{—}X \ + \ H_2O \ \longrightarrow \ R\text{—}H \ + \ HO\text{—}Metal\text{—}X$$

metallic compounds such as R_2Hg, however, have more stable carbon-to-metal bonds, and require strong acid to bring about such a decomposition.

d. Nucleophilic Substitution Reactions. A very important class of reactions shown by alkyl halides involves the displacement of the halogen atom of the halide by a **nucleophilic** (electron-rich nucleus-seeking; see Section 6-5) **agent.** This agent may be either an organic or inorganic anion or a

$$R:X \ + \ :Z^{\ominus} \ \longrightarrow \ R:Z \ + \ :X^{\ominus}$$
Nucleophilic
agent

neutral molecule containing an unshared pair of electrons. In short, nucleophilic agents are Lewis bases (Section 6-5). This type of reaction, referred to as a **nucleophilic substitution** or **displacement,** is extremely important synthetically, as can be seen (Figure 11-10) by the wide variety of compounds which can be prepared by its application.

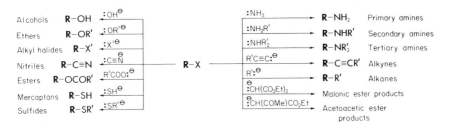

Figure 11-10. Synthetic Applications of the Nucleophilic Displacement Reaction

Nucleophilic substitution reactions have been studied quite extensively from a mechanistic viewpoint. They prove to fall into two classes mechanistically, and it will be profitable here to digress briefly and consider these two general mechanisms. Substitution reactions in which the reactant slowly ionizes to produce a carbonium ion, which then reacts rapidly with a nucleophile in its environment, are referred to as S_N1 **reactions** (substitution, nucleophilic, first order), since they obey the rate expression:

$$\text{Rate} \ = \ k\,[RX]$$

We see from this expression that the rate of S_N1 reactions depends only on the concentration of the substrate RX, and not on the concentration of the nucleophilic agent reacting with it. Since carbonium ions are flat (Section 6-6c), we might expect such two-step S_N1 reactions to yield

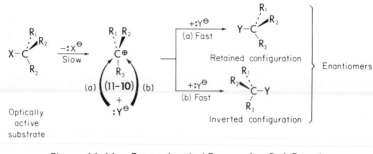

Figure 11-11. *Stereochemical Course of an S_N1 Reaction*

racemic products from optically active (Section 2-8d) substrates, as shown in Figure 11-11. That is, if the intermediate carbonium ion (11-**10**) is attacked by the nucleophile $Y:^{\ominus}$ with equal probability on either side of its plane, equal amounts of each enantiomeric product should result. In practice, substantial and often complete racemization does in fact attend S_N1 reactions. However, depending on the reaction conditions and on the nature of the groups R_1, R_2, and R_3 on the carbonium ion (11-**10**), there may be a preferred side for its attack by $:Y^{\ominus}$, in which case the product will contain unequal amounts of the two enantiomers and be partially optically active.

A second type of nucleophilic displacement reaction, called S_N2 (substitution, nucleophilic, second order), is also frequently encountered. Kinetically, this type of displacement obeys the rate law:

$$\text{Rate} = k[RX][Y]$$

Notice that here the reaction rate depends on the concentrations of *both* the substrate RX and the nucleophile Y. In S_N2 displacements there is a *synchronous attack* by the nucleophile Y upon the *rear face* of the carbon atom of the substrate bearing the reactive substituent X, such that C–X bond of the substrate breaks only as the new C–Y bond of the product is forming (Figure 11-12). We see that a "full blown" free carbonium ion is not generated in an S_N2 displacement, but that the *transition state* of the reaction

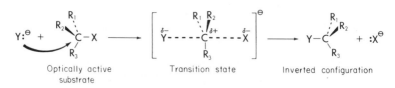

Figure 11-12. *Stereochemical Course of an S_N2 Reaction*

involves a central carbon atom which has carbonium ion character. The stereochemical consequence of S_N2 reactions involves *inversion of the original configuration* of the substrate, and the product is optically active if, as in Figure 11-12, the substrate and product possess four unlike substituents (Section 2-8d). S_N2 reactions are thus said to proceed with **Walden inversion,** named after P. Walden, a German chemist who first pointed out this phenomenon in 1895. The configurational change occurring during Walden inversion has been likened to "an umbrella turning inside out in the wind."

Nucleophilic substitution reactions of the type shown in Figure 11-10 may proceed via an S_N1 mechanism, an S_N2 mechanism, or a "mixed mechanism" which partakes kinetically and stereochemically of the characteristics of both extremes. The mechanistic path followed in a particular case depends both upon the reaction conditions and upon the structure of the substrate undergoing displacement and can often be varied at will. S_N1 mechanisms are favored, for example, in highly polar (ionization-promoting) solvents, with low concentrations of attacking nucleophile $(:Y^\ominus)$, and with weak (that is, less nucleophilic) nucleophiles. Since the various nucleophilic agents in Figure 11-10 are all Lewis bases of varying base strength, and since bases also promote the dehydrohalogenation of alkyl halides, such nucleophilic displacement reactions are often attended by varying extents of by-product alkene formation, which may occur by either the $E1$ or the $E2$ mechanism (Section 8-3b). Alkene formation rather than nucleophilic substitution may become the predominant reaction in the case of stronger bases (for example, $:OH^\ominus$ instead of H_2O as nucleophile) or with tertiary halides. Those nucleophilic displacements which occur by an S_N1 mechanism may be accompanied by the Wagner-Meerwein rearrangement (Sections 8-3a and 11-7e), if the intermediate carbonium ion produced in the slow ionization step (Figure 11-11) can rearrange to a more stable carbonium ion before it reacts rapidly and irreversibly with the nucleophile in its environment to form the product. Reactions proceeding exclusively via the S_N2 mechanism afford unrearranged (but configurationally inverted) products.

11-13. Structure and Reactivity of Organic Halides

In substitution reactions of alkyl halides of the sort discussed above, tertiary halides prove to react most rapidly, doing so primarily by way of

RCH₂X

Primary alkyl halide   Secondary alkyl halide   Tertiary alkyl halide

an $S_N 1$ mechanism, while primary alkyl halides are least reactive, reacting mainly through an $S_N 2$ mechanism. Secondary alkyl halides show intermediate reactivity, and often react via a "mixed mechanism" having characteristics of both extremes. Allyl halides, $RCH=CHCH_2X$, and benzyl halides, $ArCH_2X$, are extremely reactive (more so than tertiary halides), and usually react by way of an $S_N 1$ mechanism, because of the relatively great stability of the resonance hybrid allyl and benzyl carbonium ion intermediates (Section 6-6b). The hybrid nature of the allyl carbonium ion intermediate is confirmed in the $S_N 1$ hydrolysis of allyl bromide labeled at C1 with radioactive carbon. In the allyl alcohol product, the label is uniformly distributed between C1 and C3. In displacement reactions of

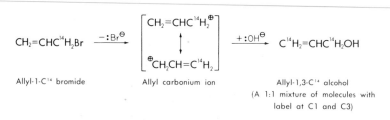

Allyl-1-C¹⁴ bromide   Allyl carbonium ion   Allyl-1,3-C¹⁴ alcohol
                                                          (A 1:1 mixture of molecules with
                                                          label at C1 and C3)

substituted allyl halides, this situation often results in the formation of re-arranged products (**allylic rearrangement**). Thus in the hydrolysis of 1-bromo-3-methyl-2-butene (11-**11**), for example, the hybrid carbonium ion intermediate 11-**12** engenders both an unrearranged alcohol (11-**13**) and a rearranged alcohol (11-**14**) by reaction of the nucleophile (:OH$^\ominus$ or H_2O) at *both* sites of electron deficiency within the carbonium ion.

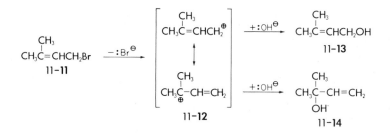

Ordinarily, as we have seen, $S_N 2$ reactions do not lead to rearranged products. Occasionally, however, allyllic halides react with $S_N 2$ kinetic behavior, but afford at the same time *rearranged* products. The mechanism for this type of reaction is believed to involve a concerted attack by the nucleophile on C3 of the allylic system, with simultaneous expulsion of a halide ion (Figure 11-13). Such a mechanism is referred to as S_N2', to distinguish it from the normal S_N2 process.

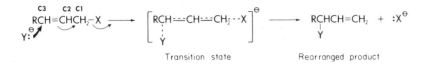

Figure 11-13. S_N2' Reaction Leading to Allylic Rearrangement

In contrast to halides of the above types, vinyl halides, RCH=CHX, and aryl halides, ArX, are quite inert in nucleophilic substitutions, reacting, if at all, only under drastic and "forcing" conditions. The low reactivity of such halides is attributed to resonance interaction between the unshared p electrons of the halogen atom and the π electrons of the adjacent ring or double bond (Figure 11-14). This resonance results in a

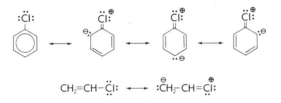

Figure 11-14. Resonance Hybrids of Chlorobenzene and Vinyl Chloride

stronger carbon-halogen bond in these halides, leading to their lower reactivity. The double bond character in the carbon-halogen bonds of such halides is reflected in their shortened C–X bond length. Vinyl chloride, for example, has a C–Cl bond measuring 1.69 Å, whereas the normal C–Cl bond distance in most alkyl chlorides is about 1.77 Å. However, when electron-withdrawing (*meta*-directing; Section 10-6) groups are located in a position *ortho* or *para* to the halogen atom of an aryl halide, reactivity toward nucleophilic substitution is enhanced. Thus *p*-nitrochlorobenzene is considerably more reactive than chlorobenzene, while 2,4,6-trinitrochlorobenzene (picryl chloride) has a very easily replaceable chlorine atom.

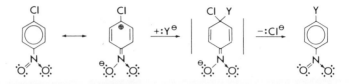

Figure 11-15. "Activation" of a Halogen Atom on the Benzene Ring by a Nitro Substituent

In Figure 11-15 we see how the nitro group in *p*-nitrochlorobenzene places a formal positive charge on the ring carbon adjacent to chlorine in one of the canonical resonance forms, and thus *activates* this ring carbon for attack by a nucleophile.

Under appropriate conditions aryl halides are also capable of undergoing replacement reactions by a completely different mechanism. When treated with very strong bases such as sodamide, $Na^{\oplus}NH_2^{\ominus}$, or certain metal alkoxides (such as $Me_3CO^{\ominus}K^{\oplus}$), for example, aryl halides undergo successive elimination-addition reactions which are believed to involve **benzyne** intermediates. Thus sodamide in liquid ammonia converts bromobenzene into aniline, while potassium *t*-butoxide in dimethyl sulfoxide (followed by addition of *t*-butyl alcohol) converts it into phenyl *t*-butyl ether. Notice that the hypothetical benzyne intermediate is formed by elimination of HBr from adjacent carbon atoms, and reacts by addition to its triple bond.

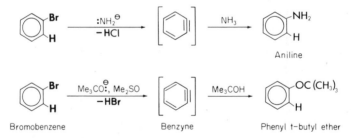

Experimental evidence for a benzyne intermediate, as postulated by Professor J. D. Roberts at the California Institute of Technology in 1953, comes from the following observations. When chlorobenzene labeled at C1 with isotopic carbon reacts with potassium amide, the aniline product has

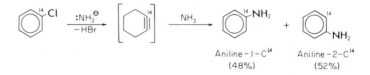

its label about equally distributed between C1 and C2, indicating a symmetrical intermediate. Similarly, when substituted halobenzenes react, isomeric amine products are formed, as shown in the following examples with *m*-chlorotoluene. Lastly, bromomesitylene fails to react with

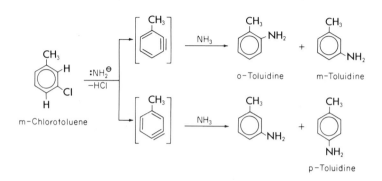

sodamide in liquid ammonia, since there is no hydrogen atom on the carbon adjacent to that bearing the halogen atom, and HBr elimination to form the benzyne intermediate therefore cannot occur.

Bromomesitylene

ETHERS

ETHERS COMPRISE a class of compounds in which two hydrocarbon-like groups are linked to an oxygen atom; that is, their general structure is of the type ROR. In **symmetrical ethers** the two groups are identical, while **unsymmetrical ethers** have nonidentical groups.

11-14. Nomenclature, Physical Properties, and Characterization of Ethers

The following examples illustrate the common method of naming ethers, the names being derived from the alkyl or aryl substituents attached to the

$C_2H_5OC_2H_5$	⟨⟩-O-⟨⟩	$C_2H_5OCH(CH_3)_2$	⟨⟩-OCH$_3$
Ethyl ether	Phenyl ether	Ethyl isopropyl ether	Methyl phenyl ether
	Symmetrical ethers		Unsymmetrical ethers

oxygen atom. IUPAC nomenclature for ethers looks upon the simpler group attached to the oxygen atom as providing an alkoxy, RO—, or aroxy, ArO—, substituent, which in turn is substituted at a numbered position in the larger group attached to the oxygen.

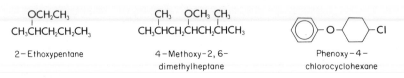

2−Ethoxypentane   4−Methoxy−2, 6−   Phenoxy−4−
dimethylheptane   chlorocyclohexane

Methyl ether (b.p. −24°) and methyl ethyl ether (b.p. 8°) are gases at room temperature. Above ethyl ether (b.p. 35°), ethers are liquids whose boiling points increase regularly with increasing molecular weight. Branching in one or both of the alkyl groups gives rise to isomers having lower boiling points, as illustrated below. Straight-chain ethers have boiling

$$CH_3CH_2CH_2OCH_2CH_2CH_3$$
Propyl ether
B.p. 91°

$$CH_3CH_2CH_2OCHCH_3$$
with CH_3 substituent
Propyl isopropyl ether
B.p. 86°

$$CH_3CHOCHCH_3$$
with CH_3 CH_3 substituents
Isopropyl ether
B.p. 68°

points roughly similar to those of normal alkanes of comparable molecular weight (compare, for example, $C_2H_5OC_2H_5$, mol. wt. 74, b.p. 35°, with $CH_3CH_2CH_2CH_2CH_3$, mol. wt. 72, b.p. 36°), indicating that ethers are normal, *nonassociated* liquids. The hydrogen bonding (Section 11-3) which gives rise to association between alcohol molecules is not possible in ethers, since they contain hydrogen atoms bonded only to carbon. The oxygen atom of ethers may hydrogen bond with other molecules, however. Thus ethers are soluble in water to about the same extent as alcohols of comparable molecular weight (for example, $C_2H_5OC_2H_5$ and $CH_3CH_2CH_2CH_2OH$, solubility about 8 g/100 ml of water at 25°), a fact attributable to hydrogen bonding between the oxygen atoms of the ether and the protons of the water molecule (Figure 11-16).

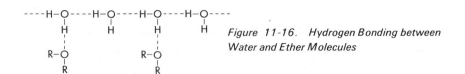

Figure 11-16. Hydrogen Bonding between Water and Ether Molecules

A large number of cyclic ethers are known, and many are commercially important. Cyclic ethers having three-membered heterocyclic rings are called **epoxides**, and will be discussed later. Those with larger rings are named as heterocyclic compounds or as **oxacycloalkanes**, the prefix *oxa-* indicating a replacement of a —CH$_2$— group by a hetero oxygen atom in the cycloalkane rings. Examples are shown below.

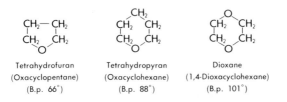

Tetrahydrofuran	Tetrahydropyran	Dioxane
(Oxacyclopentane)	(Oxacyclohexane)	(1,4-Dioxacyclohexane)
(B.p. 66°)	(B.p. 88°)	(B.p. 101°)

Ethers have limited reactivity but can be characterized chemically after cleavage (Section 11-17b). They can be recognized by their infrared spectra; the C—O—C unsymmetrical stretching frequencies are approximately 1100 cm^{-1} for aliphatic ethers and between 1270 and 1230 cm^{-1} for aryl ethers.

11-15. Occurrence and Uses of Ethers

The ether linkage, —O—, particularly in a methoxy group, CH$_3$O—, or as part of a heterocyclic ring, occurs in a wide variety of natural products, many of which have biological or practical significance. Two typical examples are shown below.

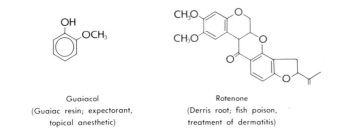

Guaiacol	Rotenone
(Guaiac resin; expectorant,	(Derris root; fish poison,
topical anesthetic)	treatment of dermatitis)

Ethyl ether, which must be prepared synthetically, is a central nervous system depressant. It has enjoyed wide medical application as a general anesthetic since its first use in surgery by Dr. C. W. Long at Jefferson, Georgia, in 1842. Tetrahydrofuran is used as a solvent in polymer fabrication, and both it and ethyl ether are widely employed as solvents in organic laboratory work, particularly in the preparation of Grignard reagents and for metal hydride reductions. For these purposes ordinary ethyl ether must be rendered absolute (that is, free of moisture, ethanol, and peroxides) by preliminary drying over sulfuric acid and distillation, followed by storage over sodium metal. Ethyl ether is probably the most common extraction solvent (Section 3-1) employed in the laboratory. The fire hazards due to its volatility and flammability, however, should be emphasized.   Phenyl ether (73.5 per cent) mixed with biphenyl (Ph—Ph, 26.5 per cent) comprises the commercial heat exchange liquid, Dowtherm (m.p. 12°, b.p. 260°, thermally stable above 400°).

11-16. Synthesis of Ethers

Ethers may be prepared by several general methods, of which the following are the most important.

a. Intermolecular Dehydration of Alcohols.   Under proper conditions the action of sulfuric acid on aliphatic alcohols affords *symmetrical* alkyl ethers by *intermolecular* dehydration.   Since secondary and tertiary alcohols

$$RO{-}H \ + \ HO{-}R \xrightarrow{H_2SO_4} ROR \ + \ H_2O$$

undergo *intramolecular* dehydration with considerable ease to form alkenes (Section 8-3a), application of this synthesis is usually limited in practice to primary alcohols. The mechanism of this reaction is believed to involve the formation of an intermediate carbonium ion (11-**16**) by loss of water from the protonated alcohol 11-**15**. The carbonium ion then reacts with

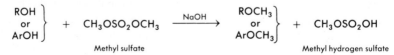

$$
\begin{array}{ccccccc}
& & & \text{Alkene} & & ROSO_3H \ + \ (RO)_2SO_2 & \\
& & & & & \text{11-18} \quad\quad \text{11-19} & \\
ROH \xrightleftharpoons{+H^\oplus} & R\overset{\oplus}{O}H_2 \xrightleftharpoons{-H_2O} & R^\oplus \xrightleftharpoons{+ROH} & \underset{H}{R\overset{\oplus}{O}R} \xrightarrow{-H^\oplus} & ROR \\
\text{11-15} & \text{11-16} & \text{11-17} &
\end{array}
$$

additional alcohol to form the protonated ether 11-**17**, which subsequently loses a proton to yield the ether product. The carbonium ion 11-**16** may also lose a proton to form an alkene (Section 8-3a), or may react with sulfuric acid to form an alkyl hydrogen sulfate (11-**18**) and/or alkyl sulfate (11-**19**) (Section 11-7c). These types of compounds tend to be by-products of the reaction. Ethyl ether is prepared commercially from ethanol by this reaction sequence, as well as from ethylene (Section 8-4d).

b. With Methyl Sulfate.   A common method for the synthesis of *unsymmetrical* methyl alkyl (or aryl) ethers involves the action of commercially available methyl sulfate (highly toxic!) on alcohols or phenols. The reaction is conducted under alkaline conditions.

$$
\left.\begin{array}{c} ROH \\ \text{or} \\ ArOH \end{array}\right\} \ + \ CH_3OSO_2OCH_3 \xrightarrow{NaOH} \left.\begin{array}{c} ROCH_3 \\ \text{or} \\ ArOCH_3 \end{array}\right\} \ + \ CH_3OSO_2OH
$$

$$\qquad\qquad\qquad\quad \text{Methyl sulfate} \qquad\qquad\qquad\qquad\qquad\qquad\quad \text{Methyl hydrogen sulfate}$$

c. Williamson Synthesis. The nucleophilic displacement of a halide ion from an alkyl halide by the action of an alkoxide or phenoxide ion as a nucleophile (Section 11-12d; Figure 11-10) provides a general method for the preparation of both symmetrical and unsymmetrical ethers (**William-son synthesis**). Since alkoxides are strong bases which promote the

$$RO^{\ominus} Na^{\oplus} \;+\; R'X \;\longrightarrow\; ROR' \;+\; Na^{\oplus} X^{\ominus}$$

dehydrohalogenation of alkyl halides (Section 8-3b), this synthesis is useful in practice only with primary alkyl halides, secondary and tertiary halides yielding primarily alkenes under these conditions. A modification of the Williamson synthesis which largely avoids this difficulty involves the reaction of an alcohol with an alkyl halide in the presence of solid silver oxide.

$$2\,ROH \;+\; 2\,R'X \;+\; Ag_2O \;\longrightarrow\; 2\,ROR' \;+\; 2\,AgX \;+\; H_2O$$

11-17. Reactions of Ethers

Ethers as a class are chemically inert, undergoing only a relatively few characteristic reactions. For this reason, OH groups of alcohols are frequently "protected" by temporary conversion to OCH_3 groups during the course of an organic synthesis involving reactions, for example, which would destroy the OH function or be prevented by its presence. The OH groups may then be regenerated (Section 11-17b) at a later stage in the synthesis. The most important reactions of ethers are the following.

a. Oxonium Salt Formation. Ethers are soluble in strong mineral acids by virtue of oxonium salt formation, the oxygen atom of the ether fulfilling the function of a Lewis base. Other Lewis acids react with ethers in a

$$R\overset{\cdot\cdot}{\underset{\cdot\cdot}{O}}R \;+\; H_2SO_4 \;\rightleftharpoons\; R\overset{\oplus}{\underset{\underset{H}{|}}{O}}R \;+\; HSO_4^{\ominus}$$

Oxonium salt of ether

similar fashion. Thus boron fluoride yields stable "etherates" with a number of ethers, and there is evidence that the magnesium atom in

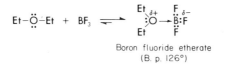

$$Et-\overset{\cdot\cdot}{\underset{\cdot\cdot}{O}}-Et \;+\; BF_3 \;\rightleftharpoons\; $$

Boron fluoride etherate
(B. p. 126°)

Grignard reagents is solvated with two molecules of ethyl ether when prepared in this solvent.

$$\text{RX} + \text{Mg} + 2\text{Et}-\overset{..}{\underset{..}{\text{O}}}-\text{Et} \rightleftharpoons R-\overset{\overset{\overset{\delta+}{\text{Et}-\overset{..}{\text{O}}-\text{Et}}}{\uparrow}}{\underset{\underset{\underset{\delta+}{\text{Et}-\underset{..}{\text{O}}-\text{Et}}}{\uparrow}}{\overset{\delta-}{\text{Mg}}-\text{X}}}$$

Alkylmagnesium halide etherate

A class of naturally occurring oxonium salts known as **anthocyanins** is mainly responsible for the red, violet, and blue colors of flowers. The heterocyclic structure on which these pigments are based is the 2-phenyl-benzopyrylium (flavylium) cation, which appears to be a resonance hybrid of the canonical structures in Figure 11-17. This oxonium cation, substi-

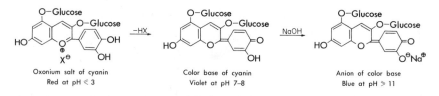

Figure 11-17. Resonance Hybrid of the Flavylium Cation

tuted with oxygen-bearing functions at various of its ring positions, comprises the anthocyanin pigments, the colors of which vary with the pH (and other factors) of the cell sap of the flowers. The first such pigment to be characterized (by Willstätter and Everest in 1913) was cyanin, which occurs in the rose, poppy, and cornflower. Its color changes with pH are interpreted in terms of the following structural changes. Acid hydrolysis

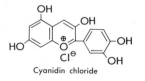

of the anthocyanins yields a sugar (frequently glucose, $C_6H_{12}O_6$) and a sugar-free oxonium salt referred to as an **anthocyanidin**. Thus hydrolysis of cyanin with hydrochloric acid affords glucose and cyanidin chloride.

Cyanidin chloride

b. Cleavage by Acids. Hydrogen halides (with reactivities: HI > HBr > HCl) are capable of cleaving the ether linkage upon heating. Aliphatic ethers yield two moles of an alkyl halide, whereas alkyl aryl ethers yield one mole each of an alkyl halide and a phenol. With HI, this type of

$$ROR' + HX \longrightarrow RX + R'OH$$
$$\xrightarrow{\quad HX \quad} R'X + H_2O$$

$$ArOR + HX \longrightarrow ArOH + RX$$

reaction may be conducted quantitatively to determine the number of methoxyl, $CH_3O—$, groups present in a complex ether. The CH_3I produced is distilled into $AgNO_3$ solution, quantitatively producing AgI. The weight of AgI formed permits a calculation of the number of methoxyl groups present in the molecule (**Zeisel methoxyl determination**). Other Lewis acids such as $AlCl_3$ and BF_3 are also capable of cleaving ethers on heating. The mechanism of ether cleavage is thought to involve a nucleophilic displacement (S_N1 or S_N2) by halide ion on the oxonium salt of the ether.

$$R-\overset{\oplus}{\underset{\underset{H}{|}}{O}}-R + :X^{\ominus} \xrightarrow{\quad S_N1 \text{ or } S_N2 \quad} RX + ROH$$

c. Peroxide Formation. On standing in contact with air, ethers slowly undergo spontaneous **autoxidation**, producing extremely unstable peroxide derivatives. These constitute a serious hazard during ether

$$CH_3CH_2OCH_2CH_3 \xrightarrow{O_2} \underset{\underset{OOH}{|}}{CH_3CHOCH_2CH_3} \longrightarrow \left(\underset{\underset{CH_3}{|}}{CHOO}\right)_x + CH_3CH_2OH$$

1-Ethoxyethyl hydroperoxide   Ethylidene peroxide polymer (explosive)

distillation since the peroxide concentrates in the undistilled residue where it is exposed to prolonged heating. Violent explosions thus may result on distilling ethers containing peroxides. The presence of peroxides may be detected by shaking the ether with a solution of ferrous ammonium sulfate and potassium thiocyanate (blood-red color of ferric thiocyanate complex), or by shaking with mercury (black color of HgO). Ethers may be freed of peroxides by shaking with an acidic solution of ferrous sulfate, among other methods. Peroxide formation may be prevented by storing the ether in the presence of iron wire, sodium, or other reducing agents. Ethers should never be distilled until the absence of peroxides has been demonstrated.

d. The Claisen Rearrangement. The interesting **Claisen rearrangement**, specific for *aryl allyl ethers*, $ArOCH_2CH=CH_2$, occurs when such ethers are heated. In this rearrangement the allyl group migrates from the ether oxygen to a position *ortho* to this oxygen. Studies with C^{14}-labeled phenyl allyl ether have shown that the allyl group "flips over" in the process, as indicated in the following *cyclic* mechanism. If both *ortho* positions in such

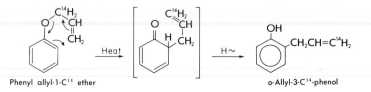

Phenyl allyl-1-C^{14} ether   o-Allyl-3-C^{14}-phenol

ethers are blocked, migration takes place to the *para* position, *without* a flipover (or with a *double* flipover) of the allyl group.

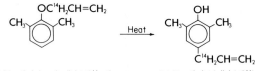

2,6-Dimethylphenyl allyl-1-C^{14} ether   2,6-Dimethyl-4-(allyl-1-C^{14})phenol

SULFUR ANALOGS OF ALCOHOLS AND ETHERS

IT IS WORTHWHILE examining briefly the sulfur analogs of alcohols and ethers. A number of compounds of these types are found in nature, and their chemistry provides for us some novel features.

11-18. Mercaptans

The sulfur analogs of alcohols, having the type formula RSH, are toxic substances called **mercaptans**. Their characteristic —SH function is variously called **thiol, mercapto,** or **sulfhydryl**. The distinguishing physical characteristic of mercaptans is their vile and repulsive odor, which diminishes with increasing molecular weight. The nose can detect one part of ethyl mercaptan (thioethanol, C_2H_5SH) in 50 billion parts of air, and the skunk depends upon this class of compounds for protection from its enemies. Mercaptans boil at much lower temperatures than do the corresponding alcohols (for example, EtSH, b.p. 36°; EtOH, b.p. 78°) and fairly close to alkanes of comparable molecular weight, indicating a lack of hydrogen bonding in mercaptans which results from the lower electronegativity (Section 2-2d) of sulfur compared to oxygen. The inability of the sulfur atom to partake in hydrogen bonds is also reflected in the lower water solubility of mercaptans as compared to alcohols.

Primary mercaptans result from a nucleophilic displacement reaction by metal hydrosulfides on primary alkyl halides (Figure 11-10). The basic

$$CH_3CH_2CH_2Br + Na^{\oplus}SH^{\ominus} \longrightarrow CH_3CH_2CH_2SH + Na^{\oplus}Br^{\ominus}$$

Sodium hydrosulfide   Propyl mercaptan
(1-Propanethiol)

$:SH^{\ominus}$ anion dehydrohalogenates secondary and particularly tertiary alkyl halides, and this reaction is therefore unsuitable for the preparation of secondary and tertiary mercaptans. To prepare the latter types the general reaction involving hydrolysis of an **S-alkylthiuronium bromide** may be employed, as illustrated below.

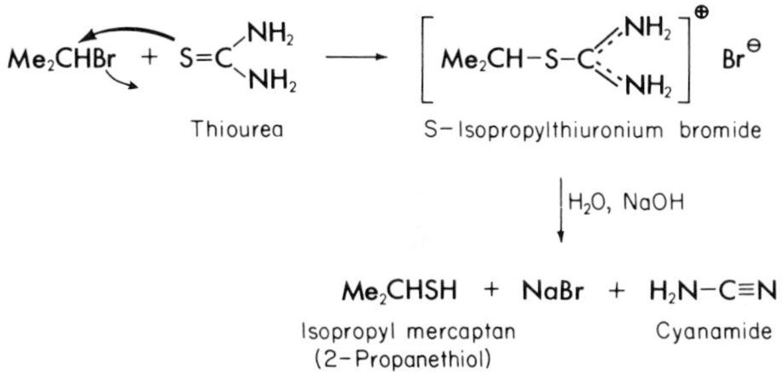

$$Me_2CHBr + S=C\begin{smallmatrix}NH_2\\NH_2\end{smallmatrix} \longrightarrow \left[Me_2CH-S-C\begin{smallmatrix}NH_2\\NH_2\end{smallmatrix} \right]^{\oplus} Br^{\ominus}$$

Thiourea   S-Isopropylthiuronium bromide

$\downarrow H_2O, NaOH$

$$Me_2CHSH + NaBr + H_2N-C\equiv N$$

Isopropyl mercaptan   Cyanamide
(2-Propanethiol)

Mercaptans are fairly acidic substances, readily forming water-soluble salts with alkalies (for example, $EtS^{\ominus}Na^{\oplus}$, sodium ethylmercaptide) and insoluble salts with heavy metals (for example, PhSHgSPh, mercury phenyl mercaptide). Under mild oxidizing conditions they form disulfides, while more vigorous oxidation converts them to sulfonic acids.

$$PhSH \underset{Reduction}{\overset{Gentle\ (O),\ H_2O_2}{\rightleftharpoons}} PhS-SPh$$

Thiophenol   Phenyl disulfide
(Phenyl mercaptan)

$$CH_3CH_2CH_2CH_2SH \xrightarrow{Vigorous\ (O),\ HNO_3} CH_3CH_2CH_2CH_2-SO_2-OH$$

Butyl mercaptan   Butanesulfonic acid

11-19. Sulfides

Alkyl sulfides, RSR', and aryl sulfides, $ArSAr'$, are the sulfur analogs of the corresponding ethers. Such compounds occur in nature in plants of the onion and garlic family and are responsible for the odors and flavors of such species. Symmetrical sulfides may be prepared by the action of sodium sulfide on alkyl halides (except tertiary), while unsymmetrical

$$2\ CH_3CH_2Br + Na_2S \longrightarrow CH_3CH_2SCH_2CH_3 + 2\ NaBr$$

Ethyl sulfide

sulfides result on reaction of sodium mercaptides with alkyl halides. Note that the latter reaction is analogous to the Williamson ether synthesis (Section 11-16c).

$$CH_3CH_2CH_2Br + Na^{\oplus\ominus}SPh \longrightarrow CH_3CH_2CH_2SPh + NaBr$$

Sodium thiophenylate
(Phenyl mercaptide)

Propyl phenyl sulfide

Sulfides react with alkyl halides to form crystalline *sulfonium salts*, which

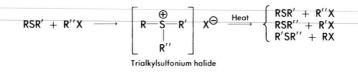

Trialkylsulfonium halide

decompose back to sulfides and halides on heating. The oxidation of sulfides occurs in two discrete steps, and may be controlled to yield either **sulfoxides** or **sulfones**, as illustrated in the following typical case.

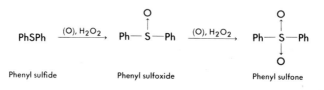

Phenyl sulfide   Phenyl sulfoxide   Phenyl sulfone

An important degradative reaction common to organic sulfur compounds in general is their **desulfuration** with **Raney nickel**, a very finely divided form of nickel having hydrogen adsorbed on its surface. Raney nickel is prepared by the action of sodium hydroxide on nickel-aluminum alloy. When organic sulfur compounds are heated with Raney nickel in

$$Ni-Al + NaOH + H_2O \longrightarrow Ni(H) + NaAlO_2 + H_2$$

Raney nickel

ethanol solvent, they are converted into hydrocarbons, the sulfur being removed as nickel sulfide. Raney nickel is also an excellent catalyst for the hydrogenation of alkenes, alkynes, and aromatic rings (Sections 8-4a, 9-4b, and 9-7a).

$$\left.\begin{array}{l} RSH \\ RSR \\ R-SO-R \\ R-SO_2-R \end{array}\right\} + Ni(H) \xrightarrow{EtOH,\ heat} RH + NiS + (H_2O)$$

SUPPLEMENTARY READING

1. "Hydrogen Bonding and the Physical Properties of Substances," L. N. Ferguson, *J. Chem. Educ.*, **33,** 267 (1956).
2. "The Evidence from Infrared Spectroscopy for Hydrogen Bonding," M. Gorman, *J. Chem. Educ.*, **34,** 304 (1957).
3. "Azeotropism. A Useful Tool Clarified," K. B. Fleer, *J. Chem. Educ.*, **22,** 588 (1945).
4. "Glycerin—Man's Most Versatile Chemical Servant," M. A. Lesser, *J. Chem. Educ.*, **26,** 327 (1949).
5. "The Chemistry of Organometallic Compounds," C. A. Kraus, *J. Chem. Educ.*, **26,** 45 (1949).
6. "The Walden Inversion in Nucleophilic Aliphatic Substitution Reactions," C. L. Deasy, *J. Chem. Educ.*, **22,** 82 (1945).
7. "Unexpected Rearrangement and Lack of Rearrangement in Allylic Systems," W. G. Young, *J. Chem. Educ.*, **39,** 455 (1962).
8. "The Chemistry of Benzyne," J. F. Bunnett, *J. Chem. Educ.*, **38,** 278 (1961).

CHAPTER 12

Aldehydes and Ketones

THESE TWO important classes of compounds each contain the reactive carbonyl group, $>C=O$. They differ structurally in that aldehydes contain at least one hydrogen atom attached to the carbonyl function, whereas in ketones both substituents are hydrocarbon-like, as shown below. Ketones are classified as *symmetrical* or *unsymmetrical*, depending upon whether the two substituents on the carbonyl group are the same or different.

RCH=O	$\begin{array}{c}R\\R\end{array}>C=O$	$\begin{array}{c}R\\R'\end{array}>C=O$
Aliphatic aldehyde	Dialkyl ketone	Alkyl alkyl′ ketone
ArCH=O	$\begin{array}{c}Ar\\Ar\end{array}>C=O$	$\begin{array}{c}R\\Ar\end{array}>C=O$
Aromatic aldehyde	Diaryl ketone	Aryl alkyl ketone
	Symmetrical Ketones	Unsymmetrical Ketones

The first member of the aldehyde family is **formaldehyde**, CH_2O, which is unique in that it possesses two hydrogen atoms joined to the carbonyl function. As a result, it has certain properties which distinguish it from other members of the aldehyde series. **Acetaldehyde, CH_3CHO,** the next homolog, is representative of the aliphatic aldehydes, while **benzaldehyde**, PhCHO, is the parent compound of the aromatic aldehydes. **Acetone, CH_3COCH_3,** is the parent aliphatic ketone, while **benzophenone** and **acetophenone,** PhCOPh and $PhCOCH_3$, respectively, are the simplest diaryl and alkyl aryl ketones.

Aldehydes and ketones occur widely throughout nature. The important carbohydrate glucose (Chapter 16) is a polyhydroxy aldehyde, while the carbohydrate fructose is a polyhydroxy ketone. The adrenal cortical hormone cortisone, the male hormone testosterone, and the female hormone progesterone are all ketones (Chapter 16). Other naturally occurring representatives include the aldehyde vanillin, which is found in the vanilla bean and used in artificial flavors. The cyclic ketone muscone, widely used in the manufacture of perfumes, is obtained from a gland of the male musk deer (*Moschus moschiferus*), a small animal found in the Himalayan mountains; the gland secretion is apparently an attractant for the female of the species. The bicyclic ketone camphor is obtainable from the camphor tree (*Cinnamonum camphora*), which is native to China, Sumatra, Japan, and elsewhere. Also available synthetically from α-pinene, a constituent of turpentine, camphor is used medicinally as a topical analgesic and commercially as a plasticizer for celluloid. The dialdehyde iridodial has been isolated from Australian ants of the *Dolichoderniae* family, who employ the substance as a protective toxin.

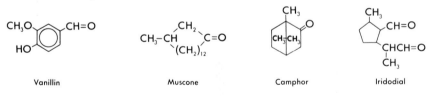

| Vanillin | Muscone | Camphor | Iridodial |

12-1. Nomenclature of Aldehydes and Ketones

Aldehydes and ketones are named either by the IUPAC system or by common names. In the IUPAC system, aldehydes are named by dropping the terminal -*e* from the name of the alkane corresponding to the longest chain of carbon atoms including the —CH=O (formyl) group, then adding the suffix -*al*. The carbon atom of the formyl group is numbered 1, and other substituents on the chain are located and named in the usual fashion, as illustrated:

$$CH_3CH_2CH=O$$

Propanal

$$CH_3\overset{\overset{\displaystyle Cl}{|}}{C}HCH_2\overset{\overset{\displaystyle CH_3}{|}}{C}HCH=O$$

2-Methyl-4-chloropentanal

Ketones are named in an analogous manner, substituting the suffix *-one* for the final *-e* of the parent alkane. The position of the carbonyl group is indicated with the lowest possible number where ambiguity exists, as in the following examples. When it is necessary to name a compound containing

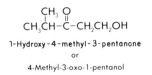

$$\overset{\overset{\displaystyle O}{\|}}{CH_3C}CH_2CH_3$$

Butanone
(No ambiguity)

$$\overset{\overset{\displaystyle O}{\|}}{CH_3C}CH_2CH_2CH_2CH_3$$

2-Hexanone

$$CH_3CH_2\overset{\overset{\displaystyle O}{\|}}{C}CH_2CH_2CH_3$$

3-Hexanone

a carbonyl group and another functional group, the presence of the carbonyl group is indicated either by the suffix *-one* or by the term *oxo* in the name, as in the following.

$$CH_3\overset{\overset{\displaystyle CH_3}{|}}{C}H-\overset{\overset{\displaystyle O}{\|}}{C}-CH_2CH_2OH$$

1-Hydroxy-4-methyl-3-pentanone
or
4-Methyl-3-oxo-1-pentanol

The common name for an aldehyde is derived from the name of its corresponding carboxylic acid, the *-ic acid* portion being replaced by the suffix *-aldehyde*. Such names will be more meaningful after considering the nomenclature for carboxylic acids (Chapter 13). By way of example, however, since the two-carbon aldehyde $CH_3CH=O$ is convertible into *ace*tic acid, CH_3COOH, the common name for the aldehyde is *ace*taldehyde. In one system common names for ketones are based on the alkyl or aryl groups attached to the carbonyl function, followed by the word *ketone*. Thus acetone is also named dimethyl ketone, butanone is methyl ethyl ketone, acetophenone is methyl phenyl ketone, and so on.

12-2. Physical Properties and Characterization of Aldehydes and Ketones

There are two principal resonance forms contributing to the structure of the carbonyl group (Figure 12-1). From dipole moment studies (Section 2-2d), it is apparent that both are important canonical structures, and that

Covalent   Ionic or dipolar

Figure 12-1. Canonical Structures of the Carbonyl Group

the ionic form is only slightly less important than the covalent form. In terms of molecular orbitals (Section 5-2), the π electrons of the carbonyl group can be thought of as being distorted, with the oxygen atom, being the more electronegative (Section 2-2d), having the greater electron density around it (Figure 12-2).

Figure 12-2. π Orbital of the Carbonyl Group

Because of the dipole moment inherent in the resonance structure of the carbonyl group, electrostatic forces of attraction exist between molecules of aldehydes and ketones. As liquids, these substances are therefore associated, and their boiling points are accordingly higher than those of hydrocarbons of comparable molecular weight. Thus acetone, propionaldehyde, and butane, each having the molecular weight 58, show boiling points of 56°, 49°, and −0.5°, respectively. The dipole-dipole attraction between molecules of aldehydes and ketones, however, is weaker than the analogous hydrogen bonding attraction between alcohol molecules (Section 11-3), as seen in the comparative boiling points of acetaldehyde (mol. wt. 44; b.p. 21°) and ethanol (mol. wt. 46; b.p. 78°).

We recall that the water solubility of hydrocarbons is very low (Section 7-3c). By constrast, among aldehydes and ketones, homologs containing up to five carbon atoms still show significant water solubility. Comparable solubilities are also found in the homologous series of alcohols, ethers, carboxylic acids, esters and the like, which also contain polar functional groups. Beyond about C_5, however, the electrostatic forces of attraction between the polar group and the water dipoles are insufficient to hold the molecule in solution, the "hydrocarbon-like" nature of the large alkyl group becomes dominant, and water solubility diminishes.

Aldehydes and ketones may be recognized by their strong infrared absorption in the 1670 to 1730 cm^{-1} region, an absorption caused by the carbon-oxygen stretching vibration. Carbonyl groups in aldehydes and ketones also show weak absorption in the ultraviolet at around 2600 to 3000 Å. This absorption is associated with the excitation of the unshared p electrons on the oxygen atom, and is referred to as a $p \rightarrow \pi^*$ electronic transition. Chemically, aldehydes and ketones may be characterized by their formation of an orange-red precipitate with 2,4-dinitrophenylhydrazine reagent (Section 12-7g). Aldehydes and ketones may be distinguished as classes by several chemical tests, as described in Section 12-7b. In addition, the position of the resonance signal (chemical shift; Section 4-10)

associated with the aldehydic protons in the NMR spectrum of aldehydes
is characteristic, permitting their easy recognition and providing a simple
distinction between aldehydes and ketones. The odors of the lower aldehydes are sharp and penetrating, while ketones may have somewhat more
agreeable odors.

12-3. Syntheses of Aldehydes and Ketones

Members of these two classes of compounds may be synthesized in a
number of ways from a variety of starting materials. Some methods of
preparation are applicable to both classes, while other methods are suitable only for either aldehydes or ketones. Let us examine first the group of
syntheses applicable to both classes.

   a. Oxidation and Dehydrogenation of Alcohols. In Section 11-7d we
learned that aldehydes could be prepared from primary alcohols and ketones from secondary alcohols either by catalytic dehydrogenation or by
employing chemical oxidants.

$$>CHOH \xrightarrow[\text{or (O)}]{\text{Cu gauze (heat)}} >C=O + H_2 \text{ (or } H_2O)$$

The name aldehyde, in fact, is derived from the original preparation of this
type of compound by *al*cohol *dehy*drogenation. Since tertiary alcohols lack
a hydrogen atom on the OH-bearing carbon, oxidation of this class of
alcohol is of no value in aldehyde and ketone synthesis. We recall also
(Section 11-7d) that aldehydes are quite susceptible to further oxidation
to carboxylic acids by chemical oxidants, whereas ketones are not. Hence
chemical oxidation is practical only for preparing ketones and lower molecular weight aldehydes, which can be readily removed from the reaction
mixture by distillation or steam distillation before they are further oxidized.
Thus acetaldehyde (b.p. 21°) may be prepared from ethanol (b.p. 78°) by
conducting the $K_2Cr_2O_7$–H_2SO_4 oxidation at 50°, which permits the acetaldehyde product to distill from the reaction mixture before it is oxidized
to acetic acid.

   b. Preparation from Alkenes. It has been noted that the *ozonization* of appropriate alkenes leads to the formation of aldehydes and ketones (Sections
4-5 and 8-4h), as does also the *hydroxylation* of alkenes (Section 8-4f), followed by *cleavage* of the resulting α-glycol with HIO_4 or $Pb(OCOCH_3)_4$
(Section 11-8a).

   c. Hydration of Alkynes. We recall also (Section 9-4e) that water may be
added catalytically to the triple bond of an alkyne, resulting in the formation of an unstable enol, which rearranges at once to the aldehyde or ketone.

d. Pyrolysis of Acid Salts. One of the oldest known reactions for preparing aldehydes and ketones is the thermal decomposition (**pyrolysis**) of suitable salts of carboxylic acids. The reaction is mainly valuable for synthesizing symmetrical ketones, as shown below. When a mixture of such

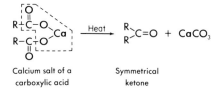

| Calcium salt of a | Symmetrical |
| carboxylic acid | ketone |

salts is employed, three ketone products result, necessitating separation. If one of the calcium salts is derived from formic acid, an aldehyde product is formed along with the ketone and formaldehyde.

$$(HCOO)_2Ca + (RCOO)_2Ca \xrightarrow{\text{Heat}} CH_2=O + RCH=O + R\overset{\overset{\displaystyle O}{\|}}{C}R$$

Calcium formate

In variations of these procedures, barium, manganese, and thorium salts of carboxylic acids have also been employed. Finally, the reaction may be conducted by passing the vapors of the carboxylic acid over the heated oxides of thorium or manganese, as illustrated in the following preparation of cyclopentanone.

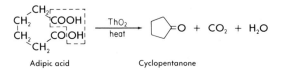

| Adipic acid | Cyclopentanone |

12-4. Synthesis of Aldehydes

There are a large number of methods available for the synthesis of aldehydes. Many of these are rather specialized and applicable only in limited areas. We shall limit our examination to only a few of the more general methods.

a. Rosenmund Reduction. Acyl chlorides are substances having structures such as R—CO—Cl and Ar—CO—Cl (Section 13-5). Acyl chlorides may be reduced to aldehydes by the so-called **Rosenmund reduction,** as in the following general example.

$$R\overset{\overset{\displaystyle O}{\|}}{C}-Cl + H_2 \xrightarrow[\text{"Poisoned"}]{\text{Pd-BaSO}_4} RCH=O + HCl$$

The success of this reaction depends upon the use of a special catalyst palladium on barium sulfate "poisoned" (that is, deactivated) with quino-line and sulfur. The catalyst is sufficiently active to bring about the de-sired reduction, but not active enough to promote further reduction of the aldehyde product to a primary alcohol (Section 11-5a). The course of the reduction is followed by sweeping the reaction vessel with nitrogen and titrating the HCl liberated with standard alkali, and the reaction is stopped when the theoretical quantity of HCl has been evolved. Such a reaction, wherein an atom or group (here Cl) is removed from a molecule by cata-lytic hydrogenation, is referred to as a *hydrogenolysis*.

b. Alkaline Decomposition of Tosylates. It has been observed that primary alcohols may be converted into aliphatic aldehydes by the decomposition of their tosylates (Section 7-5c) with sodium bicarbonate in dimethyl sulfoxide solvent.

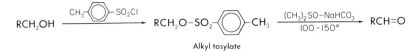

Alkyl tosylate

c. Reaction of Grignard Reagents with Ortho Esters. One of the best gen-eral laboratory preparations of aldehydes involves the reaction of a Grig-nard reagent with ethyl orthoformate (Section 13-14), followed by acid hy-drolysis of the resulting acetal (Section 12-7f).

$$\underset{\text{Ethyl orthoformate}}{\overset{\overset{\displaystyle OEt}{|}}{\underset{\underset{\displaystyle OEt}{|}}{H-C+OEt}} + X-Mg+R} \longrightarrow EtOMgX + \underset{\text{An acetal}}{\overset{\overset{\displaystyle OEt}{|}}{\underset{\underset{\displaystyle OEt}{|}}{RCH}}} \xrightarrow{H_2O,\,H^\oplus} RCH=O + 2\,EtOH$$

d. Special Methods for Aromatic Aldehydes. There are a large number of syntheses which are useful specifically for the preparation of aromatic aldehydes. Many of these are not general reactions, however, and are of only limited applicability. A few of the more important methods are sum-marized below.

Hydrolysis of Dihalomethylarenes. When a methylarene, $ArCH_3$, such as toluene is chlorinated photochemically (Section 7-6d) with two moles of chlorine, a dichloromethylarene, $ArCHCl_2$, is formed. Dibromomethyl-arenes may be formed analogously. Such dihalides are readily hydrolyzed with the formation of aromatic aldehydes.

$$PhCH_3 + 2\,Cl_2 \xrightarrow[\text{light}]{\text{Ultraviolet}} PhCHCl_2 \xrightarrow{H_2O} \left[PhCH\underset{O+H}{\overset{Cl}{\diagdown}} \right] \xrightarrow{-HCl} PhCH=O$$

Toluene   Benzal chloride   Benzaldehyde

Direct Formylation. The transformation $ArH \rightarrow ArCH=O$ may be accomplished by several alternative procedures. One of these, the **Gatter-man-Koch synthesis,** employs hydrogen chloride and carbon monoxide in the presence of aluminum chloride and bears a formal similarity to the Friedel-Crafts ketone synthesis (Section 10-4b). Another method for di-

$$HCl + CO \xrightarrow[\text{Cu}_2\text{Cl}_2]{\text{AlCl}_3} \left[H-\overset{\overset{\text{O}}{\|}}{C}-Cl \right] \xrightarrow[\text{AlCl}_3]{\text{ArH}} ArCH=O + HCl$$

rectly introducing the formyl function into an aromatic ring involves the use of *N*-methylformanilide in the presence of phosphorus oxychloride.

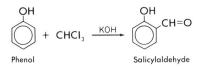

$$\underset{\text{N-Methylformanilide}}{Ph-\overset{\overset{\text{CH}_3}{|}}{N}-CH=O} + ArH \xrightarrow{POCl_3} ArCH=O + PhNHCH_3$$

The reaction fails for benzene and naphthalene, but is applicable to aromatic hydrocarbons containing ring-activating groups (Section 10-6) such as RO– and R$_2$N–, the formyl group entering the ring at positions *ortho* and *para* to the activating substituents. The reaction is also applicable to certain heterocyclic compounds, such as pyrrole.

The **Reimer-Tiemann reaction** is useful for preparing *o*-hydroxy alde-

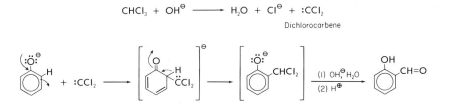

Phenol   Salicylaldehyde

hydes. It occurs when a phenol is treated with chloroform in the presence of alkali, and its mechanism appears to involve attack on the aromatic ring by a dichlorocarbene intermediate, as illustrated below.

$$CHCl_3 + OH^{\ominus} \longrightarrow H_2O + Cl^{\ominus} + :CCl_2$$
Dichlorocarbene

12-5. Synthesis of Ketones

The following are the most useful general methods for the specific synthesis of ketones.

a. Oppenauer Oxidation. This method provides a useful alternative to the direct oxidation of secondary alcohols described in Section 12-3a. The oxidation is carried out by refluxing a secondary alcohol with acetone in the presence of aluminum *t*-butoxide, which functions as a catalyst. The reaction involves the exchange of a hydrogen atom between the secondary alcohol and acetone, yielding a ketone and isopropyl alcohol. The reaction is one of equilibrium, and a large excess of acetone is therefore employed to shift it in the desired direction.

$$\underset{R'}{\overset{R}{>}}CHOH + \underset{CH_3}{\overset{CH_3}{>}}C=O \underset{}{\overset{Al\,(O-t-Bu)_3}{\rightleftharpoons}} \underset{R'}{\overset{R}{>}}C=O + \underset{CH_3}{\overset{CH_3}{>}}CHOH$$

(Excess)

The Oppenauer oxidation is particularly useful when it is desired to prepare a ketone from a secondary alcohol which contains another oxidizable function (for example, a carbon-carbon double bond) which might be attacked simultaneously if less selective oxidizing conditions were employed. The reaction cannot be used for the synthesis of aldehydes, since most aldehydes undergo condensation reactions (Section 12-7k) in the presence of aluminum *t*-butoxide. When the Oppenauer oxidation equilibrium is caused to reverse, the reaction is known as the Meerwein-Ponndorf reduction (Section 12-7c).

b. Reaction of Grignard Reagents with Nitriles. The reaction of a Grignard reagent with a nitrile, R—C≡N, leads to the formation of a ketone. The first step involves the addition of the organometallic compound to the triple bond of the nitrile. The resulting adduct is hydrolyzed to an imino derivative, which in turn hydrolyzes further to produce the desired ketone.

$$\overset{\delta^+ \ \delta^-}{R-C\equiv N} + R'MgX \longrightarrow \underset{R'}{\overset{R}{>}}C=N-MgX \overset{H_2O}{\underset{HCl}{\longrightarrow}} \underset{R'}{\overset{R}{>}}C=NH\cdot HCl \overset{H_2O}{\underset{HCl}{\longrightarrow}} \underset{R'}{\overset{R}{>}}C=O$$

Nitrile   An imino
                                                                hydrochloride

c. Reaction of Organocadmium Compounds with Acyl Halides. We recall (Section 11-12c) that the action of Grignard reagents on anhydrous cadmium chloride yielded dialkylcadmium, RCdR, and diarylcadmium, ArCdAr, derivatives. Such organocadmium compounds ("cadmium Grignard reagents") react with acyl chlorides, R—CO—Cl, or aroyl chlorides, Ar—CO—Cl, to produce ketones in good yield. The cadmium Grignard is not as reactive as an ordinary Grignard reagent, and does not convert the final ketone product into a tertiary alcohol (Section 11-5e).

$$RCdR + R'\overset{O}{\overset{\|}{C}}Cl \ (\text{or } Ar\overset{O}{\overset{\|}{C}}Cl) \longrightarrow RCdCl + R'\overset{O}{\overset{\|}{C}}R \ (\text{or } Ar\overset{O}{\overset{\|}{C}}R)$$

d. Friedel-Crafts Ketone Syntheses. The synthesis of ketones of the types RCOAr, ArCOAr, and ArCOAr' by the Friedel-Crafts ketone synthesis, involving reaction of an arene with an acid halide in the presence of aluminum chloride, has been described in Section 10-4b. In a modification of such Friedel-Crafts acylation reactions, carboxylic acid anhydrides may be used instead of acyl halides. The first step in the synthesis of anthraquinone illustrates the use of a cyclic carboxylic acid anhydride for the preparation of a keto acid, o-benzoylbenzoic acid. The ring closure in the

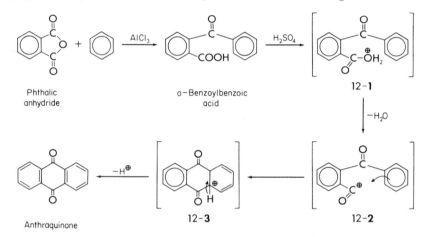

Phthalic
anhydride

o-Benzoylbenzoic
acid

12-1

−H₂O

Anthraquinone

12-3

12-2

second step of the sequence is a further nontypical extension of Friedel-Crafts acylation. The mechanism is thought to involve the addition of a proton from the sulfuric acid to the carboxyl group, forming the protonated intermediate 12-1. Water is lost, and the resulting acylium ion (12-2) attacks the adjacent ring in typical electrophilic fashion (Section 10-5), forming the cationic intermediate 12-3. Loss of a proton from this intermediate affords the final product, anthraquinone. Notice in the ring closure reaction that acylation is occurring in a deactivated ring at a position *ortho* to a *meta*-directing group. Acylation at the less deactivated *meta* position, however, would form a geometrically less favorable seven-membered central ring.

e. The Fries Reaction. In 1908 K. Fries discovered that when an ester of phenol, R—CO—OPh (Section 11-9c), is treated with aluminum chloride, it becomes rearranged into a mixture of *o*- and *p*-hydroxyphenyl alkyl ketones. The following example is typical. The relative amount of each

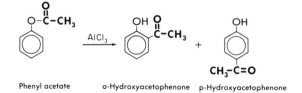

Phenyl acetate

o-Hydroxyacetophenone   p-Hydroxyacetophenone

isomer produced is influenced by the solvent, the amount of catalyst used, and the temperature. Higher temperatures (160° to 175°) generally favor production of the *ortho* isomer, while low temperatures (25°) favor the *para* isomer. The mixture of *ortho* and *para* isomers resulting from the Fries reaction can usually be separated readily by distillation or steam distillation because the chelated, intramolecularly hydrogen-bonded *ortho* isomer (Figure 12-3) has greater volatility (see Section 11-3).

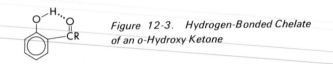

Figure 12-3. Hydrogen-Bonded Chelate of an o-Hydroxy Ketone

12-6. Industrial Syntheses of Aldehydes and Ketones

Formaldehyde, acetaldehyde, acetone, and methyl ethyl ketone are economically the most important aldehydes and ketones. The first three have a number of specific uses that are described elsewhere in the text. In addition, acetone and methyl ethyl ketone are widely employed as solvents. Formaldehyde, the production of which in the United States during 1962 (as the 37 per cent aqueous solution, **formalin**) was some 2398 million pounds, is prepared commercially by the vapor phase oxidation of methanol with air over a silver or iron oxide–molybdenum oxide catalyst. In another process, the controlled oxidation of natural gas (largely methane; Section 7-4b) is employed. Acetaldehyde is made industrially by the analogous oxidation of ethanol, the controlled oxidation of propane and butane, and the hydration of acetylene (Section 9-4e). Acetone, the United States production of which amounted to 849 million pounds in 1962, is prepared chiefly (79 per cent of total production) by the catalytic dehydrogenation and the controlled air oxidation of isopropyl alcohol. Methyl ethyl ketone (1961 production: 206 million pounds) is prepared similarly from 2-butanol. Acetone is also obtained as a by-product during the butyl alcohol fermentation of carbohydrates, and during the industrial preparation of phenol from isopropylbenzene (Section 11-9a). During World War II, for economic reasons, an interesting process known as **hydroformylation** was developed by the Germans. The reaction involves the addition of hydrogen and carbon monoxide to an alkene in the presence of a cobalt carbonyl catalyst at elevated temperature and pressure.

$$RCH=CH_2 + CO + H_2 \xrightarrow[\text{1000–6000 psi}]{Co(CO)_4,\ heat} RCH_2CH_2CH=O + \underset{\underset{CH=O}{|}}{RCHCH_3}$$
$$\text{(major product)}$$

12-7. Reactions of Aldehydes and Ketones

The carbonyl group in aldehydes and ketones is an extremely reactive function, and itself undergoes a wide variety of important transformations. In addition, its presence may confer upon other atoms in the molecule, particularly α-hydrogen atoms on a carbon atom adjacent to the carbonyl group, peculiar reactivity. Let us next examine the more important reactions associated with aldehydes and ketones.

a. Keto-Enol Tautomerization. All aldehydes and ketones having a hydrogen atom on the carbon atom adjacent to the carbonyl group (**α-hydrogen**) are capable of existing in two structurally isomeric forms. We recall (Section 9-4e) that these are referred to as **keto** and **enol** forms, and that the two forms ordinarily exist in equilibrium with one another (Figure 12-4). Isomers which are interconvertible (equilibrate) by the migration

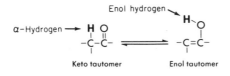

Figure 12-4. Keto-Enol Tautomerization

of a proton from one site in the molecule to another site are called **tautomers.** Keto and enol forms of an aldehyde or ketone are thus said to be **tautomeric,** their coexistence is referred to as **tautomerism,** and their equilibration is called **tautomerization.**

The classic case of keto-enol tautomerism is that of the β-keto ester ethyl acetoacetate (Section 13-11f), studied by L. Knorr in 1911. The two

forms are readily interconvertible by acid or base catalysts, and the surface of ordinary glass is sufficiently alkaline to catalyze their equilibration. The mechanism of equilibration with each catalyst is indicated in Figure 12-5. In the acid-catalyzed mechanism a protonated intermediate (12-4) of the keto form is first produced, which yields the enol form by loss of an α-hydrogen atom. In the base-catalyzed mechanism, the base B abstracts the

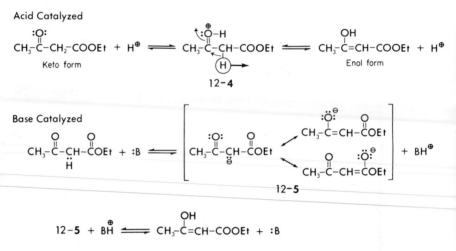

Acid Catalyzed

Base Catalyzed

Figure 12-5.   Mechanisms for the Tautomerization of Ethyl Acetoacetate

α-hydrogen atom, yielding the **enolate anion** 12-5, which is stabilized as the indicated resonance hybrid. Reaction of the latter with the conjugate acid, $BH^{\oplus}$, of the base B affords either the keto form or the enol form.

The keto form of ethyl acetoacetate may be obtained by crystallization of the mixture from various organic solvents, such as ethyl ether, at dry ice temperature ($-78°$). The enol form may be obtained by converting the ester to its sodium salt (12-6), then treating a suspension of the salt in an inert solvent, such as petroleum ether, with one mole of HCl gas at $-78°$. Either form may be kept indefinitely at this low temperature in the

$$CH_3COCH_2COOEt + Na\overset{\bullet\bullet}{O}Et \longrightarrow EtOH + Na^{\oplus}\left[CH_3CO\overset{\bullet\bullet}{C}HCOOEt\right]^{\ominus} \xrightarrow{HCl} NaCl + CH_3\overset{OH}{C}=CHCOOEt$$

12-6

absence of catalysts. By using all-quartz distillation apparatus, it is also possible to separate the keto and enol forms of this ester by fractional distillation, whereupon the enol form distills first. The apparent anomaly of an alcohol (enol) boiling lower than the corresponding ketone (Section 12-2) may be understood if we recognize the opportunity that exists for intramolecular hydrogen bonding in the enol (Figure 12-6). As a conse-

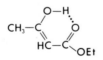

Figure 12-6.   Hydrogen-Bonded Chelate of Enol of Ethyl Acetoacetate

quence, the intermolecular forces of dipole-dipole attraction in the enol are less than those in the keto form, and the boiling point of the enol form is thus lower.

The equilibrium composition of keto-enol systems, which may be estimated by both chemical and physical methods, varies markedly with both constitution and environment. Applying infrared spectroscopy, for example, one may measure the relative areas under the absorption bands for the —OH and $>$C=O groups, respectively, as indications of the amounts of enol and keto forms present. From bond energy considerations, the keto form of a simple keto-enol pair should be the more stable. In agreement with this, liquid acetone is only 0.00015 per cent enol, and the enol content of other aldehydes and ketones varies between 10^{-4} and 10^{-1} per cent. On the other hand, the enol content of ethyl acetoacetate (7.7 per cent) is much greater, and that of 1,3-diketones, $RCOCH_2COR$, is generally even greater still. The increased stabilities of enol forms in such instances arises from the possibilities of intramolecular hydrogen bonding (Figure 12-6) or from increased resonance stabilization of the enol form over the keto form of the 1,3-diketone or β-keto ester. The influence of resonance stabilization is particularly evident in phenol, which shows no evidence of existing as either of the isomeric keto forms 12-7 and 12-8. However, 1,3,5-trihydroxybenzene (phloroglucinol) shows chemical properties of both the enol 12-9 and the triketone 12-10.

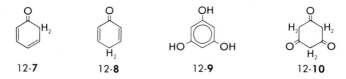

| 12-7 | 12-8 | 12-9 | 12-10 |

As far as the effect of environment is concerned, it is generally found that the enol content of a keto-enol system is enhanced in nonpolar solvents and minimized in polar solvents. Thus ethyl acetoacetate is 46.4 per cent enol in hexane solution, but only 0.4 per cent enol in water solution.

b. Qualitative Tests for Aldehydes, Ketones, and Enols. Aldehydes and ketones may be recognized by their infrared spectra, as we have seen (Section 12-2), or by their ability to form colored precipitates (2,4-dinitrophenylhydrazones) with 2,4-dinitrophenylhydrazine reagent (Section 12-7g). Aldehydes and ketones may be distinguished from one another by any of the following chemical tests, which are positive for aldehydes, but negative for ketones. (1) The magenta-colored dye fuchsin, upon treatment with sulfurous acid, forms a colorless **Schiff reagent.** Admixture of this reagent with an aldehyde regenerates the original magenta color. (2) **Tollens reagent** is prepared by reaction of silver nitrate solution with ammonium hydroxide. The silver-ammonia complex ion (12-11) of this reagent is capable of oxidizing aldehydes, but not ketones, to carboxylic acid salts (12-**12**), with simultaneous formation of a silver mirror. Silver

$$RCH{=}O + 2\,Ag(NH_3)_2^{\oplus} + 2\,OH^{\ominus} \rightarrow RCOO^{\ominus}NH_4^{\oplus} + 2\,Ag\downarrow + 3\,NH_3 + H_2O$$
$$\phantom{RCH{=}O + 2\,A}\text{12-11}\phantom{g(NH_3)_2^{\oplus} + 2\,OH^{\ominus} \rightarrow RC}\text{12-12}$$

mirrors are made commercially by this type of process. (3) **Fehling's solution** consists of a cupric ion–tartaric acid complex (12-**13**). When this

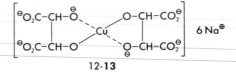

12-**13**

reagent (represented as $Cu(OH)_2$) is treated with an aldehyde, the latter is oxidized to a carboxylic acid salt, and a red precipitate of cuprous oxide is formed. **Benedict's solution** (a cupric ion–citric acid complex) reacts

$$RCH{=}O + 2\,Cu(OH)_2 + OH^{\ominus} \rightarrow RCOO^{\ominus} + Cu_2O\downarrow + 3\,H_2O$$

in a similar way. Both Fehling's and Benedict's solutions are used in the clinical analysis for reducing sugars in blood and urine. Tollen's, Fehling's, and Benedict's reagents are also useful for the specific oxidation to carboxylic acids of those aldehydes which have other oxidizable functions (for example, —OH or $>C{=}C<$) in their structure.

The **haloform reaction** serves to distinguish methyl ketones, CH_3COR, from other classes of ketones. When a methyl ketone is warmed with sodium hypoiodite solution ($NaOH + I_2$), it is cleaved into iodoform and the sodium salt of a carboxylic acid. The iodoform precipitates as a crystalline yellow solid having an unmistakable "medicinal" odor and a char-

$$\overset{\displaystyle O}{\underset{\displaystyle \|}{RC}}CH_3 + 3\,NaOI \rightarrow \overset{\displaystyle O}{\underset{\displaystyle \|}{RC}}O^{\ominus}Na^{\oplus} + \underset{\text{Iodoform}}{CHI_3} + 2\,NaOH$$

acteristic melting point (119°). The test is characteristic of both the $CH_3{-}\overset{|}{C}{=}O$ and $CH_3{-}\overset{|}{C}H{-}OH$ groupings, since the latter is oxidized to the former grouping by the hypoiodite. In an exactly analogous fashion sodium hypobromite and sodium hypochlorite yield bromoform,

$$\overset{\displaystyle OH}{\underset{\displaystyle |}{CH_3CHR}} + NaOI \rightarrow \overset{\displaystyle O}{\underset{\displaystyle \|}{CH_3CR}} + NaI + H_2O$$

$CHBr_3$, and chloroform, $CHCl_3$, respectively, and the general process is called the **haloform reaction**. The reaction is known to proceed in several

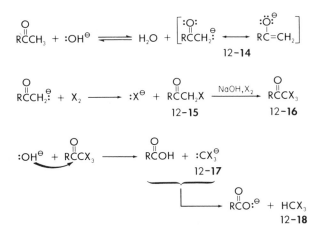

Figure 12-7. Mechanism of the Haloform Reaction

steps, as seen in Figure 12-7.   The enolate anion (12-**14**) produced by abstraction of α-hydrogen from the methyl ketone by hydroxide ion, is attacked by halogen (or HOX) to produce the halomethyl ketone 12-**15**, which then halogenates further in the same way to form the trihalomethyl ketone (12-**16**).   This ketone undergoes a nucleophilic displacement (by hydroxide ion) of the trihalomethide ion (12-**17**) and ultimately yields the haloform (12-**18**).   Methyl ketones with bulky alkyl or aryl groups frequently fail to undergo the cleavage step because such groups present steric hindrance to the nucleophilic attack by hydroxide ion; the halogenated ketone is then the final product.

Enols and phenols differ from the keto forms of aldehydes and ketones (and from ordinary alcohols) in that they frequently and characteristically give water-soluble, colored complexes with ferric chloride solution.   The color is burgundy red for simple enols and purple to green for phenols.

c. Reduction to Alcohols.   We recall that the reduction of aldehydes and ketones provides a general method for the preparation of primary and secondary alcohols, respectively (Section 11-5a).   Catalytic reductions are carried out with hydrogen gas and platinum, palladium, or Raney nickel

$$\diagdown C{=}O + 2[H] \rightarrow \diagdown CHOH$$

catalyst (Sections 7-5a and 11-19).   Chemical reducing agents include lithium aluminum hydride (Section 11-5a), sodium borohydride, $NaBH_4$, and aluminum isopropoxide, $Al(O{-}i{-}Pr)_3$.   Sodium borohydride is a weaker reducing agent than lithium aluminum hydride and, unlike the latter, may be used in hydroxylic solvents such as water and alcohol.

Aluminum isopropoxide reductions are specific for carbonyl functions, and can be used for compounds containing other reducible functions besides the carbonyl group.

The reduction with aluminum isopropoxide, known as the **Meerwein-Ponndorf reduction,** represents a reversal of the previously discussed Oppenauer oxidation of alcohols (Section 12-5a). A mixture of the aldehyde or ketone and aluminum isopropoxide in isopropyl alcohol is equilibrated by heating, and the acetone formed is allowed to distill from the mixture, displacing the equilibrium to the right. As in other reductions,

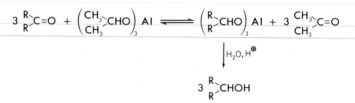

aldehydes here also yield primary alcohols, and ketones secondary alcohols, after treatment of the acetone-free mixture with dilute acid. In the Meerwein-Ponndorf reduction the initial step is an acid-base reaction between the carbonyl group (Lewis base) and the aluminum isopropoxide (Lewis acid) to form a complex (12-**19**). The hydrogen atom on the oxygen-bearing carbon of the isopropoxide group can come close enough to the carbonyl carbon in the complex for a hydride shift to occur, and the reaction proceeds by way of a six-membered cyclic transition state (12-**20**).

$$R_2C=\overset{..}{\underset{..}{O}}: \; + \; Al\,(OCHMe_2)_3 \; \rightleftharpoons \; R_2C=\overset{\delta+}{\underset{..}{O}}:\overset{\delta-}{Al}\,(OCHMe_2)_3$$

12-19

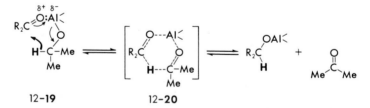

12-19   12-20

d. Reduction to Hydrocarbons.   It will be recalled (Section 7-5e) that the **Clemmenson reduction** (with HCl and Zn·Hg) and the **Wolff-Kishner reduction** (with H_2NNH_2) of aldehydes and ketones bring about complete reduction of the carbonyl groups to hydrocarbons.

$$\text{\Large$\rangle$}C=O \; + \; 4\,[H] \; \xrightarrow[\text{Wolff-Kishner}]{\text{Clemmenson or}} \; \text{\Large$\rangle$}CH_2 \; + \; H_2O$$

e. *Bimolecular Reduction of Ketones.* The reduction of ketones with metallic reducing agents is frequently accompanied by so-called **bimolecular
reduction,** in which two molecules of the ketone combine to form an α-gly-
col (pinacol; Section 11-6a). Bimolecular reduction can be made the predominant reaction if desired, as in the amalgamated magnesium conversion of acetone into pinacol, which is isolated as its stable hexahydrate

(m.p. 45°). Diaryl ketones are also reduced bimolecularly by certain
metals, as well as by "hydrogen donors" such as isopropyl alcohol in the
presence of sunlight. We recall that pinacols of these types character-

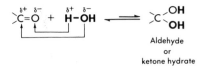

istically undergo the pinacol rearrangement in the presence of acid catalysts (Section 11-8b).

f. *Reaction with Water and Alcohols.* We have already learned that
1,1-diols are generally quite unstable with respect to their aldehyde or
ketone precursors (Erlenmeyer's rule; Section 11-6a). In a few special

$$\overset{\delta+}{\underset{}{C}}\overset{\delta-}{=}O + \overset{\delta+}{H}-\overset{\delta-}{OH} \rightleftarrows \overset{}{C}\overset{OH}{\underset{OH}{}}$$

Aldehyde
or
ketone hydrate

cases, however, such carbonyl hydrates, formed by addition of water to
the carbonyl group, are stable. Thus aqueous solutions of formaldehyde
show no carbonyl absorption in the infrared, presumably because of hydrate formation, and a formaldehyde polymer (paraformaldehyde) results
on evaporation of such solutions. The reaction of acetone with water is

$$CH_2{=}O + H_2O \longrightarrow HOCH_2OH$$

Formaldehyde hydrate

$$\{H!O{-}CH_2{-}!OH + H!O{-}CH_2{-}!OH + H!O{-}CH_2{-}!OH\} \xrightarrow{-nH_2O} -OCH_2OCH_2OCH_2-$$

Paraformaldehyde

negligible, on the other hand, as shown by the absence of oxygen exchange when acetone is mixed with water containing H_2O^{18} (which would result if water added reversibly to acetone; such exchange occurs only in the presence of acidic or basic catalysts). The stability of hydrates is greatly enhanced if electron-withdrawing groups are located on the carbon atom adjacent to the hydrated carbonyl group. Chloral hydrate, for example, is a stable, crystalline substance (m.p. 57°) which is convertible to its aldehyde precursor, chloral (trichloroacetaldehyde), only under dehydrating

Chloral hydrate

conditions such as azeotropic distillation (Section 11-4b). Chloral hydrate is a rapid-acting soporific, and constitutes the "knock-out drops" of criminal lore. Its introduction into medicine is an interesting story of medicinal chemistry. Chloroform was long known as an anesthetic, and since it is formed from chloral by the haloform reaction (Section 12-7b) the conclusion was made that administration of chloral hydrate should result in the slow release of chloroform in the body. Therapeutic trials confirmed its soporific action, though this action is now known to be due primarily to trichloroethanol, Cl_3CCH_2OH, which is produced *in vivo* from the chloral hydrate.

The reaction of aldehydes with alcohols closely parallels their reaction with water. In the presence of acidic or basic catalysts, alcohols add to the carbonyl group to form adducts known as **hemiacetals,** as shown in the following equation with ethanol. Like hydrates, hemiacetals are unstable,

$$RCH{=}O \ + \ \textbf{EtOH} \ \underset{}{\overset{H^{\oplus} \text{ or } OH^{\ominus}}{\rightleftharpoons}} \ RCH\overset{OH}{\underset{OEt}{<}}$$

Ethyl hemiacetal
of an aldehyde

except again with such aldehydes as chloral, and in certain cyclic structures (see Section 16-5). In the presence of excess alcohol and an acidic catalyst, the hemiacetal in solution is converted into an **acetal,** as shown in the following mechanism. Basic catalysts do not promote acetal forma-

$$RCH\overset{OH}{\underset{OEt}{<}} \ \underset{-H^{\oplus}}{\overset{+H^{\oplus}}{\rightleftharpoons}} \ RCH\overset{\overset{\oplus}{O}H_2}{\underset{OEt}{<}} \ \underset{+H_2O}{\overset{-H_2O}{\rightleftharpoons}} \ RCH\overset{\oplus}{\underset{OEt}{<}} \ \underset{-EtOH}{\overset{+EtOH}{\rightleftharpoons}} \ RCH\overset{\overset{H}{\underset{|}{\oplus}}OEt}{\underset{OEt}{<}} \ \underset{+H^{\oplus}}{\overset{-H^{\oplus}}{\rightleftharpoons}} \ RCH\overset{OEt}{\underset{OEt}{<}}$$

Ethyl acetal
of an
aldehyde

tion, and acetals themselves are stable in neutral or basic media. With aqueous acids, however, as we would anticipate from the above mechanism, they readily hydrolyze back to the original aldehyde.

$$\text{RCH}\!\!<_{\!\!OEt}^{\!\!OEt} + H_2O \xrightarrow{\ H^\oplus\ } \text{RCH=O} + 2\ EtOH$$

In reactions of ketones with alcohols, the equilibria generally lie far to the left. The analogous addition compounds (**ketals,** $R_2C(OR')_2$) must accordingly be prepared by other means, such as the reaction of the ketone with ethyl orthoformate.

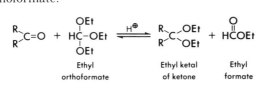

| Ethyl
orthoformate | Ethyl ketal
of ketone | Ethyl
formate |

Thiols react similarly with aldehydes and ketones to yield **thioacetals** and **thioketals,** respectively. These are more stable to acid hydrolysis than

$$\text{RCH=O} + 2\ R'SH \ \rightleftharpoons^{\ H^\oplus\ }\ \text{RCH}\!\!<_{\!\!SR'}^{\!\!SR'} + H_2O$$

A thioacetal

$$\text{R}\!\!>_{\!\!R}^{\!\!R}\!\!C\!\!=\!\!O + 2\ R'SH \ \rightleftharpoons^{\ H^\oplus\ }\ \text{R}\!\!>_{\!\!R}^{\!\!R}\!\!C\!\!<_{\!\!SR'}^{\!\!SR'} + H_2O$$

A thioketal

are acetals, but may be hydrolyzed readily in the presence of mercuric oxide. Reaction of acetone with ethyl mercaptan yields a product which upon oxidation with potassium permanganate is converted into a disulfone (Section 11-19) known as sulfonal. This compound was formerly used

$$\text{CH}_3\!\!>_{\!\!CH_3}^{\ }\!\!C\!\!=\!\!O + 2\ EtSH \xrightarrow{\ H^\oplus\ } \text{CH}_3\!\!>_{\!\!CH_3}^{\ }\!\!C\!\!<_{\!\!SEt}^{\!\!SEt} \xrightarrow{\ KMnO_4\ } \text{CH}_3\!\!>_{\!\!CH_3}^{\ }\!\!C\!\!<_{\!\!SO_2-Et}^{\!\!SO_2-Et}$$

Sulfonal

medically as a hypnotic, but its use has been largely discontinued since the introduction of the barbiturates (Section 13-18).

It is sometimes necessary to protect an aldehyde or ketone group in a molecule to prevent it from reacting during the course of transformation of some other functional group in the molecule. This is often done by converting the carbonyl group into an acetal, thioacetal, or thioketal as described above, then subsequently regenerating the carbonyl group by hydrolysis. Another reaction used for the temporary blocking of aldehyde groups is that with acetic anhydride, whereby an **acylal** is formed. Acylals,

which are esters of the hydrated form of the aldehyde, are readily reconverted to aldehydes by acid hydrolysis.

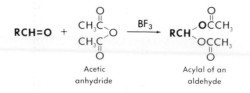

Acetic
anhydride

Acylal of an
aldehyde

g. Reaction with Ammonia and Derivatives.

Ammonia and a number of its
derivatives react with aldehydes and ketones in a manner which is initially
similar to the reaction of these compounds with water and alcohols,
namely, by initial *addition* to their carbonyl groups. Chloral, for example,
forms a stable addition compound with ammonia. More generally, how-

$$Cl_3CCH=O + H-\overset{..}{N}H_2 \longrightarrow Cl_3CCH\overset{OH}{\underset{NH_2}{<}}$$

Chloral ammonia

ever, such initial addition is followed by intramolecular dehydration and
other changes. Thus acetaldehyde forms a 1:1 addition compound (12-**21**)
with ammonia, known as an **aldehyde ammonia.** This is unstable, and
spontaneously dehydrates to form an **aldimine** (12-**22**). The latter in turn
polymerizes to a cyclic trimer (12-**23**), which is isolated as a crystalline
trihydrate.

$$CH_3CH=O + NH_3 \rightleftharpoons CH_3CH\overset{OH}{\underset{NH_2}{<}} \underset{+H_2O}{\overset{-H_2O}{\rightleftharpoons}} CH_3CH=NH \longrightarrow$$

12-**21**   12-**22**   12-**23**

The reaction of formaldehyde with ammonia yields hexamethylenetetramine, $(CH_2)_6N_4$ (hexamine, urotropine), a compound of interest for
several reasons. It was the first organic compound whose structure, initi-

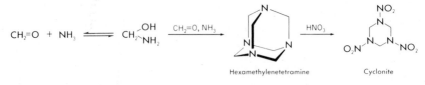

Hexamethylenetetramine

Cyclonite

ally deduced from valence theory and chemical reactions, was confirmed
by X-ray diffraction. Notice its structural similarity to adamantane (Section 9-6). It is used to a certain extent medically as a urinary antiseptic,

where its action depends upon the slow release of formaldehyde in the urine. Finally, during World War II it was of importance in the manufacture of the high explosive Cyclonite (RDX) which is a more powerful explosive than TNT.

Benzaldehyde condenses with ammonia to form hydrobenzamide, and a number of aromatic aldehydes react similarly.

$$PhCH{=}O + NH_3 \xrightarrow{-H_2O} [PhCH{=}NH] \xrightarrow[-H_2O]{PhCH{=}O} PhCH{=}N{-}\overset{\overset{\displaystyle Ph}{|}}{CH}{-}N{=}CHPh$$
$$\text{Hydrobenzamide}$$

The reaction of aldehydes with primary amines proceeds in a similar fashion, and can be generalized as follows. The resulting condensation

$$RCH{=}O + R'NH_2 \rightleftharpoons \left[RCH\underset{NHR'}{\overset{OH}{\diagdown}}\right] \xrightarrow{-H_2O} RCH{=}NR'$$
$$\text{Schiff base}$$

products are commonly called **Schiff bases,** and those derived from aromatic amines are also known as **anils.** Anils derived from aromatic aldehydes, in contrast to aliphatic Schiff bases, are more stable and show less tendency to polymerize. Their stability is attributed to the conjugation of the azomethine linkage, $-CH{=}N-$, with both aromatic rings.

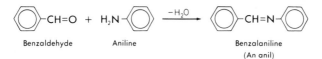

Benzaldehyde	Aniline	Benzalaniline
		(An anil)

A number of *derivatives* of ammonia condense in a similar manner with the carbonyl groups of aldehydes and ketones, that is, by initial addition followed by intramolecular dehydration. These derivatives and the classes of compounds which they afford are depicted with the specific examples of Figure 12-8 which illustrate the nomenclature involved.

Oximes, phenylhydrazones, 2,4-dinitrophenylhydrazones, and semicarbazones are useful types of derivatives for the characterization of aldehydes and ketones, since they are usually crystalline compounds which may be identified by their characteristic melting points. The use of 2,4-dinitrophenylhydrazine as a diagnostic test for aldehydes and ketones has already been mentioned (Section 12-2). Hydrazones are important intermediates in the Wolff-Kishner reduction (Section 7-5e). Girard's reagent, being an ionic salt, converts carbonyl compounds into water-soluble derivatives, and is therefore sometimes useful both in the isolation and purification of aldehydes and ketones. It was first used, for example, in the isolation of the female hormone estrone from urine. The carbonyl

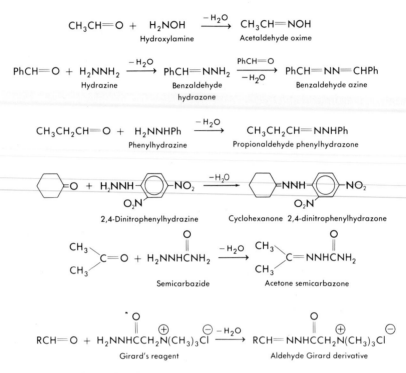

Figure 12-8. Carbonyl Derivatives of Aldehydes and Ketones

derivatives listed above can be hydrolyzed (acid catalyst) to regenerate the original aldehyde or ketone.

Oxime, phenylhydrazone, and semicarbazone formation are all acid-catalyzed reactions. Oxime formation is also found to be base catalyzed. In the acid-catalyzed formation of these derivatives, protonation of the carbonyl group is the first step. The protonated species 12-**24** is then

$$\overset{\delta+}{\underset{}{C}}\!=\!\overset{\delta-}{\ddot{O}}\!: \;+\; H^{\oplus} \;\rightleftharpoons\; \overset{\oplus}{C}\!-\!\ddot{O}H$$

12-**24**

$$\underset{\text{12-}\mathbf{24}}{\overset{\oplus}{C}\!-\!\ddot{O}H} \;+\; \underset{\text{12-}\mathbf{25}}{:NH_2NHR} \quad\xrightarrow{\text{Slow}}\quad \underset{\text{12-}\mathbf{26}}{C\!\!\overset{OH}{\underset{\overset{\oplus}{NH_2}NHR}{}}} \quad\underset{\text{Fast}}{\overset{-H^{\oplus}}{\rightleftharpoons}}\quad C\!\!\overset{OH}{\underset{NHNHR}{}} \quad\underset{\text{Fast}}{\overset{-H_2O}{\rightleftharpoons}}\quad \underset{\text{12-}\mathbf{27}}{C\!=\!NNHR}$$

subject to nucleophilic attack by the ammonia derivative (12-**25**), yielding an intermediate adduct (12-**26**) which rapidly loses a proton and a water molecule to form the final product (12-**27**). One might conclude from this mechanism that an increase in acidity, increasing the concentration of the protonated species 12-**24,** should increase the rate of the reaction.   We must bear in mind, however, that increasing acidity also increases the concentration of the protonated ammonia derivative 12-**28,** which is unable

$$RN\ddot{H}\ddot{N}H_2 + H^\oplus \rightleftharpoons RN\ddot{H}\overset{\oplus}{N}H_3$$

12-**25**   12-**28**

to participate in a nucleophilic attack on 12-**24.** Since the concentration of the attacking nucleophile 12-**25** is thereby reduced with increasing acidity, a rate decrease would be expected. .Since the two consequences of increased acidity work in opposite directions on the overall rate, it is not surprising that such reactions show a rate dependence on pH, and a maximum rate at an optimum pH.

   h. Isomerism of Oximes—The Beckmann Rearrangement. Oximes (except for symmetrical ketoximes of the type $R_2C{=}NOH$) frequently show an interesting type of geometrical isomerism. In the $>C{=}N{-}OH$ system both the carbon atom and the nitrogen atom are essentially trigonally hybridized (sp^2; Section 5-3), and oximes are accordingly planar molecules with essentially 120° bond angles. Thus oximes, like alkenes, can exist as stable geometrical isomers owing to lack of free rotation about their double bond. The following example of the oximes of benzaldehyde is typical. As first formed, benzaldoxime exists as the *syn* isomer (m.p. 35°)

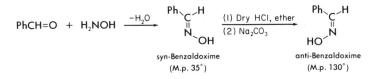

$$PhCH{=}O + H_2NOH \xrightarrow{-H_2O}$$

syn-Benzaldoxime
(M.p. 35°)

(1) Dry HCl, ether
(2) Na$_2$CO$_3$

anti-Benzaldoxime
(M.p. 130°)

which is convertible to the *anti* isomer (m.p. 130°) by the action of dry HCl in ether, followed by sodium carbonate. Note that the prefixes *cis* and *trans* used in describing the geometrical isomers of alkenes are replaced by *syn* and *anti* when referring to oximes. For aldoximes the prefixes refer to the relative positions of H and OH about the $>C{=}N{-}$ grouping. For ketoximes, they refer to the positions of the OH group and the group following the prefix, as illustrated below.

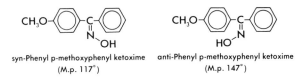

syn-Phenyl p-methoxyphenyl ketoxime
(M.p. 117°)

anti-Phenyl p-methoxyphenyl ketoxime
(M.p. 147°)

Oxime isomers vary in their stability and are interconvertible in a number of ways. Thus, as mentioned above, dry HCl converts *syn*-benzaldoxime into the *anti* form. The isomeric phenyl *p*-methoxyphenyl ketoximes are interconvertible to an equilibrium mixture of the two by means of ultraviolet light. Other reagents which have been reported to transform less stable oxime isomers into more stable ones include lithium chloride, bromine, and charcoal containing adsorbed oxygen.

Syn and *anti* configurations of oximes have been established in a number of ways. A general method for aldoximes involves their conversion into *O*-acetates with acetic anhydride, followed by treatment of the *O*-acetate with sodium carbonate, which merely hydrolyzes the *O*-acetate of the *syn*-

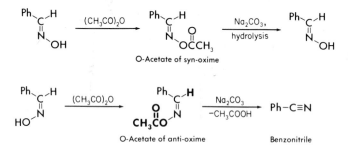

aldoxime back to the original *syn* oxime, but converts the *O*-acetate of the *anti*-oxime into a nitrile by *trans* elimination (Section 8-3b) of the elements of acetic acid.

In confirmation of the above configurational criteria, one of the oximes (12-**29**) of 2-chloro-5-nitrobenzaldehyde readily affords the heterocyclic compound 5-nitrobenzoxazole (12-**30**) on treatment with sodium hydroxide, and is therefore assigned the *anti* configuration. The corresponding *syn* isomer (12-**31**) yields 12-**30** only with difficulty, presumably after first rearranging into the *anti* isomers (12-**29**). Notice that the *anti* configuration of 12-**29** is such that facile intramolecular loss of HCl may occur, whereas in the *syn* isomer (12-**31**) the Cl and OH functions are too far apart to permit this. Moreover, the *anti*-oxime (12-**29**) is transformed into

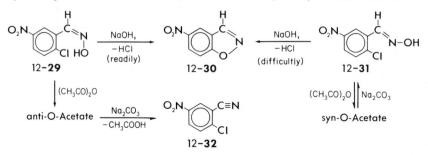

2-chloro-5-nitrobenzonitrile (12-**32**) on conversion to its *O*-acetate, fol-lowed by treatment with sodium carbonate, whereas the *syn*-oxime (12-**31**) is recovered unchanged after such treatment.

In the presence of acidic catalysts (H_2SO_4, PCl_5, BF_3, P_2O_5, etc.; usually in ether solution), ketoximes, $R_2C{=}NOH$, undergo an interesting and important transformation into *N*-substituted amides, R—CO—NHR. This reaction, known as the **Beckmann rearrangement,** was first observed for benzophenone oxime by E. Beckmann in 1886. Extensive investigation

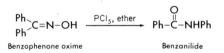

Benzophenone oxime   Benzanilide

of the Beckmann rearrangement of unsymmetrical ketoximes has disclosed that the reaction is *stereospecific*, and that the alkyl or aryl group which migrates to the nitrogen atom is invariably *trans* (*anti*) to the OH group of the oxime function. Accordingly, by identification of the amide product

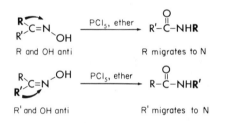

from the Beckmann rearrangement of an unsymmetrical ketoxime, the con-figuration of the original ketoxime may be established. The stereochemical course of the reaction has been elucidated by using appropriately substi-tuted, isomeric ketoximes whose configurations have been determined in-dependently—for example by their ease of cyclization to oxazole deriva-tives, as described above for aldoximes.

The mechanism of the Beckmann rearrangement has been extensively studied. We know that the migrating group never becomes fully detached during the reaction, for when the migrating group contains an asymmetric carbon atom adjacent to the $>C{=}NOH$ function, the group *migrates with retention of its configuration* and without racemization (Section 2-8d). Fur-thermore, when the rearrangement is conducted in the presence of H_2O^{18}, it is found that the resulting amide contains O^{18} to the same extent as the original H_2O^{18}, although neither unreacted oxime nor the amide product exchanges its oxygen with H_2O^{18} under the conditions of the reaction. The mechanism in Figure 12-9 accords with these facts, as well as with the observed stereochemistry of the rearrangement.

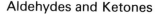

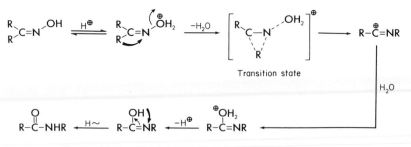

Transition state

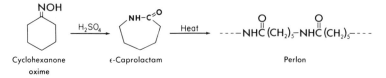

Figure 12-9.   Mechanism of the Beckmann Rearrangement

The Beckmann rearrangement has important synthetic applications, including the preparation of amines (by hydrolysis of the amide products; Section 13-12) and the formation of ε-caprolactam (from cyclohexanone oxime). Heating this cyclic amide produces a linear polymeric amide, which may be spun into the synthetic fiber Perlon.

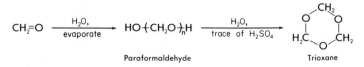

Cyclohexanone   ε-Caprolactam   Perlon
oxime

i. Polymerization. The lower aldehydes show a marked tendency to polymerize. Formaldehyde, for example, polymerizes spontaneously at a temperature slightly above its freezing point ($-92°$), and its existence as a polymer in aqueous solution has already been noted (Section 12-7f). A 37 per cent solution of formaldehyde (and/or its polymer) in water containing 10 to 15 per cent methanol, **formalin,** is used as a germicide, fungicide, insecticide, and embalming agent. Evaporation of formalin solution yields a solid polymer, $HO(CH_2O)_xH$, known as **paraformaldehyde.** On heating, paraformaldehyde depolymerizes into gaseous formaldehyde, and thus finds use as a fumigant. Treatment of a 60 to 65 per cent aqueous solution of formaldehyde with a trace of sulfuric acid affords a crystalline cyclic trimer, **trioxane.**

$$CH_2{=}O \xrightarrow[\text{evaporate}]{H_2O,} HO{-}(CH_2O){-}_nH \xrightarrow[\text{trace of } H_2SO_4]{H_2O,}$$

Paraformaldehyde   Trioxane

Acetaldehyde is also readily polymerized. When treated with a trace of sulfuric acid at ordinary temperature, it is converted into a stable cyclic trimer called **paraldehyde,** which finds use as an efficient soporific of low toxicity. When heated with sulfuric acid, paraldehyde may also be depolymerized. If acetaldehyde is polymerized with dry hydrogen chloride at a low temperature, a solid cyclic tetramer, **metaldehyde,** is formed. Although a solid, metaldehyde has sufficient vapor pressure to be ignited readily, and thus is marketed as "canned heat" for limited heating purposes. Metaldehyde is also attractive as well as toxic to slugs and snails, and thus finds extensive use as a garden bait. Aromatic aldehydes and ketones in general show little or no tendency to polymerize.

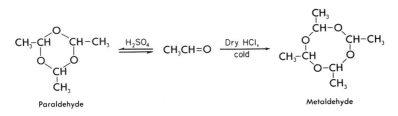

Paraldehyde   Metaldehyde

j. Further Addition Reactions. There are several further addition reactions which are important and characteristic for aldehydes and some ketones. The following general equations and examples summarize each of these reactions, which are in turn discussed briefly below. Notice in each addition reaction that the electron-rich (δ^-) end of the addendum adds to the electrophilic (δ^+) carbon atom end of the carbonyl group, and that the electrophilic (δ^+) end of the addendum adds to the nucleophilic (δ^-) carbonyl oxygen atom.

1. Cyanohydrin Formation

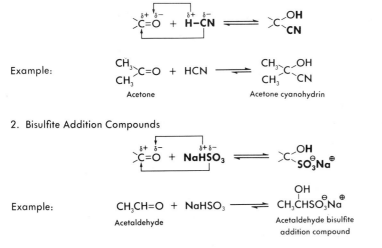

3. Reformatsky Reaction

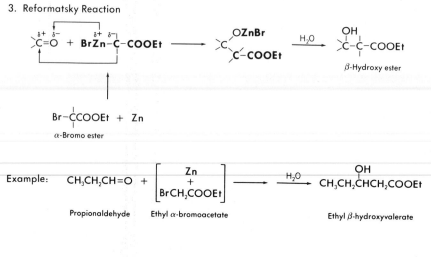

Example:

Propionaldehyde   Ethyl α-bromoacetate   Ethyl β-hydroxyvalerate

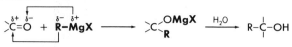

4. Grignard Addition

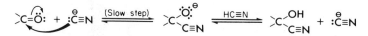

Example: See Section 11-5e

Cyanohydrins are formed by the action of hydrogen cyanide on aldehydes and many ketones. The reaction is one of equilibrium, and in the case of ketones having aryl groups or bulky substituents on the carbonyl group, yields are generally low because of steric hindrance to the addition. In the case of aryl ketones, diminished electrophilic character of the carbonyl carbon atom (due to resonance interaction with the aromatic ring; Section 10-6) also contributes to incomplete addition. Cyanohydrin formation is catalyzed by cyanide ion, according to the following mechanism:

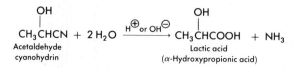

Cyanohydrins are important in that their hydrolysis provides a means of preparing α-hydroxy acids, for example:

$$\underset{\substack{\text{Acetaldehyde}\\\text{cyanohydrin}}}{CH_3\overset{\displaystyle OH}{\underset{|}{C}}HCN} + 2\,H_2O \xrightarrow{H^{\oplus} \text{ or } OH^{\ominus}} \underset{\substack{\text{Lactic acid}\\(\alpha\text{-Hydroxypropionic acid})}}{CH_3\overset{\displaystyle OH}{\underset{|}{C}}HCOOH} + NH_3$$

When a saturated aqueous solution of sodium bisulfite is shaken with an aldehyde, a white crystalline **bisulfite addition compound** forms in equilibrium. Again, as a result of steric hindrance or resonance effects, the equilibrium lies far to the left for ketones with bulky substituents and for aryl ketones. Like cyanohydrin formation, bisulfite addition is thus satisfactory only for relatively unhindered methyl ketones, $RCOCH_3$, or for cyclic ketones like cyclohexanone, whose carbonyl substituents are effectively "tied back out of the way" due to their ring structure. Bisulfite addition compounds are sometimes useful as a means of separating aldehydes from other substances, since the aldehyde may be regenerated from the addition compound with dilute acid or base. The action of sodium cyanide on bisulfite addition compounds also provides a convenient alternative preparation of cyanohydrins.

$$RCH\!=\!O \xleftarrow{\;H^{\oplus}\text{or }OH^{\ominus}\;} RCHSO_3^{\ominus}Na^{\oplus} \xrightarrow{\;NaCN\;} R\overset{\overset{\displaystyle OH}{|}}{C}HCN$$

The **Reformatsky reaction,** which involves the reaction of an α-bromo ester, $RCH(Br)COOEt$, plus zinc dust with an aldehyde or ketone, is useful for the synthesis of β-hydroxy esters and (after hydrolysis) β-hydroxy acids. The reaction is believed to involve the initial formation of the organozinc derivative $RCH(ZnBr)COOEt$, which then adds to the carbonyl group of the aldehyde or ketone in the same manner as does the Grignard reagent. Such organozinc compounds, however, are less reactive in carbonyl additions than are Grignard reagents; they do not, for example, undergo addition to the carbonyl group of esters.

Grignard addition reactions to aldehydes and ketones have been previously discussed as methods for the preparation of primary, secondary, and tertiary alcohols (Section 11-5e).

k. Aldol Condensation. When acetaldehyde is warmed with a trace of base catalyst, it undergoes a self-addition reaction known as the **aldol condensation.** Notice that the hydrogen atom on a carbon adjacent to the

$$CH_3CH\!=\!O\ +\ H\!-\!CH_2CH\!=\!O \xrightleftharpoons{\;Base\;} CH_3\overset{\overset{\displaystyle OH}{|}}{C}HCH_2CH\!=\!O$$

Aldol
(B.p. 83°/20 mm)

carbonyl group (α-hydrogen) of one acetaldehyde molecule adds to the carbonyl oxygen of another acetaldehyde molecule, that the remainder of the former aldehyde molecule adds to the carbonyl carbon of the latter, and that the reaction is an equilibrium. The product obtained, "aldol" (3-hydroxybutanal), provides also the class name for analogous β-hydroxyaldehydes. Aldol products form similarly from any aldehydes having one or more α-hydrogen atoms. In the following example with propionaldehyde, note again the specific involvement of the α-hydrogen. Because the aldol condensation is an equilibrium, aldols themselves may be reconverted into aldehydes by heating with dilute alkali (**reverse aldol reaction**).

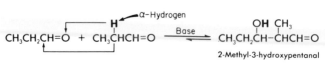

When a *mixture* of two different aldehydes, each possessing an α-hydrogen, is treated with base, four different aldol products result. In the general example shown, we see that the aldehyde 12-**33** may add to itself to yield the aldol 12-**35**, or add to 12-**34** to yield the **crossed aldol** 12-**36**. Similarly, 12-**34** may add to itself to give 12-**37**, or to 12-**33** to give the crossed aldol 12-**38**. Because of the mixtures obtained, such reactions are of little preparative value.

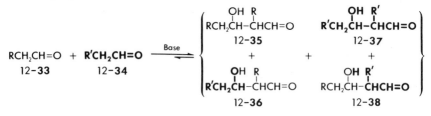

Aldol condensations do not take place between aldehydes containing no α-hydrogen atoms. Such aldehydes, however, may act as "acceptors" to aldehydes which do contain α-hydrogens. The addition of acetaldehyde, for example, to trimethylacetaldehyde (12-**39**) satisfactorily affords the crossed aldol 12-**40**. Note that 12-**39** contains no α-hydrogen and hence

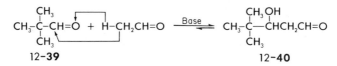

cannot condense with itself. Benzaldehyde, which also contains no α-hydrogen, reacts with acetaldehyde in an analogous manner. In this case the crossed aldol product (12-**41**) spontaneously dehydrates, however, and the α,β-unsaturated aldehyde cinnamaldehyde results (**Claisen-Schmidt con-**

$$PhCH=O + H-CH_2CH=O \xrightarrow{Base} \left[\overset{OH}{\underset{|}{PhCH}}-CH_2CH=O \right] \xrightarrow{-H_2O} \overset{\beta}{PhCH}=\overset{\alpha}{CH}CH=O$$

12-**41**   Cinnamaldehyde

densation). Cinnamaldehyde is the chief constituent of oil of cinnamon, and is widely used in flavoring and perfumery. Aldols in general may be dehydrated to α,β-unsaturated aldehydes by heating them alone or with a trace of mineral acid, as in the following conversion of aldol into croton-aldehyde.

$$\underset{\substack{| \quad | \\ }}{\overset{\text{OH H}}{CH_3CH-CHCH=O}} \xrightarrow{H^\oplus, \text{heat}} CH_3\overset{\beta}{CH}=\overset{\alpha}{CH}CH=O + H_2O$$

Crotonaldehyde

Ketones containing α-hydrogen atoms undergo the aldol condensation to only a limited extent; that is, the equilibria lie far to the left, presumably as a consequence of steric hindrance to the carbonyl addition. Thus, at equilibrium, acetone is only slightly converted to its aldol ("diacetone alcohol," 12-42). By allowing hot acetone to percolate through insoluble

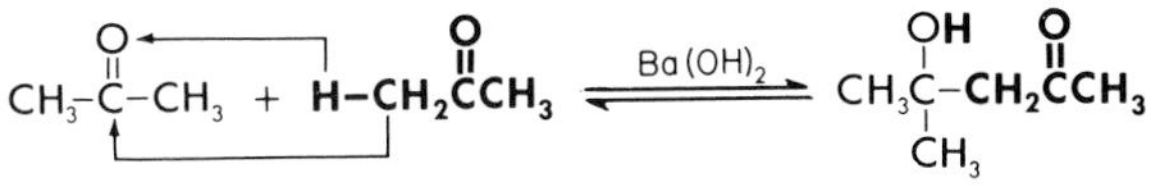

$$CH_3\overset{\overset{\text{O}}{\|}}{C}-CH_3 + H-CH_2\overset{\overset{\text{O}}{\|}}{C}CH_3 \underset{}{\overset{Ba(OH)_2}{\rightleftharpoons}} \underset{\substack{| \\ CH_3}}{CH_3\overset{\text{OH}}{\underset{}{C}}-CH_2\overset{\overset{\text{O}}{\|}}{C}CH_3}$$

12-42

barium hydroxide catalyst contained in a Soxhlet thimble (see Figure 3-1), however, the aldol 12-42 may be obtained in excellent yield, since the catalyst is thereby kept out of contact with the bulk of the aldol product which accumulates in the Soxhlet extractor flask. Acetone also undergoes the following Claisen-Schmidt condensation with benzaldehyde.

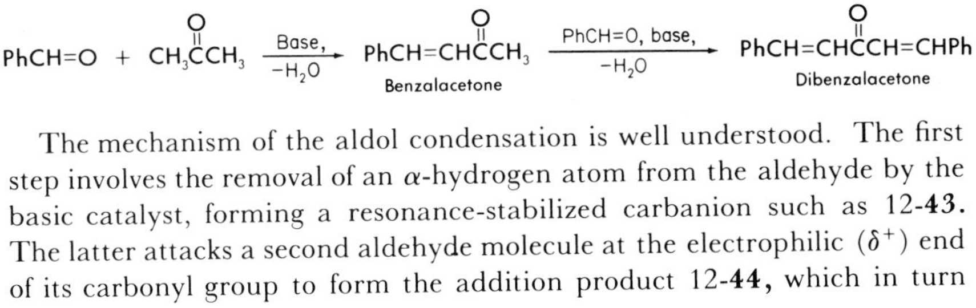

$$PhCH=O + CH_3\overset{\overset{\text{O}}{\|}}{C}CH_3 \xrightarrow[-H_2O]{Base,} PhCH=CH\overset{\overset{\text{O}}{\|}}{C}CH_3 \xrightarrow[-H_2O]{PhCH=O, base,} PhCH=CH\overset{\overset{\text{O}}{\|}}{C}CH=CHPh$$

Benzalacetone   Dibenzalacetone

The mechanism of the aldol condensation is well understood. The first step involves the removal of an α-hydrogen atom from the aldehyde by the basic catalyst, forming a resonance-stabilized carbanion such as 12-43. The latter attacks a second aldehyde molecule at the electrophilic (δ^+) end of its carbonyl group to form the addition product 12-44, which in turn

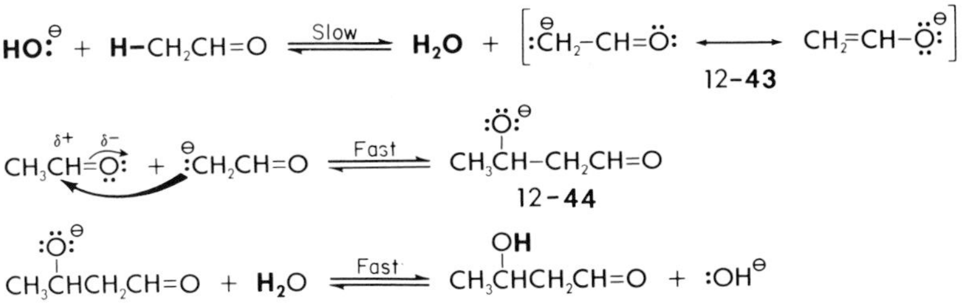

$$HO\overset{\ominus}{:} + H-CH_2CH=O \underset{}{\overset{\text{Slow}}{\rightleftharpoons}} H_2O + \left[:\overset{\ominus}{C}H_2-CH=\overset{..}{O}: \longleftrightarrow CH_2=CH-\overset{..}{\underset{..}{O}}{:}^\ominus \right]$$

12-43

$$\underset{\substack{\delta^+ \quad \delta^- }}{CH_3CH=\overset{..}{\underset{..}{O}}:} + \overset{\ominus}{:}CH_2CH=O \xrightarrow{\text{Fast}} \underset{\substack{| \\ }}{CH_3CH-CH_2CH=O}$$
(with $:\overset{..}{\underset{..}{O}}{:}^\ominus$ above)

12-44

$$\underset{\substack{| \\ }}{CH_3CHCH_2CH=O} + H_2O \xrightarrow{\text{Fast}} \underset{\substack{| \\ }}{CH_3CHCH_2CH=O} + :OH^\ominus$$
(with $:\overset{..}{\underset{..}{O}}{:}^\ominus$ and OH above)

Figure 12-10. Mechanism of the Aldol Condensation

exchanges a proton with water (or another proton source), yielding the aldol product and regenerating the catalyst. Kinetic experiments indicate that the first step in the reaction sequence is slow, as does the fact that when the condensation is allowed to proceed incompletely in the presence of D_2O, very few C–D bonds are found either in the aldol product or in the unreacted aldehyde.

I. Related Condensations. In light of the previous discussion it is not surprising that other types of carbanions are also frequently capable of adding to carbonyl groups. Under the influence of suitable basic catalysts, α-hydrogen atoms may be removed from carboxylic esters, carboxylic anhydrides, nitriles, and nitroalkanes, for example, and the resulting resonance-stabilized carbanions may add to the carbonyl groups of aldehydes and ketones as described above. A variety of important types of products result from such condensation reactions, which are illustrated briefly by the following examples.

Condensation with Ester (Claisen Condensation)

$$CH_3COOEt + EtO:^{\ominus} \rightleftharpoons EtOH + \left[:CH_2\overset{:O:}{\underset{\|}{C}}OEt \longleftrightarrow CH_2=\overset{:\ddot{O}:}{\underset{|}{C}}OEt \right]^{\ominus}$$

Ethyl acetate

$$RCH=O + {}^{\ominus}:CH_2COOEt \xrightarrow{Etc.} RCH=CHCOOEt$$

α,β-Unsaturated ester

Condensation with Malonic Ester (Knoevenagel Condensation)

$$CH_2(COOEt)_2 + EtO:^{\ominus} \rightleftharpoons EtOH + \left[EtO\overset{O}{\underset{\|}{C}}\overset{O}{\underset{\|}{C}}HCOEt \longleftrightarrow EtO\overset{:\ddot{O}:}{\underset{|}{C}}=CH\overset{O}{\underset{\|}{C}}OEt \longleftrightarrow EtO\overset{O}{\underset{\|}{C}}CH=\overset{:\ddot{O}:}{\underset{|}{C}}OEt \right]^{\ominus}$$

Ethyl malonate

$$RCH=O + {}^{\ominus}:CH(COOEt)_2 \xrightarrow{Etc.} RCH=C\overset{COOEt}{\underset{COOEt}{\diagdown}}$$

α,β-Unsaturated malonic ester

Condensation with Carboxylic Acid Anhydride (Perkin Reaction)

$$PhCH=O + CH_3\overset{O}{\underset{\|}{C}}O\overset{O}{\underset{\|}{C}}CH_3 \xrightarrow[(-H_2O)]{CH_3COONa} PhCH=CH\overset{O}{\underset{\|}{C}}O\overset{O}{\underset{\|}{C}}CH_3 \xrightarrow{H_2O} PhCH=CHCOOH + CH_3COOH$$

Acetic anhydride α,β-Unsaturated β-aryl acid

Coumarin, a constituent of lavender oil used in perfumery, is prepared synthetically by application of the Perkin reaction to salicylaldehyde. Note that sodium acetate is used as the base in these condensations.

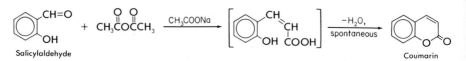

Salicylaldehyde   Coumarin

Condensation with Nitrile

$$CH_3C{\equiv}N + EtO:^{\ominus} \rightleftharpoons EtOH + \left[:CH_2{-}C{\equiv}\ddot{N} \longleftrightarrow CH_2{=}C{=}\ddot{N}:\right]^{\ominus}$$

Acetonitrile

$$RCH{=}O + {}^{\ominus}\!:CH_2CN \xrightarrow{\text{Etc.}} RCH{=}CHCN$$

α,β-Unsaturated nitrile

Condensation with Nitroalkane

$$CH_3NO_2 + EtO:^{\ominus} \rightleftharpoons EtOH + \left[:CH_2{-}N{\overset{\ddot{\ddot{O}:}}{\underset{O}{\diagdown}}} \longleftrightarrow CH_2{=}N{\overset{\ddot{\ddot{O}:}}{\underset{O}{\diagdown}}}\right]^{\ominus}$$

Nitromethane

$$RCH{=}O + {}^{\ominus}\!:CH_2NO_2 \xrightarrow{\text{Etc.}} \overset{\overset{\displaystyle OH}{|}}{RCH}{-}CH_2NO_2$$

β-Hydroxynitroalkane

m. Benzoin Condensation. With cyanide ion as catalyst, benzaldehyde undergoes an unusual self-condensation to produce the α-hydroxy ketone

$$2\ PhCH{=}O \xrightarrow[\text{EtOH, H}_2\text{O}]{\text{NaCN}} \overset{\overset{\displaystyle OH\ \ O}{|\quad\ \parallel}}{PhCH}{-}\overset{}{C}Ph$$

Benzoin

(M.p. 134°)

benzoin. The reaction is also shown by certain other armomatic aldehydes, and the resulting products of the type ArCH(OH)COAr are generally called **acyloins**. Treatment of a mixture of aromatic aldehydes
with sodium cyanide likewise produces **mixed acyloins** of the types
ArCH(OH)COAr' and Ar'CH(OH)COAr, with one of the isomers usually
predominating. Since cyanide ion is basic in aqueous solution (that is,
$CN^{\ominus} + H_2O \rightleftharpoons HCN + OH^{\ominus}$), aliphatic aldehydes generally undergo
the aldol condensation under these conditions. However, in the presence
of yeast, acetaldehyde is transformed into acetoin, $CH_3CH(OH)COCH_3$,
while a mixture of acetaldehyde and benzaldehyde forms the mixed acyloin
benzacetoin, $PhCH(OH)COCH_3$.

The mechanism in Figure 12-11 is in accord with the kinetics of the ben-

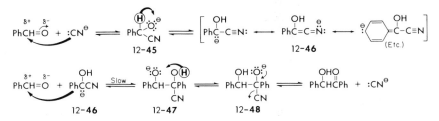

Figure 12-11. Mechanism of the Benzoin Condensation

zoin condensation. Addition of cyanide ion to the carbonyl group of benz-aldehyde produces an anion (12-**45**) which, underoing a proton shift from carbon to oxygen, affords the resonance-stabilized carbanion 12-**46**. This in turn adds to benzaldehyde to form 12-**47**, which by proton migration gives 12-**48**. The latter loses cyanide ion to form the benzoin product and regenerate the catalyst. The reversibility of the entire scheme is shown by the fact that mixed acyloins result when benzoin and a substituted benzaldehyde are treated with sodium cyanide.

Benzoin is readily oxidized to the α-diketone known as benzil, and other acyloins may be oxidized analogously. With phenylhydrazine, acyloins form bisphenylhydrazones (two phenylhydrazone residues) called **osa-zones** (Section 16-4a).

$$\underset{\text{PhCHCPh}}{\overset{\text{HO O}}{|\ \ ||}} + (O) \xrightarrow[\text{pyridine, H}_2\text{O}]{\text{CuSO}_4,} \underset{\text{PhCCPh}}{\overset{\text{OO}}{||\ ||}} + \text{H}_2\text{O}$$

Benzil
(M. p. 95°)

$$\begin{matrix}\overset{\text{OHO}}{\underset{|\ ||}{\text{PhCHCPh}}} \\ + \\ \text{PhNHNH}_2\end{matrix} \longrightarrow \begin{bmatrix}\text{PhC=NNHPh} \\ | \\ \text{PhCHOH}\end{bmatrix} \xrightarrow{\text{PhNHNH}_2} \begin{bmatrix}\text{PhC=NNHPh} \\ | \\ \text{PhC=O}\end{bmatrix} \xrightarrow{\text{PhNHNH}_2} \begin{matrix}\text{PhC=NNHPh} \\ | \\ \text{PhC=NNHPh}\end{matrix}$$

$$+ \ \text{PhNH}_2 \ + \ \text{NH}_3$$

Benzil osazone

Benzil and related α-diketones undergo the interesting **benzilic acid rearrangement** when heated with aqueous or alcoholic alkali, a reaction for which the following mechanism is known to be operative.

$$\underset{\text{PhCCPh}}{\overset{\text{OO}}{||\ ||}} + :\text{OH}^\ominus \rightleftharpoons \begin{bmatrix}\underset{\text{(Ph)}}{\overset{\ddot{\text{O}}:^\ominus \text{O}}{\text{HO–C–C–Ph}}}\end{bmatrix} \xrightarrow{\text{Ph}\sim} \begin{matrix}\overset{\text{O}\ \ddot{\text{O}}:^\ominus}{\text{HO–C–C–Ph}} \\ \text{Ph}\end{matrix} \longrightarrow \underset{\text{Ph}}{\overset{\text{Ph}}{}}\text{C–C}\overset{\text{O}}{\underset{\ddot{\text{O}}:^\ominus}{}} \xrightarrow{\text{H}^\oplus} \underset{\text{Ph}}{\overset{\text{Ph}}{}}\text{CCOOH}$$

Benzilic acid
(M.p. 151°)

n. Cannizzaro Reaction. Aldehydes *lacking an α-hydrogen atom,* and hence incapable of participating in the aldol condensation, undergo a re-markable oxidation-reduction reaction when heated with strong alkali, a process discovered by S. Cannizzaro in 1853. The following examples with formaldehyde and benzaldehyde are typical.

$$2\,\text{CH}_2{=}\text{O} + \text{NaOH} \rightarrow \underset{\text{Sodium formate}}{\text{HCOO}^\ominus\text{Na}^\oplus} + \underset{\text{Methanol}}{\text{CH}_3\text{OH}}$$

$$2\,\text{PhCH}{=}\text{O} + \text{NaOH} \rightarrow \underset{\text{Sodium benzoate}}{\text{PhCOO}^\ominus\text{Na}^\oplus} + \underset{\text{Benzyl alcohol}}{\text{PhCH}_2\text{OH}}$$

Notice that one molecule of the aldehyde is oxidized to the salt of a carbox-ylic acid, while a second molecule of the aldehyde is reduced to the cor-

responding alcohol.   Such self-oxidation-reduction processes are called
disproportionation reactions.

The mechanism of this important reaction has been well studied, and is believed to proceed as shown in Figure 12-12. Hydroxide ion attacks the

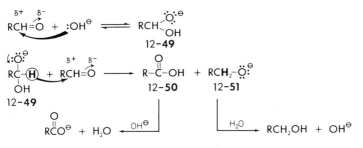

Figure 12-12.   Mechanism of the Cannizzaro Reaction

aldehyde carbonyl group to form the adduct 12-**49.** This in turn transfers a hydride ion ($H:^{\ominus}$) *intermolecularly* to another aldehyde molecule, forming the carboxylic acid 12-**50** and the alkoxide ion 12-**51,** which ultimately form the final products. In support of the hydride ion transfer step, it is found that if the Cannizzaro reaction is carried out in D_2O, no C–D bonds are found in the resulting alcohol product.

When a mixture of formaldehyde and another aldehyde having no α-hydrogen is heated with strong alkali, the formaldehyde is preferentially oxidized and the other aldehyde is reduced.

$$ArCH{=}O + CH_2{=}O \xrightarrow{\text{NaOH}} HCOO^{\ominus}Na^{\oplus} + ArCH_2OH$$

This process, called a **crossed Cannizzaro reaction,** is useful as a means of preparing alcohols of the type $ArCH_2OH$. The technically important tetrahydric alcohol pentaerythritol (United States production in 1961, over 32 million pounds) is prepared from acetaldehyde and formaldehyde by a

Aldol step

$$3\ CH_2{=}O + H{-}\overset{\displaystyle H}{\underset{\displaystyle H}{C}}{-}CH{=}O \xrightarrow{OH^{\ominus}} HOCH_2{-}\overset{\displaystyle CH_2OH}{\underset{\displaystyle CH_2OH}{C}}{-}CH{=}O$$

Crossed Cannizzaro step

$$HOCH_2\overset{\displaystyle CH_2OH}{\underset{\displaystyle CH_2OH}{CCH}}{=}O + CH_2{=}O \xrightarrow{OH^{\ominus}} HCOO^{\ominus} + HOCH_2\overset{\displaystyle CH_2OH}{\underset{\displaystyle CH_2OH}{CCH_2OH}}$$

Pentaerythritol

combination of the aldol condensation and the crossed Cannizzaro reaction. Pentaerythritol is esterified with polybasic acids to produce **alkyd resin** polymers. Its nitrate ester, pentaerythritol tetranitrate (PETN), is used as an explosive and medicinally as a vasodilator.

    o. Wittig Reaction.   In 1954, G. Wittig discovered a novel procedure for the conversion of the carbonyl group of aldehydes or ketones into the methylene group, $=CH_2$. This general method for the preparation of 1-alkenes involves the reaction of the carbonyl group with triphenylphosphinemethylene, which is a resonance hybrid of a **methylene structure** and an **ylide structure**.   The triphenylphosphinemethylene reagent is generated in

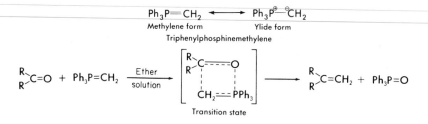

ether from triphenylphosphine by the following sequence of reactions, and the aldehyde or ketone is added directly to the ether solution to accomplish the Wittig reaction illustrated above.

$$Ph_3P \xrightarrow{CH_3Br} Ph_3\overset{\oplus}{P}CH_3, \overset{\ominus}{Br} \xrightarrow[\text{(Phenyllithium)}]{PhLi} \overset{\oplus}{Li}\overset{\ominus}{Br} + PhH + Ph_3P=CH_2$$

Triphenyl-   Methyltriphenyl-
phosphine   phosphonium
             bromide

    p. Baeyer-Villiger Reaction.   Around 1900, A. Baeyer and V. Villiger discovered that ketones could be converted into esters by oxidation with permonosulfuric acid, $HO—SO_2—OOH$ (Caro's acid). Other peracids, such as peracetic, CH_3CO_3H, and perbenzoic, $PhCO_3H$, acids, are also effec-

$$\underset{RCR}{\overset{\overset{\displaystyle O}{\|}}{}} \xrightarrow{H_2SO_5} \underset{RCOR}{\overset{\overset{\displaystyle O}{\|}}{}}$$

tive, and the reaction proves to be acid catalyzed. In 1953, W. von E. Doering used O^{18}-labeled benzophenone to demonstrate that a mechanism such as that in Figure 12-13 was operative. Notice that the phenyl group migrates *with its pair of electrons* from carbon to oxygen, a 1,2 shift reminiscent of that occurring during the Wagner-Meerwein (Section 8-3a) and pinacol (Section 11-8b) rearrangements. The reaction takes place with both aliphatic and aromatic ketones, and unsymmetrical ketones, RCOR', can lead to two ester products, RCOOR' and R'COOR. In such cases it is found that the group migrating to the positively charged oxygen atom is

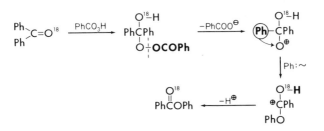

Figure 12-13. Mechanism of the Baeyer-Villiger Reaction

the one more capable of electron release. Thus the order of migratory aptitude in the alkyl ketone series is tertiary > secondary > primary, and in
the aryl series p-CH$_3$OC$_6$H$_4$— > Ph > p-O$_2$NC$_6$H$_4$—. The migrating
group in such rearrangements is found to retain its stereochemical configuration:

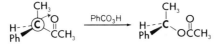

q. **Reaction with Diazomethane.** Diazomethane, CH$_2$N$_2$, in water or alcohol reacts with simple aldehydes and ketones with the liberation of nitrogen and the formation of a mixture of a ketone and an epoxide. Notice in

$$RCH=O + CH_2N_2 \longrightarrow N_2 + RCCH_3 + RCH-CH_2$$

$$RCR + CH_2N_2 \longrightarrow N_2 + RCCH_2R + \underset{R}{\overset{R}{\diagdown}}C-CH_2$$

each of the examples shown that a methylene group, —CH$_2$—, has been
inserted adjacent to the carbonyl group in the ketonic product. The reaction is particularly useful when applied to cyclic ketones, which undergo
an analogous ring expansion to the next higher cyclic ketone. Thus cyclohexanone may be converted into cycloheptanone in acceptable yield. The

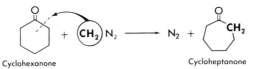

Cyclohexanone   Cycloheptanone

mechanism of this interesting **methylene insertion** reaction is believed to
involve preliminary addition of the diazomethane hybrid (12-52) to the
carbonyl group of the aldehyde or ketone, forming an adduct (12-53) which

loses nitrogen to form the dipolar ion 12-**54**. The latter may undergo direct ring closure to the epoxide 12-**55**, or alternatively undergo a 1,2 shift of an alkyl (or aryl) group to yield the homologous ketone 12-**56**.

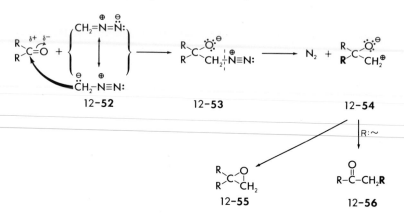

| 12-**52** | 12-**53** | 12-**54** |

12-**55**   12-**56**

12-8. α,β-Unsaturated Aldehydes and Ketones

In Section 12-7k we learned that α,β-unsaturated aldehydes and ketones could be prepared by the dehydration of aldols. Notice that the α,β-alkene linkage in such structures (for example, $RCH=CHCH=O$) is *conjugated* with the double bond of the carbonyl group. As with conjugated dienes and polyenes (Section 8-5), this conjugation alters both the physical and chemical properties of α,β-unsaturated carbonyl compounds.

Physically, both the infrared and ultraviolet spectra of aldehydes and ketones are markedly affected by α,β-unsaturation. While aliphatic aldehydes have carbonyl stretching frequencies in the infrared region 1740 to 1720 cm^{-1}, α,β-unsaturated aldehydes display their carbonyl frequencies between 1705 and 1685 cm^{-1}. Similar shifts to lower carbonyl absorption frequencies (longer wavelengths) are found in α,β-unsaturated ketones. In the ultraviolet region, acetaldehyde shows very weak carbonyl absorption at 293 mμ. In crotonaldehyde, $CH_3CH=CHCH=O$, this band is shifted to 322 mμ, its intensity increases almost tenfold, and a new very intense absorption band characteristic of the conjugated chromophore appears at 220 mμ. Analogous ultraviolet spectral differences are noted between other aldehydes or ketones and their α,β-unsaturated analogs.

Chemically, again as with conjugated dienes, α,β-unsaturated carbonyl compounds may undergo 1,2 and/or 1,4-addition (**conjugate addition**) in typical addition reactions involving the carbonyl group. In the general case, the α,β-unsaturated carbonyl group may be represented as the resonance hybrid 12-**57**, and we note that the nucleophilic (δ⁻) end of an ad-

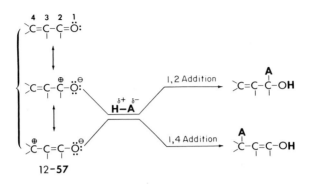

12-57

dendum $H^{\delta+}$—$A^{\delta-}$ may add to the hybrid at the electron-deficient center either at position 2 (1,2 addition) or position 4 (1,4 addition). The particular mode of addition followed in a specific case depends both upon the addendum and the structure of the α,β-unsaturated compound. In general, conjugate addition is favored when steric factors in either reactant hinder direct 1,2 addition to the carbonyl group. A few typical examples of 1,4 addition are shown in the equations below.

12-58

Notice that the initial adduct 12-58 is an unstable enol, and undergoes spontaneous isomerization to the more stable keto structure. α,β-Unsaturated aldehydes, in contrast to such ketones, generally undergo 1,2 addition with hydrogen cyanide. A similar pattern is observed during reaction with sodium bisulfite, α,β-unsaturated aldehydes tending to give 1,2 addition and ketones 1,4 addition.

Although 1,2 addition of hydrogen halides to the carbonyl group of aldehydes and ketones does not occur, conjugate addition is observed in the reaction of hydrogen halides with α,β-unsaturated carbonyl compounds. Note that the 1,4 addition process results in an apparent anti-Markownikoff addition in such cases.

$$RCH{=}CHCH{=}O \ + \ HX \longrightarrow \left[\overset{X}{\underset{|}{R}CHCH{=}CHOH} \right] \xrightarrow{\text{Ketonization}} \overset{X}{\underset{|}{R}CHCH_2CH{=}O}$$

Grignard reagents show an increasing preference for 1,4 over 1,2 addition as the size of the R group in either $RMgX$ or $R'CH{=}CHCOR$ increases. Benzaldeoxybenzoin (12-**59**), for example, reacts with phenyl-magnesium bromide to give a 1,4 adduct (12-**60**), which yields the enol (12-**61**) on hydrolysis. The latter undergoes slow ketonization to the more stable keto isomer (12-**62**). Having carbonyl groups which are sterically less hindered, α,β-unsaturated aldehydes generally undergo 1,2 addition with Grignard reagents.

$$PhCH=\underset{\underset{Ph}{|}}{\overset{\overset{O}{\|}}{C}}CPh \xrightarrow{PhMgBr} \underset{Ph}{\overset{Ph}{>}}CH\underset{\underset{Ph}{|}}{C}=\overset{\overset{OMgBr}{|}}{C}Ph \xrightarrow{H_2O} \underset{Ph}{\overset{Ph}{>}}CH\underset{\underset{Ph}{|}}{C}=\overset{\overset{OH}{|}}{C}Ph \longrightarrow \underset{Ph}{\overset{Ph}{>}}CH\underset{\underset{Ph}{|}}{CH}\overset{\overset{O}{\|}}{C}Ph$$

$$\quad\quad\quad 12\text{-}59 \quad\quad\quad\quad\quad 12\text{-}60 \quad\quad\quad\quad\quad 12\text{-}61 \quad\quad\quad\quad\quad 12\text{-}62$$

Probably the most useful, synthetically, of the conjugate additions is the so-called **Michael reaction,** which involves the 1,4 addition of resonance-stabilized carbanions from dicarboxylic esters such as ethyl malonate and related compounds (Section 12-71) to α,β-unsaturated aldehydes, ketones, and other derivatives. The following addition of the carbanion (12-**64**) of ethyl malonate (12-**63**) to benzalacetophenone (12-**65**) is a typical example of this important reaction. Notice in all 1,4 additions which are followed by a ketonization step, that the net result of the overall process is a 3,4 addition.

$$CH_2(COOEt)_2 + EtO:^{\ominus} \rightleftharpoons EtOH + :\overset{\ominus}{C}H(COOEt)$$
$$\quad\quad 12\text{-}63 \quad\quad\quad\quad\quad\quad\quad\quad\quad\quad 12\text{-}64$$

$$PhCH=\overset{\overset{\overset{\ddot{O}:}{\|}}{\curvearrowleft}}{CH}CPh + {}^{\ominus}:CH(COOEt)_2 \longrightarrow PhCHCH=\overset{\overset{:\overset{\ominus}{\ddot{O}}:}{|}}{C}Ph \xrightarrow{H_2O} PhCHCH_2\overset{\overset{O}{\|}}{C}Ph$$
$$\quad\quad\quad\quad\quad\quad\quad\quad\quad\quad\quad\quad\quad\quad\quad\quad\quad | \quad\quad\quad\quad\quad\quad\quad\quad | $$
$$\quad\quad\quad\quad\quad\quad\quad\quad\quad\quad\quad\quad\quad\quad\quad CH(COOEt)_2 \quad\quad\quad\quad CH(COOEt)_2$$
$$12\text{-}65$$

α,β-Unsaturated carbonyl compounds having γ-hydrogen atoms display γ-hydrogen activation analogous to the α-hydrogen activation observed in saturated aldehydes and ketones. Crotonaldehyde (12-**66**), for example, will undergo a typical aldol condensation with other aldehydes not having an α-hydrogen atom, as shown. Notice that the carbanion obtained by

$$\overset{\gamma}{C}\overset{\beta}{H_3}CH=\overset{\alpha}{C}HCH=O + :\overset{\ominus}{O}H \rightleftharpoons H_2O + \left[:\overset{\ominus}{C}H_2CH=CHCH=O \longleftrightarrow CH_2=CHCH=CH-\overset{..}{\overset{\ominus}{\ddot{O}}}: \right]$$
$$\quad 12\text{-}66 \quad\quad\quad\quad\quad\quad\quad\quad\quad\quad\quad 12\text{-}67$$

$$\overset{\delta+}{P}hC\overset{\delta-}{H}=O + {}^{\ominus}:CH_2CH=CHCH=O \longrightarrow PhCHCH_2CH=CHCH=O \xrightarrow{H_2O} PhCHCH_2CH=CHCH=O + :OH^{\ominus}$$
$$\quad\quad\quad\quad\quad\quad\quad\quad\quad\quad\quad\quad\quad\quad | \quad\quad\quad\quad\quad\quad\quad\quad\quad\quad\quad | $$
$$\quad\quad\quad\quad\quad\quad\quad\quad\quad\quad\quad\quad\quad :\overset{..}{\overset{\ominus}{\ddot{O}}}: \quad\quad\quad\quad\quad\quad\quad\quad\quad OH$$

removing the γ-hydrogen atom is stabilized as the resonance hybrid 12-**67**, which adds as before to the carbonyl group of the second aldehyde molecule. The above example illustrates the **principle of vinylogy,** which states that a resonance interaction involving groups A and B in a compound A—B will also operate in compounds of the type A–$(CH=CH-)_n B$, that is, **vinylogs** of A—B which contain one or more vinyl groups, —CH=CH—, interposed between A and B. We see above, for example, how α-hydrogen activation in CH_3CH=O may be transferred to the terminal hydrogen atom in CH_3—(CH=CH—)$_n$CH=O.

12-9. Quinones

Quinones comprise an interesting special class of cyclic α,β-unsaturated diketones. They are prepared generally by the oxidation of dihydroxy, hydroxyamino, or diamino aromatic derivatives whose OH and NH_2 functions are located *ortho* or *para* to one another. The following conversions of hydroquinone into *p*-benzoquinone, 1,4-diaminonaphthalene into 1,4-naphthoquinone, and catechol into *o*-benzoquinone are typical. *p*-Benzo-

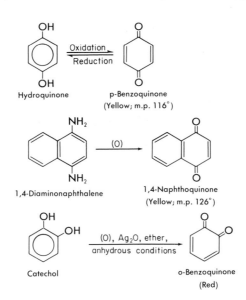

Hydroquinone   p-Benzoquinone
(Yellow; m.p. 116°)

1,4-Diaminonaphthalene   1,4-Naphthoquinone
(Yellow; m.p. 126°)

Catechol   o-Benzoquinone
(Red)

quinone (usually called simply quinone) is also prepared commercially by the oxidation of aniline ($PhNH_2$; Section 14-10d) with manganese dioxide and sulfuric acid. It finds use in photography, in the dyestuff industry, and for the tanning of hides. Its ready reduction by a variety of reducing agents provides a commercial preparation of hydroquinone (Section 11-9).

Numerous quinone derivatives are found among natural sources, where their colors early attracted attention, and where they comprise important classes of plant, mold, and fungus pigments. The following examples are typical, but represent only a small segment of the structural variations which natural quinones display.

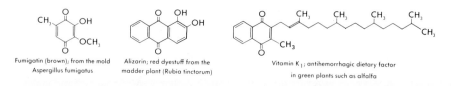

Fumigatin (brown); from the mold
Aspergillus fumigatus

Alizarin; red dyestuff from the
madder plant (Rubia tinctorum)

Vitamin K₁; antihemorrhagic dietary factor
in green plants such as alfalfa

Quinones in general are readily reduced, as indicated above with
p-benzoquinone. p-Quinones react typically by way of 1,4 addition with
reagents capable of adding to the carbonyl group, but occasionally 1,2 addition is also observed. Thus HCN adds conjugatively to p-quinones, as
do also HCl, ethyl malonate, and many other reagents, while Grignard
reagents show both 1,2 and 1,4 additions. Note that in 1,4 additions, the
product is a substituted hydroquinone, formed by rearrangement of the
initial 1,4 adduct. The use of quinones as a dienophile in the Diels-Alder
reaction has already been discussed (Section 9-7c).

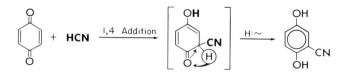

12-10. Tropolones

Another important class of unsaturated ketones which is found among
natural products is the **tropolones,** which are structural modifications of
an unusual parent molecule called tropolone. The accompanying formulas
depict the skeletal structures of tropolone and several of its derivatives
found among various plants and molds. Tropolones are chemically un-

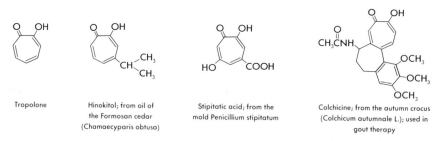

Tropolone

Hinokitol; from oil of
the Formosan cedar
(Chamaecyparis obtusa)

Stipitatic acid; from the
mold Penicillium stipitatum

Colchicine; from the autumn crocus
(Colchicum autumnale L.); used in
gout therapy

usual, and their properties are inadequately rationalized by the simple
structures shown. Thus their hydroxyl groups are phenolic in character
(they show a color reaction with ferric chloride, for example; Section
12-7b), their ketonic properties are masked, and their double bonds are
hydrogenated only with difficulty. They undergo aromatic type electro-

philic substitution reactions, such as nitration and bromination. Further-more, tropolone reacts with hydrochloric acid to form a salt whose X-ray diffraction pattern indicates that all of its carbon-carbon bond lengths are identical, and equal to the value found for benzene (1.39 Å; Section 5-1). Lastly, heat of combustion data indicate that tropolone has a resonance energy (Section 5-1) of about 22 kcal/mole, 61 per cent that of benzene.

In 1945, M. J. S. Dewar at Queen Mary's College in London proposed a structure for tropolone (unknown in its unsubstituted form at the time) which accorded with the peculiar chemical properties of its derivatives.

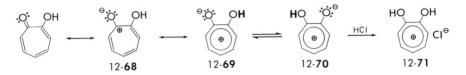

12-**68**   12-**69**   12-**70**   12-**71**

If tropolone is rewritten with its carbonyl group in the dipolar form 12-**68,** we see immediately that the positive charge may be distributed over the seven-membered cycloheptatriene ring to give the resonance hybrid 12-**69** (see Figure 6-9). By simple proton migration this may equilibrate with the equivalent resonance hybrid 12-**70**. Notice also that the hybrids 12-**69** and 12-**70** obey Hückel's rule for aromaticity (Section 10-9), in that the cyclic conjugated system has $4n + 2$ $(n = 1)$ π electrons. The above-men-tioned chemical peculiarities of tropolone are readily understandable in terms of such hybrid structures, as is its reaction with hydrochloric acid to yield the salt 1,2-dihydroxytropylium chloride (12-**71**).

12-11. Epoxides

Epoxides are 1,2 cyclic ethers related to the parent molecule epoxy-ethane (ethylene oxide). Their nomenclature is illustrated in the examples

Epoxyethane   2,3-Epoxybutane   4-Methyl-1,2-epoxycyclohexane
(Ethylene oxide)

shown. Ethylene oxide, prepared commercially by the direct oxidation of ethylene with air in the presence of finely divided silver catalyst (Section 11-6a), is a colorless, flammable gas (b.p. 13° to 14°) which is used as a fumigant, agricultural fungicide and precursor for ethylene glycol and acrylonitrile; the United States produced some 1.36 billion pounds in 1961. Epoxides in general are most conveniently prepared by the epoxidation of alkenes with perbenzoic acid, a reaction for which the following mechanism has been proposed. The action of alkali on halohydrins (Section 8-4e) also provides a general synthesis for epoxides.

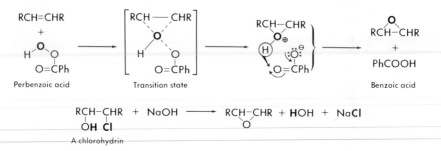

Perbenzoic acid   Transition state   Benzoic acid

$$RCH-CHR + NaOH \longrightarrow RCH-CHR + HOH + NaCl$$
$$\overset{|}{OH} \overset{|}{Cl} \qquad\qquad \overset{\diagdown O \diagup}{}$$

A chlorohydrin

   Because of the bond angle strain (Section 9-6) inherent in its three-membered heterocyclic ring, the epoxide function behaves chemically rather more like the carbonyl group than like a cyclic ether. That is, a variety of reagents which add to the carbonyl group of aldehydes and ketones, also rupture the epoxide ring—under conditions where the ordinary ether linkage is quite stable. The examples of epoxide ring cleavage shown for ethylene oxide in Figure 12-14 are typical. Under proper conditions

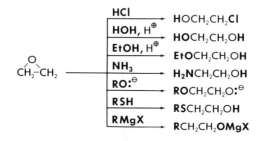

Figure 12-14.   Ring Cleavage Reactions of Ethylene Oxide

ethylene oxide may also be polymerized to a waxy, water-soluble polymer called polyethylene glycol (Carbowax).

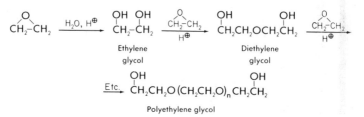

Ethylene   Diethylene
glycol   glycol

Polyethylene glycol

SUPPLEMENTARY READING

1. "Keto-Enol Tautomerism of Ethyl Acetoacetate," C. H. Ward, *J. Chem. Educ.*, **39,** 95 (1962).
2. "Enolization: An Electronic Interpretation," S. Zuffanti, *J. Chem. Educ.*, **22,** 230 (1945).
3. "The Iodoform Reaction," R. N. Seelye and T. A. Turney, *J. Chem. Educ.*, **36,** 572 (1959).
4. "The Pyrolytic Decomposition of Carboxylate Salts to Ketones," H. P. Schultz and J. P. Sichels, *J. Chem. Educ.*, **38,** 300 (1961).

CHAPTER 13

Carboxylic Acids and Their Derivatives

CARBOXYLIC ACIDS

THE CARBOXYL GROUP, $-\overset{\overset{\textstyle O}{\|}}{C}-OH$, is the functional unit characteristic of carboxylic acids, which may be of the aliphatic, RCOOH, aromatic, ArCOOH, or heterocyclic series. This class of compounds also includes di- and polycarboxylic acids (two or more —COOH groups per molecule), as well as carboxylic acids also possessing other functional groups. Carboxylic acids of great variety occur throughout nature, and these compounds serve countless important functions both in nature and in industry. Acetic acid, the acidic component of vinegar, is the most important carboxylic acid industrially; it is used as a solvent and in the manufacture of plastics, rubber, drugs, and a variety of organic chemicals. Its United States production in 1962 was some 985.8 million pounds. Citric acid, the sour constituent of citrus fruits, is an important intermediate in carbohydrate metabolism, and is widely used commercially as an acidulant in beverages. Cholic acid is a constituent of animal bile, and gallic acid, from nutgalls and other plant sources, is employed in ink manufacture, in

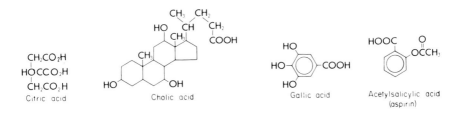

photography and in tanning. The common pain reliever *aspirin* (acetyl-salicylic acid) enjoyed a United States production of over 22 million pounds in 1961. We shall encounter further examples of naturally occurring and commercially important carboxylic acids later. In addition, many carboxylic acid derivatives, particularly esters and amides, are widespread in nature and are of great importance and interest because of their functions and uses. These compounds, too, will be discussed in this and subsequent chapters.

13-1. Nomenclature and Physical Properties of Carboxylic Acids

The IUPAC names for aliphatic carboxylic acids are obtained by deleting the terminal -*e* from the names of the corresponding alkanes and then adding the suffix -*oic acid* (Table 13-1). The carboxyl group defines the

Table 13-1. Some Physical Properties of Aliphatic Carboxylic Acids

Structure	IUPAC Name (—— Acid)	Common Name (—— Acid)	B.p., °C	M.p., °C
HCOOH	Methanoic	Formic	101	8.4
CH_3COOH	Ethanoic	Acetic	118	16
CH_3CH_2COOH	Propanoic	Propionic	142	−21
$CH_3CH_2CH_2COOH$	Butanoic	Butyric	164	−5
$(CH_3)_2CHCOOH$	2-Methylpropanoic	Isobutyric	154	−47
$CH_3(CH_2)_3COOH$	Pentanoic	Valeric	186	−35
$CH_3(CH_2)_6COOH$	Octanoic	Caprylic	239	16
$CH_3(CH_2)_{14}COOH$	Hexadecanoic	Palmitic	139/1 mm	63
$CH_3(CH_2)_{16}COOH$	Octadecanoic	Stearic	160/1 mm	69

longest chain in the molecule and its carbon is numbered 1, other substituents on the chain being numbered in the usual way. Aromatic acids are named as substitution products of benzoic acid, PhCOOH (m.p. 122°), or of the aromatic hydrocarbon from which they are derived. Carboxylic acids are also frequently named as "alkanecarboxylic acids," particularly in the cycloalkane series. These principles are illustrated in the examples below.

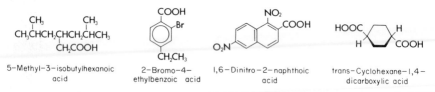

5–Methyl–3–isobutylhexanoic acid	2–Bromo–4– ethylbenzoic acid	1,6–Dinitro–2–naphthoic acid	trans–Cyclohexane–1,4– dicarboxylic acid

The common names of many carboxylic acids reflect their historic origin in natural sources. This is evident in such names as formic (Latin: *formica,* ant), acetic (Latin: *acetum,* vinegar), butyric (Latin: *butyrum,* butter), palmitic (palm oil), stearic (Greek: *stear,* tallow), cerotic (Latin: *cera,* wax), and vanillic (vanilla bean) acids. The long-chain, normal aliphatic acids, $CH_3(CH_2)_nCOOH$ (n = 12 to 20), occur as esters (Section 13-8) in fats and oils of both animal and vegetable origin. Hence the designation **fatty acid,** which is used for the aliphatic carboxylic acid series.

In Table 13-1 we see that the lower carboxylic acids are liquids, while the higher ones are solids at room temperature. Their boiling points increase in the usual regular fashion with increasing molecular weight, but their melting points increase in an irregular, "sawtooth" manner. The boiling points of carboxylic acids are even higher than those of alcohols of comparable molecular weight; for example, $HCOOH$ and CH_3CH_2OH (mol. wt. 46) boil at 101° and 78°, respectively; CH_3COOH and $CH_3CH_2CH_2OH$ (mol. wt. 60) boil at 118° and 98° respectively. This indicates an even greater degree of association due to hydrogen bonding in the case of acids than in the case of alcohols (Section 11-3). Simple carboxylic acids are known to form hydrogen-bonded "dimers" whose association persists even in the vapor state (Figure 13-1). Carboxylic acids are

$$CH_3C \begin{matrix} O\cdots H-O \\ \diagup \qquad \diagdown \\ O-H\cdots O \end{matrix} CCH_3 \qquad \textit{Figure 13-1. Hydrogen-Bonded "Dimer" of Acetic Acid}$$

"abnormally" soluble in water also as a consequence of their ability to form hydrogen bonds. Carboxylic acids show a characteristic bonded O—H stretching frequency in the infrared region, 3300 to 2500 cm^{-1}, as well as strong infrared band between 1725 and 1700 cm^{-1} due to the carbonyl stretching vibration of the associated dimer. Saturated carboxylic acids (and their esters) display weak ultraviolet absorption around 200 to 210 mμ. The lower fatty acids have pungent, unpleasant odors, while higher homologs are odorless.

13-2. Acidity of Carboxylic Acids

The distinctive chemical feature of the carboxyl group is its acidity. Carboxylic acids are typical **weak acids,** because of the tendency of the

$$\overset{O}{\underset{\parallel}{R\overset{}{C}}}O—H$$ bond to rupture heterolytically in the presence of a base (proton acceptor), as illustrated by their ionization in water. Water-insoluble

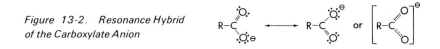

(base)   Carboxylate anion

carboxylic acids may accordingly be recognized by their ability to dissolve as soluble carboxylate salts in dilute sodium bicarbonate solution. The

$$PhCOOH + Na^{\oplus}HCO_3^{\ominus} \longrightarrow PhCOO^{\ominus}Na^{\oplus} + H_2O + CO_2$$

Benzoic acid   Sodium benzoate
                                        (soluble)

acidity of carboxylic acids is attributable to the fact that the carboxylate ion may stabilize itself as a resonance hybrid whose negative charge is distributed over a three-atom system, as shown in Figure 13-2. Such charge

Figure 13-2. Resonance Hybrid
of the Carboxylate Anion

delocalization makes the carboxylate ion a far weaker base, for example, than the alkoxide anion ($RO:^{\ominus}$), whose negative charge is not delocalized. If the carboxylate anion is a true resonance hybrid, we would expect complete equivalence of its carbon-oxygen bonds. This is confirmed by X-ray and electron diffraction studies, which show that formic acid has two distinct C–O bond distances, whereas the formate ion has only a single C—O distance, which is intermediate between the —C=O and —C—O— bond lengths (Figure 13-3).

Figure 13-3. Bond Lengths in
Formic Acid and Sodium Formate

Formic acid   Sodium formate

The acidities of carboxylic acids may be compared quantitatively by comparing the measurable equilibrium constants (K_a) of their ionization in water.

$$K_a = \frac{[H_3O^{\oplus}][RCOO^{\ominus}]}{[RCOOH]} \qquad pK_a = \log_{10}\frac{1}{K_a}$$

The greater the degree of ionization, the greater is K_a, and the stronger is the acid. It is usually more convenient to compare values of pK_a, the logarithm of $1/K_a$. Lower pK_a values indicate stronger acids, and higher pK_a values weaker acids, each unit of pK_a decrease indicating a factor of 10 increase in the value of K_a. Thus an acid having $pK_a = 3$ is 100 times stronger (K_a 100 times larger) than an acid having $pK_a = 5$. Typically, aliphatic carboxylic acids have pK_a about 5 (that is, $K_a = 10^{-5}$). The more weakly acidic phenol (Section 11-9b), for example, has pK_a about 10 ($K_a = 10^{-10}$). Phenols are thus soluble in sodium hydroxide solution, but insoluble in less basic sodium bicarbonate solution, and can therefore be distinguished from carboxylic acids by this chemical difference.

Any structural unit attached to the carboxylate anion which permits greater delocalization of its negative charge has the effect of making the corresponding carboxylic acid a stronger one. High electronegative (electron-withdrawing; Section 2-2d) substituents, such as halogen, on the α-carbon atom adjacent to the carboxyl group, for example, have such acidity-increasing effects. We see this in comparing the acidities of acetic, CH_3COOH, chloroacetic, $ClCH_2COOH$, dichloroacetic, $Cl_2CHCOOH$, and trichloroacetic, Cl_3CCOOH acids, whose respective pK_a values are 4.75, 2.81, 1.29, and 0.04 (corresponding to $K_a = 1.76 \times 10^{-5}$, 1.55×10^{-3}, 5.14×10^{-2}, and 0.9 respectively). Trichloroacetic acid is classed as a strong acid, and the effect of the chlorine atoms in stabilizing the trichloroacetate anion hybrid may be symbolized as shown in 13-1. Similarly,

13-1

electron-withdrawing groups (*m*-directors; Section 10-6) in the *para* position of benzoic acid lead to increased acidity, while electron-releasing substituents (*o,p*-directors) in the *para* position give rise to weaker benzoic acids, as seen in Figure 13-4. Note how the *p*-NO$_2$ group tends to place a positive charge on the carboxyl group, making for a stronger acid, while

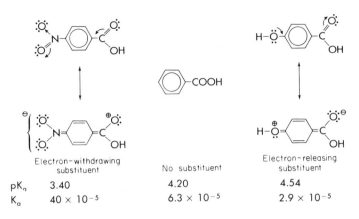

	Electron-withdrawing substituent	No substituent	Electron-releasing substituent
pK$_a$	3.40	4.20	4.54
K$_a$	40 × 10^{-5}	6.3 × 10^{-5}	2.9 × 10^{-5}

Figure 13-4. Acidities of Some Benzoic Acids

the *p*-OH group tends to place a negative charge on the carboxyl group, making for a weaker acid.

13-3. Synthesis of Carboxylic Acids

Acetic acid is prepared commercially by the catalytic air oxidation of acetaldehyde (from acetylene; Section 9-4e) and of low molecular weight alkanes, and to a small extent by the fermentation of ethanol and the destructive distillation of wood (Section 11-4a). Formic acid is made industrially by the reaction of carbon monoxide with 25 per cent aqueous sodium hydroxide, followed by acidification.

$$CO + NaOH \xrightarrow{200°, 250 \text{ psi}} HCOO^{\ominus}Na^{\oplus} \xrightarrow{H_2SO_4} HCOOH$$

Higher carboxylic acids are obtained either synthetically or from natural sources. The following are the most important general methods for the laboratory preparation of individual carboxylic acids.

a. Oxidation of Primary Alcohols. We recall that chemical oxidizing agents will convert primary alcohols into aldehydes (Section 11-7d), and that these in turn are very readily oxidized further to carboxylic acids (Section 11-7d). The overall oxidation thus forms a convenient method for preparing carboxylic acids from primary alcohols.

$$RCH_2OH \xrightarrow{(O)} [RCH{=}O] \xrightarrow{(O)} RCOOH$$

b. Carbonation of Grignard Reagents. When carbon dioxide is passed into an ethereal solution of a Grignard reagent, an addition reaction takes place and the halomagnesium salt (13-2) of a carboxylic acid is formed.

$$R{-}MgX \ + \ O{=}C{=}O \ \longrightarrow \ R{-}\overset{\overset{\displaystyle O}{\|}}{C}{-}OMgX \ \xrightarrow{\ H^{\oplus},H_2O\ } \ RCOOH \ + \ Mg(OH)X$$

13-2

Subsequent treatment with water liberates the free acid. This **carbona-tion** reaction is frequently accomplished by merely pouring the solution of the Grignard reagent onto dry ice.

c. Hydrolysis of Nitriles. Heating a nitrile, $RC{\equiv}N$, with aqueous acid or base results in hydrolysis to a carboxylic acid (or its salt). In the latter case the free acid is obtained by acidification of the alkaline solution with strong mineral acid.

$$RC{\equiv}N \ + \ 2\,H_2O \ + \ H^{\oplus}Cl^{\ominus} \ \longrightarrow \ RCOOH \ + \ NH_4^{\oplus}Cl^{\ominus}$$

$$RC{\equiv}N \ + \ H_2O \ + \ Na^{\oplus}OH^{\ominus} \ \longrightarrow \ RCOO^{\ominus}Na^{\oplus} \ + \ NH_3$$

$$RCOO^{\ominus}Na^{\oplus} \ + \ H^{\oplus}Cl^{\ominus} \ \longrightarrow \ RCOOH \ + \ Na^{\oplus}Cl^{\ominus}$$

We thus have two convenient general methods for the conversion of alkyl halides into carboxylic acids one carbon atom higher:

$$RX\ \Bigg\lbrace\ \begin{array}{l} \xrightarrow[\text{ether}]{\text{Mg}}\ RMgX\ \xrightarrow[\text{(2) H}_2\text{O}]{\text{(1) CO}_2}\ RCOOH \\[2ex] \xrightarrow{\text{KCN}}\ RC{\equiv}N\ \xrightarrow{\text{Hydrolysis}}\ RCOOH \end{array}$$

d. Oxidation of Alkenes and Arenes. The oxidation of certain alkenes to carboxylic acids has already been discussed (Section 8-4g), as has also the side-chain oxidation of alkylated aromatic hydrocarbons to benzoic acid and its analogs (Section 10-4d). These reactions are sometimes useful in preparing specific carboxylic acids. In connection with the side-chain oxidation of arenes, it should be noted that nuclear substituents such as $-NO_2$, halogen, $-SO_3H$, $ArCO{-}$, and $RO{-}$ are stable under ordinary oxidizing conditions. $RCO{-}$, like alkyl groups, is oxidized to $-COOH$, while $-OH$ and $-NH_2$ substituents render the aromatic ring itself susceptible to oxidation. The transformations shown in the following equations are representative.

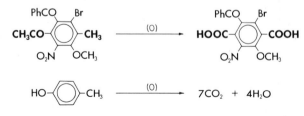

13-4. Reactions of Carboxylic Acids

Carboxylic acids display a variety of reactions which may involve either the hydrogen atom of the carboxyl group, $-COOH$, the hydroxyl portion, $-CO-OH$, or other parts of the molecule. Many of these reactions transform carboxylic acids into important **derivatives,** whose preparations, properties, and reactions are discussed in subsequent sections of this chapter. The following are several important reactions worth noting at this point.

a. Salt Formation. The conversion of carboxylic acids into stable metal salts has been mentioned in Section 13-2. Many of these metal salts are technically useful as such. Thus basic copper acetate, $Cu(OH)_2 \cdot 2Cu(OCOCH_3)_2$, is used as an insecticide; aluminum acetate, $Al(OCOCH_3)_3$, is used to impregnate cotton fibers in the mordant process of dyeing (Section 14-22); calcium propionate, $Ca(OCOC_2H_5)_2$, and sodium benzoate, $PhCOONa$, are used as food preservatives; and the sodium salts of long-chain fatty acids comprise common soap (Section 13-9). Recalling that stronger acids will replace weaker acids from their metal salts, we note that free carboxylic acids may be quantitatively regenerated from their salts by treatment with strong mineral acid.

$$RCOO^{\ominus}M^{\oplus} + H^{\oplus}X^{\ominus} \longrightarrow RCOOH + M^{\oplus}X^{\ominus}$$

b. Reduction to Primary Alcohols. In Section 11-5a we learned that carboxylic acids may be reduced quantitatively to primary alcohols by action of the powerful reducing agent lithium aluminum hydride.

c. α-Halogenation. When an aliphatic carboxylic acid is treated with chlorine or bromine in the presence of red phosphorus, the α-hydrogen atoms on the carbon adjacent to the carboxyl group are replaced by Cl or

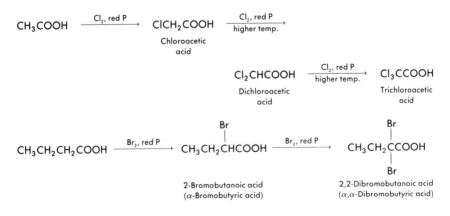

Br. By appropriate control of reaction conditions, this **Hell-Volhard-Zelinsky reaction** may be caused to proceed stepwise, to produce either mono- or polyhalogenated acids. Note that with higher aliphatic acids only the α-hydrogen atoms are replaced, and that after their full replacement, no further halogenation occurs.

ACYL HALIDES

13-5. Preparation and Properties of Acyl Halides

A very important reaction of the carboxyl group is the replacement of its OH function by halogen to produce an **acyl halide** or (in the aromatic series) an **aroyl halide**.

$$\underset{\text{An acyl halide}}{RC-X} \quad \xleftarrow{} \quad RC-OH$$

$$\underset{\text{An aroyl halide}}{ArC-X} \quad \xleftarrow{} \quad ArC-OH$$

These reactive compounds, usually liquids but occasionally solids, are synthetically important intermediates in a variety of transformations of carboxylic acids. They are generally prepared by the action of phosphorus halides or thionyl halides on carboxylic acids, as seen in the following equations, which also illustrate their nomenclature.

$$3\,CH_3COOH + PBr_3 \longrightarrow 3\,CH_3COBr + P(OH)_3$$
$$\underset{\substack{\text{Ethanoyl bromide} \\ \text{(Acetyl bromide)}}}{}$$

$$(CH_3)_2CHCOOH + PCl_5 \longrightarrow (CH_3)_2CHCOCl + POCl_3 + HCl$$
$$\underset{\substack{\text{2-Methylpropanoyl chloride} \\ \text{(Isobutyryl chloride)}}}{}$$

$$CH_3O-\!\!\bigcirc\!\!-COOH + SOCl_2 \longrightarrow CH_3O-\!\!\bigcirc\!\!-COCl + SO_2 + HCl$$
$$\underset{\text{p–Methoxybenzoyl chloride}}{}$$

We recall that these same reagents brought about analogous transformations of alcohols into alkyl halides (Section 11-7e). Acyl halides, as seen in the above examples, are named by deleting *-ic acid* from the name of the parent acid and adding *-yl halide*.

The more important general reactions of acyl halides, leading to other

classes of compounds, are summarized in Figure 13-5. Many of these reactions will be discussed in greater detail in appropriate subsequent sec-

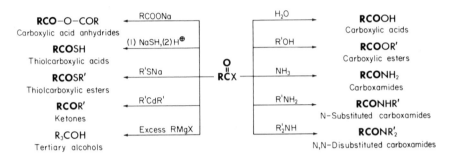

Figure 13-5. Reactions of Acyl Halides

tions. We see that the synthetic utility of the acyl halides is indeed im-
pressive.

CARBOXYLIC ACID ANHYDRIDES

13-6. Preparation and Properties of Carboxylic Acid Anhydrides

Carboxylic acid anhydrides are derivatives which formally arise by
intermolecular dehydration between two molecules of a carboxylic acid.

$$\text{RCO-O+H + HO+COR'} \longrightarrow \text{RCO-O-COR' + H}_2\text{O}$$

Carboxylic acid anhydride

They may be of two types: (1) simple anhydrides, derived from a single
acid (R = R'), and (2) mixed anhydrides, derived from two acids
(R ≠ R'). Simple anhydrides are the more common and important type.
Nomenclature for anhydrides is quite simple. One simply adds the term
anhydride following the names of the acids involved, as in the examples

$$\text{CH}_3\text{CO—O—COCH}_3 \qquad \text{PhCO—O—COC}_2\text{H}_5$$

Acetic anhydride   Benzoic propionic anhydride
                          (Benzoyl propionyl oxide)

shown. Anhydrides, having no hydroxylic hydrogen atoms, are "normal,"
unassociated liquids having boiling points roughly approximating those of
hydrocarbons of comparable molecular weight (for example, $\text{CH}_3\text{CO—}$
O—COCH_3, mol. wt. 102, b.p. 118°; $n\text{-C}_7\text{H}_{16}$, mol. wt. 100, b.p. 98°).
Higher anhydrides may be low-melting solids.

Carboxylic acid anhydrides are generally prepared by the action of acyl halides on the metal salts of carboxylic acids. The most important an-

$$RCO-X \ + \ Na^{\oplus} \ \overset{\ominus}{O}COR' \ \longrightarrow \ RCO-O-COR' \ + \ Na^{\oplus} \ X^{\ominus}$$

hydride, acetic anhydride, is prepared commercially by the reaction of ketene with acetic acid. Ketene, an extremely reactive gaseous substance,

$$CH_3COCH_3 \ \xrightarrow{\ 700° \ } \ CH_4 \ + \ \underset{\text{Ketene}}{CH_2{=}C{=}O}$$

$$CH_2{=}C{=}O \ + \ CH_3COOH \ \rightarrow \ CH_3CO{-}O{-}COCH_3$$

is formed by pyrolysis of acetone vapors at a dull red heat. Other transformations illustrating the reactivity of ketene are shown in Figure 13-6.

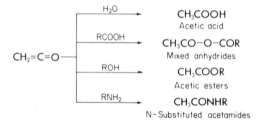

Figure 13-6. Some Reactions of Ketene

The principal use of carboxylic acid anhydrides is as an *O*-acylating agent in the preparation of esters from alcohols (Section 13-10b). They may also be employed in place of acyl halides in the preparation of aromatic ketones by the Friedel-Crafts ketone synthesis (Section 10-4b).

CARBOXYLIC ESTERS

13-7. Nomenclature and Physical Properties of Esters

We have seen that esters result from the reaction of acids with alcohols (Section 11-7c), and that carboxylic esters arise *formally* by the intermolecular loss of water between a carboxylic acid and an alcohol, either of which may itself belong to the aliphatic, aromatic, or heterocyclic series. Esters

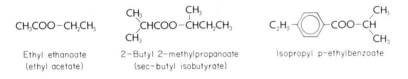

are named as if they were alkyl salts of carboxylic acids, because of the formal analogy of the above equation to that of neutralization. Their nomenclature is apparent in the following examples, and we note the use of two-word names in both the IUPAC and common systems.

CH₃COO–CH₂CH₃

Ethyl ethanoate
(ethyl acetate)

2–Butyl 2–methylpropanoate
(sec–butyl isobutyrate)

Isopropyl p–ethylbenzoate

Low molecular weight esters are nonassociated liquids having boiling points approximating those of alkanes of comparable molecular weight (for example, $CH_3COOC_2H_5$, mol. wt. 88, b.p. 77°; $n\text{-}C_6H_{14}$, mol. wt. 86, b.p. 69°). Their low degree of hydrogen bonding makes them quite insoluble in water, but they have excellent solvent properties for organic compounds. The principal industrial use for low molecular weight esters is as solvents, and the United States production of ethyl acetate and butyl acetate, mainly for solvent purposes, was 86.9 and 69.8 million pounds, respectively, in 1961. In their infrared spectra, esters show two characteristic absorption bands, one at around 1740 cm^{-1} (C=O stretching), and the other in the region 1300 to 1100 cm^{-1} (—C—O— stretching), with their exact positions depending upon other structural features. Weak ultraviolet absorption is noted for esters in the 200 to 220 mμ region.

13-8. Natural Esters

Esters constitute a most important class of compounds owing to their widespread natural occurrence. The low molecular weight esters are liquids with agreeable, fruity odors, and many of the distinctive fragrances of fruits and flowers are due to their constituent mixtures of esters. Thus isoamyl acetate occurs in bananas, amyl butyrate is found in apricots, and ethyl acetate occurs in pineapples, although the true natural odors of such fruits depend upon complex mixtures of esters and other components. Esters of long, straight-chain aliphatic acids make up the oils, waxes, and fats which occur throughout the animal and plant kingdoms. **Waxes** are mixtures of esters of high molecular weight, straight-chain monohydric alcohols with the higher straight-chain fatty acids. Thus **beeswax** from honeycombs could be represented chiefly as $CH_3(CH_2)_{24}COO(CH_2)_{27}CH_3$ or $CH_3(CH_2)_{26}COO(CH_2)_{25}CH_3$. **Carnauba wax**, from the leaves of the Brazilian palm (*Copernicia cerifera*), is commercially important as a constituent of automobile and floor waxes and of candles. It may be thought of as containing principally components such as $C_{31}H_{63}COOC_{32}H_{65}$ and $C_{33}H_{67}COOC_{34}H_{69}$, while **spermaceti** from the head of the sperm whale is mainly $C_{15}H_{31}COOC_{16}H_{33}$. Paraffin "wax" from petroleum, however, we recall to be a mixture of normal alkanes in the C_{20} to C_{30} range (Section 7-3b).

Natural **fats** and **oils** are esters of fatty acids and the trihydric alcohol glycerol (Section 11-6b). In the general structure for an oil or fat, shown below, each of the substituents R_1, R_2, and R_3 may be,

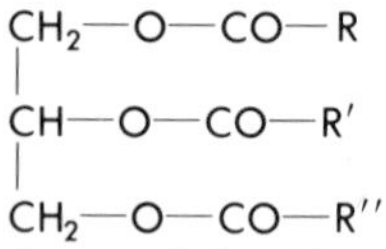

$$CH_2-O-CO-R$$
$$CH-O-CO-R'$$
$$CH_2-O-CO-R''$$

Structure of oils and fats

ordinarily, any straight-chain alkyl group in the range C_3 to C_{25} which contains an odd number of carbon atoms, and which may either be saturated or contain from one to four conjugated or nonconjugated double bonds. Fats derived from saturated fatty acids (for example, tallow, lard) are higher melting, and are solids at room temperature. Those derived from mono- or polyunsaturated fatty acids (for example, corn oil, peanut oil) have lower melting points and are oily liquids at room temperature. Liquid fats, such as cottonseed oil, are **hardened** commercially by catalytic hydrogenation of their double bonds, to produce saturated fats which are solids. The butter substitute oleomargarine, for example, consists of partially hydrogenated vegetable oils to which flavor and color have been added. The fatty acid contents of several typical fats and oils are shown in Table 13-2. Note how the unsaturated and polyunsaturated fatty acid content is higher in the liquid oils, and the saturated fatty acid content is higher in the solid fats. Fats and oils make up one of the principal foodstuffs of mankind, and medical research has suggested that those derived from unsaturated fatty acids are the more beneficial from the point of view of avoiding arteriosclerosis (hardening of the arteries). Unsaturated oils (for example, linseed oil, tung oil) are also used in the paint industry as **drying oils** since, on exposure to air, they rapidly undergo *autooxidation* and *polymerization* to produce resin-like materials which form tough, protective coatings. Oil cloth, for example, is prepared by coating canvas with linseed oil paint, then "drying" the sheet in a warm oven while exposing it to air. Edible oils and fats derived from unsaturated fatty acids turn *rancid* on exposure to air, the autooxidation here giving rise to degradation products (volatile aldehydes, ketones, and acids) which cause the off-odor

Table 13-2. Fatty Acid Composition (%) of Typical Fats and Oils

Fatty Acid	Fats		Oils		
	Tallow	Butter	Peanut Oil	Linseed Oil	Whale Oil
Myristic[1]	2–3	7–9	—	—	4–6
Palmitic[2]	24–32	23–26	6–9	4–7	11–18
Stearic[3]	14–32	10–13	2–6	2–5	2–4
Palmitoleic[4]	1–3	5	1	—	13–18
Oleic[5]	35–48	30–40	50–70	9–38	33–38
Linoleic[6]	2–4	4–5	13–26	3–43	—

1. Saturated: $CH_3(CH_2)_{12}COOH$
2. Saturated: $CH_3(CH_2)_{14}COOH$
3. Saturated: $CH_3(CH_2)_{16}COOH$
4. Unsaturated: $CH_3(CH_2)_5CH{=}CH(CH_2)_7COOH$
5. Unsaturated: $CH_3(CH_2)_7CH{=}CH(CH_2)_7COOH$
6. Polyunsaturated: $CH_3(CH_2)_4CH{=}CHCH_2CH{=}CH(CH_2)_7COOH$

and taste. The degree of unsaturation in fats and oils is expressed in terms of their **iodine number,** the number of grams of ICl or IBr (expressed as grams of I_2) which will add to the double bonds of 100 g of the fat. The greater the iodine number, the more unsaturated fatty acids are present. Thus tallow, has an iodine number in the range 31 to 47, while that of peanut oil is 83 to 98.

13-9. Soaps and Detergents

When an oil or fat is heated with aqueous alkali, the ester undergoes **hydrolysis** (here frequently called **saponification**), yielding glycerol and a mixture of the sodium salts of the constituent fatty acids. The latter

$$
\begin{array}{c}
CH_2OCOR \\
| \\
CHOCOR' \\
| \\
CH_2OCOR''
\end{array}
\; + \; 3\,NaOH
\; \xrightarrow[\text{heat}]{H_2O} \;
\begin{array}{c}
CH_2OH \\
| \\
CHOH \\
| \\
CH_2OH
\end{array}
\; + \;
\left\{
\begin{array}{c}
RCOO^{\ominus}Na^{\oplus} \\
R'COO^{\ominus}Na^{\oplus} \\
R''COO^{\ominus}Na^{\oplus}
\end{array}
\right.
$$

Fat   Glycerol   Soap

water-soluble mixture of fatty acid salts, when purified from excess alkali, makes up the common cleansing agent soap, while the by-product glycerol is utilized for other commercial purposes (Section 11-6b). The cleansing action of soap resides in the ability of the hydrocarbon-like portion of the soap molecule to "dissolve" water-insoluble grease spots ("like dissolves like"), and the simultaneous ability of the $—COO^{\ominus}$ portion of the soap molecule to render the whole conglomerate water soluble through solvation of the carboxylate ions, as symbolized in Figure 13-7.

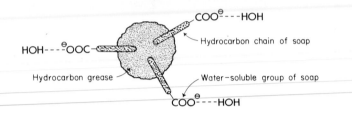

$Figure\ 13\text{-}7.\ \ The\ Cleansing\ Action\ of\ Soap$

The calcium and magnesium salts of long-chain fatty acids, in contrast to the sodium and potassium salts, are water insoluble. Thus in "hard water" (containing Ca^{2+} and Mg^{2+}) soaps tend to precipitate as insoluble salts, producing an undesirable scum. This limitation of soaps as cleansing agents gave impetus to the multimillion dollar detergent industry, which today saturates the market (as well as the streams and rivers) with synthetic detergents whose alkaline earth salts are water soluble. Their cleansing action is similar to that of soaps; that is, their molecules contain a long-chain, hydrocarbon-solubilizing portion and an ionic, water-soluble portion. Structurally, synthetic detergents are mainly of two types: (1) sodium salts of alkyl hydrogen sulfates derived from long-chain alcohols, such as Dreft, and (2) sodium salts of long-chain alkylbenzenesulfonic acids, such as Nacconol. Examples of each structural type are shown below.

$$C_{12}H_{25}O-SO_2O^{\ominus}\ Na^{\oplus} \qquad\qquad C_{12}H_{25}-\!\!\left\langle\bigcirc\right\rangle\!\!-SO_2O^{\ominus}\ Na^{\oplus}$$

Sodium lauryl sulfate   Sodium p-dodecylbenzenesulfonate

An important property of soaps and detergents is their **surface activity,** or their ability to lower the surface tension of water—that is, to weaken the "skin" on a water surface. The practical consequence of this is that a soap solution will wet an object more readily than does water itself. This is easily demonstrated by carefully floating a steel needle on the surface of a cup of water, then adding a few particles of soap powder, whereupon the needle will sink. The surface activity of detergents arises from the fact that at a water surface the water-soluble (**hydrophilic**) ionic $-COO^{\ominus}$ or $-SO_2O^-$ group "buries itself" into the surface, while the water-insoluble (**hydrophobic**) alkyl portion of the molecule tends to remain outside of the

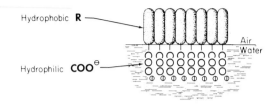

Hydrophobic **R**

Air
Water

Hydrophilic **COO**$^{\ominus}$

Figure 13-8. Behavior of Soap at an Air–Water Interface

surface (Figure 13-8). By carefully setting up such a system, it is possible to cover the surface of the water with a **monomolecular film** of soap molecules.

13-10. Synthesis of Esters

Esters may be prepared from carboxylic acids (or their derivatives) and alcohols (or their derivatives) by several general methods. The most important of these are described below.

a. Direct Esterification (Fischer Esterification). When a mixture of an alcohol and a carboxylic acid is heated in the presence of a mineral acid catalyst, *intermolecular* dehydration occurs and an ester is formed.

$$RCOOH + HOR' \underset{}{\overset{H^{\oplus}}{\rightleftharpoons}} RCOOR' + H_2O$$

This **direct esterification** is an equilibrium reaction. Its reverse, when carried to completion, is known as **hydrolysis** of the ester. The exact point of equilibrium for the esterification reaction depends upon the structures of both the alcohol and the carboxylic acid precursors, but the reaction may be caused to go substantially to completion in either direction by the use of a large excess of one of the reactants (mass action law). Thus esterification of an acid is forced toward completion by using a large excess of alcohol, while complete hydrolysis is achieved in the presence of a large excess of water. Complete esterification is also accomplished by removing the by-product water as it is formed, thus driving the equilibrium to the right. This may be done by conducting the esterification in benzene solvent, and continuously distilling off the benzene-water azeotrope (Section 11-4b).

The intermolecular dehydration involved in esterification may be visualized as occurring in two alternative ways, as symbolized below. It is im-

RCO–OH   H–OR   RCOO–H   HO–R
    Path A   Path B

portant theoretically to know which path is actually followed during esterification, that is, whether the —OH group is lost from the alcohol or from the carboxylic acid. This question has been answered through the esterification of an acid with an alcohol isotopically labeled with O^{18}. We find that the O^{18} isotope ends up exclusively in the ester product, indicating

$$PhCO\overline{{}-OH \quad H}{}-O^{18}CH_3 \xrightarrow{H^{\oplus}} PhCO-O^{18}CH_3 + H_2O$$

O^{18}-Labeled methanol O^{18}-Labeled methyl benzoate

that path A above is the mode of dehydration. Had path B been followed, the O^{18} label would have ended up as $HO^{18}H$, and the methyl benzoate would be label-free.

In accord with the above and other studies, the mechanism indicated in Figure 13-9 is generally accepted as applicable to direct esterification. The

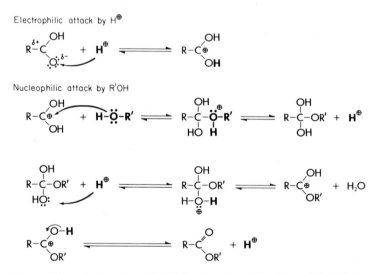

Electrophilic attack by $H^{\oplus}$

Nucleophilic attack by $R'OH$

Figure 13-9. Mechanism of Acid-Catalyzed Esterification and Hydrolysis

order of reactivity of alcohols during esterification is primary > secondary > tertiary, with tertiary alcohols being substantially unreactive. Acid reactivity is in the order $CH_3COOH > RCH_2COOH > R_2CHCOOH > R_3CCOOH$. Both reactivity orders are understandable in terms of *steric hindrance* and its effect on the equilibria in the above mechanism. Thus the bulk of the alkyl substituents in R_3COH and in R_3CCOOH hinders the close approach of the intermediates, particularly in the second step of the mechanism. We see that this same mechanism in reverse explains the acid-catalyzed hydrolysis of an ester. The base-catalyzed hydrolysis of esters (saponification; Section 13-9), however, is an irreversible reaction believed to proceed through the alternate mechanism in Figure 13-10. The irre-

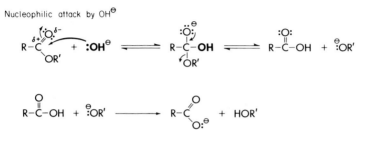

Figure 13-10.   Mechanism of Base-Catalyzed Ester Hydrolysis

versibility of the last step in the sequence, due to the vastly greater acid strength of RCOOH over R'OH (Section 13-2), renders the overall saponi-fication irreversible. For this reason also, bases do not catalyze the esteri-fication of carboxylic acids.

The acid-catalyzed esterification of *aromatic carboxylic acids* proceeds satis-factorily unless there are nuclear substituents in positions *ortho* to the carboxyl group, in which case esterification is slowed or stopped. The same generalization holds for the acid-catalyzed hydrolysis of esters of such

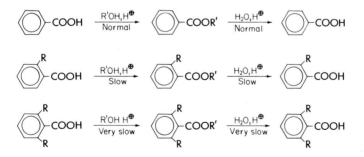

acids. The rate-retarding effect of *ortho* substituents is thought to be due to their *steric hindrance* to the second step of the normal esterification mech-anism (Figure 13-9), since larger *ortho* substituents have greater retarding effects, and the retardation is not dependent upon the electron-withdraw-ing or -releasing characteristics of the substituent. Furthermore, *ortho*-sub-

stituted phenylacetic acids such as 13-3, where the bulk of the *ortho* substituents is further removed from —COOH, show normal esterification

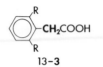

13-3

behavior. Sterically hindered benzoic acids such as described above may
be esterified by the **Newman esterification** procedure, which consists of
dissolving the acid in concentrated sulfuric acid, then adding the mixture
to excess alcohol. Here the strong sulfuric acid apparently converts the
carboxylic acid into the resonance-stabilized acylium cation 13-4, which
subsequently reacts directly with the added alcohol. Figure 13-11 indi-

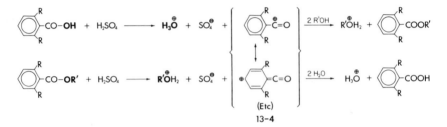

Figure 13-11. *Mechanism of Newman Esterification and Hydrolysis*

cates that the same mechanism applies to the hydrolysis of sterically hindered benzoate esters, which may be effectively accomplished in a similar
manner, namely, by dissolving the ester in concentrated sulfuric acid and
subsequently quenching the mixture with water.

b. O-Acylation of Alcohols. The action of an acyl halide on an alcohol
yields an ester.

$$Ph-CO-CI + H-OCH_2CH_2CH_3 \longrightarrow PhCOOCH_2CH_2CH_3 + HCI$$
Benzoyl chloride   Propyl benzoate

This **O-acylation** reaction (introduction of an acyl group onto oxygen)
may be driven to completion by neutralizing the HX by-product with an
organic base (amine) or an inorganic base such as aqueous sodium hydroxide (**Schotten-Baumann reaction**). The reaction is limited to primary and secondary alcohols, since tertiary alcohols tend to dehydrate
intramolecularly under the influence of the acyl halide.

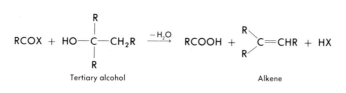

Tertiary alcohol Alkene

A closely related synthesis of esters involves the use of an acid anhydride as the acylating agent for alcohols. This reaction is subject to the same limitations as that involving acyl halides.

$$CH_3CO{-}O{-}COCH_3 + PhOH \longrightarrow CH_3COOPh + CH_3COOH$$

Acetic anhydride $\qquad\qquad$ Phenyl acetate

Occasionally it is desirable to employ the alkali metal salt of an alcohol, instead of the free alcohol, in such reactions. We notice the analogy of this technique to the Williamson ether synthesis (Section 11-16c).

$$\left. \begin{array}{c} RCOX \\ \text{or} \\ RCO{-}O{-}COR \end{array} \right\} + R'O^{\ominus}Na^{\oplus} \longrightarrow RCOOR' + \left\{ \begin{array}{c} Na^{\oplus}X^{\ominus} \\ \text{or} \\ RCOO^{\ominus}Na^{\oplus} \end{array} \right.$$

c. Reaction of Alkyl Halides with Carboxylate Salts. Metal salts of carboxylic acids will react with alkyl halides to produce esters, and dry silver carboxylate salts are frequently employed to prepare esters when the above methods prove inadequate.

$$RCOO^{\ominus}Ag^{\oplus} + R'X \longrightarrow RCOOR' + AgX$$

d. Methyl Ester Formation with Diazomethane. When the white solid *N*-methyl-*N*-nitrosourea is treated with aqueous potassium hydroxide at 0°,

$$CH_3N{-}\overset{NO}{\underset{\underset{O}{\|}}{C}}{-}NH_2 + 2KOH \xrightarrow{0°} CH_2N_2 + K_2CO_3 + NH_3 + H_2O$$

N-Methyl-N-nitrosourea $\qquad\qquad$ Diazomethane

diazomethane is evolved. Other aliphatic *N*-methyl-*N*-nitroso derivatives may also be employed, and some of these are commercially available. Diazomethane is a toxic yellow gas (b.p. –23°, m.p. –145°) which explodes violently when heated. Its preparation is ordinarily conducted in the presence of ethyl ether, providing a yellow etheral solution of diazomethane which is safe and relatively stable at 0°. The yellow color of diazomethane is attributed to its structure as the resonance hybrid 13-**5**.

$$CH_2{=}\overset{\oplus}{N}{=}\overset{\ominus}{\underset{..}{N}}{:} \longleftrightarrow {:}\overset{\ominus}{C}H_2{-}\overset{\oplus}{N}{\equiv}N{:}$$

13-**5**

Treatment of a carboxylic acid with a yellow ethereal solution of diazomethane results in quantitative and almost instantaneous conversion of the acid into its methyl ester, with concomitant decolorization of the solution and liberation of nitrogen gas.

$$RCOOH + CH_2N_2 \longrightarrow RCOOCH_3 + N_2\uparrow$$

Completion of this convenient reaction may be estimated when the yellow color of excess diazomethane persists in the reaction mixture.

Diazomethane will also methylate phenols and enols, which are weakly acidic. It is without action on alcohols, however, except in the presence of an acidic catalyst such as fluoroboric acid, HBF_4, whereupon it converts primary and secondary alcohols into their methyl ethers in high yield.

$$PhOH + CH_2N_2 \longrightarrow PhOCH_3 + N_2\uparrow$$
Methyl phenyl ether
(Anisole)

$$\underset{\text{Enol}}{\overset{\overset{\displaystyle OH}{|}}{RCH{=}CR}} + CH_2N_2 \longrightarrow \underset{\text{Enol methyl ether}}{\overset{\overset{\displaystyle OCH_3}{|}}{RCH{=}CR}} + N_2\uparrow$$

$$ROH + CH_2N_2 \xrightarrow{HBF_4} ROCH_3 + N_2\uparrow$$

13-11. Reactions of Esters

Esters undergo a wide variety of important chemical transformations. Those which have been discussed in previous sections are summarized first below.

a. Reduction to Primary Alcohol. This process, using lithium aluminum hydride or other reducing agent, has been discussed in Section 11-5a.

b. Reaction with Grignard Reagents. We recall that Grignard reagents react with esters to produce tertiary alcohols (Section 11-5e). It should be emphasized at this point that carboxylic acids, in contrast with their esters, do not undergo a carbonyl addition reaction with Grignard reagents. Rather, like alcohols and water, they merely react to form halomagnesium salts.

$$RCOOH + R'MgX \longrightarrow RCOOMgX + R'H$$
Halomagnesium
carboxylate

c. Hydrolysis. The techniques and mechanisms of the hydrolysis of esters to carboxylic acids in the presence of acidic or basic catalysts have been discussed in Section 13-10a.

d. *Alcoholysis (Transesterification).* When an ester derived from one alcohol is heated with another alcohol in the presence of an acidic or basic catalyst, exchange of the O-alkyl group of the ester occurs (**transesterification**).

$$RCOOR' + R''OH \xrightleftharpoons{H^{\oplus} \text{ or } OR^{\ominus}} RCOOR'' + R'OH$$

The reaction is one of equilibrium and may be driven in either direction desired by employing one of the alcohol components in large excess (mass action law). The mechanisms of transesterification are entirely analogous to those of acid-catalyzed esterification and hydrolysis and of base-catalyzed saponification (Section 13-10a). The transesterification of fats with methanol provides a commercially important route to the preparation of long-chain aliphatic acids and alcohols having even numbers of carbon atoms. The mixture of long-chain methyl esters resulting from the transesterification may be separated by fractional distillation, and the resulting pure methyl esters may then be saponified or reduced to the corresponding primary alcohols.

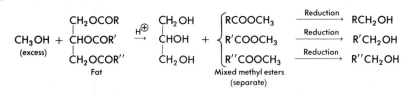

e. *Ammonolysis.* When an ester is treated with an excess of ammonia under anhydrous conditions, it is converted into a carboxamide—a class of compound which will be discussed in greater detail below.

$$RCOOR' + NH_3 \longrightarrow \underset{\text{A carboxamide}}{RCONH_2} + R'OH$$

The reaction is referred to as **ammonolysis** of the ester, and we see at once the formal similarity among hydrolysis, alcoholysis, and ammonolysis of esters.

$$RCO\underset{}{\vdots}OR' + \begin{cases} H\vdots OH \\ H\vdots OR'' \\ H\vdots NH_2 \end{cases} \begin{array}{l} \xrightarrow{\text{Hydrolysis}} RCOOH \\ \xrightarrow{\text{Alcoholysis}} RCOOR'' \\ \xrightarrow{\text{Ammonolysis}} RCONH_2 \end{array} \Bigg\} + R'OH$$

f. *Ester Condensations.* Esters undergo a wide variety of mechanistically similar base-catalyzed transformations loosely termed **condensation reactions**. The common feature of these reactions is the intermolecular elimination of an alcohol molecule (usually ethanol) between the alkoxy group of the ester and the α-hydrogen atom on a carbon adjacent to an activating

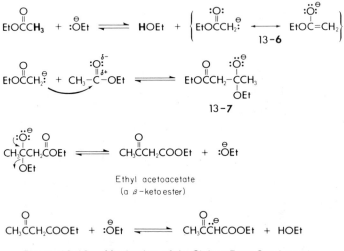

(electron-withdrawing) group. Notice that the activating groups are the same ones which are *meta* directors in aromatic substitution reactions (Section 10-6), and that the net result of the condensation involves **C-acylation** of the α-carbon atom adjacent to the activating group.

There is abundant evidence that the mechanism common to such condensations involves carbanion intermediates which are resonance stabilized by distribution of their negative charge over the adjacent electron-withdrawing group. The principal features of this mechanism are illustrated in Figure 13-12, which depicts the alkoxide-catalyzed self-condensation of ethyl acetate to produce ethyl acetoacetate (**Claisen ester condensation**).

Figure 13-12.   *Mechanism of the Claisen Ester Condensation*

The latter ester, as will be seen later, is an extremely important starting material for further organic syntheses. Notice that the first stage of the reaction involves formation of the resonance-stabilized ester carbanion 13-**6,** which partakes in a nucleophilic attack on the carbonyl group of another ester molecule to form the adduct 13-**7.** Loss of ethoxide ion from the latter affords the β-keto ester product and regenerates the catalyst.

Notice also the fundamental similarity of such ester condensations to the aldol and related base-catalyzed condensations of aldehydes and ketones, previously discussed in Section 12-7 and 12-71. The several additional examples of other ester condensations illustrated below typify the versatility of this general reaction. The last reaction, called the **Dieckmann condensation**, is the intramolecular analog of the Claisen ester condensation. It provides an important route to the synthesis of cyclopentane and cyclohexane derivatives. The student should practice writing the detailed carbanion mechanism for each example.

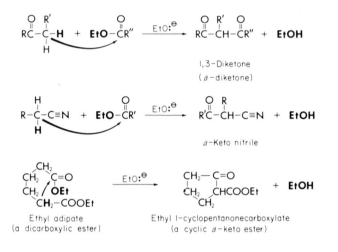

1,3–Diketone
(β–diketone)

β–Keto nitrile

Ethyl adipate
(a dicarboxylic ester)

Ethyl 1-cyclopentanonecarboxylate
(a cyclic β–keto ester)

CARBOXAMIDES

13-12. Preparation and Properties of Carboxamides

Simple carboxamides are N-acyl derivatives of ammonia, while N-substituted amides are analogous derivatives of primary $(RNH_2, ArNH_2)$ or secondary $(R_2NH, Ar_2NH, ArNHR)$ amines. They arise formally by intermolecular dehydration between the OH group of RCOOH and a hydrogen atom of the ammonia derivative:

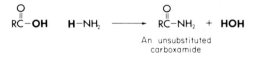

An unsubstituted
carboxamide

Amides are named by deleting the *-oic* or *-ic acid* suffix from the IUPAC or common name of the parent acid and adding the suffix *-amide*. The nomenclature of simple and substituted amides is illustrated in the following examples.

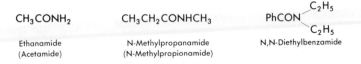

$$CH_3CONH_2 \qquad CH_3CH_2CONHCH_3 \qquad PhCON\begin{smallmatrix}C_2H_5\\C_2H_5\end{smallmatrix}$$

Ethanamide   N-Methylpropanamide   N,N-Diethylbenzamide
(Acetamide)   (N-Methylpropionamide)

With the exception of formamide, $HCONH_2$ (m.p. 2.5°), unsubstituted amides are all solids. Their boiling points are vastly higher than the boiling points of their parent acids, even though their molecular weights are essentially identical (for example, compare HCOOH, mol. wt. 46, b.p. 100°, with $HCONH_2$, mol. wt. 45, b.p. 211°, and CH_3COOH, mol. wt. 60, b.p. 118°, with CH_3CONH_2, mol. wt. 59, b.p. 222°). Such abnormally high boiling points, as well as their general crystallinity, are indicative of the extensive association between simple amide molecules, which is due to intermolecular hydrogen bonding involving the protons on their nitrogen atoms and their oxygen atoms. The importance of the N-protons in determining the physical properties of amides is seen in Table 13-3,

Table 13-3. Physical Properties of Some Amides

Structure	Mol. Wt.	B.p., °C	M.p., °C
CH_3CONH_2	59	222	81
$CH_3CONHCH_3$	73	206	28
$CH_3CON(CH_3)_2$	87	166	Liquid

which shows the effect of replacing the N-protons of acetamide successively with methyl groups, thus permitting progressively less hydrogen bonding. Simple amides show a strong carbonyl stretching absorption band at around 1690 to 1650 cm^{-1}, Nh stretching vibrations in the region 3500 to 3180 cm^{-7}, an N—H bending absorption band at 1650 to 1590 cm^{-1} region, and an additional characteristic band around 1420 to 1400 cm^{-1}.

Amides are prepared from ammonia or amines by N-acylation reactions conducted with acyl halides, carboxylic acid anhydrides, or esters, as illustrated with the following specific examples. The former two reagents

$$CH_3COCl + 2CH_3NH_2 \longrightarrow CH_3CONHCH_3 + CH_3NH_3^{\oplus}Cl^{\ominus}$$
Acetyl chloride   Methylamine   N-Methylacetamide

$$CH_3CH_2CO—O—COCH_2CH_3 + (CH_3)_2NH \longrightarrow$$
Propionic anhydride   Dimethylamine

$$CH_3CH_2CON(CH_3)_2 + CH_3CH_2COOH$$
N,N-Dimethylpropionamide

$$PhCOOC_2H_5 + NH_3 \longrightarrow PhCONH_2 + C_2H_5OH$$

Ethyl benzoate   Benzamide

are generally more widely utilized. Nitrogen-substituted acetamides may also be prepared by the acetylation of amines with ketene (Figure 13-6), while unsubstituted amides in general are accessible by the pyrolysis of ammonium salts of carboxylic acids. The partial hydrolysis of nitriles

$$RCOO^\ominus NH_4{}^\oplus \xrightarrow{\text{Heat}} RCONH_2 + H_2O$$

Ammonium carboxylate

(Section 13-13) is also useful in preparing unsubstituted amides.

Simple and substituted amides are readily hydrolyzed to the parent acid (or its salt) by heating with dilute acid (or alkali).

$$RCONH_2 + H_3O^\oplus \xrightarrow{H_2O} RCOOH + NH_4{}^\oplus$$

$$RCONHR' + OH^\ominus \xrightarrow{H_2O} RCOO^\ominus + R'NH_2$$

Conversion to the parent acid also occurs on treatment of *unsubstituted* amides with nitrous acid, nitrogen being liberated quantitatively.

$$RCONH_2 + HONO \xrightarrow{H_2O, 0°} RCOOH + N_2 + H_2O$$

Simple and substituted amides may be reduced to amines by the action of lithium aluminum hydride,

$$RCONH_2 \xrightarrow{LiAlH_4} RCH_2NH_2$$

$$RCONR'_2 \xrightarrow{LiAlH_4} RCH_2NR'_2$$

and the reaction of lithium diethoxyaluminum hydride (13-8) with N,N-dimethylamides provides an excellent general synthesis of aldehydes.

$$2RCONMe_2 + Li^\oplus[AlH_2(OEt)_2]^\ominus \longrightarrow 2RCH{=}O + Li^\oplus[(Me_2N)_2Al(OEt)_2]^\ominus$$
13-8

Because of their crystallinity and characteristic melting points, amides are widely utilized in the identification (through melting points and mixture melting points) of carboxylic acids, after the acid has been converted to its amide derivative as described above. Liquid amides, especially N,N-dimethylformamide, have excellent solvent properties because of the ability of the amide oxygen atom to form hydrogen bonds to other molecules. N,N-Dimethylformamide is thus frequently used in the laboratory as a solvent.

The **amide group,** $-CONH-$, is believed to be a resonance hybrid

Figure 13-13. Resonance Hybrid
of the Amide Group

such as illustrated in Figure 13-13. This linkage is widely distributed
throughout nature in protein molecules, which are polymeric **polyamides**
of a very special sort (see Section 16-19), whose properties are largely determined by the polar nature of the amide group. Simpler polyamides
make up the industrially important nylon polymers (Section 13-16g).

$$\left(\begin{array}{c} CH-CO-NH-CH-CO-NH \\ | \qquad\qquad | \\ R \qquad\qquad R \end{array}\right)_n$$

A polyamide polymer

NITRILES

13-13. Preparation and Properties of Nitriles

Nitriles, or organic cyanides, $RC\equiv N$ and $ArC\equiv N$, are frequently
looked upon as derivatives of carboxylic acids since their hydrolysis, like
that of esters, amides, and acyl halides, leads ultimately to carboxylic acids.
Such hydrolysis of nitriles proceeds via an intermediate carboxamide
which, under proper conditions, may be isolated if desired.

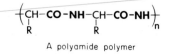

Lower nitriles are water-insoluble liquids, while higher ones (above C_{14})
are solids. Their abnormally high boiling points (compare $CH_3CH_2C\equiv N$,
mol. wt. 55, b.p. 97°, and $CH_3CH_2CH_2CH_3$, mol. wt. 58, b.p. 0.5°) are
attributed to the high polarity of the $-C^{\delta+}\equiv^{\delta-}N$ bond and the dipole-
dipole attraction (Section 2-2d) which this engenders. As seen in the following examples, nitriles may be named as alkyl cyanides or cyanoalkanes
or by deleting -ic acid from the name of the parent acid and adding the
suffix -onitrile.

CH₃CN

$$\begin{array}{c} CH_3 \\ | \\ CH_3CHCN \end{array}$$

Methyl cyanide	Isopropyl cyanide	p-Nitrophenyl cyanide
Cyanomethane	2-Cyanopropane	p-Cyanonitrobenzene
Acetonitrile	Isobutyronitrile	p-Nitrobenzonitrile
Methanenitrile (IUPAC)	2-Propanenitrile (IUPAC)	

Nitriles may be prepared by the following general methods, several of
which have already been encountered.

a. The Action of Metal Cyanides on Alkyl Halides. We recall that the nucleophilic displacement of halide from an alkyl halide by cyanide ion affords nitriles (Section 11-12d).

$$RX \; + \; Na^{\oplus}CN^{\ominus} \; \xrightarrow{\text{S}_N\text{I or S}_N\text{2}} \; RCN \; + \; Na^{\oplus}X^{\ominus}$$

b. The Dehydration of Unsubstituted Carboxamides. With vigorous dehydrating agents, such as phosphorus pentoxide, simple amides may be dehydrated to nitriles.

$$RCONH_2 \; \xrightarrow{P_2O_5} \; RCN \; + \; H_2O$$

c. The Dehydration of anti-Aldoximes. We recall (Section 12-7h) that the action of acetic anhydride followed by base on *anti*-aldoximes results in their overall dehydration into nitriles.

$$\underset{HO-N}{\overset{R-C-H}{\|}} \; \xrightarrow{(CH_3CO)_2O} \; \text{O-Acetate} \; \xrightarrow{Na_2CO_3} \; RCN$$

Acetonitrile finds some use as a solvent, but the principal uses of nitriles are in the field of organic synthesis. The reactions summarized in Figure 13-14 are typical of the more important conversions of nitriles into other

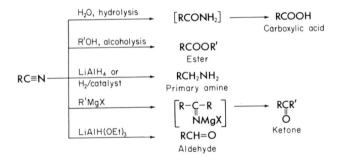

Figure 13-14. *Some Synthetic Transformations of Nitriles*

classes of organic compounds. The last reaction, employing lithium triethoxyaluminum hydride, illustrates a novel as well as general synthesis of aldehydes. We should also recall (Section 13-11f) that the cyano group activates α-hydrogen atoms on carbon atoms adjacent to it, and that nitriles accordingly undergo Claisen-type condensation reactions with esters. Highly reactive nitriles such as ethyl cyanoacetate, $N\equiv C-CH_2-COOEt$, whose α-hydrogens are "doubly activated" by the presence of a second electron-withdrawing group, are even more reactive in such ester condensations and in other reactions involving addition of the intermediate carbanion to an unsaturated group (for example, Knoevenagel condensation, Section 12-7l, and Michael reaction, Section 12-8).

The α,β-unsaturated nitrile acrylonitrile, CH_2=CHCN, is commercially the most important nitrile, United States production in 1961 having been some 250 million pounds. It is mainly prepared by the catalytic addition of hydrogen cyanide to acetylene.

$$HC \equiv CH \ + \ \textbf{HCN} \quad \xrightarrow[\text{heat}]{Cu_2Cl_2, \ NH_4Cl} \quad CH_2\text{=}CHCN$$

Over 60 per cent of its utilization is as a monomer for the production of vinyl polymers and copolymers (Section 8-4l). In the presence of basic catalysts, the double bond of acrylonitrile also undergoes addition of a number of reagents, according to the following general pattern.

$$CH_2\text{=}CHCN \qquad \textbf{HA} \xrightarrow{Base} \textbf{A}-CH_2CH_2CN$$

This addition, which introduces the β-cyanoethyl group, $-CH_2CH_2CN$, into the moiety A, is referred to as the **cyanoethylation reaction.** A few general examples of the cyanoethylation reaction are illustrated in Figure 13-15.

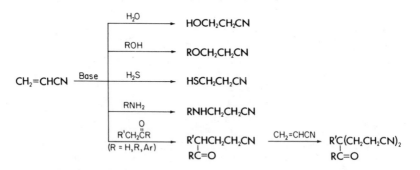

Figure 13-15.   Cyanoethylation Reactions of Acrylonitrile

ORTHO ACIDS AND ORTHO ESTERS

13-14. Organic Ortho Acids and Esters

Ortho acids, those acids containing the largest possible number of hydroxyl groups, can be thought of as arising by addition of water to unsaturated oxygen bonds in the parent acid. While inorganic ortho acids

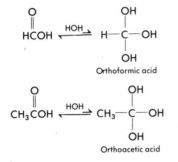

Orthoformic acid

Orthoacetic acid

are known (for example, orthophosphoric acid, $(HO)_3P=O$), the equilibria of such addition reactions of water to the carbonyl group of carboxylic acids lie *far to the left* (see Erlenmeyer's rule; Section 11-6a), and organic ortho acids as such have accordingly never been isolated. On the other hand, just as acetals are stable as compared to aldehyde and ketone hydrates (Section 12-7f), *esters of ortho acids are stable compounds* as compared to ortho acids. Ethyl orthoformate may be prepared, for example, by the action of sodium ethoxide on chloroform, while ethyl orthocarbon-

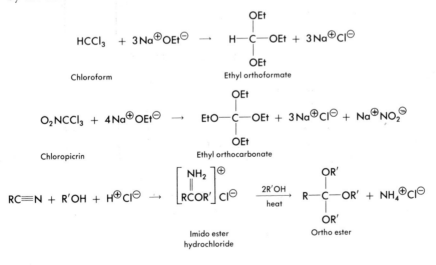

Chloroform   Ethyl orthoformate

Chloropicrin   Ethyl orthocarbonate

Imido ester
hydrochloride   Ortho ester

ate results from a similar reaction with trichloronitromethane (chloropicrin). Ortho esters may also be prepared by the acid-catalyzed alcoholysis of nitriles (**Pinner reaction**).

Lacking a carbonyl group, ortho esters, like acetals, are stable under neutral or alkaline conditions and partake in none of the carbonyl reactions characteristic of normal esters. Under acidic conditions, however, they are (again like acetals) readily hydrolyzed, first to the normal ester and finally to the parent carboxylic acid.

$$R'C(OR)_3 + HOH \xrightarrow{H^\oplus} 2ROH + R'COOR \xrightarrow{H_2O, H^\oplus} R'COOH + ROH$$

Ethyl orthoformate (and occasionally other ortho esters) is of use synthetically in two main connections: (1) its acid-catalyzed reaction with aldehydes and ketones yields acetals and ketals, respectively, and (2) its reaction with Grignard reagents affords acetals, whose hydrolysis provides a synthesis of aldehydes.

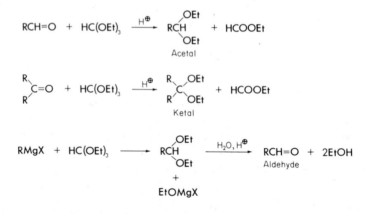

HYDROXY ACIDS AND LACTONES

13-15. Hydroxy Acids and Lactones

Aliphatic carboxylic acids having an —OH function along the alkyl chain are called **hydroxy acids.** Two important types chemically are the so-called γ- and δ-hydroxy acids, representatives of which are seen in the equations below. These acids are unique in that they spontaneously

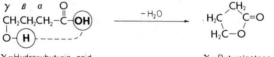

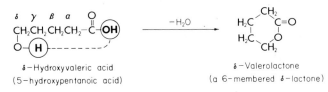

δ−Hydroxyvaleric acid   δ−Valerolactone
(5−hydroxypentanoic acid)   (a 6−membered δ−lactone)

cyclize by *intramolecular* dehydration, affording five- and six-membered ring heterocyclic esters referred to as γ- and δ-lactones, respectively.   These reactions, which emphasize the ease and natural tendency toward the formation of stable five- and six-membered rings when cyclization is possible, can be reversed by hydrolysis of the lactones under alkaline conditions. The resulting sodium salts of the hydroxy acids are stable toward spontaneous cyclization.   Under dehydrating conditions β-hydroxy acids lose water *intramolecularly* in an alternative fashion, yielding α,β-unsaturated acids.   β-Lactones are known, but must be prepared by special methods, such as the addition of formaldehyde to ketene.   α-Hydroxy acids dehy-

$$\underset{OH}{\overset{\beta \quad \alpha}{CH_2-CH_2-COOH}} \xrightarrow{-H_2O} CH_2=CHCOOH$$

β−Hydroxypropionic acid   Acrylic acid

$$\begin{array}{c} CH_2=C=O \\ + \\ CH_2=O \end{array} \xrightarrow{ZnCl_2} \underset{CH_2-O}{\overset{CH_2-C=O}{|\qquad|}}$$

β−Propiolactone

drate intermolecularly in two alternative ways, producing either linear polymeric esters called polyglycolides or cyclic dimeric esters called glycolides. The behavior of glycolic acid is representative.   γ- and δ-Lactones

$$HO-CH_2-COOH \begin{cases} \xrightarrow{-H_2O} (OCH_2-COOCH_2-COOCH_2-CO)_n \\ \qquad\qquad\qquad \text{Polyglycolide} \\ \xrightarrow{-H_2O} \quad O=C\underset{CH_2-O}{\overset{O-CH_2}{\diagdown\quad\diagup}}C=O \end{cases}$$

Glycolic acid

Glycolide

also form quite readily in the aromatic series when the —OH function is in a position *ortho* to a chain bearing the —COOH group, as seen in the following lactonization of β-(*o*-hydroxyphenyl)propionic acid (13-**9**) to 3,4-dihydrocoumarin (13-**10**).

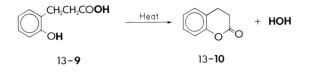

13-**9**   13-**10**

α-Hydroxy acids are found commonly in natural sources, as illustrated by lactic acid in milk, malic acid in apples, tartaric acid in grapes, and

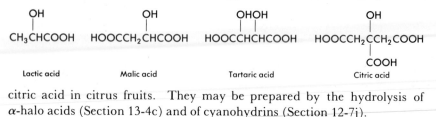

| Lactic acid | Malic acid | Tartaric acid | Citric acid |

citric acid in citrus fruits. They may be prepared by the hydrolysis of α-halo acids (Section 13-4c) and of cyanohydrins (Section 12-7j).

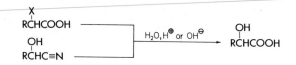

Lactone rings derived from hydroxy acids are also found extensively among natural products. Examples of naturally occurring lactones are ambrettolide, from the musk pear, which is used in perfumery; nepetalactone, the cat-attracting principle of catnip (*Nepeta cataria*); and digitoxigenin, a constituent of digitalis, from the purple foxglove (*Digitalis purpurea*).

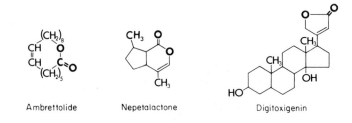

Ambrettolide   Nepetalactone   Digitoxigenin

DICARBOXYLIC ACIDS

13-16. Preparation, Properties, and Uses of Dicarboxylic Acids

Aliphatic and aromatic acids with two —COOH functions are called **dicarboxylic acids.** Chemically and industrially, they are the most important representatives of the **polycarboxylic acids,** acids having more than one —COOH group per molecule. The structures, names, and some physical properties of the most important dicarboxylic acids are presented in Table 13-4. With the exception of carbonic acid (Section 13-16a), the dicarboxylic acids are solids. Each carboxyl group of a dicarboxylic acid may ionize separately, and we see in Table 13-4 that the first carboxyl

Table 13-4. Important Dicarboxylic Acids

Structure	Name (—— Acid)	M.p., °C	$K_{a_1} \times 10^5$	$K_{a_2} \times 10^5$
HO—CO—OH	Carbonic	Unstable		
HOOC—COOH	Oxalic	189	3500	4.0
HOOCCH$_2$COOH	Malonic	136	140	0.22
HOOC(CH$_2$)$_2$COOH	Succinic	185	6.4	0.25
HOOC(CH$_2$)$_3$COOH	Glutaric	98	4.5	0.38
HOOC(CH$_2$)$_4$COOH	Adipic	151	3.7	0.24
cis-HOOCCH=CHCOOH	Maleic	130	1200	0.03
trans-HOOCCH=CHCOOH	Fumaric	302	93	2.9
[phthalic structure]	Phthalic	231	120	0.3
[isophthalic structure]	Isophthalic	348	29	2.7
HOOC—[benzene]—COOH	Terephthalic	300 (sublimes)	15	—

group is generally considerably more acidic (higher pK_a; Section 13-2) than the second carboxyl group, particularly when the two carboxyl groups are close (Why?). The chemical reactions of the dicarboxylic acids are similar to those of monocarboxylic acids. The more important specific additional reactions of individual dicarboxylic acids are described below.

a. Carbonic Acid ($CO_2 + H_2O \rightleftharpoons H_2CO_3$) This acid is known only in aqueous solution, as its stable salts (metal carbonates), and as certain organic derivatives, the most important of which are its acid chloride (carbonyl chloride, phosgene, a toxic gas used in World War I), its amide (urea, a constituent of urine), and its ethyl ester. The preparations of these derivatives from carbon monoxide and chlorine are illustrated in the following equation.

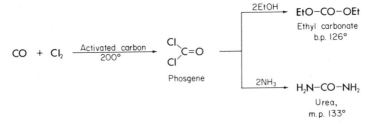

b. Oxalic Acid (IUPAC name: ethanedioic acid). Oxalic acid is prepared commercially by fusing sodium formate with alkali, followed by acidifica-

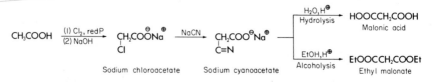

$$2\,HCOO^\ominus Na^\oplus \xrightarrow[360°]{NaOH} Na^{\oplus\ominus}OOC—COO^\ominus Na^\oplus \xrightarrow{H_2SO_4} HOOC—COOH$$

Sodium formate   Sodium oxalate   Oxalic acid

tion. It is a toxic substance which occurs naturally in rhubarb, spinach, sorrel, and other plants. It is used commercially in bleaching straw and leather, as a rust and stain remover, in the dyeing industry, and in photo-engraving. Its esters are used in organic syntheses.

c. Malonic Acid (propanedioic acid). Malonic acid is prepared indus-trially from acetic acid by the sequence of reactions shown below. Its

$$CH_3COOH \xrightarrow[(2)\ NaOH]{(1)\ Cl_2,\ red\ P} \underset{\underset{Cl}{|}}{CH_2COONa} \xrightarrow{NaCN} \underset{\underset{C\equiv N}{|}}{CH_2COO^\ominus Na^\oplus}$$

$$\xrightarrow[\text{Hydrolysis}]{H_2O,\,H^\oplus} HOOCCH_2COOH \quad \text{Malonic acid}$$

$$\xrightarrow[\text{Alcoholysis}]{EtOH,\,H^\oplus} EtOOCCH_2COOEt \quad \text{Ethyl malonate}$$

Sodium chloroacetate   Sodium cyanoacetate

ethyl ester is very important in organic syntheses, and is discussed sep-arately in Section 13-18. The most significant chemical reaction of ma-lonic and substituted malonic acids is their facile **decarboxylation** (loss of CO_2), which occurs on heating the acid above its melting point.

$$HOOCCH_2COOH \xrightarrow{\text{Heat above m.p.}} CH_3COOH + CO_2$$

Facile decarboxylation of monocarboxylic acids also occurs when the acid possesses electron-withdrawing substituents on the α-carbon. Thus tri-chloroacetic acid and nitroacetic acid smoothly decarboxylate to chloro-form and nitromethane, respectively, under mild conditions. The decar-boxylation of ordinary aliphatic monocarboxylic acids, however, is usually accompanied by fragmentation of the aliphatic chain, leading to mixtures of alkanes, alkenes, and hydrogen. When an aromatic carboxylic acid (or its salt) is heated with soda lime, NaOH–CaO, simple decarboxylation occurs.

$$ArCOOH \xrightarrow[\text{heat}]{NaOH–CaO} ArH + CO_2$$

d. Succinic Acid (butanedioic acid). This acid, first prepared in the 16th century by the destructive distillation of amber (Latin, *succinum*), is ob-tained commercially by the catalytic hydrogenation of maleic acid (butene-dioic acid), which is prepared in turn by the catalytic oxidation of benzene.

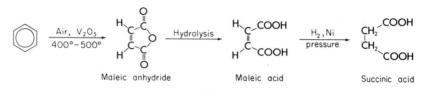

Maleic anhydride   Maleic acid   Succinic acid

Succinic acid and its derivatives are used in the manufacture of lacquers, in perfumery, and in medicine, while maleic acid finds use in the plastic and dyeing industries. The important synthetic use of maleic anhydride as a dieneophile in the Diels-Alder synthesis has already been discussed (Section 9-7c).

e. Other Acids. The important dibasic acids **adipic, phthalic, and terephthalic acids** are prepared commercially by the methods shown in the following equations. Their uses are discussed below.

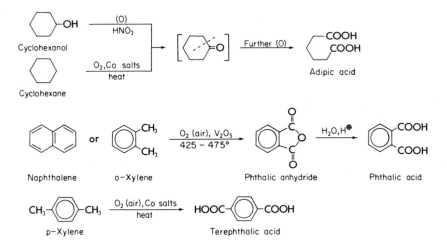

Cyclohexanol

Cyclohexane

Adipic acid

Naphthalene   o-Xylene   Phthalic anhydride   Phthalic acid

p-Xylene   Terephthalic acid

f. Cyclic Anhydrides. An important reaction shared by succinic, maleic, and phthalic acids is the *intramolecular dehydration* which they undergo on heating, whereby in each case a five-membered heterocyclic acid anhydride is formed. Glutaric acid undergoes the same type of intramolecular dehydration on heating, forming a six-membered cyclic anhydride. These

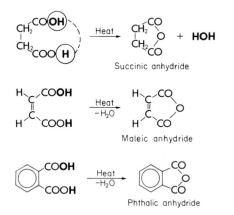

Succinic anhydride

Maleic anhydride

Phthalic anhydride

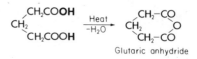

Glutaric anhydride

reactions illustrate again the ease with which five- and six-membered rings form *when the molecular geometry is favorable*. In contrast to the examples above, fumaric acid (the geometrical isomer of maleic acid), whose two carboxyl groups are "frozen" in an unfavorable *trans* orientation, fails to yield a cyclic anhydride on simple heating because its carboxyl groups are too far apart. With vigorous heating, however, it does isomerize into maleic acid, which then yields maleic anhydride. Similarly, isophthalic and terephthalic acids (the *meta* and *para* isomers of phthalic acid) give no cyclic anhydrides on dehydration, since the "frozen geometry" of the benzene ring also places their carboxyl groups too far apart to permit cyclization. Finally, the dehydration of adipic acid leads to a linear, polymeric anhydride, since its dehydration to a cyclic anhydride would involve the "improbable" formation of a seven-membered ring (see Section 9-7b). When adipic acid and pimelic acid are heated in the presence of barium hydroxide, however, **cyclodecarboxylation** occurs, and five- and six-membered cyclic ketones, respectively, are formed. The generalization that succinic and glutaric acids yield cyclic anhydrides, while adipic and pimelic acids give cyclic ketones under the above conditions is known as **Blanc's rule.**

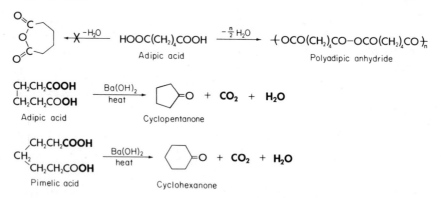

Cyclic anhydrides undergo exactly the same types of reactions which we have seen to be characteristic of anhydrides in general (Sections 13-6, 13-10b, and 13-12). They thus act as O-acylating, N-acylating, and C-acylating agents, as illustrated in the following specific examples. Notice that the only difference in their reactions, as compared to acyclic anhydrides, is that they lead to a *single* product bearing both of the functional groups produced.

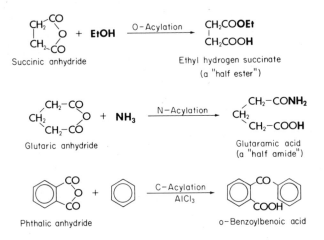

Succinic anhydride + EtOH →(O-Acylation) Ethyl hydrogen succinate (a "half ester")

Glutaric anhydride + NH₃ →(N-Acylation) Glutaramic acid (a "half amide")

Phthalic anhydride + benzene →(C-Acylation, AlCl₃) o-Benzoylbenoic acid

g. Condensation Polymerization. When a dibasic acid or one of its derivatives reacts with a polyhydroxy alcohol, a polymeric ester results. Such a polymer is said to be formed by **condensation polymerization** since (formally and often actually) water is formed as a by-product of the reaction. With a diol, a *linear* polymeric ester is formed, as in the production of Dacron from terephthalic acid and ethylene glycol. Triols, on the other hand, lead to *cross-linked* (three-dimensional) polyesters, as typified by the Glyptal type resins. Linear polyesters are commercially important

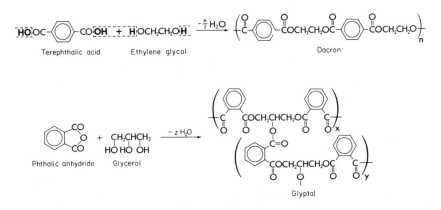

Terephthalic acid + Ethylene glycol →(-n/2 H₂O) Dacron

Phthalic anhydride + Glycerol →(-z H₂O) Glyptal

as fibers, while cross-linked polyesters find extensive use as protective coatings, in lacquers, and as adhesives. The term **alkyd resin** is applied to a large variety of important polyesters formed by reaction of maleic or phthalic anhydride with various polyhydric alcohols. A similar condensation polymerization between a dibasic acid and a difunctional amine yields linear **polyamide** polymers, as illustrated by the reaction of adipic acid with 1,6-diaminohexane to form nylon, whose molecular weight is in

$$\underline{HOOC(CH_2)_4COOH} + \underline{H_2N(CH_2)_6NH_2} \xrightarrow{\text{Heat}, -\frac{n}{2}H_2O} \{CO(CH_2)_4CONH(CH_2)_6NHCO(CH_2)_4CONH(CH_2)_6NH\}_n$$

  Adipic acid   1,6-Diaminohexane   Nylon

the range 12,000 to 15,000. Nylon polymer is fabricated into fibers by melting (m.p. 264°), extruding the melt under pressure through small holes (spinnerets), and finally cooling the extruded monofilament. When linear polyester and polyamide fibers are "worked" by stretching, their long molecular chains tend to assume a parallel alignment, producing a strand of relatively ordered molecules. Such ordering of polymer molecules permits the establishment of hydrogen bonds between adjacent molecules, and results in an increase in the density, strength, and elasticity of the fiber. Condensation polymerizations, which involve the by-product formation of water, should be clearly distinguished from addition polymerizations, such as Vinyl polymerization (Section 8-41) and diene polymerization (Section 8-5b), which entail the formation of no by-product.

KETO ACIDS AND KETO ESTERS

13-17. Preparation and Properties of Keto Acids and Esters

Keto acids have both a carboxyl group and an extra carbonyl group in the same molecule. Two types are of primary interest, α-keto acids and β-keto acids. The esters of β-keto acids are particularly important in organic syntheses, as discussed in Section 13-18 below.

α-Keto acids may be prepared by the action of cuprous cyanide on acyl halides, followed by hydrolysis of the resulting α-keto nitrile, and by the Claisen condensation of ethyl oxalate with a carboxylic ester, followed by hydrolysis and decarboxylation of the o-oxalyl ester so formed.

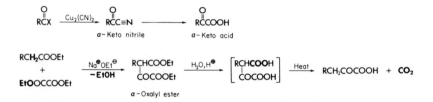

On heating, both α-keto acids and their esters undergo **decarbonylation** (loss of carbon monoxide). By labeling the α-keto group with radioactive C^{14}, it has been shown that the carbon monoxide obtained during decarbonylation of α-keto esters comes from the ester function. The most

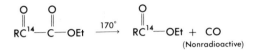

important α-keto acid is pyruvic acid, $CH_3COCOOH$, which is a key intermediate in a variety of biochemical transformations in plant and animal organisms.

We recall that β-keto esters may be obtained by the Claisen condensation of carboxylic esters (Section 13-11f), and that they characteristically

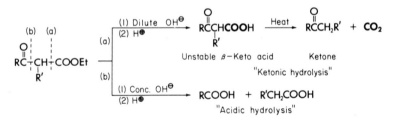

exist partially as enols (Section 12-7a). β-Keto acids, which result on hydrolysis of β-keto esters with dilute alkali (followed by acidification), are notable for their ease of decarboxylation to form ketones. Such facile decarboxylation is reminiscent of the behavior of malonic acid and other carboxylic acids having electron-withdrawing groups on their α-carbon atoms (Section 13-16c). The overall process (path a) affording the ketone product is sometimes called **ketonic hydrolysis** of the β-keto ester. Hydrolysis

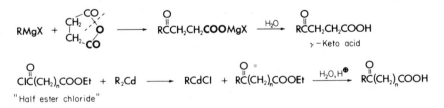

of β-keto esters with concentrated alkali (path b), on the other hand, causes reversal of the Claisen ester condensation and cleaves the molecule into two molecules of carboxylic acid. This procedure is sometimes called **acidic hydrolysis,** because acidic products are formed.

γ-Keto acids may be prepared by the action of Grignard reagents on succinic anhydride. Keto acids with more distant carbonyl groups are available by the reaction of organocadmium compounds with "half ester chlorides" of higher dicarboxylic acids (see Section 12-5c).

13-18. Malonic and Acetoacetic Ester Syntheses

Owing to the "activating" influence of *two* electron-withdrawing groups adjacent to their α-carbon atoms, the α-hydrogen atoms of ethyl malonate and ethyl acetoacetate are unusually acidic. Thus in the presence of a strong base such as ethoxide ion, one of the α-hydrogens of each ester is removed and the esters are converted into their sodium salts, the anions of which are particularly effectively stabilized as the resonance hybrids 13-**11** and 13-**12** (see Section 12-7a). The anions of such sodium salts are

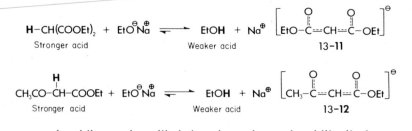

strong nucleophiles, and readily bring about the nucleophilic displacement of halide ions from alkyl halides (Section 11-12d), with the formation of *C*-alkyl derivatives of malonic and acetoacetic ester. Notice that the *C*-alkyl-

$$\text{Na}^{\oplus} \left[\text{:CH(COOEt)}_2 \right]^{\ominus} + \text{RX} \longrightarrow \text{RCH(COOEt)}_2 + \text{Na}^{\oplus}\text{X}^{\ominus}$$

Ethyl alkylmalonate

$$\text{Na}^{\oplus} \left[\text{CH}_3\text{CO}\ddot{\text{C}}\text{HCOOEt} \right]^{\ominus} + \text{RX} \longrightarrow \overset{\text{R}}{\underset{}{\text{CH}_3\text{COCHCOOEt}}} + \text{Na}^{\oplus}\text{X}^{\oplus}$$

Ethyl alkylacetoacetate

ated ester products still have one activated α-hydrogen atom each. Accordingly such products may again be converted to their sodium derivatives, and a second alkyl group may be introduced into each by a similar reaction with a second alkyl halide. Such reactions are practical only for primary and

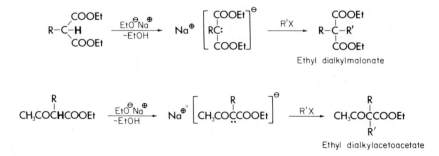

secondary alkyl halides, since tertiary alkyl halides generally suffer dehydrohalogenation (Section 8-3b) under the influence of the strongly basic sodium derivatives, while aryl halides are too inert toward nucleophilic attack (Section 11-13) to be usable.

$$Na^{\oplus}[:CH(COOEt)_2]^{\ominus} + CH_3-\underset{\underset{R}{|}}{\overset{\overset{R}{|}}{C}}-X \longrightarrow CH_2(COOEt)_2 + CH_2=\underset{\underset{R}{|}}{\overset{\overset{R}{|}}{C}} + Na^{\oplus}X^{\ominus}$$

Tertiary halide

The importance of these reactions lies in the fact that the alkylated ester products may be hydrolyzed to the corresponding acids, which then behave as their unsubstituted prototypes. Thus substituted malonic esters afford substituted malonic acids, which in turn decarboxylate on simple heating to yield mono- or disubstituted acetic acids. Similarly, alkylated

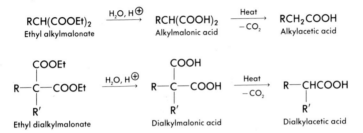

acetoacetic esters may be subjected to either *ketonic hydrolysis* (path a) or *acidic hydrolysis* (path b) (Section 13-17), to yield alkylated methyl ketones (13-13, 13-15) or alkylated acetic acids (13-14, 13-16), respectively.

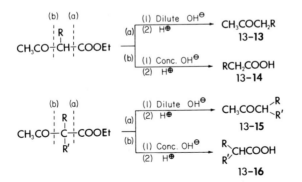

Another important synthetic use of alkylated malonic esters is their condensation with urea to form barbituric acid derivatives (**barbiturates**). Such derivatives have been used widely as sedatives and hypnotics since

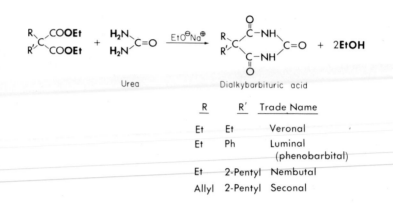

Urea   Dialkybarbituric acid

R	R'	Trade Name
Et	Et	Veronal
Et	Ph	Luminal (phenobarbital)
Et	2-Pentyl	Nembutal
Allyl	2-Pentyl	Seconal

1903, and variations in the substituents R and R' provide a series of drugs of varying speed of action, duration and depth of action, and toxicity. United States production of barbiturate drugs in 1961 was some 700,000 pounds, attesting to their widespread medical application. Their indiscrimminate use is quite hazardous, however, since their anesthetic dose is sometimes as high as 50 to 70 per cent of their lethal dose.

Substituted malonic and acetoacetic ester derivatives (as their sodium salts) undergo a variety of other synthetically useful transformations. Among these, illustrated with their resulting product types in the following equations, are C-acylation with acyl halides, dimerization with iodine, and C-alkylation with dihaloalkanes.

$$R'COX + Na^{\oplus}[RCO\ddot{C}HCOOEt]^{\ominus} \xrightarrow{-NaX} \underset{\substack{| \\ COR'}}{RCOCHCOOEt} \xrightarrow[(2) -CO_2]{(1)\ Hydrolysis} RCOCH_2COR'$$

1,3−Diketone

$$2\ Na^{\oplus}[RCO\ddot{C}HCOOEt]^{\ominus} + I_2 \xrightarrow{-2NaI} \underset{\substack{| \\ RCOCHCOOEt}}{RCOCHCOOEt} \xrightarrow[(2) -2\,CO_2]{(1)\ Hydrolysis} RCOCH_2CH_2COR$$

1,4−Diketone

$$2\ Na^{\oplus}[RCO\ddot{C}HCOOEt]^{\ominus} + X(CH_2)_nX \xrightarrow{-2NaX} \underset{\substack{EtOOC \quad COOEt \\ | \qquad\qquad | \\ RCOCH(CH_2)_nCHCOR}}{} \xrightarrow[(2) -2CO_2]{(1)\ Hydrolysis} RCOCH_2(CH_2)_nCH_2COR$$

ω −Diketone

$$2\ Na^{\oplus}[R\ddot{C}(COOEt)_2]^{\ominus} + I_2 \xrightarrow{-2\,NaI} \underset{\substack{RC(COOEt)_2 \\ | \\ RC(COOEt)_2}}{} \xrightarrow[(2)-2CO_2]{(1)\ Hydrolysis} \underset{\substack{RCHCOOH \\ | \\ RCHCOOH}}{}$$

Substituted succinic acid

$$2\ Na^{\oplus}[:CH(COOEt)_2]^{\ominus} + X(CH_2)_nX \xrightarrow{-2\,NaX} (EtOOC)_2CH(CH_2)_nCH(COOEt)_2 \xrightarrow[(2) -2CO_2]{(1)\ Hydrolysis}$$

$$HOOCCH_2(CH_2)_nCH_2COOH$$

ω −Dicarboxylic acid

PEROXY ACIDS AND DERIVATIVES

13-19. Preparation and Uses of Peroxy Acids and Acyl Peroxides

The acid-catalyzed reaction between 30 to 90 per cent aqueous hydrogen peroxide and a carboxylic acid converts the acid into a **peroxy acid** or **per acid.** The reaction, which is formally analogous to Fisher esterification

$$CH_3CO-OH \; + \; H-OOH \; \underset{}{\overset{H^\oplus}{\rightleftharpoons}} \; CH_3\overset{O}{\overset{\|}{C}}-OOH \; + \; HOH$$
Peracetic acid

(Section 13-10a), is reversible, and per acids slowly hydrolyze in the presence of excess water. The principal use of per acids is in the epoxidation of alkenes to epoxides (Section 12-11), which may in turn be hydrolized to α-glycols (Section 11-6a).

Acyl peroxides, formally analogous to acid anhydrides, are formed by the reaction of acyl chlorides with sodium peroxide. Acyl peroxides are

$$2\,PhCOCl \; + \; Na_2O_2 \; \longrightarrow \; PhCO-OO-COPh \; + \; 2\,NaCl$$
Benzoyl chloride   Benzoyl peroxide

heat sensitive, and violent explosions have resulted during their preparation and use. Benzoyl peroxide, which is considerably more stable, is used as a chain-initiating catalyst in free radical polymerizations (Section 8-41) and as a bleaching agent.

SULFUR AND NITROGEN ANALOGS OF CARBOXYLIC ACIDS

13-20. Typical Sulfur and Nitrogen Analogs

One or both of the oxygen atoms in the —COOH group of a carboxylic acid may be "replaced," using appropriate synthetic methods, with nitrogen or sulfur atoms. The resulting nitrogen and sulfur analogs of the carboxylic acids are not particularly important classes of compounds, but it is worthwhile to give several representative examples to illustrate the types of structures which may result.

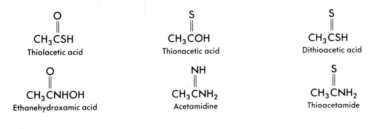

$\overset{O}{\overset{\|}{CH_3CSH}}$	$\overset{S}{\overset{\|}{CH_3COH}}$	$\overset{S}{\overset{\|}{CH_3CSH}}$
Thiolacetic acid	Thionacetic acid	Dithioacetic acid
$\overset{O}{\overset{\|}{CH_3CNHOH}}$	$\overset{NH}{\overset{\|}{CH_3CNH_2}}$	$\overset{S}{\overset{\|}{CH_3CNH_2}}$
Ethanehydroxamic acid	Acetamidine	Thioacetamide

SULFONIC ACIDS AND THEIR DERIVATIVES

13-21. Preparation and Uses of Sulfonic Acids and Derivatives

Aliphatic sulfonic acids, $R—SO_2—OH$, and, particularly, aromatic sulfonic acids, $Ar—SO_2—OH$, and their derivatives constitute important classes of compounds. We notice immediately that the sulfonic acids are S-alkyl or S-aryl derivatives of sulfuric acid, $HO—SO_2—OH$, and it is therefore not surprising to find that they are strong acids. Such acids are named by merely adding the suffix *-sulfonic acid* to the name of the parent hydrocarbon, as shown in the following examples.

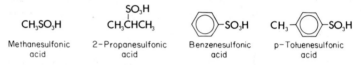

CH₃SO₃H	CH₃CHCH₃	⬡—SO₃H	CH₃—⬡—SO₃H
Methanesulfonic acid	2-Propanesulfonic acid	Benzenesulfonic acid	p-Toluenesulfonic acid

Aryl sulfonic acids, the more important class, are generally prepared by direct sulfonation of the appropriate aromatic hydrocarbon (Section 10-4b). They find use as strong acid catalysts in the laboratory and as intermediates in the synthesis of other aromatic compounds. Some of the transformations of the sulfonic acid group which are synthetically useful are shown in Figure 13-16. In addition, it is sometimes advantageous to

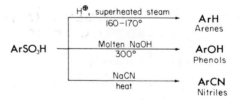

Figure 13-16.   Some Transformations of Aryl Sulfonic Acids

utilize the powerful *meta*-directing influence of the sulfonic acid function (Section 10-6) to *direct the introduction of other groups* into specific positions in the benzene ring, as illustrated in the preparation of *o*-bromophenol.

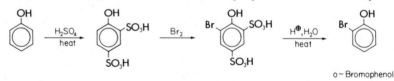

The sodium salts of alkylated aromatic sulfonic acids make up an important class of synthetic detergents (Section 13-9), and the water-solubilizing characteristics of the ionic —$SO_3^{\ominus}Na^{\oplus}$ group make it an extremely important functional group in dyestuff molecules (Section 14-22). The most important derivatives of sulfonic acids are their acid chlorides and amides.

The sulfonyl chlorides are prepared by the action of phosphorus pentachloride on sodium salts of sulfonic acid or by direct **chlorosulfonation** of the aromatic ring using chlorosulfonic acids. Sulfonyl chlorides show re-

$$3\,PhSO_2\!-\!O^{\ominus}Na^{\oplus} + PCl_5 \longrightarrow 3\,PhSO_2Cl + 2NaCl + NaPO_3$$

Benzenesulfonyl
chloride

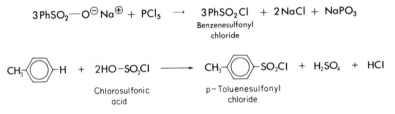

Chlorosulfonic
acid

p–Toluenesulfonyl
chloride

actions analogous to those of carboxylic acid halides, and are employed in the laboratory to prepare crystalline sulfonamides, which are useful in characterizing both sulfonic acids and amines. The cyclic sulfonamide

$$PhSO_2Cl + 2NH_3 \longrightarrow PhSO_2NH_2 + NH_4Cl$$

Benzenesulfonyl
chloride

Benzenesulfonamide

saccharin is widely used as a sweetening agent by diabetics and patients who require a sugar-free diet. It is about 300 times "sweeter" than table sugar, and is prepared commercially as shown in the accompanying equation.

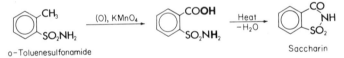

o–Toluenesulfonamide

Saccharin

The "sulfa drugs," which were widely used in combating bacterial infections prior to the advent of the more recent antibiotics, are simple or nitrogen-substituted aromatic sulfonamides containing a *para*-NH_2 group, as seen in the following typical examples.

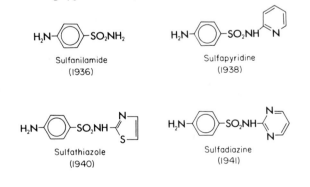

Sulfanilamide
(1936)

Sulfapyridine
(1938)

Sulfathiazole
(1940)

Sulfadiazine
(1941)

Reaction of sulfonyl halides with alcohols or phenols (in the presence of pyridine), or with their sodium salts, leads to the formation of sulfonic esters. *p*-Toluenesulfonates (usually abbreviated as **tosylates**) are gener-

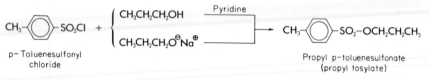

p-Toluenesulfonyl   Propyl p-toluenesulfonate
chloride   (propyl tosylate)

ally crystalline derivatives which have several useful synthetic applications, as summarized in Figure 13-17. These transformations are typical nucleophilic displacement reactions (Section 11-12d) of the tosylate group (p-$CH_3C_6H_4SO_3^{\ominus}$, and mechanistic studies of them have provided much information about the intimate details of S_N1 and S_N2 reactions.

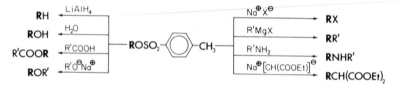

Figure 13-17.   Some Transformations of Tosylates

ORGANIC OXIDATION-REDUCTION REACTIONS

13-22. Balancing Organic Oxidation-Reduction Reactions

In past chapters we have considered conditions under which the following sequence of oxidation reactions could be achieved.

$$R-CH_3 \xrightarrow{(O)} R-CH_2OH \xrightarrow{(O)} R-CH=O \xrightarrow{(O)} R-COOH$$

In this sequence we note a progressive increase in the oxidation level of each compound; that is, each consecutive compound contains more oxygen and/or less hydrogen than its predecessor. Recalling the concept from inorganic chemistry, we see that *formal* **oxidation numbers** of -3, -1, $+1$, and $+3$, respectively, may be assigned to the carbon atom in the four consecutive members of this series. Having been previously noncommittal on the nature and details of the oxidation process, let us now examine it in greater detail.

In the first place, how are organic oxidation equations balanced? This is quite important from a practical, preparative standpoint. For example, the oxidation of an alkene of the type $RCH{=}CHR$ with a limited amount of potassium permanganate in dilute acidic solution at room temperature affords an α-glycol, whereas the use of additional permanganate results in further oxidation of the α-glycol and ultimately cleaves it into a carboxylic acid.

$$RCH{=}CHR \xrightarrow{KMnO_4} \underset{\displaystyle RCH{-}CHR}{\overset{\displaystyle OH\ \ OH}{}} \xrightarrow{KMnO_4} \underset{\displaystyle RC{-}CR}{\overset{\displaystyle O\ \ \ O}{}} \xrightarrow{KMnO_4} 2\,RCOOH$$

How can we calculate the proper amount of oxidant for any stage of the reaction? The first requirement, of course, is a correctly balanced equation for the reaction of interest.

Organic oxidations may be balanced most simply by the **half reaction method**. We recall that *oxidation involves the loss of electrons from the reductant*, and *reduction involves the gain of electrons by the oxidant*. In addition, most organic oxidations also involve the organic molecule either *gaining oxygen* or *losing hydrogen*. In the half reaction method we assume formally that oxygen for the oxidation is provided by water molecules (forming protons and electrons), and that reduction of the oxidant is accomplished by protons and electrons (regenerating the water). The overall reaction is thus divided into two stages, one of oxidation and one of reduction. A balanced half reaction is written for each stage, and the balanced half reactions (multiplied by appropriate integers to equalize the number of electrons involved in each) are finally summed algebraically to provide the balanced overall equation. Let us apply the method to the above oxidation of an alkene to an α-glycol.

First, write an equation showing all reactants and products, but ignoring coefficients, water molecules, $H^{\oplus}$ ions, and $OH^{\ominus}$ ions.

Second, write the balanced half reaction for the oxidation stage, using water as a source of oxygen atoms to combine with the reductant. Excess hydrogens are written as hydrogen ions on the product side, and a sufficient number of electrons are written as "released" to give a net charge balance.

$$RCH{=}CHR + 2H_2O \longrightarrow \underset{\displaystyle RCH{-}CHR}{\overset{\displaystyle OH\ \ OH}{}} + 2H^{\oplus} + 2e^{\ominus}$$

Third, write a balanced half reaction for the reduction stage, using hydrogen ions to combine with the oxygen atoms lost from the oxidant, and writing a number of electrons "gained" which is sufficient for a net charge balance.

$$MnO_4^{\ominus} + 8H^{\oplus} + 5e^{\ominus} \longrightarrow Mn^{2+} + 4H_2O$$

Finally, multiply each balanced half reaction by a coefficient which will make the number of electrons in each half reaction equal, then add the two half reactions, canceling out appropriate numbers of all species appearing on each side of the overall equation.

$$5RCH{=}CHR + 10H_2O \longrightarrow 5RCH\overset{\overset{\displaystyle OH}{|}}{-}\overset{\overset{\displaystyle OH}{|}}{C}HR + 10H^{\oplus} + 10e^{\ominus}$$

$$2MnO_4^{\ominus} + 16H^{\oplus} + 10e^{\ominus} \longrightarrow 2Mn^{2+} + 8H_2O$$

Balanced
equation:

$$5RCH{=}CHR + 2MnO_4^{\ominus} + 6H^{\oplus} + 2H_2O \longrightarrow 5RCH\overset{\overset{\displaystyle OH}{|}}{-}\overset{\overset{\displaystyle OH}{|}}{C}HR + 2Mn^{2+}$$

As an additional example, consider the oxidation of benzyl alcohol to benzoic acid, using potassium dichromate as oxidant:

1.

$$\overset{\text{Oxidation}}{\underset{\text{Reduction}}{PhCH_2OH \underset{\text{Reductant}}{} + \underset{\text{Oxidant}}{Cr_2O_7^{2-}} \longrightarrow PhCOOH + Cr^{3+}}}$$

2. Oxidation stage:
$$(PhCH_2OH + H_2O \longrightarrow PhCOOH + 4H^{\oplus} + 4e^{\ominus}) \times 3$$

3. Reduction stage:
$$(Cr_2O_7^{2-} + 14H^{\oplus} + 6e^{\ominus} \longrightarrow 2Cr^{3+} + 7H_2O) \times 2$$

4. Add:

$$3PhCH_2OH + 3H_2O \longrightarrow 3PhCOOH + 12H^{\oplus} + 12e^{\ominus}$$
$$2Cr_2O_7^{2-} + 28H^{\oplus} + 12e^{\ominus} \longrightarrow 4Cr^{3+} + 14H_2O$$

Balanced equation:
$$3PhCH_2OH + 2Cr_2O_7^{2-} + 16H^{\oplus} \longrightarrow 3PhCOOH + 4Cr^{3+} + 11H_2O$$

A number of nonselective inorganic oxidizing agents which are used to oxidize a variety of organic compounds are listed, along with their reduced forms, in Table 13-5.

Table 13-5. Some Oxidants and Their Reduced Forms

Oxidant	Reduced Form
$K_2Cr_2O_7$ (in H_2SO_4)	Cr^{3+}
CrO_3 (in CH_3COOH)	Cr^{3+}
$KMnO_4$ (in acid media)	Mn^{2+}
$KMnO_4$ (in neutral or basic media)	MnO_2
HNO_3	NO_2 (or NO)
H_2O_2 (in acid media)	H_2O

13-23. Mechanism of Organic Oxidations

The majority of the oxidations brought about by the inorganic oxidants in Table 13-5 occur in polar solvents, where heterolytic bond-breaking processes are prevalent (Sections 6-2 and 6-3). Furthermore, we have seen that the types of organic compounds most readily oxidized (for example, alkenes, alkynes, alcohols, and aldehydes) are those containing unshared electrons. Now, since the oxidizing power of the common inorganic oxidizing agents generally increases with the acidity of the oxidizing medium, it is apparent that the actual oxidizing agent must be a protonated, or other positively charged, species, as seen in Table 13-6. While

Table 13-6. Probable Oxidizing Species in Acidic Solution

Oxidant	Probable Oxidizing Species
$K_2Cr_2O_7$ (H_2SO_4)	$\overset{\oplus}{Cr}O_3H$, $\overset{\delta+\,\delta-}{CrO_3}$
CrO_3 (CH_3COOH)	$\overset{\oplus}{Cr}O_3H$, $\overset{\delta+\,\delta-}{CrO_3}$
$KMnO_4$ (CH_3COOH)	$\overset{\oplus}{Mn}O_4H_2$, $\overset{\oplus}{Mn}O_3$
HNO_3	$H_2\overset{\oplus}{O}NO_2$, $\overset{\oplus}{N}O_2$, NO_2
H_2O_2 (H^+)	$H_2\overset{\oplus}{O}OH$, $\overset{\oplus}{O}H$

many such positively charged, electrophilic species may have only a transitory existence during oxidation, others are known as stable substances (for example, CrO_3, NO_2), as constituents of known substances (for example, $MnO_3^{\oplus}F^{\ominus}$, $NO_2^{\oplus}ClO_4^{\ominus}$), or as reaction intermediates (for example, $OH^{\oplus}$).

From such considerations L. S. Levitt proposed in 1955 a general three-step mechanism for the oxidation of organic substances in acidic media. This may be illustrated by the oxidation of a secondary alcohol with chromic acid in acid solution (Figure 13-18). The first step involves an

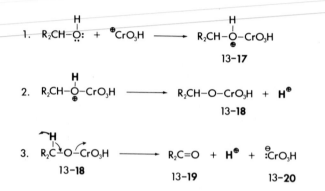

Figure 13-18.   Mechanism of Oxidation by Chromic Acid

electrophilic attack by the positively charged oxidizing species ($CrO_3H^{\oplus}$; Table 13-6) on the unshared electrons of the alcohol (reductant). The resulting positively charged adduct (13-17) loses a proton to form a chromic ester (13-18; step 2). This in turn loses its chromium moiety with its bonding pair of electrons (step 3) to produce the reduced chromium species 13-20, with simultaneous loss of a proton to afford the ketone product 13-19. It is of interest that the oxidation of secondary alcohols has been shown experimentally to proceed via chromic esters, and that the proton loss in step 3 has been established as rate determining by isotope effect studies with deuterated analogs (for example, R_2CDOH), which oxidize at a slower rate.

In Figure 13-18 the oxidation is consummated (step 3) by a proton loss. However, the loss of a sufficiently stabilized carbonium ion may also occur. This is demonstrated in the chromic acid oxidation of optically active 3-methyl-3-phenyl-2-pentanol (13-21), where the planar 2-phenyl-2-butyl carbonium ion (13-23), expelled during decomposition of the chromic ester 13-22, yields optically inactive 2-phenyl-2-butanol (13-24) as the final oxidation product.

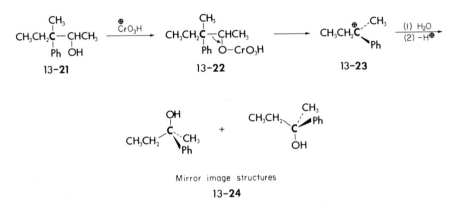

13-21   13-22   13-23

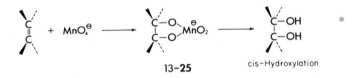

Mirror image structures

13-24

Permanganate oxidations are complicated by the varying oxidation states available to manganese (+2 to +7). In view of the formation of *cis*-α-glycols during the permanganate oxidation of cyclic alkenes (Section 8-4f), however, it is thought likely that a cyclic permanganate ester intermediate (13-**25**), analogous to the intermediate in osmium tetroxide oxidations (Section 8-4f), intervenes during the hydroxylation of alkenes by potassium permanganate in neutral or alkaline (but not acidic) media.

13-25   cis-Hydroxylation

SUPPLEMENTARY READING

1. "Acids and Bases in Organic Chemistry," D. Davidson, *J. Chem. Educ.*, **19**, 154 (1942).
2. "The Early History of Detergent Substances," M. Levey, *J. Chem. Educ.*, **31**, 521 (1954).
3. "Soap and Glycerol," F. D. Snell, *J. Chem. Educ.*, **19**, 172 (1942).
4. "The Metallic Soaps," R. G. Bossert, *J. Chem. Educ.*, **27**, 10 (1950).
5. "Syndets and Surfactants," F. D. Snell and C. T. Snell, *J. Chem. Educ.*, **35**, 271 (1958).
6. "Synthetic Detergents and Surface Activity," C. T. Snell, *J. Chem. Educ.*, **24**, 505 (1947).
7. "Nylon," M. Shor, *J. Chem. Educ.*, **21**, 88 (1944).
8. "Synthetic Fibers," W. W. Heckert, *J. Chem. Educ.*, **30**, 166 (1953).
9. "Sulfanilamide and Related Chemotherapeutic Agents," L. H. Amundsen, *J. Chem. Educ.*, **19**, 167 (1942).

10. "Phosgene," K. E. Jackson, *J. Chem. Educ.*, **10**, 622 (1933).
11. "Oxidation Numbers and Valence," S. Glasstone, *J. Chem. Educ.*, **25**, 278 (1948).
12. "More on Oxidation Numbers," D. F. Swinehart, *J. Chem. Educ.*, **29**, 284 (1952).
13. "A Simplified Electronic Interpretation of Oxidation-Reduction," D. C. Gregg, *J. Chem. Educ.*, **22**, 548 (1945).
14. "Balancing Equations for Organic Oxidation-Reduction Reactions," L. N. Ferguson, *J. Chem. Educ.*, **23**, 550 (1946).
15. "A Consistent Treatment of Oxidation-Reduction," C. A. VanderWerf, *J. Chem. Educ.*, **25**, 547 (1948).
16. "The Common Basis of Organic Oxidations in Acidic Solution," L. S. Levitt, *J. Org. Chem.*, **20**, 1297 (1955).

CHAPTER 14

Organic Nitrogen Compounds

NITROGEN-CONTAINING compounds rank among the most important classes of organic substances. In nature they occur among proteins, alkaloids, vitamins, and hormones, while synthetic examples include polymers, explosives, dyestuffs, and drugs. The nitrogen atoms in such compounds are found in various degrees of substitution and of oxidation, and they may be part of a simple functional group or of more complex heterocyclic ring systems. The present chapter is concerned with the chemistry of simpler nitrogen compounds, while in Chapter 16 we shall examine some of the important complex nitrogenous substances which occur in nature.

AMINES

14-1. Nomenclature of Amines

Amines are alkyl or aryl derivatives of ammonia. They are classed as primary, secondary, or tertiary depending upon the number of organic groups attached to the nitrogen atom.

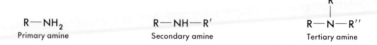

R—NH$_2$	R—NH—R′	R—N—R″
Primary amine	Secondary amine	Tertiary amine

Simple amines are named by naming the alkyl or aryl groups bonded to nitrogen, and adding the suffix *-amine*. If the same group appears more than once, the proper prefix (*di-*, *tri-*, etc.) is used. The names of the different groups may be arranged either in order of increasing complexity or alphabetically. The following examples are representative.

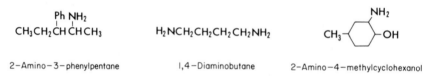

CH$_3$CH$_2$NH$_2$ (CH$_3$)$_2$NH   CH$_3$NHCH$_2$CH$_3$ (CH$_3$CH$_2$)$_3$N   CH$_3$NCH$_2$CH(CH$_3$)$_2$

Ethylamine   Dimethylamine   Methylethylamine   Triethylamine   Methylethylisobutylamine

In more complex structures the **amino group** is named as a substituent in the chain or ring involved:

Ph NH$_2$
CH$_3$CH$_2$CH CHCH$_3$

H$_2$NCH$_2$CH$_2$CH$_2$CH$_2$NH$_2$

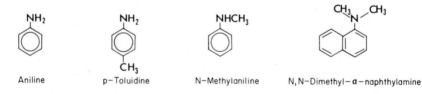

2–Amino–3–phenylpentane   1,4–Diaminobutane   2–Amino–4–methylcyclohexanol

The simplest aromatic amine, aminobenzene, PhNH$_2$, is commonly called aniline. Its homologs with methyl groups on the ring are called toluidines (*o-*, *m-*, and *p-*). If the methyl group is on nitrogen, however, the derivative is named *N*-methylaniline, to indicate that the methyl group is located on the nitrogen atom and not the ring. The prefix is repeated if there are two substituents on nitrogen, as illustrated by the naphthylamine derivative shown below.

Aniline   p–Toluidine   N–Methylaniline   N, N–Dimethyl–a–naphthylamine

Long-chain polyamines and cyclic amines are frequently named as **aza** derivatives. The compound is named as though all of its atoms were carbon, and the positions of the nitrogen atoms in the structure are indicated by numbers and the prefix *aza-*.

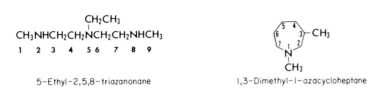

5-Ethyl-2,5,8-triazanonane   1,3-Dimethyl-1-azacycloheptane

14-2. Structure of Ammonia and Amines

Recalling the electron distribution in the nitrogen atom $(1s^2 2s^2 2p_x 2p_y 2p_z$; Table 5-1), and the angular direction of p orbitals, we might anticipate that the bonds from nitrogen in ammonia and amines would make $90°$ angles. It is found, however, that they are in fact larger than this, and the bond angles are nearly tetrahedral. Thus the H–N–H bond angle in ammonia is about $107°$, while the C–N–C bond angle in trimethylamine is about $108°$. Two principal factors are considered responsible, the repulsion between the nonbonded atoms on the nitrogen and the hybridization of the bonds to nitrogen. In ammonia, repulsion forces act between the electrons of all three N–H bonds, as well as between these and the unshared pair of p electrons on the nitrogen atom. Repulsion also exists between the partial positive charges residing on each hydrogen atom as a result of the polarity of the N–H bond. Concerning hybridization, we recall that the bond angles of hybrid orbitals increase with increasing s character (Section 5-3), and we conclude therefore that there is appreciable sp^3 hybridization of the unshared pair of electrons on the nitrogen atom of ammonia. The greater bond angle in trimethylamine is attributed to the greater bulk of the CH_3 groups in this molecule, as compared to the H atoms in ammonia.

It is known that ammonia and amines undergo a rapid interconversion between their two pyramidal forms (Figure 14-1). This *inversion*, which

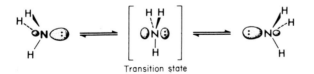

Transition state

Figure 14-1. Spontaneous Inversion of the Ammonia Molecule

necessitates that the molecule pass through a planar transition state ($120°$ bond angles), requires an activation energy of only about 6 kcal/mole for ammonia, and thus occurs spontaneously at room temperature.

14-3. Physical Properties of Amines

From its position in the periodic table of the elements (Figure 2-1), nitrogen is seen to be less electronegative (electron-attracting; Section 2-2d) than is oxygen. Hence, the lone pair of electrons on the nitrogen atom of ammonia and amines is understandably more readily shared than are the comparable unshared electron pairs on oxygen in water, alcohols, and ethers. Concomitantly, the N–H bonds in ammonia and amines have less ionic character than the O–H bonds in water and alcohols. The overall result is that ammonia and amines are less strongly hydrogen bonded than are water and alcohols (Section 11-3). This is immediately seen in comparing the boiling points of water and ammonia, and of methylamine and methanol (Table 14-1). That hydrogen bonding does exist between molecules of amines having N–H bonds, however, is evident from the boiling points of dimethylamine and trimethylamine (Table 14-1). The 4° lower boiling point of trimethylamine, despite its 14 unit increase in molecular weight, is attributable to its lack of hydrogen bonding due to the absence of N–H bonds.

Table 14-1. Boiling Points of Some Nitrogen and Oxygen Compounds

Compound	Molecular Weight	B.p., °C
NH_3	17	−33
H_2O	18	100
CH_3NH_2	31	−6.5
CH_3OH	32	65
$(CH_3)_2NH$	45	7.4
$(CH_3)_3N$	59	3.5

Because the unshared pair of electrons on the nitrogen atom in amines is more readily shared than the electron pairs on the oxygen atom of alcohols, amines form stronger hydrogen bonds with water than do alcohols. They are thus more soluble in water than are alcohols of comparable molecular weight. Butylamine, for example, is infinitely miscible with water, whereas 1-butanol has only limited water solubility.

Primary amines in dilute solution show two infrared absorption bands in the 3500 to 3300 cm^{-1} region of the spectrum, corresponding to symmetrical and unsymmetrical N–H stretching vibrations. N–H bending vibrations for primary amines occur in the 1650 to 1580 and 900 to 650 cm^{-1} regions. Both types of bands may be shifted somewhat by hydrogen bonding in more concentrated solutions. C–N stretching vibrations are seen as weak bands in the 1220 to 1020 cm^{-1} region for aliphatic amines and as strong bands between 1360 and 1250 cm^{-1} for aromatic amines.

Lower aliphatic amines have characteristic unpleasant odors, reminiscent of ammonia and dead fish. Decay of fish, in fact, is accompanied by the liberation of trimethylamine, while putrescine (1,4-diaminobutane) and cadaverine (1,5-diaminopentane) are present in decaying flesh. As in other series, the odor of amines decreases with increasing molecular weight (and consequent decreasing vapor pressure).

14-4. Basicity of Amines

Ammonia and amines are characteristically basic, as a consequence of the ability of the lone pair of electrons on their nitrogen atoms to be shared by electron acceptors (Lewis acids). They are stronger Lewis bases than water because of the lower electronegativity of nitrogen as compared to oxygen (Section 2-2d). Thus the position of equilibrium for the transfer of a proton between ammonia and water lies to the right,

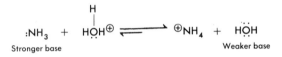

$$:NH_3 \ + \ HO\overset{\underset{\displaystyle H}{|}}{H}{}^{\oplus} \ \rightleftharpoons \ {}^{\oplus}NH_4 \ + \ H\ddot{O}H$$

Stronger base   Weaker base

and various acids in aqueous solution will accordingly form ammonium salts with ammonia. Amines, having comparable base strengths, behave similarly, forming substituted ammonium salts. The following examples are typical, and illustrate the nomenclature of such salts.

$$NH_3 + CH_3COOH \xrightarrow{H_2O} NH_4^{\oplus}CH_3COO^{\ominus}$$
Ammonium acetate

$$CH_3NH_2 + HCl \xrightarrow{H_2O} CH_3NH_3^{\oplus}Cl^{\ominus}$$
Methylammonium chloride

$$(CH_3CH_2)_3N + PhCOOH \xrightarrow{H_2O} (CH_3CH_2)_3NH^{\oplus}PhCOO^{\ominus}$$
Triethylammonium benzoate

Since ammonia and amines are much weaker bases than hydroxide ion, however, they may be liberated from their salts by the action of strong inorganic bases such as sodium hydroxide.

$$RNH_3^{\oplus}Cl^{\ominus} + Na^{\oplus}OH^{\ominus} \longrightarrow RNH_2 + H_2O + Na^{\oplus}Cl^{\ominus}$$
Stronger base   Weaker base

The strength of a base may be described quantitatively by the equilibrium constant (K_b) for its ionization with water. As with acids (pK_a; Sec-

$$B: + HOH \rightleftharpoons B:H^{\oplus} + :OH^{\ominus}$$

$$K_b = \frac{[B:H^{\oplus}][:OH^{\ominus}]}{[B:]} \qquad pK_b = \log_{10}\frac{1}{K_b}$$

tion 13-2), the strengths of bases are more conveniently compared by their pK_b values defined as the logarithm of the reciprocal of the basic dissociation constant K_b. From this relationship, a base with a dissociation constant of 10^{-4} would have $pK_b = 4$. It is evident that the stronger the base, the larger will be the value of K_b and the smaller will be that of pK_b. In Table 14-2 are listed values for K_b and pK_b of a number of amine bases.

Table 14-2. Base Strengths of Some Amines

Base	K_b	pK_b
Ammonia	1.8×10^{-5}	4.74
Methylamine	4.4×10^{-4}	3.36
Dimethylamine	5.1×10^{-4}	3.29
Trimethylamine	5.3×10^{-5}	4.28
Aniline	4.2×10^{-10}	9.38
Diphenylamine (Ph_2NH)	6.3×10^{-14}	13.2
Triphenylamine (Ph_3N)	$\sim 10^{-20}$	~ 20
o-Nitroaniline	5×10^{-15}	14.3
m-Nitroaniline	2.5×10^{-12}	11.6
p-Nitroaniline	10^{-13}	13.0
p-Methoxyaniline	2×10^{-9}	8.7

The influence of electronic and other factors on the base strength of amines is evident from Table 14-2. The greater base strength of methylamine over ammonia is thought to result from the greater capability of electron release of the methyl group as compared to hydrogen, which effectively increases the electron density on the nitrogen atom, as symbolized in 14-1. Dimethylamine (14-2) is slightly stronger than methylamine

$$CH_3 \rightarrow \overset{..}{N}H_2 \qquad\qquad\qquad CH_3 \rightarrow \overset{..}{N}H \leftarrow CH_3$$
$$14\text{-}1 \qquad\qquad\qquad\qquad 14\text{-}2$$

for the same reason. Trimethylamine, surprisingly, is about a 10-fold *weaker* base than dimethylamine. The electron-release effect of the third methyl group is apparently offset by another factor, namely, diminished hydration of the trimethylammonium cation. One of the driving forces for ionization in water is the hydration of the ions formed (Section 2-3). Because of the steric (bulk) shielding effect of *three* alkyl groups, the hydrated trimethylammonium ion (14-**4**) is less effectively hydrated than, for ex-

$$CH_3\ddot{N}H_2 + x\,H_2O \rightleftharpoons CH_3NH_3^{\oplus} \cdot (H_2O)_y + OH^{\ominus} \cdot (H_2O)_z$$
14-3

$$(CH_3)_3\ddot{N} + x'\,H_2O \rightleftharpoons (CH_3)_3NH^{\oplus} \cdot (H_2O)_{y'} + OH^{\ominus} \cdot (H_2O)_{z'}$$
14-4

ample, the hydrated methylammonium ion (14-3). In addition, hydration is favored by the presence of N–H bonds capable of hydrogen bonding
with water molecules. We notice that the primary ammonium ion 14-3
has three such bonds, whereas the tertiary ammonium ion 14-**4** has but
one. Thus hydration is again disfavored in trialkylammonium ions, and
tertiary amines are accordingly the weaker bases.

The vastly lower basicity of aniline, which is some million-fold weaker
than methylamine, is attributed to resonance. Notice in the resonance
hybrid for aniline (14-**5**) that the pair of electrons on nitrogen is distributed
over the aromatic ring, and is thus less available for sharing in reaction

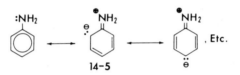

14–5

with an acid. Diphenylamine, with *two* aromatic rings wherein the electrons on nitrogen may be analogously "lost" in a resonance hybrid, is in
turn almost 10,000-fold weaker a base than aniline, and in triphenylamine
the resonance effect is dramatically continued.

Electron-withdrawing substituents on the aromatic ring decrease the
basicity of substituted anilines as well. Thus *m*-nitroaniline is 100-fold
weaker a base than aniline owing to the *inductive withdrawal* of electrons
occasioned by the *m*-nitro group, as symbolized in 14-**6**. In *o*- and *p*-nitro-
anilines a resonance effect (such as 14-**7**) is superimposed on the inductive

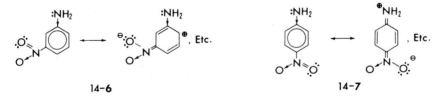

14–6   14–7

withdrawal of electrons by the nitro group, and these amines are accordingly even weaker bases. The opposite effect of electron *release* by a ring

substituent is found in *p*-methoxyaniline (*p*-anisidine). Here the resonance hybrid (14-**8**) involving the methoxy group and the ring induces a higher electronic charge on nitrogen, and *p*-methoxyaniline is a five-fold *stronger* base than aniline.

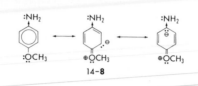

14-**8**

Steric effects also influence the basic strength of amines in certain circumstances. 2,4,6-Trinitroaniline (14-**9a**) is an extremely weak base because of the resonance effect (14-**9b**) of its three nitro groups. *N,N*-Dimethyl-2,4,6-trinitroaniline (14-**10a**) is a 40,000 fold stronger base, however, since contributing resonance structures such as 14-**10b**, which *require a coplanar disposition* of the *o*-nitro and *N*-methyl groups, are prevented because of the bulk interference between these substituents. This phenomenon, referred to as **steric inhibition of resonance,** results here in a greater availability of the nitrogen electrons in 14-**10a** and consequent higher basic-

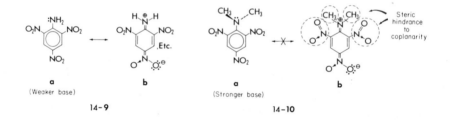

14-**9**   14-**10**

ity. In 14-**9a** the smaller *N*-hydrogen atoms do not interfere sterically with the *o*-nitro groups, coplanarity may be largely achieved, and the canonical forms such as 14-**9b** may contribute to the hybrid, making for lower basicity. The same phenomenon affects the acidity of phenols (Section 11-9b) as well. The *p*-nitrophenoxide anion (14-**11a**), for example, is a weaker base (that is, the corresponding phenol is a stronger acid, pK_a = 7.16) than the 3,5-dimethyl-4-nitrophenoxide ion (14-**12a**) (corresponding phenol, pK_a = 8.25). In this example, contributing coplanar structures such as 14-**11b**, which decrease the basicity of the *p*-nitrophenoxide ion, are hindered by steric interference between the methyl groups and oxygen atoms in 14-**12b**, making for higher basicity of 14-**12a** and lower acidity for its corresponding phenol.

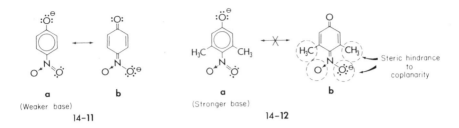

14-11   14-12

The increased basicity resulting from the inaccessibility of coplanarity for contributing resonance structures is also illustrated by N,N-dimethylaniline (14-**13a**, pK_b = 8.94) and the 540-fold stronger base benzoquinuclidine (14-**14a**, pK_b = 6.21). Coplanar contributing resonance forms such as 14-**13b** in N,N-dimethylaniline are not possible for benzoquinuclidine

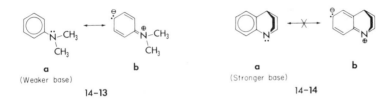

14-13   14-14

since, as seen in 14-**14b**, they would require that the formal double bond be at the nitrogen bridgehead atom, in violation of Bredt's rule (Section 8-3c). The unshared nitrogen electrons in benzoquinuclidine are thus more localized, making for its greater basicity.

Dr. H. C. Brown of Purdue University has provided much interesting evidence on the steric factors influencing the basicity of amines toward bulky Lewis acids such as tri-t-butylboron. In this acid-base reaction, adducts such as 14-**15** are reversibly formed, and base strength is measured

Tri-t-butylboron

by the equilibrium constant of the reaction. With ethylamines the stability of the adducts varies as NH_3 > $EtNH_2$ > Et_2NH > Et_3N. This order is opposite to that predicted on the basis of the electronic inductive effects of the ethyl groups, and suggests that a steric factor must be in control. The stability of the adduct is weakened, and its formation is impaired, because of the steric interference between the ethyl and the bulky t-butyl

Steric interference
at front

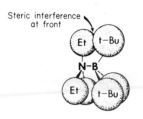

Figure 14-2. F Strain in Trialkylboron–Amine Adducts

substituents, and the greater the number of *N*-ethyl groups present, the greater the steric interference. Since this interference occurs at the *front sides* of the reacting molecules, it is called **front strain** or **F strain** (Figure 14-2). It is noteworthy that quinuclidine (14-**16**), whose alkyl groups are

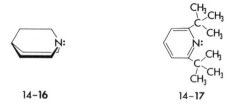

14-16   14-17

"tied back out of the way" by its caged ring structure, shows much less evidence of F strain, and is a far stronger base than triethylamine in such reactions. One of the largest F-strain effects is seen in 2,6-di-*t*-butylpyridine (14-**17**), which fails completely to coordinate with the powerful Lewis acid BF$_3$, and which even shows diminished basicity towards protons.

In trialkylborons the bulky alkyl groups lie as far apart as possible (at or near 120°), since boron would be expected to utilize sp^2 orbitals when tricovalent. In adducts such as 14-**15,** however, the boron bond angles are forced into something closer to tetrahedral (109.5°), since the bond hybridization becomes sp^3-like. The diminished bond angles accordingly give rise to a steric compression between the alkyl groups on the *back side* of the boron atom. This situation, referred to as **B strain** (Figure 14-3; see Sec-

Steric interference
at back

Figure 14-3. B Strain in Trialkylboron–Amine Adducts

tion 8-3a), also decreases the stability of such boron adducts as the bulk of the alkyl substituents on boron increases. B strain may operate in the amine moiety also, especially as augmented by the already present F strain.

We have seen previously (Section 9-6) that small ring compounds often show peculiar behavior due to the internal angle strain, sometimes called **I strain,** of their rings. These three types of strain have been collectively referred to as "FBI" effects.

The ability of amines to form stable salts is often utilized for their isolation and characterization. Salts with hydrochloric acid ("hydrochlorides") are often used for these purposes, as are salts ("picrates") with the strongly acidic 2,4,6-trinitrophenol (picric acid, $pK_a = 0.8$; Section 11-9b). The regeneration of free amines from such salts has been discussed earlier in this Section.

Salt formation in certain cyclic amino ketones is instructive in showing the opportunity for *transannular participation* (Section 9-8c) during such reactions. As seen in Figure 14-4, cyclic amino ketones (A) of various ring

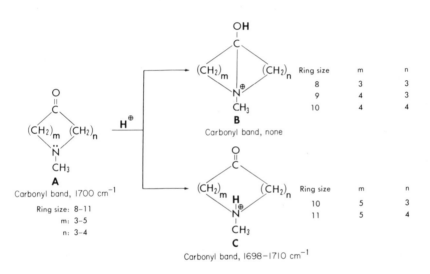

Figure 14-4. Infrared Spectra of Cyclic Amino Ketones

sizes show carbonyl absorption frequencies around 1700 cm^{-1} in neutral solution. Let us now place such amino ketones in acid solution to form their amine salts. We find that the carbonyl adsorption band vanishes for those cyclic amino ketones (B) whose ring sizes are 8 to 10 and which are capable of protonation at the carbonyl function via transannular participation of the unshared electrons on the nitrogen atom across the ring. Notice that 5-5, 6-5 and 6-6 bicyclic ring systems are formed in the process. On the other hand, those amino ketones (C) having 10- or 11-membered rings, which would yield sterically improbable 7-5 or 7-6 bicyclic ring systems by a similar transannular process, undergo normal neutralization at their nitrogen atoms and show their customary carbonyl absorption bands.

14-5. Characterization of Amines

Primary and secondary amines may be readily distinguished from tertiary amines by the N–H stretching vibration (characteristic of the first two types) in the infrared region close to 3300 cm^{-1} (Section 14-3). Primary and secondary amines may be further distinguished since only the former yields an *isocyanide* (isonitrile, carbylamine) upon heating with chloroform and sodium hydroxide. The isocyanides are toxic compounds having disagreeable and readily detectable odors, particularly those with lower molecular weights.

$$RNH_2 + CHCl_3 + 3\,NaOH \longrightarrow R\overset{\oplus}{-}N\equiv\overset{\ominus}{C} + 3\,NaCl + 3\,H_2O$$

Alkyl isocyanide

The three types of amines may also be distinguished chemically by their differing behavior toward nitrous acid. Primary amines yield nitrogen quantitatively, and afford a mixture of organic products (Section 14-10b).

$$RNH_2 + HONO \longrightarrow N_2 + H_2O + \text{Organic products}$$

Volumetric measurement of nitrogen after reaction with nitrous acid is thus frequently employed in the quantitative estimation of primary —NH$_2$ groups (**Van Slyke method**), particularly among amino acids and proteins (Section 16-20e). Secondary amines are converted into oily, yellow *N*-nitroso derivatives (*N*-nitrosoamines) which, being neutral amides of nitrous acid, are insoluble in dilute acids.

$$R_2NH + HONO \longrightarrow R_2N—NO + H_2O$$

N-Nitrosodialkylamine

Tertiary amines react with nitrous acid to form soluble nitrite salts. Under more vigourous conditions, these may undergo further complex transformations.

$$R_3N + HONO \longrightarrow R_3NH^{\oplus}NO_2^{\ominus}$$

Trialkylammonium nitrite

Tertiary aromatic amines are exceptional in that they yield ring-substituted nitroso derivatives. If the position *para* to the dialkylamino group is free, substitution occurs exclusively at this position. If the *para* position is substituted, the *C*-nitrosation occurs at the *ortho* position.

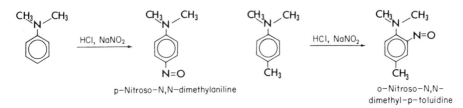

p—Nitroso—N,N—dimethylaniline   o—Nitroso—N,N—
dimethyl—p—toluidine

Finally, the three types of amines may be differentiated by the **Hinsberg method.** This test reaction is based on the differences in behavior of each type of amine with benzenesulfonyl chloride in the presence of base, and on the differences in the properties of the products obtained from each type. Primary amines afford N-alkylbenzenesulfonamides (14-**18**), which are soluble in excess sodium hydroxide, since their sulfonyl group is suf-

$$RNH_2 + PhSO_2Cl + NaOH \longrightarrow RNHSO_2Ph + NaCl + H_2O$$
14—18

$$\xrightarrow{NaOH} \left[R\overset{\ominus}{N}SO_2Ph \right] \overset{\oplus}{Na} + H_2O$$
Water soluble

ficiently electron attracting to render their N-proton acidic enough to react with base. Acidification of the solution precipitates the solid sulfonamide 14-**18**, and such solid sulfonamides are frequently used to charactarize primary amines by their melting points. Secondary amines yield solid N,N-dialkylbenzenesulfonamides (14-**19**), which, lacking a proton on their nitrogen atom, are insoluble in excess alkali. The solid sulfonamide is

$$R_2NH + PhSO_2Cl + NaOH \longrightarrow R_2NSO_2Ph + NaCl + H_2O$$
14-**19**
Insoluble in dilute
acid or base

again useful for characterization purposes. Tertiary amines, lacking a proton on nitrogen, are unreactive toward benzenesulfonyl chloride and remain unchanged.

$$R_3N + PhSO_2Cl + NaOH \longrightarrow \text{No reaction}$$

14-6. General Synthesis of Amines

Syntheses of amines fall into two categories: (1) general methods which afford the three classes of amines simultaneously and (2) specific methods which yield either primary, secondary, or tertiary amines as individual classes. In the former category, which we shall consider first, reaction conditions may often be varied so as to maximize the yield of the particular class of amine desired.

    a. Alkylation of Ammonia and Amines.   Ammonia reacts with alkyl halides in a typical nucleophilic displacement reaction (Section 11-12d) to form, initially, a primary alkylammonium salt (14-**20**), from which the free amine may be obtained by treatment with strong base. As a syn-

$$H_3N: + R:X \longrightarrow \overset{\oplus}{R}NH_3 \ X:^{\ominus} \xrightarrow{\text{NaOH}} RNH_2$$
$$\text{14-20}$$

thetic procedure for primary amines, however, the method suffers from the disadvantage that the initial reaction is followed by a series of subsequent reactions leading to more highly alkylated products. Since primary amines are comparable to ammonia in basicity (Table 14-2), the alkylammonium salt 14-**20** comes into an equilibrium in which substantial amounts of free primary amine are present. The resulting free amine is then capable of reaction with more alkyl halide to form the dialkylammonium salt 14-**21.** This in turn equilibrates with ammonia to form a secondary amine, which again is alkylated by the alkyl halide to produce the trialkylammonium salt 14-**22.** The same process ultimately leads to the tetraalkylammonium salt 14-**23.** On subsequent treatment with base, the reaction thus leads to a mixture of primary, secondary, and tertiary amines, and is of practical value only when the mixture may be conveniently separated into its

$$\overset{\oplus}{R}NH_3 \ \overset{\ominus}{X} + NH_3 \rightleftharpoons RNH_2 + \overset{\oplus}{NH_4} \ \overset{\ominus}{X}$$
$$\text{14-20}$$

$$RNH_2 + RX \longrightarrow R_2\overset{\oplus}{N}H \ \overset{\ominus}{X} \overset{NH_3}{\rightleftharpoons} R_2NH + \overset{\oplus}{NH_4} \ \overset{\ominus}{X}$$
$$\text{14-21}$$

$$R_2NH + RX \longrightarrow R_3\overset{\oplus}{N} \overset{\ominus}{X} \overset{NH_3}{\rightleftharpoons} R_3N + \overset{\oplus}{NH_4} \ \overset{\ominus}{X}$$
$$\text{14-22}$$

$$R_3N + RX \longrightarrow R_4\overset{\oplus}{N} \overset{\ominus}{X}$$
$$\text{14-23}$$

individual components. From the above equilibria, it is apparent that by using a very large excess of ammonia, the yield of primary amine will be favored. Similarly, using a large excess of a primary amine and an alkyl halide, the maximum yield of a secondary amine may be expected.

$$\text{Excess } RNH_2 + R'X \longrightarrow RR'NH_2^{\oplus}X^{\ominus} \xrightarrow{\text{NaOH}} RR'NH$$

In the same manner, the method may be utilized to synthesize a tertiary amine from a secondary amine and an alkyl halide. The alkylation of

$$\text{Excess } RR'NH + R''X \longrightarrow RR'R''NH^\oplus X^\ominus \xrightarrow{\text{NaOH}} RR'R''N$$

ammonia and amines with alkyl halides is referred to as the **Hofmann reaction**. Because of their basicity, amines may act as dehydrohalogenating agents (Section 8-3b) toward alkyl halides. The Hofmann reaction is thus further limited by the formation of olefin by-products. This competing elimination reaction may be significant with secondary alkyl halides and, as indicated in the accompanying equation, becomes the major reac-

$$(CH_3)_3CBr + NH_3 \longrightarrow (CH_3)_2C{=}CH_2 + NH_4^\oplus Br^\ominus$$

tion with tertiary halides. The Hofmann method is therefore not applicable to the synthesis of amines of the type R_3CNH_2.

The low reactivity of aryl and vinyl halides in nucleophilic displacement reactions (Section 11-13) precludes their use in the Hofmann reaction. Nevertheless, under more vigorous conditions aniline is synthesized commercially from chlorobenzene and ammonia.

$$PhCl + 2NH_3 \xrightarrow{Cu_2Cl_2,\ heat,\ pressure} PhNH_2 + NH_4^\oplus Cl^\ominus$$

Aryl halides whose halogen atoms are "activated" by the presence of electron-withdrawing substituents *ortho* or *para* to them (Section 11-13), however, react more readily with amines and ammonia. Thus the chlorine atom of *o*-nitrochlorobenzene is considerably more readily displaced than that of chlorobenzene, while 2,4-dinitrochlorobenzene is even more reactive.

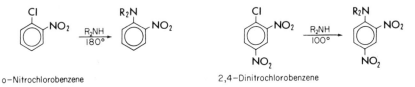

o−Nitrochlorobenzene   2,4−Dinitrochlorobenzene

b. Reductive Amination of Aldehydes and Ketones. It will be recalled (Section 12-7g) that ammonia and amines add to the carbonyl groups of aldehydes and ketones to form unstable adducts and Schiff bases. These may in turn be reduced catalytically to form amines. To accomplish the reaction, a mixture of the amine (or ammonia), the carbonyl compound, and

$$RCH{=}O + NH_3 \rightleftharpoons \begin{bmatrix} RCHNH_2 \\ | \\ OH \end{bmatrix} \begin{array}{c} \\ \\ \end{array} \xrightarrow[\text{heat, pressure}]{H_2,\ Catalyst} RCH_2NH_2$$
$$\Big\downarrow -H_2O$$
$$\big[RCH{=}NH\big]$$

Raney nickel (or platinum) catalyst is treated directly with hydrogen at elevated pressure (100 to 2000 psi) and temperature (50° to 200°). The reaction affords a *mixture* of amine products, however, since the initially formed primary amine, for example, may react in a similar manner to form secondary amine, which in turn may yield tertiary amine.

$$RCH_2NH_2 \xrightarrow{RCH=O} [RCH_2N=CHR] \xrightarrow[\text{heat, pressure}]{H_2, \text{ catalyst}}$$

$$RCH_2NHCH_2R \xrightarrow[\text{etc.}]{RCH=O} (RCH_2)_3N$$

Symmetrical and unsymmetrical secondary amines can also be synthesized by this procedure. For symmetrical secondary amines, two moles of the carbonyl compound per mole of ammonia are employed.

$$2\,ArCH=O + NH_3 + H_2 \xrightarrow[\text{heat, pressure}]{\text{Catalyst}} (ArCH_2)_2NH + H_2O$$

The reaction is most successful using aromatic aldehydes. Unsymmetrical secondary amines may be prepared using a mixture of primary amine and an aldehyde or ketone.

$$RCH=O + R'NH_2 + H_2 \xrightarrow[\text{heat, pressure}]{\text{Catalyst}} RCH_2NHR' + H_2O$$

The catalytic reduction of carbonyl compounds in the presence of secondary amines may also be employed for the synthesis of unsymmetrical tertiary amines.

A useful variation of the reductive amination method, known as the **Leuckart reaction,** employs a mixture of the aldehyde or ketone and ammonium formate.

$$RCH=O + HCOO^{\ominus}NH_4^{\oplus} \xrightarrow{150-200°} RCH_2NH_2 + CO_2 + H_2O$$

The reaction presumably occurs by thermal decomposition of the ammonium formate, whereupon the resulting ammonia reacts with the carbonyl compound as usual and the formic acid acts as a reducing agent.

$$HCOO^{\ominus}NH_4^{\oplus} \xrightarrow{\text{Heat}} NH_3 + HCOOH$$

$$RCH=O \xrightarrow[-H_2O]{NH_3} [RCH=NH] \xrightarrow{HCOOH} RCH_2NH_2 + CO_2$$

With *N*-substituted ammonium formates, secondary amines may be prepared, while *N*,*N*-disubstituted analogs yield tertiary amines. Similarly,

$$RCH=O + HCOO^{\ominus}R'NH_3^{\oplus} \xrightarrow{150-200°} RCH_2NHR' + CO_2 + H_2O$$

successive Leuckart reactions may lead to secondary and tertiary amine by-products in reactions of the above types. The presence of formic acid in the reaction mixture frequently converts the primary or secondary amine products into their N-formyl derivatives (14-**24**). These substituted form-amides, however, may be readily hydrolyzed to the desired free amine.

$$RCH_2NH_2 + HCOOH \xrightarrow[-H_2O]{Heat} \underset{14\text{-}24}{RCH_2NH-CH=O} \xrightarrow{H_2O, H^{\oplus}} RCH_2NH_2 + HCOOH$$

14-7. Synthesis of Primary Amines

The following methods are useful as specific syntheses of primary amines.

a. Reduction of Unsaturated Nitrogen Derivatives. The reduction of several types of unsaturated nitrogen-containing derivatives leads to aliphatic or aromatic primary amines. Such derivatives include nitro compounds, nitriles, oximes, and amides, as indicated in the accompanying general equations. The experimental conditions for these reductions are varied,

$$\underset{\text{Nitro compounds}}{RNO_2} + 6(H) \longrightarrow RNH_2 + 2H_2O$$

$$\underset{\text{Nitriles}}{RC\equiv N} + 4(H) \longrightarrow RCH_2NH_2$$

$$\underset{\text{Oximes}}{RCH=NOH} + 4(H) \longrightarrow RCH_2NH_2 + H_2O$$

$$\underset{\text{Amides}}{\overset{\overset{\text{O}}{\|}}{RCNH_2}} + 4(H) \longrightarrow RCH_2NH_2 + H_2O$$

and may involve either catalytic hydrogenation (Raney nickel, platinum, or copper–chromium catalyst; elevated temperature and pressure), or chemical agents (lithium aluminum hydride; sodium and ethanol; tin or iron and hydrochloric acid). Optimum conditions depend upon the derivative undergoing reduction. During the catalytic reduction of nitriles and oximes, as in catalytic reductive aminations (Section 14-6b), secondary and tertiary amine by-products may often be formed. These are thought to arise by addition of the primary amine product to intermediate imines such as 14-**25**, forming adducts (14-**26**) which ultimately yield secondary

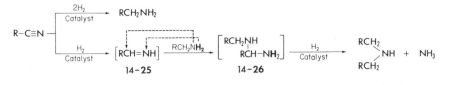

amines and ammonia. Tertiary amine by-products arise by an analogous path. The yield of undesired secondary and tertiary amines may be minimized by conducting such catalytic reductions in the presence of a large excess of ammonia.

The important aromatic primary amine *aniline* is prepared commercially (United States production in 1961: over 122 million pounds) by the reduction of nitrobenzene using iron turnings in the presence of water and a small amount of hydrochloric acid, or by the ammonolysis of chlorobenzene in the presence of copper oxide at elevated temperature and pressure. Aniline is used as a raw material in a variety of industries, particularly in dyestuffs, pharmaceuticals, rubber vulcanization accelerators, and antioxidants.

$$4\,PhNO_2 + 9\,Fe + 4\,H_2O \xrightarrow{\;HCl\;} 4\,PhNH_2 + 3\,Fe_3O_4$$

$$PhCl + 2\,NH_3\,(aqueous) \xrightarrow[\text{pressure}]{CuO,\,200°} PhNH_2 + NH_4^{\oplus}Cl^{\ominus}$$

b. Gabriel Synthesis.   When phthalic anhydride reacts with ammonia at elevated temperature, the cyclic imide phthalimide is formed.   Because of

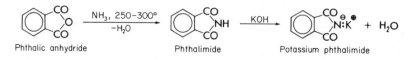

Phthalic anhydride   Phthalimide   Potassium phthalimide

the two electron-attracting groups attached to nitrogen, its N-hydrogen atom is somewhat acidic (pK_a = 8.30), and phthalimide thus readily forms a potassium salt with potassium hydroxide.   A useful procedure for preparing primary amines is the **Gabriel synthesis,** which involves nucleophilic displacement of halide ions from alkyl halides by the phthalimide group, to form N-substituted phthalimides (14-**27**).   Hydrolysis of the latter cleanly affords primary amines in good yield.

![reaction scheme]

14-**27**

c. Hofmann and Related Rearrangements.   In the **Hofmann rearrangement,** a carboxamide is converted into a primary amine by the action of sodium hypohalite.

$$\overset{O}{\overset{\|}{RCNH_2}} + NaOX + 2\,NaOH \longrightarrow RNH_2 + Na_2CO_3 + NaX + H_2O$$

The reaction provides a means for the controlled removal of a carbon atom from a carboxylic acid chain, and also represents a useful method for synthesizing primary amines. It is usually conducted by using a mixture of Cl_2 or Br_2 and NaOH, and yields are generally satisfactory. The transformation has been studied in detail mechanistically, and is believed to proceed by way of the steps shown in Figure 14-5. The action of hypo-

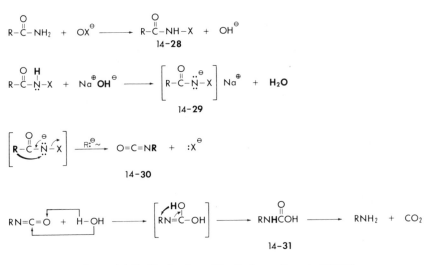

Figure 14-5. Mechanism of the Hofmann Rearrangement

halite on the amide first produces the *N*-haloamide (14-**28**) which, having electron-withdrawing acyl and halogen functions, possesses a somewhat acidic *N*-hydrogen atom. In the presence of base this proton is removed, forming a transient ionic species 14-**29**, which undergoes a 1,2 shift of the adjacent alkyl (or aryl) group, expelling halide ion and forming the intermediate alkyl isocyanate (14-**30**). This in turn is hydrolyzed to an intermediate *N*-alkylcarbamic acid (14-**31**), which finally decarboxylates into the primary amine. The last step in the sequence is a well-known reaction of isocyanates, which may actually be isolated if the reaction is conducted in nonaqueous media. Further evidence for the mechanism comes from the isolation, under proper conditions, of the *N*-haloamide (14-**28**) and ionic intermediates (14-**29**), which in turn may be separately transformed into the amine product under the usual reaction conditions. The loss of halogen from 14-**29** and the 1,2 shift of $R:^{\ominus}$ from carbon to nitrogen to form 14-**30** is thought to occur *synchronously* (as in analogous carbonium ion rearrangements), since the rearrangement occurs with only small loss of optical activity and with retention of configuration when an asymmetric alkyl group migrates. If R:⊖ becomes free, a racemic product would be expected (Section 6-7).

96% Retained configuration

The **Curtius reaction** of carboxylic acid azides is another synthesis of primary amines which is mechanistically related to the Hofmann rearrangement. The acid azide is prepared by action of sodium azide on an acyl chloride, or by reaction of nitrous acid with a carboxylic acid hydrazide. The azide is decomposed by heating whereupon it loses nitrogen and rearranges to the isocyanate 14-30. The latter, as before, hydrolyzes to

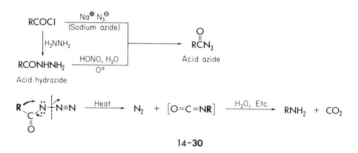

14-30

the primary amine product. The conversion RCOOH → RNH$_2$ may also be accomplished by the **Schmidt reaction,** in which a carboxylic acid is treated with hydrazoic acid in the presence of sulfuric acid. The process is mechanistically similar to the Curtius reaction. In both of these reactions, as in the Hofmann rearrangement, retention of configuration of the migrating group R is the rule.

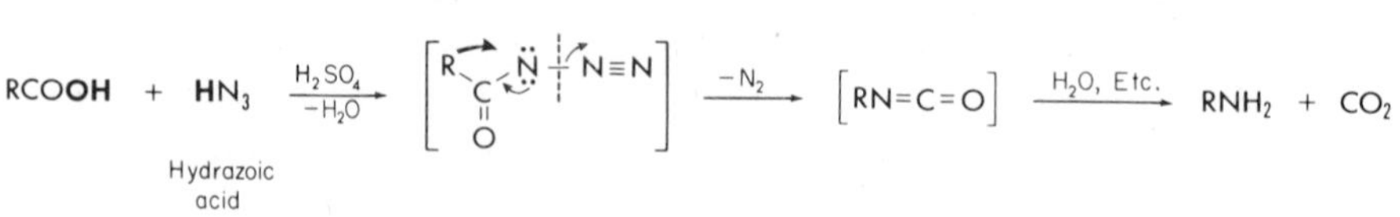

RCOOH + HN$_3$ $\xrightarrow[-H_2O]{H_2SO_4}$ $\left[\overset{R}{\underset{O}{C}}\ddot{N}\text{—}N{\equiv}N \right]$ $\xrightarrow{-N_2}$ $\left[RN{=}C{=}O \right]$ $\xrightarrow{H_2O, \text{Etc.}}$ RNH$_2$ + CO$_2$

Hydrazoic
acid

14-8. Synthesis of Secondary Amines

Besides the nonspecific methods previously discussed for the preparation of secondary amines, the following specific procedures are sometimes useful.

a. Reaction of Grignard Reagents with Schiff Bases. The addition of Grignard reagents to carbonyl groups of aldehydes and ketones has an analogy in the addition of these reagents to the C=N linkage of Schiff bases (Section 12-7g). Hydrolysis of the adducts from such additions provides a general method for preparing secondary amines of the type shown in 14-**32**.

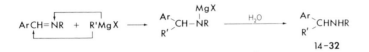

b. Hydrogenolysis of N,N-Dialkylbenzylamines. The benzyl group, PhCH$_2$—, in benzylamines, as in benzyl alcohols and benzyl ethers, may be removed by catalytic hydrogenolysis. Application of this reaction to *N,N*-dialkylbenzylamines (14-**33**) provides an excellent procedure for the synthesis of secondary dialkylamines. The dialkylbenzylamine precursor

$$PhCH_2 \!+\! N\!\!<^R_R \;+\; H_2 \;\xrightarrow[Raney\ Ni]{Pt,\ Pd,\ or}\; PhCH_3 \;+\; HN\!\!<^R_R$$

14-**33**

may be prepared by the alkylation of benzylamine with the desired alkyl halide (Section 14-6a).

14-9. Synthesis of Tertiary Amines

These compounds are most frequently prepared by the alkylation of secondary amines with alkyl halides (Section 14-6a). In addition, the introduction of the dialkylaminomethyl group onto the α-carbon of an aldehyde or ketone having an α-hydrogen may be accomplished using formaldehyde and a secondary amine (**Mannich reaction**), producing in fair yields tertiary β-keto amines of the type 14-**34**. The Mannich reaction also proceeds with the activated *o*- and *p*-hydrogen atoms of phenols, permitting the introduction of one, two, or three dialkylamino groups into the phenol nucleus.

$$\overset{O}{\underset{}{Ar\overset{\shortparallel}{C}CH_2}}\!\!-\!\overset{\alpha\text{-}H}{H} \;+\; CH_2{=}O \;+\; HNR_2 \;\xrightarrow{H^\oplus,\ heat}\; \overset{O}{\underset{}{Ar\overset{\shortparallel}{C}CH_2}}CH_2NR_2 \;+\; HOH$$

14-**34**

14-10. Reactions of Amines

Many important reactions of amines have been discussed in previous sections. These include salt formation (Section 14-4), *N*-alkylation (Section 14-6a), *N*-acylation (Sections 13-5 and 13-6), isocyanide formation (Section 14-5), reaction with nitrous acid (Section 14-5), and the Hinsberg reaction (Section 14-5). Let us now examine a few of these reactions in greater detail, as well as several new reactions characteristic of certain types of amines.

a. Reaction with Grignard Reagents. As with the hydroxylic hydrogen atoms of alcohols and carboxylic acids, the hydrogen atoms of primary and secondary amines react with Grignard reagents to form halomagnesium salts (14-35, 14-36) of the amines and to liberate the alkane corresponding to the Grignard reagent. With methylmagnesium halide and

$$RNH_2 + CH_3MgX \longrightarrow RNH—MgX + CH_4$$
$$14\text{-}35$$

$$R_2NH + R'MgX \longrightarrow R_2N—MgX + R'H$$
$$14\text{-}36$$

measurement of the volume of methane liberated, such reactions constitute the **Zerevitinoff method** for the quantitative estimation of "active hydrogen" in —OH and $>$NH compounds. Tertiary amines have no active hydrogen atom on nitrogen, and thus cannot form analogous halomagnesium salts. Instead, the form complexes with Grignard reagents, which are analogous to, but more stable than, the complexes between Grignard reagents and ethers (Section 11-17a). Thus *N*,*N*-dimethylaniline, $PhN(CH_3)_2$, may be used as a solvent for the Grignard reagent, thereby permitting higher reaction temperatures than when ethyl ether is employed. In contrast, pyridine forms an insoluble complex with Grignard reagents.

b. Reaction with Nitrous Acid. In Section 14-5 we learned that nitrous acid was a useful reagent to distinguish amines, since it reacts with primary amines to liberate nitrogen, with secondary amines to form *N*-nitroso amines, with tertiary amines to yield nitrite salts, and with *N*, *N*-dialkyl aromatic amines to produce *C*-nitroso derivatives. Let us here consider in more detail the reaction of nitrous acid with primary amines.

The initial product from an aliphatic primary amine and nitrous acid is thought to be a **diazonium salt** (14-37). In the aliphatic series such diazonium cations are extremely unstable, however, and immediately lose nitrogen to form a carbonium ion (14-38), which may then react in alternative ways depending upon its structure and environment. In aqueous media, alcohols are the principal final products, although alkenes may

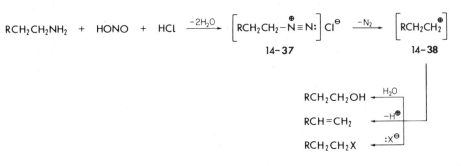

$$14-37 \qquad\qquad 14-38$$

also be formed, as well as alkyl halides. Furthermore, rearrangement of the carbonium ion may occur prior to its final reaction, leading to rearranged products. Thus the reaction of butylamine with nitrous acid in dilute hydrochloric acid affords a mixture of 1-butanol, 2-butanol, 1-chlorobutane, 2-chlorobutane, 1-butene, and 2-butene. Alkyl 1,2 shifts are also common, as seen in the following examples, where we note that cyclic primary amines often react with ring expansion or ring contraction. Such Wagner-Meerwein rearrangements in the amine series are referred to as **Demjanov rearrangements.** The complexity of products usually obtained from the reaction of aliphatic primary amines with nitrous acid precludes the general synthetic utility of the reaction. Its analytical application, however, has been mentioned (Section 14-5).

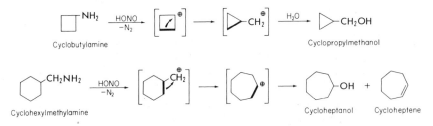

The reaction of aromatic primary amines with nitrous acid likewise produces diazonium salts, as seen in the following examples with aniline and β-naphthylamine. Such aromatic diazonium salts were discovered by

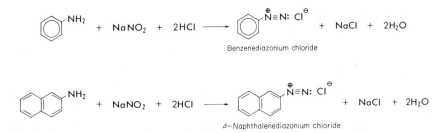

P. Griess in 1858, and the reaction producing them is referred to as **diazo-tization** of the aromatic amine. In contrast to aliphatic diazonium salts which immediately lose nitrogen, aromatic diazonium salts are stable in aqueous solution. This is accounted for by the resonance stabilization (Figure 14-6) possible for aromatic diazonium salts, but not for aliphatic

Figure 14-6. Resonance Hybrid of the Benzendiazonium Cation

analogs. Aromatic diazonium salts are unstable as dry solids, however, and explode when heated or subjected to mechanical shock. They are accordingly always employed in aqueous solution or as wet pastes, and find widespread application in organic syntheses and in the preparation of azo dyestuffs, as discussed in Sections 14-20 and 14-21.

    c. N-Acylation. We have learned previously (Section 13-12) that primary and secondary amines, respectively, react with acyl halides, acid anhydrides, and esters to form *N*-alkyl- and *N*,*N*-dialkylcarboxamides, and that ammonia reacts similarly to yield unsubstituted carboxamides. We recall also that such crystalline amide products, having sharp and characteristic melting points, find use in the characterization of carboxylic acids (Section 13-12). Such derivatives are equally useful for characterizing liquid amines. Tertiary amines, having no replaceable hydrogen atom on nitrogen, do not undergo such *N*-acylation reactions.

    N-Acylation is further used frequently as a means of protecting or blocking amino groups prior to a subsequent synthetic sequence involving the remainder of the molecule. An excellent example is found in the synthesis of the chemotherapeutic agent, sulfanilamide (*p*-aminobenzenesulfonamide, 14-**42**) from aniline. The aniline is first acetylated to form acetanilide (14-**39**). Acetylation of the amino group prevents its subsequent reaction with chlorosulfonic acid which, with aniline itself, would yield phenylsulfamic acid, $PhNHSO_2OH$. Since —$NHCOCH_3$ is an *o*,*p*-directing group, nuclear chlorosulfonation at the *p*-position of 14-**39** occurs instead, forming *p*-acetylaminobenzenesulfonyl chloride (14-**40**). Ammon-

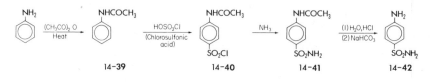

olysis of the sulfonyl chloride 14-**40** affords *p*-acetylaminobenzenesulfon-
amide (14-**41**), which is subsequently hydrolyzed to produce sulfanilamide
(14-**42**). Acetanilide (14-**39**) itself is widely used as an antipyretic and
analgesic drug.

   d. Oxidation. Aliphatic amines are fairly resistant to oxidation, particularly in acid solution owing to salt formation, but aromatic amines
oxidize readily and darken on standing, owing to oxidation by atmospheric
oxygen. With stronger oxidizing agents, aniline is converted to a complex
mixture of oxidation products which, by a poorly understood sequence of
secondary reactions, condense and oxidize further to form polymeric materials of imperfectly understood constitution, such as the jet-black dyestuff Aniline Black. Further oxidation affords *p*-quinone (Section 12-9)

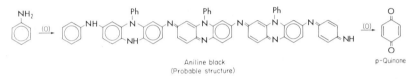

Aniline black
(Probable structure)

p-Quinone

   The oxidation of *tertiary* aliphatic or aromatic amines with aqueous hydrogen peroxide yields *N*-oxide derivatives.

$$R_3N + H_2O_2 \longrightarrow R_3\overset{\delta+}{N}\longrightarrow\overset{\delta-}{O}$$

Tertiary amine oxide

The presence of the semipolar N–O bond in such molecules gives rise to a
high dipole moment (Section 2-2d), and the dipole-dipole attractions between amine oxide molecules make for abnormally high boiling points.
Thus trimethylamine boils at 3.5°, but trimethylamine oxide does not distill at temperatures up to 180°, where it decomposes. Trimethylamine
oxide has been isolated from octopus and other marine organisms. The
thermal decomposition of tertiary amine oxides is an important reaction
to be discussed later (Section 14-12).

   e. Enamines. Under proper conditions in the presence of a trace of
p-toluenesulfonic acid, *secondary* amines will condense with aldehydes or
ketones having α-hydrogen atoms to form **enamines**. The reaction may be
formulated as analogous to Schiff base formation (Section 12-7g) except

$$R'CH_2CH=O \ + \ HNR_2 \xrightarrow{\ H^{\oplus}\ } \left[\begin{matrix} R'CH_2CHNR_2 \\ | \\ OH \end{matrix} \right] \xrightarrow[\text{Heat}]{-H_2O} R'CH=CHNR_2$$

Enamine

that, there being no hydrogen on the nitrogen atom of the intermediate,
its dehydration occurs toward the α-carbon rather than toward nitrogen.
Enamines prove to be useful intermediates for a number of subsequent
synthetic transformations. Their reduction with formic acid, for example,

provides an excellent method for preparing tertiary amines of the type
14-**43**. Oxidation of enamines, particularly those derived from pyrrolidine

$$R'CH{=}CHNR_2 + HCOOH \longrightarrow R'CH_2CH_2NR_2 + CO_2$$

14-**43**

(14-**44**) and piperidine, provides a good method for converting aldehydes
to aldehydes or ketones with one less carbon atom. Enamines are readily

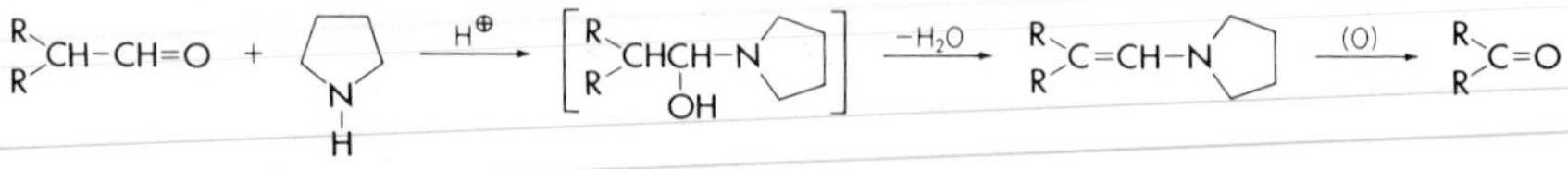

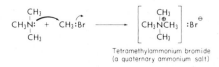

14-44

hydrolyzed by dilute acid, and are accordingly sometimes useful as protective derivatives for aldehydes and ketones. Lastly, the nucleophilic

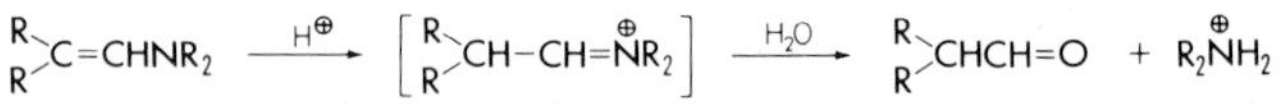

double bond of enamines makes them useful intermediates for the α-alkyl-
ation or α-acylation of aldehydes and ketones.

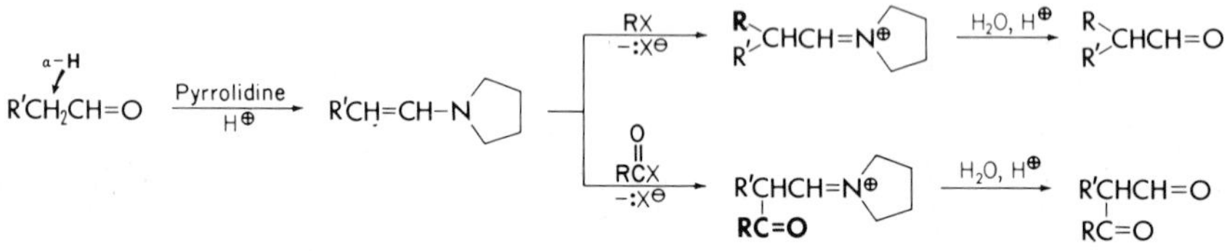

QUARTERNARY AMMONIUM SALTS AND BASES

14-11. Preparation and Properties of Quaternary Ammonium Derivatives

Quaternary ammonium salts, with all four hydrogen atoms of the $NH_4^{\oplus}$
cation substituted by alkyl or aryl groups, may be prepared generally by
the reaction of tertiary amines with alkyl halides, as in the following specific example. We have already seen (Section 14-6a) that this nucleo-

Tetramethylammonium bromide
(a quaternary ammonium salt)

philic displacement reaction results in such compounds as by-products in the Hofmann preparation of primary, secondary, and tertiary amines. It is obvious that by using an alkyl halide having a different R group, and amines with nonidentical R groups, tetraalkylammonium halides with any number up to four of nonidentical substituents may be prepared. Alkyl sulfates may also be employed in place of the halides as the alkylating agent.

$$RR'R''N: + R'''X \longrightarrow RR'R''R'''N^{\oplus}:X^{\ominus}$$

When tetraalkylammonium halides in aqueous solution are treated with silver hydroxide, or when quaternary ammonium sulfates (or acid sulfates) are treated with barium hydroxide, quaternary ammonium hydroxides are produced, as seen in the following examples. Such quaternary ammonium salts and bases are named straightforwardly as substituted ammonium derivatives, as is apparent in the specific examples shown.

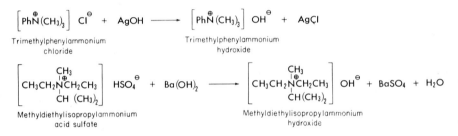

$$\left[Ph\overset{\oplus}{N}(CH_3)_3 \right] Cl^{\ominus} + AgOH \longrightarrow \left[Ph\overset{\oplus}{N}(CH_3)_3 \right] OH^{\ominus} + AgCl$$

Trimethylphenylammonium chloride   Trimethylphenylammonium hydroxide

$$\left[\begin{array}{c} CH_3 \\ | \oplus \\ CH_3CH_2\overset{}{N}CH_2CH_3 \\ | \\ CH\,(CH_3)_2 \end{array} \right] HSO_4^{\ominus} + Ba(OH)_2 \longrightarrow \left[\begin{array}{c} CH_3 \\ | \oplus \\ CH_3CH_2\overset{}{N}CH_2CH_3 \\ | \\ CH(CH_3)_2 \end{array} \right] OH^{\ominus} + BaSO_4 + H_2O$$

Methyldiethylisopropylammonium acid sulfate   Methyldiethylisopropylammonium hydroxide

Quaternary ammonium derivatives of the above sorts are completely ionized in aqueous solution and, as strong electrolytes, are very soluble. Quaternary ammonium hydroxides are thus extremely strong bases, comparable in base strength to sodium and potassium hydroxides. Their base strength contrasts to those of ammonium hydroxide and the hydroxides derived from primary, secondary, and tertiary amines. These each contain one or more hydrogen atoms on their nitrogen, and accordingly dissociate with a resulting low equilibrium concentration of hydroxide ion.

$$R\overset{\oplus}{N}H_3\,\overset{\ominus}{O}H \;\rightleftharpoons\; RNH_2 + H_2O$$

Quaternary ammonium salts possessing an alkyl group with a long hydrocarbon chain, as found in trimethylhexadecylammonium chloride, $CH_3(CH_2)_{15}N^{\oplus}(CH_3)_3\,Cl^{\ominus}$ have soap-like properties. Since the charge on the ion responsible for the detergent action of the salt is opposite to that on the ion responsible for the same action in an ordinary soap, for example, $CH_3(CH_2)_{16}COO^{\ominus}Na^{\oplus}$, quaternary ammonium salts having detergent properties are called **invert soaps.** Many of these are useful as germicides.

The quaternary ammonium ion called **choline,** $(CH_3)_3N^{\oplus}CH_2CH_2OH$, which occurs in all plant and animal cells either free or as a derivative, is considered to be a member of the vitamin B complex, but its proper nutritional classification is undecided. Growth inhibition, fatty degeneration of the liver, and hemorrhagic kidney disintegration result from choline deficiency. It is also the precursor in the animal organism of **acetylcholine** (14-**45**), a quaternary ion of utmost importance in controlling the func-

$$(CH_3)_3N^{\oplus}CH_2CH_2OCCH_3$$
$$\overset{\displaystyle O}{\overset{\|}{}}$$

14-45

tions of the body, in that it acts as a mediator of nerve impulses. Released at nerve endings, acetylcholine is involved in the control of nerve impulses to muscle fibers. Its action is localized by an enzyme in the blood, **acetylcholine esterase**, which rapidly causes acetylcholine to hydrolyze to choline, thus limiting its inhibitory action. It is of interest that the most active toxins known deactivate the acetylcholinesterase enzyme, thereby permitting widespread distribution of acetylcholine, with ensuing total muscle relaxation and paralysis. In plant and animal cells, choline is also esterified with phosphoric acid in the **lecithins**, members of a group of fat-like substances (**phospholipids**) which are required for the normal transport and utilization of other fats.

$$
\begin{array}{l}
CH_2OCOR \\
| \\
CHOCOR' \\
| \\
CH_2O-PO_2-OCH_2CH_2N^{\oplus}(CH_3)_3
\end{array}
$$

Lecithins

14-12. Pyrolysis of Quaternary Ammonium Derivatives

On heating, quaternary ammonium bases undergo an important thermal decomposition referred to as **Hofmann elimination** or **degradation**. When trimethylethylammonium hydroxide, for example, is heated to 125° to 150°, it decomposes into ethylene, trimethylamine, and water.

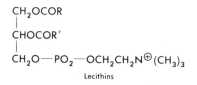

$$\overset{\beta-H}{\overset{\curvearrowright}{CH_3CH_2}}\overset{\oplus}{N}(CH_3)_3 \ \ \overset{\ominus}{OH} \xrightarrow{\text{Heat}} CH_2=CH_2 \ + \ (CH_3)_3N: \ + \ H_2O$$

Higher trimethylalkylammonium bases pyrolyze analogously, and we note that in both cases a β-hydrogen atom is eliminated from the larger group to form the alkene, and that the three methyl groups remain attached to the nitrogen atom.

$$\overset{\beta-H}{\overset{\curvearrowright}{RCH_2CH_2}}\overset{\oplus}{N}(CH_3)_3 \ \ \overset{\ominus}{OH} \xrightarrow{\text{Heat}} RCH=CH_2 \ + \ (CH_3)_3N: \ + \ H_2O$$

The mechanism of the Hofmann degradation is known to involve a typ-

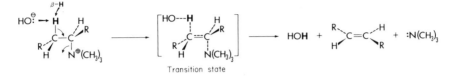

Figure 14-7. Mechanism of the Hofmann Elimination

ical *E*2 elimination (Figure 14-7; Section 8-3b). Attack by :OH$^\ominus$ at the
β-hydrogen atom of the larger alkyl group in the quaternary base occurs
synchronously with *trans* elimination of trimethylamine, forming the alkene
product. Notice that in the transition state the reacting groups are in a
trans orientation to one another (Section 8-3b). The elimination of $(CH_3)_3N$
in this reaction, like the loss of H_2O in the dehydration of alcohols via the
protonated species $ROH_2^\oplus$ (Section 8-3a), is favored by the positive charge
on the hetero atom, which increases its attraction for the electron pair
bonding it to carbon.

When an *unsymmetrical* dimethyldialkylammonium hydroxide such as
14-**46** is pyrolyzed, the question arises as to which β-hydrogen atom will
be abstracted and, therefore, which of the two larger alkyl groups will become the alkene. Unlike dehydrohalogenation and dehydration reactions

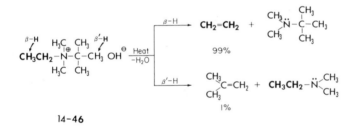

14-**46**

in which the most highly substituted alkene is the major product (Saytzeff
rule; Section 8-3a), in the Hofmann elimination the least substituted alkene is the one most generally formed. This generalization is referred to
as the **Hofmann rule.** Thus in the pyrolysis of 14-**46**, ethylene is formed
almost exclusively. When there is a choice of β-hydrogen atoms within
the *same* alkyl group, as in 14-**47,** the Hofmann rule also applies, and the
least substituted alkene is again the predominant product. There are two

$$CH_3CH_2-CH-CH_3 \xrightarrow[-H_2O]{Heat,} CH_3CH_2CH=CH_2 + CH_3CH=CHCH_3 + (CH_3)_3N:$$

$$\underset{(CH_3)_3\overset{\oplus}{N}\ OH^\ominus}{} \qquad\qquad 95\% \qquad\qquad\quad 5\%$$

14-**47**

principal reasons for the validity of the Hofmann rule: (1) the β-hydrogens on the β-carbon atoms having the fewer alkyl substituents are usually sterically more accessible to attack by :OH$^\ominus$, and (2) greater numbers of alkyl substituents on the β-carbon atom more effectively decrease the acidity of the β-hydrogens through the electron-releasing inductive effect of the substituents, thus making them less subject to attack by :OH$^\ominus$. Groups which, by inductive or resonance effects, are able to *increase* the acidity of the β-hydrogens, however, enhance the ease of elimination. Thus dimethylethyl-2-phenylethylammonium hydroxide (14-**48**) pyrolyzes, in defiance of Hofmann's rule, to yield mainly styrene (14-**49**) because of the greater acidity of its benzylic β-hydrogen atoms. More complex steric and

Benzylic β-H   CH$_3$ β-H
$$PhCH_2CH_2-\overset{CH_3}{\underset{CH_3}{\overset{\oplus}{N}}}-CH_2CH_3 \; OH^\ominus \xrightarrow[-H_2O]{Heat} PhCH=CH_2 + (CH_2=CH_2) + (CH_3)_2\ddot{N}CH_2CH_3$$

14-**48**   93%   Trace only
                                         14-**49**

electronic effects are sometimes important in determining the course of Hofmann elimination, but these are beyond our scope.

Lacking β-hydrogen atoms, a methyl group itself cannot be converted to an alkene, but it may be removed pyrolytically in a nucleophilic displacement reaction by OH$^\ominus$. Thus tetramethylammonium hydroxide yields methanol and trimethylamine in heating.

$$(CH_3)_4N^\oplus OH^\ominus \xrightarrow{Heat} CH_3OH + (CH_3)_3N:$$

By an analogous nucleophilic displacement, quaternary ammonium halides are also decomposed thermally into alkyl halides and tertiary amines, a reversal of their synthesis. With very strong bases such as alkyllithium, tetramethylammonium bromide suffers proton abstraction from one of its methyl groups and forms an ylide (trimethylammonium methylide, 14-**50**; Section 12-7o).

$$R_4N^\oplus X^\ominus \xrightarrow{Heat} RX + R_3N:$$

$$(CH_3)_4N^\oplus Br^\ominus + RLi \longrightarrow (CH_3)_3\overset{\oplus}{N}-\overset{\ominus}{\ddot{C}}H_2 + RH + LiBr$$
14-**50**

We recall (Section 11-19) that trialkylsulfonium halides may be prepared by the action of alkyl halides on alkyl sulfides. When such sulfonium salts are heated in the presence of bases such as ethoxide ion, or when the corresponding trialkylsulfonium hydroxides (made analogously by the action of silver hydroxide on the halide) are pyrolyzed, a similar *E*2 elimination reaction takes place, and Hofmann's rule again generally applies. The following example is typical.

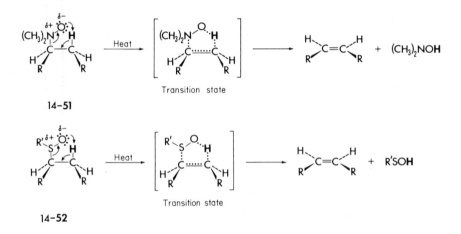

$$CH_3CH-CH-CH_2 \xrightarrow[-EtOH]{Heat} CH_3CH_2CH=CH_2 + CH_3CH=CHCH_3 + CH_3\ddot{S}CH_3 + Br\overset{\ominus}{:}$$

74%   26%

Dimethyl-2-butylsulfonium bromide

Two further alkene syntheses, formally analogous to the Hofmann degradation in that they involve elimination of β-hydrogen atoms, are the pyrolyses of dimethylalkylamine oxides (14-**51**; Section 14-10d) (**Cope elimination**) and of dialkyl sulfoxides (14-**52**; Section 11-19). Like the Chugaeff reaction (Section 8-3a) and the pyrolysis of esters (Section 8-3a), however, these decompositions involve *cis* elimination, presumably via cyclic transitions states of the types illustrated.

Transition state

14-51

Transition state

14-52

14-13. A Problem in Structure Determination

The Hofmann degradation has proved particularly useful in the structure determination of alkaloids (Section 16-40) and other natural nitrogen-containing derivatives which may be converted into quaternary bases. The amine under investigation is *exhaustively methylated* with an excess of methyl iodide, the resulting quaternary ammonium iodide is converted into the corresponding hydroxide using silver hydroxide, and the quaternary ammonium base is pyrolyzed. Knowing the course of the Hofmann elimination, the structure of the original amine may then be deduced from the nature of the pyrolysis products. Let us consider a specific example of the complete structure elucidation of a simple naturally occurring nitrogen base and see the types of structural information which the Hofmann and other degradative and diagnostic reactions may provide.

From mescal buttons or peyote, the flowering tops of a small south-western cactus (*Lophophora williamsii*), the nitrogen base mescaline, $C_{11}H_{17}NO_3$, may be extracted. The chief physiologically active principle of peyote, mescaline is responsible for the hallucinatory and psychogenic action which for centuries has involved this plant in the religious cere-monies of southwestern and Mexican Indian tribes. Zerevitinoff analysis (Section 14-10a) of mescaline shows the presence of active hydrogen, and the Hinsberg test (Section 14-5) indicates a primary amine function. Ex-haustive methylation with methyl iodide, followed by conversion to the quaternary hydroxide and pyrolysis, yields trimethylamine and a new ole-finic substance, $C_{11}H_{14}O_3$. Ozonolysis (Section 8-4h) of the latter pro-

$$C_{11}H_{15}O_3NH_2 \xrightarrow[\text{(2) AgOH}]{\text{(1) Excess CH}_3\text{I}} C_{11}H_{15}O_3N^{\oplus}(CH_3)_3{}^{\ominus}OH \xrightarrow{\text{Heat}}$$
Mescaline

$$C_{11}H_{14}O_3 + (CH_3)_3N + H_2O$$

duces formaldehyde and a new aldehyde, $C_{10}H_{12}O_4$, indicating the pres-ence of a methylene group, $=CH_2$, in the alkene $C_{11}H_{14}O_3$. A Zeisel

$$C_{11}H_{14}O_3 + O_3 \longrightarrow CH_2{=}O + C_{10}H_{12}O_4$$

analysis (Section 11-17b) on the aldehyde $C_{10}H_{12}O_4$ shows the presence of three methoxy groups, and 3,4,5-trihydroxybenzaldehyde (14-**54**) can be isolated from the demethylation reaction, indicating that the aldehyde pre-cursor must have been 3,4,5-trimethoxybenzaldehyde (14-**53**). Piecing

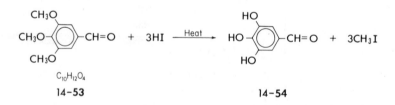

14-**53**   14-**54**

together the ozonolysis products, we see that the previous $C_{11}H_{14}O_3$ alkene must have been 3,4,5-trimethoxystyrene (14-**55**), which would result from Hofmann degradation of either of the quaternary hydroxides 14-**56** or 14-**57**. Mescaline itself must then be the free primary amine correspond-ing to one of the quaternary bases 14-**56** or 14-**57**. The final structure of mescaline was unequivocally established by synthesis, which provided a

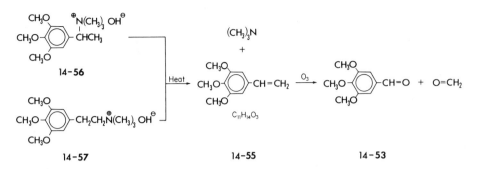

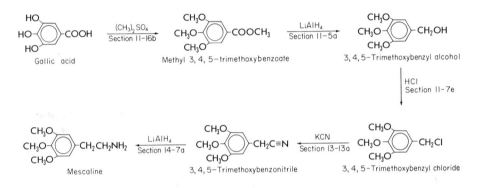

product identical in all respects with the natural material. One convenient synthesis of mescaline, starting with gallic acid, is the following.

NITRO COMPOUNDS

14-14. Nomenclature and Uses of Nitro Compounds

Nitro compounds are molecules containing the nitro group, $-NO_2$, bonded directly to carbon. In past chapters we have encountered briefly both aliphatic, RNO_2 (Section 7-6e), and aromatic, $ArNO_2$ (Section 10-4b), nitro compounds; we shall now examine these derivatives in somewhat greater detail. At the outset, nitro compounds should be clearly distinguished from both their isomeric nitrous esters, $RONO$ (Section 11-7c), and from nitric esters, $RONO_2$ (Section 11-7c), each of which have their nitrogen atom bonded to oxygen only, rather than to carbon and oxygen.

Nitro compounds are named systematically by merely inserting the prefix *nitro-* with appropriate numbers when necessary, before the name of the alkane or arene in which the nitro group is substituted. The following examples are representative.

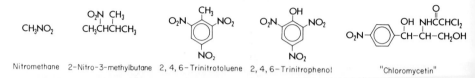

Nitromethane   2-Nitro-3-methylbutane   2,4,6-Trinitrotoluene   2,4,6-Trinitrophenol   "Chloromycetin"

Nitro compounds have a variety of specific uses, and we can consider only a few. Nitromethane finds use as a racing fuel, while 2,4,6-trinitro-toluene is the well-known explosive TNT. 2,4,6-Trinitrophenol (picric acid; Section 11-9b) was formerly employed as a yellow dye for wool and silk and as a germicide, while ammonium picrate is used as an explosive in armor-piercing shells. Chloromycetin (chloramphenicol, 3-*p*-nitro-phenyl-2-*N*-dichloroacetylamino-1,3-propanediol) is a broad-spectrum antibiotic substance first isolated from a strain of bacteria (*Strepto-myces venezuelae*) found in Venezuelan soil. 2,4,6-Trinitro-3-*t*-butyltoluene ("Baur musk") has an odor similar to natural musks and is used as a perfume in cheap soaps. Nitrobenzene is used primarily for the produc-tion of aniline (Section 14-7a) and as a constituent of shoe polishes, while the reduction of nitroalkanes analogously affords primary alkylamines. Nitro compounds are generally toxic substances. Nitrobenzene, for ex-ample, which may enter the body by ingestion, inhalation, or absorption through the skin, causes death by cyanosis, turning the blood a chocolate-brown color.

14-15. Structure and Physical Properties of Nitro Compounds

The electronic structure of the nitro group is a resonance hybrid derived from the canonical structures A and B in Figure 14-8. In support of this,

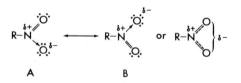

Figure 14-8. Resonance Hybrid of the Nitro Group

electron diffraction measurements on nitromethane show only a single N–O bond distance (1.21 Å), and not two as would be the case if a single discrete structure (such as A or B) prevailed. We recall also (Section 10-6) that aromatic nitro compounds are resonance hybrids which also involve the aromatic π electrons and that the nitro group is accordingly ring deactivating and *meta* directing. In accord with the electron structure of the nitro group, nitro compounds are characterized by high dipole moments (Section 2-2d), and consequently have abnormally high boiling points due to dipole-dipole attraction. Thus nitromethane (mol. wt. 61) has a boiling point of 101.5°, as compared to −0.5° for butane (mol. wt. 58). All nitro compounds are liquids or solids at room temperature, and are quite insoluble in water.

As previously mentioned (Section 12-71), the α-hydrogen atoms of nitroalkanes, like those of aldehydes, ketones, and esters, have enhanced acidic character owing to resonance stabilization (14-**58**) of their carbanion. Nitroalkanes thus form water-soluble salts (14-**58**) with strong bases. When such salt solutions are acidified, a product is sometimes isolable which is isomeric with the original nitro compound, but rearranges to it on standing. The explanation for this behavior is that such nitro compounds may exist in tautomeric equilibria involving **nitro** forms and **aci**

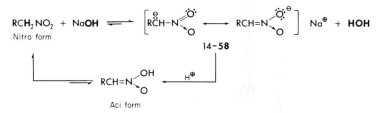

forms. Phenylnitromethane, $PhCH_2NO_2$, for example, may be readily obtained in its *nitro* form, which is a light yellow oil, or its *aci* form, which is a white solid, m.p. 84°. We recognize that this *aci-nitro* tautomerism is completely analogous to the *keto-enol* tautomerism which we have previously encountered (Section 12-7a).

Nitro compounds are characterized by two strong infrared absorption bands resulting from symmetrical and unsymmetrical stretching of the NO_2 group. These bands occur in the 1650 to 1500 cm^{-1} and 1350 to 1250 cm^{-1} regions of the spectrum, their exact positions depending upon the structure adjacent to the nitro function. In the ultraviolet, low intensity absorption occurs in the 2700 to 2800 Å region, analogous to carbonyl absorption (Section 12-2).

14-16. Synthesis of Nitro Compounds

Nitroalkanes are prepared in the laboratory by the reaction of an alkyl halide with silver nitrite, AgONO. In this nucleophilic displacement, both a nitroalkane and the isomeric alkyl nitrite ester are produced. This situa-

$$RX + AgONO \longrightarrow RNO_2 + RONO + AgX$$

Nitroalkane   Alkyl nitrite

tion arises because of the so-called **ambident** character of the nitrite ion hybrid (14-**59**), which has unshared electrons (capable of reacting nucleo-

$$:\overset{\ominus}{\underset{..}{\text{O}}}-\overset{..}{\text{N}}=\overset{..}{\text{O}}: \longleftrightarrow :\overset{..}{\text{O}}=\overset{..}{\text{N}}-\overset{\ominus}{\underset{..}{\text{O}}}:$$

14-**59**

philically) on both oxygen and nitrogen. Reaction at the nitrogen electron site gives the nitroalkane, while reaction of the oxygen electrons yields the alkyl nitrite ester. Silver nitrite generally favors the nitro product, while alcoholic sodium nitrite yields mainly the alkyl nitrite. However, using N,N-dimethylformamide or dimethyl sulfoxide as solvent, satisfactory yields of primary and secondary nitroalkanes may be obtained using sodium or potassium nitrite. Tertiary halides afford alkenes rather than nitroalkanes. The industrially important vapor phase nitration of alkanes to produce mixtures of nitroalkanes, introduced by Dr. H. B. Hass of Purdue University in 1936, has been previously discussed (Section 7-6e).

Aromatic nitro compounds are generally prepared by the direct nitration of the aromatic ring using nitric acid (Section 10-4b). Since nitric acid is an oxidizing agent, however, sensitive ring substituents frequently require protection prior to conducting a ring nitration. Aniline, for example, is readily oxidized (Section 14-10d). Oxidation may be minimized by conducting its nitration in the presence of sulfuric acid, whereby the anilinium bisulfate (14-**60**) is nitrated chiefly in the *meta* position. *o*- and *p*-Nitro-

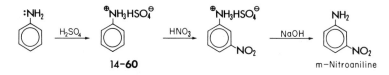

14-**60**   m−Nitroaniline

anilines may be prepared by protecting the amino group through acetylation. Nitration of acetanilide in acetic acid solvent then yields mainly p-nitroacetanilide, while nitration in acetic anhydride gives chiefly o-nitro-

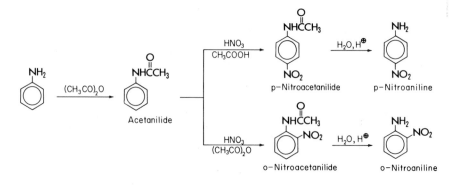

acetanilide. Hydrolysis of the nitroacetanilides subsequently affords the corresponding nitroanilines.

14-17. Reactions of Aliphatic Nitro Compounds

We have already considered several reactions of nitroalkanes. These are listed below by reference only, along with a number of reactions not previously discussed.

a. Reduction to Primary Amines. See Section 14-7a.

b. Condensation with Aldehydes and Ketones. See Section 12-7l.

c. Bromination. Primary (14-**61**) and secondary nitroalkanes (14-**62**), like aldehydes and ketones containing α-hydrogen atoms (Section 12-7b), readily undergo bromination in alkaline solution. 1-Bromo-1-nitroalkanes (14-**63**, 14-**64**) are the resulting products, and we note that bromination occurs only at the α-carbon atom, via intermediate sodium salts (Section

$$RCH_2NO_2 \xrightarrow{NaOH} \left[R\ddot{C}HNO_2\right]^{\ominus} \overset{\oplus}{Na} \xrightarrow{Br_2} \overset{Br}{\underset{14-63}{R CHNO_2}} + NaBr$$
14-61

$$R_2CHNO_2 \xrightarrow{NaOH} \left[R_2\ddot{C}NO_2\right]^{\ominus} \overset{\oplus}{Na} \xrightarrow{Br_2} \overset{Br}{\underset{14-64}{R_2 CNO_2}} + NaBr$$
14-62

14-15). Tertiary nitroalkanes, R_3CNO_2, having no α-hydrogen atom, do not undergo bromination.

d. Alkylation. Silver salts of primary and secondary nitroalkanes react with primary and secondary alkyl halides to give C-alkylation products such as 14-**65**. Diazomethane (Section 13-10d), as with enols, O-alkylates primary and secondary nitroalkanes through their *aci* form, yielding O-methyl-*aci*-nitroalkanes (14-**66**).

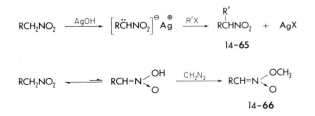

$$RCH_2NO_2 \xrightarrow{AgOH} \left[R\ddot{C}HNO_2\right]^{\ominus} \overset{\oplus}{Ag} \xrightarrow{R'X} \overset{R'}{\underset{14-65}{R CHNO_2}} + AgX$$

$$RCH_2NO_2 \rightleftharpoons RCH{=}N\overset{OH}{\underset{O}{\diagdown}} \xrightarrow{CH_2N_2} RCH{=}N\overset{OCH_3}{\underset{O}{\diagdown}}$$
14-66

e. Hydrolysis. On heating with concentrated hydrochloric acid, primary nitroalkanes are hydrolyzed to carboxylic acids and hydroxylamine hydrochloride (14-**67**). Notice that this reaction involves a **disproportionation,**

$$RCH_2NO_2 + HCl + H_2O \longrightarrow RCOOH + HONH_3^{\oplus} Cl^{\ominus}$$
$$14\text{-}67$$

wherein the CH_2 group is oxidized and the NO_2 group is reduced. Hydroxylamine, $HONH_2$, is prepared commercially by this process. In contrast, if a primary or secondary nitroalkane is first converted to its sodium salt and the latter is hydrolyzed with 25 per cent sulfuric acid, an aldehyde or ketone is formed along with nitrous oxide. This preparation of aldehydes and ketones is known as the **Nef reaction.**

f. Reaction with Nitrous Acid. Primary nitroalkanes react with nitrous acid to form blue C-nitroso derivatives (14-**68**) known as **nitrolic acids.** These dissolve in alkali to form soluble red salts (14-**69**). Secondary nitro-

$$RCH_2NO_2 \xrightarrow{HONO} \underset{\substack{14\text{-}68 \\ (blue)}}{\overset{\overset{\displaystyle NO}{|}}{RCHNO_2}} \xrightarrow{NaOH} \underset{\substack{14\text{-}69 \\ (red)}}{\overset{\overset{\displaystyle NO}{|}}{RCNO_2^{\ominus}}\ Na^{\oplus}}$$

alkanes give blue C-nitroso derivatives (17-**70**) which are insoluble in alkali since they have no acidic hydrogen. Tertiary nitroalkanes, R_3CNO_2,

$$R_2CHNO_2 \xrightarrow{HONO} \underset{\substack{14\text{-}70 \\ (Blue)}}{\overset{\overset{\displaystyle NO}{|}}{R_2CNO_2}}$$

lacking an α-hydrogen atom, fail to react with nitrous acid. These diagnostic color tests for primary, secondary, and tertiary nitroalkanes are sometimes referred to as the "red, white, and blue reaction."

14-18. Reactions of Aromatic Nitro Compounds

These generally differ from the reactions of aliphatic nitro compounds. The most important reactions of nitroarenes are the following types.

a. Nucleophilic Displacements. Ordinarily, the nitro group does not undergo nucleophilic displacement. In certain polynitro aromatic compounds, however, one nitro group may frequently be displaced by nucleophilic agents, with liberation of nitrite ion. The reactions of o-dinitrobenzene shown below are typical. p-Dinitrobenzene reacts similarly, but m-dinitrobenzene does not. The ease of displacement of one nitro group from the *ortho* and *para* isomers, but not from the *meta*, is readily under-

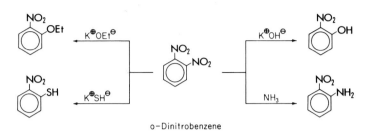

o–Dinitrobenzene

standable in terms of the explanation already given for the reactivity of the chlorine atom in *o*- and *p*-chloronitrobenzenes (see Figure 11-15).

b. Molecular Complex Formation.   Polynitro aromatic compounds have the unusual ability of forming molecular complexes with a wide variety of aromatic hydrocarbons. Such complexes, which usually contain one molecule of each component, are frequently colored, have sharp and characteristic melting points, and are widely used for characterization purposes, particularly of polynuclear arenes.   A few representative examples are listed in Table 14-3. The complexes may generally be readily decomposed

Table 14-3. Molecular Complexes of Polynitroarenes

Polynitroarene	Second Component	M.p. of Complex, °C	Color of Complex
1,3,5-Trinitrobenzene	Naphthalene	152	Colorless
	Phenanthrene	158	Orange
	Anthracene	174	Scarlet
	Aniline	124	Red
	N,N-Dimethylaniline	107	Violet
2,4,6-Trinitrotoluene	Naphthalene	98	Colorless
	α-Naphthol	110	Orange
	Aniline	84	Red

into their components, particularly by means of column chromatography (Section 3-5a). Complex formation is not limited exclusively to polynitroarenes. Hexanitroethane, for example, yields red complexes with naphthalene, aniline, and phenol, while tetranitromethane gives orange-colored solutions with alkenes and aromatic hydrocarbons, and is used as a diagnostic reagent for these classes of substances.   The nature of the bonding forces in such π complexes has been discussed previously (Section 10-4c).

c. Reduction.   The most important reaction of nitroarenes is their chemical or catalytic reduction to aminoarenes.

$$ArNO_2 + 6(H) \longrightarrow ArNH_2 + 2H_2O$$

The commercial reduction of nitrobenzene to aniline has already been mentioned (Section 14-7a). Such reductions are not always simple processes, however, and hence merit our further attention.

In the first place, if two or more nitro groups are present in the aromatic ring, it is possible to reduce one of them without the others. Such selective reductions may be accomplished using the calculated quantity of sodium or ammonium sulfides, as in the following typical conversion of *m*-dinitrobenzene into *m*-nitroaniline.

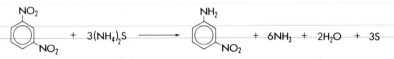

Secondly, although aniline is the end product from the reduction of nitrobenzene, it is possible to isolate a number of intermediate reduction products by choosing proper reducing agents and reaction conditions. Some of these intermediates are formed by direct partial reduction, while others arise from subsequent secondary changes. These products, together with the conditions for their formation and interconversion, are

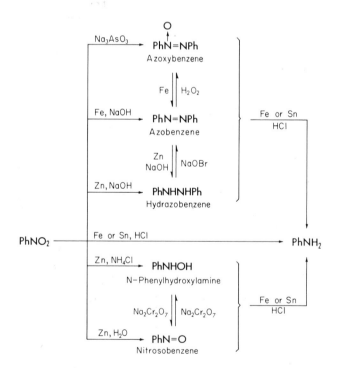

Figure 14-9. Reduction Products of Nitrobenzene

summarized in Figure 14-9. Note that all of the products may be reduced to aniline using more vigorous reducing agents.

Additional comments concerning several of the compounds in Figure 14-9 are in order. Nitrosobenzene exists as a green monomer in solution, but crystallizes as a white dimer. Azobenzene is capable of existing as *cis* and *trans* isomers because of the —N═N— double bond. On exposure to light, the ordinarily more stable isomer (m.p. 68°) if transformed into the less stable one (m.p. 71°), which reverts to the more stable form in solution.

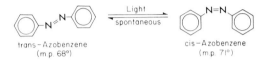

trans–Azobenzene
(m.p. 68°)

cis–Azobenzene
(m.p. 71°)

On steric grounds one would expect the *trans* isomer to be the more stable, and this is confirmed by X-ray diffraction, Furthermore, in the *trans* form the rings prove to be almost coplanar, thus permitting maximum resonance stabilization (Figure 14-10). In the *cis* isomer, the rings are forced out of

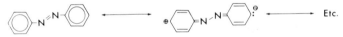

Figure 14-10. Resonance Stabilization of trans-*Azobenzene*

coplanarity by their proximity, thereby militating against the opportunity for analogous resonance stabilization. Azobenzene derivatives constitute an important class of dyestuffs which will be discussed in greater detail in Section 14-22.

Hydrazobenzene, which is simply the 1,2-diphenyl derivative of hydrazine, H_2NNH_2, undergoes an unexpected reaction in acid solution. Instead of forming a simple salt (analogous to $H_2NNH_3^{\oplus} Cl^{\ominus}$ or $Cl^{\ominus} H_3N^{\oplus}NH_3^{\oplus} Cl^{\ominus}$), reaction with hydrochloric acid affords the salt of a new base, 4,4′-diaminobiphenyl (benzidine). Detailed kinetic studies of

Hydrazobenzene

Benzidine hydrochloride

Benzidine

this unique **benzidine rearrangement** show that the rate of the reaction is proportional to the molar concentration of hydrazobenzene and to the square of the molar concentration of hydrogen ion; that is,

$$Rate = k[\text{PhNHNHPh}] [H^{\oplus}]^2$$

In agreement with these kinetics, the mechanism in Figure 14-11 has been proposed to account for the benzidine rearrangement. The *intramolecular*

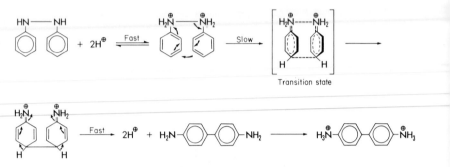

Figure 14-11. *Mechanism of the Benzidine Rearrangement*

nature of the transformation is further evident from the fact that no "crossed products" arise when a *mixture* of two substituted hydrazoben- zenes is subjected to the benzidine arrangement. Note in the **example** shown that the rearrangement of each hydrazobenzene again occurs to its own *para* positions only.

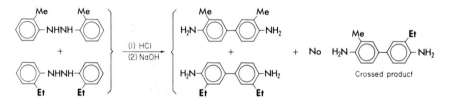

AROMATIC DIAZONIUM AND DIAZO COMPOUNDS

IN SECTION 14-10b we learned that the action of nitrous acid on primary aromatic amines leads to the formation of **aromatic diazonium salts,** which are stable in aqueous solution. Such diazonium salts are extremely important synthetic intermediates, and we shall next consider them in greater detail.

14-19. Formation of Diazonium Salts

Several mechanisms have been proposed for the overall **diazotization** reaction leading to aromatic diazonium salts (14-**71**).

$$ArNH_2 + NaNO_2 + 2\,HX \longrightarrow ArN_2^{\oplus}\,X^{\ominus} + NaX + 2\,H_2O$$
$$14\text{-}71$$

At high acid concentration the rate of diazotization follows the law

$$\text{Rate} = k[H^{\oplus}]\,[HNO_2]\,[ArNH_2]$$

and the mechanism in Figure 14-12 has been proposed to account for diazotization under these conditions. Notice that the N-nitroso primary

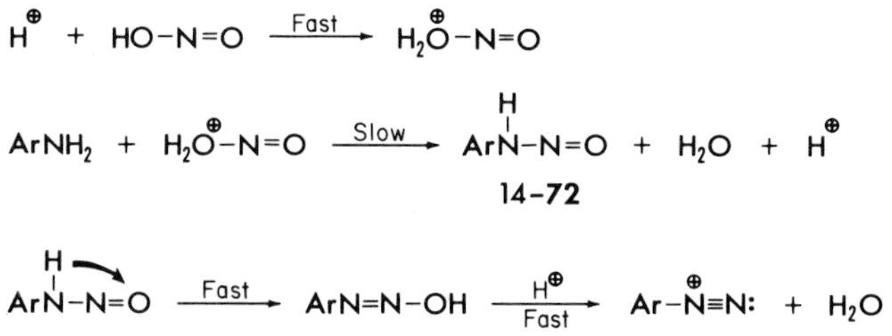

$$H^{\oplus} + HO\text{-}N\text{=}O \xrightarrow{\;Fast\;} H_2\overset{\oplus}{O}\text{-}N\text{=}O$$

$$ArNH_2 + H_2\overset{\oplus}{O}\text{-}N\text{=}O \xrightarrow{\;Slow\;} Ar\overset{\overset{\displaystyle H}{|}}{N}\text{-}N\text{=}O + H_2O + H^{\oplus}$$
$$14\text{-}72$$

$$Ar\overset{\overset{\displaystyle H}{|}\,\curvearrowleft}{N}\text{-}N\text{=}O \xrightarrow{\;Fast\;} ArN\text{=}N\text{-}OH \xrightarrow[\;Fast\;]{H^{\oplus}} Ar\text{-}\overset{\oplus}{N}\text{≡}N: + H_2O$$

Figure 14-12. A Mechanism for Diazotization

amine intermediate (14-**72**) is unstable, in contrast to stable N-nitroso secondary amines (Section 14-5). At low acid concentrations the nitrosating agent appears to be dinitrogen trioxide, N_2O_3 (formed by $2\,HNO_2 \rightleftharpoons N_2O_3 + H_2O$), instead of the species $H_2O^{\oplus}\text{-}N\text{=}O$.

14-20. Diazonium Salt Reactions with Loss of Nitrogen

The reactions of aromatic diazonium salts fall into two classes, depending upon whether the diazonium nitrogen atoms are lost during the reaction or are retained as part of the reaction product. We shall consider the first class of reactions first. These reactions involve *replacement* of the diazonium function with other substituents.

a. Replacement by Hydrogen. Hypophosphorous acid, H_3PO_2, as well as several other reducing agents, brings about the replacement of the diazonium group by hydrogen.

$$ArN_2^{\oplus}X^{\ominus} + H_3PO_2 + H_2O \longrightarrow ArH + N_2 + HX + H_3PO_3$$

This reaction is useful in that it permits us to make use of the powerful o,p-directing influence of the amino group, and then subsequently to remove this group from the aromatic ring. The synthesis of 1,3,5-tribromo-benzene from aniline illustrates this type of application.

2,4,6-Tribromoaniline   2,4,6-Tribromobenzene-   1,3,5-Tribromobenzene
                                     diazonium bisulfate

b. Replacement by Hydroxyl and Alkoxyl. When an aqueous diazonium salt solution is heated, nitrogen is liberated and a phenol is formed.

$$ArN_2^{\oplus}X^{\ominus} + H_2O \xrightarrow{Heat} ArOH + N_2 + HX$$

The reaction is usually conducted in an acidic medium to prevent coupling of the phenol product with the unreacted diazonium salt (Section 14-21b). In a similar way, heating diazonium salts in the presence of an excess of alcohol leads to the formation of alkyl aryl ethers. These replacements appear to be examples of aromatic S_N1 reactions, and are believed to proceed via **aronium ion** intermediates (14-73).

$$ArN_2^{\oplus}X^{\ominus} + ROH \xrightarrow{Heat} ArOR + N_2 + HX$$

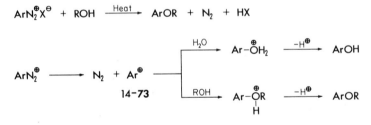

c. Replacement by Halogen. Aryl chlorides and bromides may be prepared by the **Sandmeyer reaction,** wherein a diazonium salt solution is heated with cuprous chloride or bromide, or by the **Gattermann reaction,** wherein finely divided copper is used as catalyst.

$$ArN_2^{\oplus}X^{\ominus} \xrightarrow[\text{heat}]{\text{CuX or Cu}} ArX + N_2 \qquad (X = Cl, Br)$$

Higher yields usually result from the Sandmeyer process. The diazonium group may be replaced by iodine by merely heating diazonium salt solutions in the presence of potassium iodide.

$$ArN_2^{\oplus}X^{\ominus} + KI \xrightarrow{Heat} ArI + N_2 + KX$$

Aryl fluorides are conveniently prepared by diazotizing the aromatic amine in the presence of fluoroboric acid, HBF_4, whereupon a diazonium fluoroborate (14-**74**) precipitates. Heating converts the dry fluoroborate salt into an aryl fluoride (**Schiemann reaction**).

$$ArNH_2 \xrightarrow[HBF_4]{NaNO_2} ArN_2^{\oplus}BF_4^{\ominus} \xrightarrow{Heat} ArF + N_2 + BF_3$$
$$\text{14-74}$$

d. Replacement by Cyano (and Carboxyl). By using curpous cyanide (instead of cuprous halide) in the Sandmeyer reaction, the diazonium group may be replaced by a cyano group. Hydrolysis of the cyano function results in the overall replacement of an amino group by a carboxyl group.

$$ArNH_2 \xrightarrow[HX]{NaNO_2} ArN_2^{\oplus}X^{\ominus} \xrightarrow{CuCN, \; heat} ArC{\equiv}N \xrightarrow{H_2O, \; H^{\oplus}} ArCOOH$$

e. Replacement of Nitro. When diazonium fluoroborates are heated with aqueous sodium nitrite, the diazonium function is replaced by the nitro group. This reaction makes possible the synthesis of nitro compounds which cannot be prepared by direct nitration, as in the following preparation of *p*-dinitrobenzene.

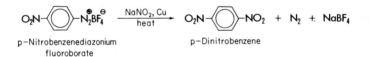

$$O_2N-\!\!\!\!\bigcirc\!\!\!\!-N_2^{\oplus}BF_4^{\ominus} \xrightarrow[heat]{NaNO_2, \; Cu} O_2N-\!\!\!\!\bigcirc\!\!\!\!-NO_2 + N_2 + NaBF_4$$

| p–Nitrobenzenediazonium fluoroborate | p–Dinitrobenzene |

f. Replacement by Arsono. The arsono group, $-AsO_3H_2$, may be introduced into the aromatic ring by heating diazonium salt solutions with sodium arsenite in the presence of curpic salts, whereby salts of arylarsonic acids, $ArAsO_3H_2$, are formed (**Bart reaction**).

$$ArN_2^{\oplus} Cl^{\ominus} + Na_3AsO_3 \xrightarrow{CuSO_4} ArAsO_3Na_2 + N_2 + NaCl$$

Arsenic compounds have been used therapeutically since the 5th century B.C., when Hippocrates reportedly recommended arsenic trisulfide ointments for the treatment of ulcerative abscesses. Today, tryparsamide (sodium hydrogen *N*-(carbamoylmethyl)arsanilate) is used in the treatment of syphilis and African trypanosomiasis.

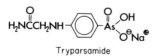

Tryparsamide

g. Replacement by Aryl. The reaction of a diazonium salt with an aromatic hydrocarbon in the presence of sodium hydroxide, known as the

Gomberg reaction, is used to prepare unsymmetrical diaryls, Ar—Ar′, in fair yield.

$$ArN_2^{\oplus}X^{\ominus} + Ar'H + NaOH \longrightarrow Ar—Ar' + N_2 + H_2O + NaX$$

The reaction is believed to occur by a free radical mechanism. When the diazonium salt is treated with base, it is reversibly converted into an aryldiazoic acid, and then into the sodium salt of the latter. Aryldiazoic acids

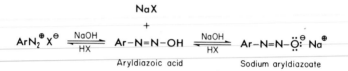

$$\underset{\text{Aryldiazoic acid}}{Ar-N=N-OH} \qquad \underset{\text{Sodium aryldiazoate}}{Ar-N=N-\overset{..}{\underset{..}{O}}{:}^{\ominus}\ Na^{\oplus}}$$

are unstable and tend to dissociate into free radicals. When the decomposition takes place in the presence of benzene or other arenes, the free radicals attack these hydrocarbons and the diaryl product is formed. Aryl-

$$\left.\begin{array}{l} Ar-N=N-OH \longrightarrow Ar\cdot + N_2 + \cdot OH \\ Ar\cdot + Ar'H \longrightarrow Ar-Ar' + \cdot H \end{array}\right\} \longrightarrow HOH$$

diazoic acids themselves have not been isolated, but certain aryldiazoate salts are known, and have been obtained as geometrical isomers, analogous to *syn* and *anti* oximes (Section 12-7h). Addition of acid to solutions of such salts regenerates the original diazonium salt.

$$\underset{\text{anti Isomer}}{\overset{Ar}{\underset{}{\diagdown}}N=N\diagdown_{O^{\ominus}\ Na^{\oplus}}} \qquad \underset{\text{syn Isomer}}{\overset{Ar}{\underset{}{\diagdown}}N=N\diagup^{O^{\ominus}\ Na^{\oplus}}}$$

Heating diazonium salt solutions with copper bronze is also used as a low yield method for the synthesis of symmetrical diaryls. This reaction also yields diaryls as by-products in the above Gattermann synthesis of aryl halides (Section 14-20c).

$$2\,ArN_2^{\oplus}X^{\ominus} + 2\,Cu \longrightarrow Ar—Ar + N_2 + 2\,CuX$$

14-21. Diazonium Salt Reactions with Retention of Nitrogen

In the following important transformations of diazonium salts, the diazonium nitrogen atoms are retained in the reaction product.

a. Reduction to Substituted Hydrazines. Reduction of diazonium salts with stannous chloride–hydrochloric acid, or with sodium sulfite, leads to the formation of arylhydrazines. The preparation of the carbonyl reagent, phenylhydrazine (Section 12-7g), is typical.

$$PhN_2^{\oplus}Cl^{\ominus} \xrightarrow[\text{4 (H)}]{SnCl_2-HCl} \underset{\text{Phenylhydrazinium chloride}}{PhNHNH_3^{\oplus}Cl^{\ominus}} \xrightarrow{NaOH} \underset{\text{Phenylhydrazine}}{PhNHNH_2}$$

b. Diazonium Coupling Reactions. Diazonium salts react with phenols and tertiary amines to form highly colored *azo compounds*. Depending upon the reactant, these **coupling reactions** occur in weakly acidic, neutral, or alkaline media, with the diazonium ion attacking electrophilically the *para* position of the phenol or amine. If the *para* position is already occupied, substitution occurs alternatively at the *ortho* position. The following reactions of benzenediazonium chloride with *N,N*-dimethylaniline and with *p*-cresol are typical, and illustrate the nomenclature of the azobenzene derivatives produced.

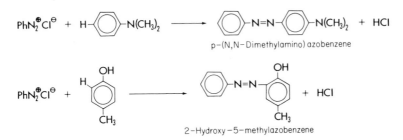

p-(N,N-Dimethylamino) azobenzene

2-Hydroxy-5-methylazobenzene

Diazonium coupling is a typical electrophilic aromatic substitution (Section 10-5). The diazonium ion is a very weak electrophile, however, and coupling ordinarily occurs only when strongly activating substituents, such as $-NR_2$ or $-OH$, are present in the nucleus of the arene undergoing substitution. Diazonium ions become more reactive electrophiles, however, when electron-withdrawing substituents such as $-NO_2$ are present in the *ortho* or *para* positions of their aromatic rings. Thus 2,4,6-trinitrobenzene-diazonium chloride (14-**75**) will couple with mesitylene (14-**76**), although the latter hydrocarbon is inert toward benzenediazonium chloride itself.

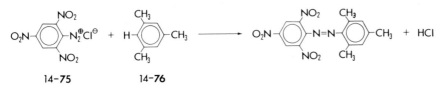

14-**75**   14-**76**

With primary and secondary amines, coupling occurs at the nitrogen atom to form **diazoamino compounds** (14-**77**). Certain primary and secondary aromatic amines behave similarly. Thus aniline affords diazoaminobenzene. If such aromatic diazoamino compounds are allowed to

$$ArN_2^{\oplus}Cl^{\ominus} + 2 RNH_2 \longrightarrow ArN{=}N{-}NHR + RNH_3^{\oplus}Cl^{\ominus}$$
14-**77**

$$PhN_2^{\oplus}Cl^{\ominus} + H_2NPh \xrightarrow{CH_3COONa}$$
Diazoaminobenzene

stand in acid solution, they rearrange to the aminoazo isomer (**diazo-amino rearrangement**), with substitution occurring at the *para* position if it is free, or at the *ortho* position (if *para* is blocked). Diazoaminobenzene reverts to *p*-aminoazobenzene under these conditions. Notice that such

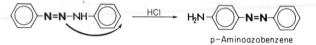

rearrangement products are the same as would be obtained by direct coupling in the nucleus. In fact, many primary aromatic amines undergo the diazoamino rearrangement so rapidly after initial coupling at the nitrogen that the nuclear coupling product is the only one isolated. 1-Naphthylamine is illustrative of this situation.

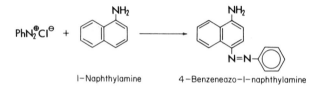

Diazonium salts will also couple with compounds containing highly activated methylene groups, such as nitroalkanes, β-keto esters, and malonic esters. The following examples are representative. Notice that the initial coupling products tautomerize into arylhydrazones, $>C{=}NNHAr$.

$$RCH_2NO_2 + ArN_2^{\oplus}X^{\ominus} \xrightarrow{-HX} \underset{\overset{|}{NO_2}}{RCH-N{=}NAr} \longrightarrow \underset{\overset{|}{NO_2}}{RC{=}NNHAr}$$

$$CH_3COCH_2COOEt + ArN_2^{\oplus}X^{\ominus} \xrightarrow{-HX} \underset{\overset{|}{N{=}NAr}}{CH_3COCHCOOEt} \longrightarrow \underset{\overset{||}{NNHAr}}{CH_3COCCOOEt}$$

14-22. Dyestuffs

It is appropriate to consider dyes and dyeing at this point, since azo derivatives make up the most important class of dyestuffs. The United States production of azo dyes in 1961 was over 44 million pounds, with sales at an average price of \$1.67 per pound. A dye is a colored substance capable of becoming permanently attached to the fibers of a material, thereby coloring it. Dyestuff molecules are colored because they are capable of absorbing light in the visible region of the spectrum (Section 4-6). Light absorption is made possible by the presence in the molecule of **chromophores** (Greek: *chroma*, color + *phoros*, bearer), groups such as $-N{=}O$, $-NO_2$, $-N{=}N-$, etc., which are themselves capable of absorbing light in the near ultraviolet. If such groups are appropriately situated in a molecule whose structure permits resonance stabilization of their photoexcited states (Section 8-5c), however, absorption occurs at longer wavelengths (visible light) and the substance appears colored. Thus the azo chromophore, —N=N—, in aliphatic compounds absorbs ultraviolet light around 3400 Å, but azobenzene is orange (absorption bands at 3190 and 4450 Å) because the conjugation of the aromatic π electrons with the nitrogen electrons constitutes an *extended* chromophoric system capable of photoexcitation at lower energies (longer wavelengths) through the possibility of resonance stabilization (14-**78**) of the photo-excited molecule. Dyestuff molecules also usually contain **auxochromes**

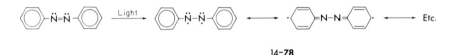

14-78

(Latin: *auxilium*, aid), groups such as —NH$_2$, —NR$_2$, —OH, —OR, etc., which, when located in the molecule in positions where they can further increase the resonance stabilization of the photoexcited state, shift the light absorption to even longer wavelengths and "deepen" the color of the dyestuff. Auxochromic groups also frequently function in the capacity of helping to anchor the dyestuff to the fabric, through chemical interaction with its fibers. We should note that the color of a dyestuff is not the color corresponding to its absorption wavelengths, but rather the *complementary* color which is "left over" when these absorption wavelengths are deleted from white light. Approximate relationships between observed color and light absorption by a colored substance are shown in Table 14-4.

Table 14-4. Relation Between Color and Absorption Maxima

Wavelength Absorbed, Å	Color Absorbed	Color Observed
4350–4800	Blue	Yellow
4900–5000	Blue-green	Red
5000–5600	Green	Purple
5800–5950	Yellow	Blue
6050–7500	Red	Blue-green

Dyestuffs, or colored substances in general, are thus molecules containing ultraviolet- (or visible-) light-absorbing chromophores which are conjugated with a large π-electron system in the remainder of the molecule.

This situation may be achieved by a variety of structures. The following are a very few representative examples, classified as to structure, of the hundreds of known dyestuffs.

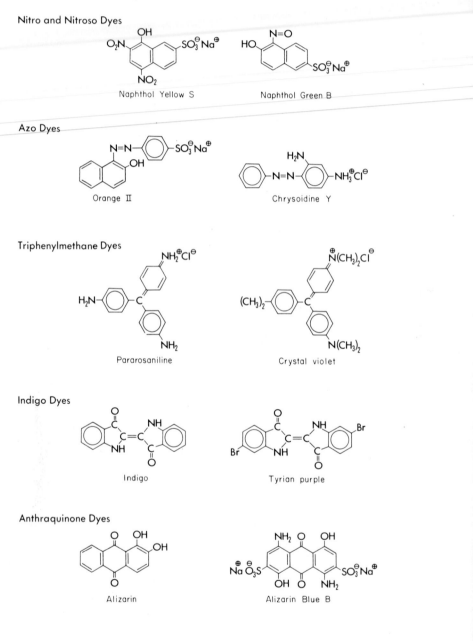

Nitro and Nitroso Dyes

Naphthol Yellow S

Naphthol Green B

Azo Dyes

Orange II

Chrysoidine Y

Triphenylmethane Dyes

Pararosaniline

Crystal violet

Indigo Dyes

Indigo

Tyrian purple

Anthraquinone Dyes

Alizarin

Alizarin Blue B

Phthaleins

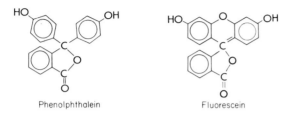

Phenolphthalein   Fluorescein

Phenolphthalein is not a dyestuff, but finds use as an indicator (see below) and laxative. Fluorescein, even on dilution to 1 part in 44 million of water, gives an intense yellow-green fluorescence in sunlight. It is used to follow the course of underground streams, and as a sea marker for downed aircraft.

Dyestuffs are applied to fabrics in various ways, depending upon the chemical nature of both the dye and the fiber. **Direct dyes** are applied by merely immersing the fabric in a water solution of the dye, and are useful for dyeing animal fibers. **Mordant dyes** form insoluble complexes with certain metal hydroxides (**mordants;** Latin: *mordere*, to bite). The hydroxide is first precipitated on the fiber, and then treated with the dye. For example, if cotton is soaked in aluminum acetate solution and then steamed (producing $Al(OH)_3$ on the fibers), it may be dyed with the mordant dye alizarin, which forms the insoluble colored chelate compound 14-**79** in the fibers. **Ingrain dyes** are water-insoluble dyes which are syn-

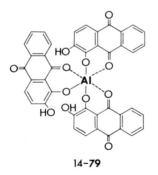

14–79

thesized directly on the fiber. Thus cotton may be impregnated with an aromatic amine or phenol, then treated with a solution of a diazotized amine, whereupon diazo coupling occurs to produce the azo dye within the fiber. **Vat dyes** (such as indigo) are water insoluble, but may be made soluble by reduction in alkaline solution. The fiber is steeped in the solution and then exposed to air or chemical oxidizing agents, whereupon the reduced dyestuff is reoxidized to the insoluble form. The reduction stage was formerly accomplished by fermentation in large vats, hence the term, vat dye. There are many other methods of applying dyes to fabrics, but dyestuff technology is beyond our scope.

Many dyestuffs also act as **indicators;** that is, their colors are changeable with changing acidity. Indicator action occurs when the overall chromophoric system of the molecule may be altered by the addition or deletion of protons. A straightforward example of indicator action is shown by the behavior of phenolphthalein in solutions of varying pH (Figure 14-13). Note the *auxochromic effect* of the phenoxide group in the structure of the red form.

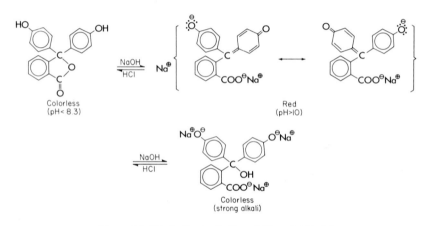

Figure 14-13. Indicator Action of Phenolphthalein

MISCELLANEOUS NITROGEN COMPOUNDS

IN CLOSING our survey of simpler nitrogen derivatives, it is worthwhile considering a few miscellaneous classes of important nitrogen compounds.

14-23. Isonitriles and Related Compounds

Isonitriles or isocyanides, $R—\overset{\oplus}{N}\equiv C:\overset{\ominus}{}$, are isomeric with nitriles or cyanides, $R—C\equiv N$. They are highly toxic substances and possess vile odors. We recall that the latter property is useful in the qualitative recognition of primary amines (Section 14-5), from which isonitriles may be prepared using chloroform and sodium hydroxide. Isonitriles are also formed as by-products when a metal cyanide acts on an alkyl halide to form a nitrile.

$$RX + M^{\oplus}C{\equiv}N^{\ominus} \longrightarrow R{-}C{\equiv}N + R{-}^{\oplus}N{\equiv}C{:}^{\ominus} + MX$$

The two products arise from the fact that the cyanide ion, like the nitrite ion (Section 14-16), is an **ambident ion** (14-80) having alternative pairs

$$:N{\equiv}C{:}^{\ominus}$$
14-80

of unshared electrons capable of reacting nucleophilically. With silver cyanide, the isonitrile becomes the main product.

Because of the unshared pair of electrons on carbon, isonitriles are much more reactive than nitriles. On heating, they rearrange into the more stable nitriles. Their catalytic reduction affords secondary amines, in contrast to nitriles which yield primary amines (Section 14-7a). Mild oxidizing agents such as mercuric oxide convert isonitriles into alkyl isocyanates, $RN{=}C{=}O$, while the action of sulfur yields alkyl isothiocyanates, $RN{=}C{=}S$. Hydrolysis of isonitriles ($H^{\oplus}$ or $OH^{\ominus}$ catalyst) leads to a primary amine and formic acid. These reactions are summarized in Figure 14-14. Isonitriles have no commercial importance.

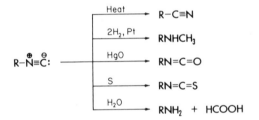

Figure 14-14. Some Reactions of Isonitriles

14-24. Urea, Cyanamide, and Guanidine

Urea or carbamide, $H_2N{-}CO{-}NH_2$, is the most important derivative of carbonic acid (Section 13-16a). It is the end product of protein metabolism in animals, and an adult man excretes about 30 g of urea each day in the urine, from where urea was first isolated in 1773. Its synthesis from ammonium cyanate (Section 1-1) by F. Wöhler in 1828 was one of the first preparations of an organic from an inorganic substance. Urea is manufactured in vast quantities by the reaction of ammonia with carbon dioxide.

$$CO_2 + NH_3 \xrightarrow{150°, 5000 \text{ psi}} [H_2NCOO^{\ominus}NH_4^{\oplus}] \longrightarrow \overset{\overset{\displaystyle O}{\|}}{H_2NCNH_2} + H_2O$$

Its United States production in 1962 was some 1.8 billion pounds, at a cost of $0.05 per pound. It is used as a fertilizer, as a protein supplement in cattle feed, and in the manufacture of **urea–formaldehyde plastics,** which are insoluble condensation polymers (14-**81**) of urea and formaldehyde.

$$H_2NCONH_2 + CH_2=O \longrightarrow H_2NCONHCH_2OH \xrightarrow{H_2NCONH_2} H_2NCONHCH_2NHCONH_2 \xrightarrow[\text{Etc.}]{CH_2=O, H_2NCONH_2}$$

$$\begin{array}{c} -(\text{NHCONCH}_2)_x \\ | \\ \text{CH}_2 \\ | \\ -(\text{NCONHCH}_2)_y \end{array}$$

14-81

Polymerization is stopped at a syrupy stage, wood pulp or other inert filler is added, and the mixture is subjected to heat and pressure, whereupon cross-linking occurs and an infusible, molded solid results. The use of urea in the preparation of barbiturate sedatives has been previously mentioned (Section 13-18).

When calcium carbide is heated with nitrogen at 1100° in the presence of about 10 per cent calcium oxide, calcium cyanamide is formed. This

$$CaC_2 + N_2 \xrightarrow{1100°, 10\% \text{ CaO}} \underset{\text{Calcium cyanamide}}{Ca-N-C\equiv N}$$

cyanamide process was the first important method for the fixation of atmospheric nitrogen, and calcium cyanamide constitutes an important fertilizer. Its hydrolysis leads to **cyanamide,** which is stable at pH <5, but dimerizes to **dicyanamide** at pH >7. If dicyanamide is heated with

$$CaNC\equiv N + 2 H_2O \longrightarrow Ca(OH)_2 + \underset{\text{Cyanamide}}{H_2N-C\equiv N} \xrightarrow{H_2NC\equiv N} \underset{\text{Dicyanamide}}{H_2N-\overset{\overset{\displaystyle NH}{\|}}{C}-NHC\equiv N}$$

an excess of ammonia, **guanidine,** the nitrogen analog of urea, is formed.

$$\underset{}{H_2N-\overset{\overset{\displaystyle NH}{\|}}{C}-NHC\equiv N} + 2 NH_3 \longrightarrow 2 \underset{\text{Guanidine}}{H_2N-\overset{\overset{\displaystyle NH}{\|}}{C}-NH_2}$$

In contrast to urea which (being an amide) is a very weak base, guanidine is one of the strongest organic bases known, comparable in strength to hydroxide ion. Its base strength is attributed to the resonance stabilization of the guanidinium ion (Figure 14-15) which is formed when a proton

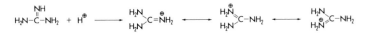

Figure 14-15. Resonance Hybrid of the Guanidinium Cation

adds to guanidine. The guanidine structure is found distributed among biological materials. Thus a phosphoric ester derivative of **creatine** (*N*-methylguanidinoacetic acid) is involved in muscular activity, its cyclic amide **creatinine** is excreted in the urine, and **tetrodotoxin** is the extremely active neurotoxin of the Japanese pufferfish and the California newt. Its complex, adamantane-like structure was elucidated in 1964 by Professors H. S. Mosher at Stanford University, R. B. Woodward at Harvard University, and K. Tsuda at Tokyo University.

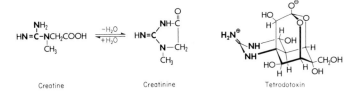

14-25. Isocyanates and Related Products

When urea is heated above its melting point, it decomposes into ammonia and **isocyanic acid,** which in turn polymerizes into a mixture of a cyclic trimer, **cyanuric acid,** and a linear polymer, **cyamelide.** If cyanuric

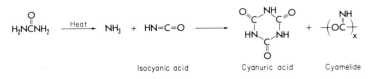

acid is heated, it depolymerizes into isocyanic acid, which may be condensed and kept below 0° as a colorless liquid. Isocyanic acid is tautomeric with **cyanic acid,** and spectral and chemical evidence indicates that isocyanic acid is the preferred structure. **Fulminic acid,** $HO^{\oplus}{-}N{\equiv}C{:}^{\ominus}$,

$$HN{=}\!{=}C{=}\!{=}\ddot{O}: \quad \longleftrightarrow \quad :N{\equiv}C{-}OH$$

Isocyanic acid   Cyanic acid

another isomer having a structure analogous to an isonitrile, is unknown in the free state, and known only as certain metal salts. Mercuric fulminate, $Hg(ONC)_2$, for example, is an explosive used in percussion caps as a detonator for dynamite. The discovery that silver fulminate and silver cyanate have the same composition (J. Liebig, 1823) constituted the first recognition of isomerism.

Alkyl cyanates, $ROC\equiv N$, are unknown in the monomeric form, but alkyl isocyanates, $RN\equiv C\equiv O$ are stable, if reactive, substances. We recall that isocyanates are intermediates in the Hofmann rearrangement of carboxamides to amines (Section 14-7c). Isocyanates and isothiocyanates, $RN\equiv C\equiv S$, have a cumulative system of double bonds analogous to ketene, $CH_2\equiv C\equiv O$ (Section 13-6), and accordingly undergo a number of addition reactions similar to those of ketene. The examples in Figure 14-16 are representative. The addition of similar reagents across the

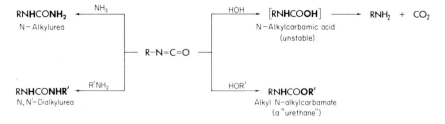

Figure 14-16. Some Reactions of Isocyanates

$-N\equiv C\equiv S$ bond of isothiocyanates affords analogous derivatives, such as N-alkylthiocarbamates (thiourethanes), $RNH-CS-OR'$, thioureas, $RNH-CS-NH_2$, and the like. Phenyl isocyanate, $PhN\equiv C\equiv O$, and phenyl isothiocyanate, $PhN\equiv C\equiv S$, are useful reagents for characterizing amines and alcohols, since the substituted urea and urethane products obtained from them are usually crystalline solids. The isothiocyanates are sometimes called **mustard oils,** since allyl isothiocyanate, $CH_2\equiv CHCH_2N\equiv C\equiv S$, may be obtained by the enzymatic hydrolysis of black mustard seed. Benzyl isothiocyanate, $PhCH_2N\equiv C\equiv S$, is found in the nasturtium plant, and 2-phenylethyl isothiocyanate, $PhCH_2CH_2N\equiv C\equiv S$, has been isolated from watercress. The well-known tranquilizer meprobamate (Miltown, Equanil) is a diurethane of 2-methyl-2-propyl-1,3-propanediol.

$$HOCH_2\underset{\underset{CH_2CH_2CH_3}{|}}{\overset{\overset{CH_3}{|}}{C}}CH_2OH \ + \ 2\,H_2NCONH_2 \ \xrightarrow{\text{Heat}} \ H_2N\overset{O}{\overset{\|}{C}}O-CH_2\underset{\underset{CH_2CH_2CH_3}{|}}{\overset{\overset{CH_3}{|}}{C}}CH_2-O\overset{O}{\overset{\|}{C}}NH_2$$

Meprobamate

SUPPLEMENTARY READING

1. "A. W. Hofmann and the Founding of the Royal College of Chemistry," J. J. Beer, *J. Chem. Educ.*, **37**, 248 (1960).
2. "Faraday, Hofmann and Wurtz," F. E. Wall, *J. Chem. Educ.*, **28**, 355 (1951).
3. "Reaction of Tertiary Amines with Nitrous Acid," G. E. Hein, *J. Chem. Educ.*, **40**, 181 (1963).
4. "Peter Griess—Discoverer of Diazo Compounds," V. Heines, *J. Chem. Educ.*, **35**, 187 (1958).
5. "The Mechanism of Diazotization," R. G. Gillis, *J. Chem. Educ.*, **31**, 344 (1954).
6. "Dyes and Dyeing in Ancient Mesopotamia," M. Levey, *J. Chem. Educ.*, **32**, 625 (1955).
7. "The Story of Dyes and Dyeing," C. Decelles, *J. Chem. Educ.*, **26**, 583 (1949).
8. "The Role of Chemistry in the Development of Dyeing and Bleaching," S. M. Edelstein, *J. Chem. Educ.*, **25**, 144 (1948).
9. "Dyes and Dyeing," H. A. Webb, *J. Chem. Educ.*, **19**, 460 (1942).
10. "Use of Metal Complexes in Organic Dyes and Pigments," O. Stallmann, *J. Chem. Educ.*, **37**, 220 (1960).
11. "Sulfanilamide and Related Chemotherapeutic Agents," L. H. Amundsen, *J. Chem. Educ.*, **19**, 167 (1942).
12. "The Chemotherapy of Tuberculosis," H. H. Fox, *J. Chem. Educ.*, **29**, 29 (1952).
13. "Gerhard Domagk and Chemotherapy," R. E. Oesper, *J. Chem. Educ.*, **31**, 188 (1954).
14. "Organic Isocyanates—Versatile Chemical Intermediates," R. G. Arnold, J. A. Nelson, and J. J. Verbanc, *J. Chem. Educ.*, **34**, 158 (1957).
15. "Urea in the History of Organic Chemistry," F. Kurzer and P. M. Sanderson, *J. Chem. Educ.*, **33**, 452 (1956).
16. "Nitrogen Fixation," H. A. Curtis, *J. Chem. Educ.*, **19**, 161 (1942).
17. "Tarichatoxin—Tetrodotoxin: A Potent Neurotoxin," H. S. Mosher, F. A. Fuhrman, H. D. Buchwald, and H. G. Fischer, *Science*, **144**, 1100 (1964).

CHAPTER 15

Optical Isomerism

In Section 2-8d we learned that an asymmetric carbon atom, with its four nonidentical substituents, gives rise to **enantiomers,** or nonsuperimposable, three-dimensional mirror-image structures. Such "right-handed" or "left-handed" enantiomers containing a single asymmetric carbon atom constitute the simplest structural situation permitting the occurrence of **optical isomerism** and the phenomenon of **optical activity.** In this chapter we shall examine these subjects in greater detail.

15-1. Plane Polarized Light

It will be recalled (Figure 4-6) that light consists of an electromagnetic disturbance which is wave-like in nature and which is propagated in a straight line through a transparent medium. With ordinary light, this electromagnetic wave train is actually cylindrically symmetrical about its axis of propagation; that is, the crests, troughs, and curvatures of each wave have a symmetrical radial distribution perpendicular to the axis of propa-

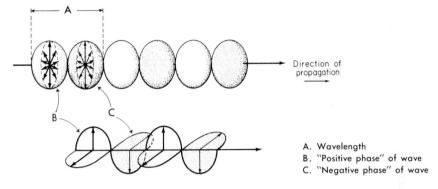

A. Wavelength
B. "Positive phase" of wave
C. "Negative phase" of wave

Figure 15-1. Schematic Representations of Unpolarized Monochromatic Light

gation. Thus the wave nature of ordinary monochromatic light must be represented three dimensionally as shown in Figure 15-1. We see that this representation is akin to a string of short, fat footballs which arise by rotating the wave train of Figure 4-6 through 360° about its axis of propagation. Ordinary light of this sort, whose electric vector "vibrates" in all directions perpendicular to the propagation axis, is called **unpolarized light.** Its representation may be simplified, as shown in the bottom drawing of Figure 15-1, by emphasizing any two electric vectors vibrating at right angles to one another. (The magnetic vectors at right angles to the electric vectors may be ignored.)

In 1808 the French physicist E. L. Malus discovered that when ordinary unpolarized light was reflected at a particular angle from a mirror surface, the reflected beam had properties which could be ascribed to an electromagnetic wave with crests and troughs alternating in a single plane, as shown in Figure 15-2. Such light, with its electric vector vibrating in a

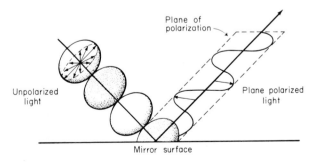

Figure 15-2. Plane Polarization of Light by Reflection

single plane, is called **plane polarized light** (or simply, polarized light), and the plane in which the vector vibrations occur is called the **plane of polarization**. Malus also found that the two rays of light emerging from a doubly refracting crystal of Iceland spar (calcite; transparent, crystalline calcium carbonate) were plane polarized at right angles to each other (Figure 15-3), and in 1828 William Nicol of Edinburgh discovered how to

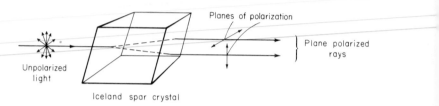

Figure 15-3. Double Refraction and Plane Polarization of Light by Iceland Spar

cut such a crystal, cement the two pieces together with Canada balsam, and mount it so that the emergent light beam was completely plane polarized in a single plane, as shown in Figure 15-4. This optical device, called

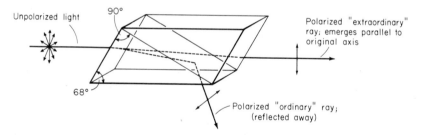

Figure 15-4. Plane Polarization of Light by a Nicol Prism

a **Nicol prism,** is the most convenient and commonly employed means of obtaining completely plane polarized light. In recent years it has been possible to produce substantially plane polarized light by the use of **Polaroid** sheets, whose operation is based on the phenomenon of **dichroism** shown by certain crystals. If light is passed through a dichroic crystal (for example, tourmaline, a complex metallic silicate, or quinine periodide sulfate, an alkaloid derivative), the electromagnetic vectors oscillating in one plane are much more strongly absorbed than those oscillating in a perpendicular plane. If the crystal is thick enough, the emergent light will be mainly polarized in the latter plane, as seen in Figure 15-5.

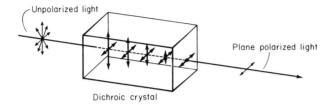

Figure 15-5. Plane Polarization of Light by a Dichroic Crystal

Polaroid sheets contain myriads of uniformly oriented, microscopic dichroic crystals embedded in a plastic film. These act as a single large dichroic crystal, and produce light which is substantially, but not completely, plane polarized. A schematic representation of polarizers such as Nicol prisms and Polaroid films is shown in Figure 15-6. We see that the

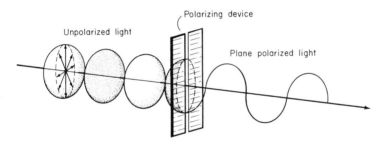

Figure 15-6. Schematic Operation of a Polarizer

polarizer acts as a "slit" which permits only a single plane of electric vector oscillations to pass through it.

An important property of polarizers is that they will "pass" *plane polarized light* fully only when the plane of polarization of the incoming polarized light coincides with the plane of polarization produced by the polarizer (Figure 15-7A). If the two planes are "crossed" (at 90°) to each other, the incoming polarized light is stopped (Figure 15-7B). At angles between 0° and 90° between the planes, only part of the incoming polarized light beam will be passed, namely, that component of the beam which is in a plane parallel to the plane of polarization produced by the polarizer.

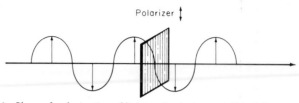

A. Plane of polarization of light and polarizer coincide (0° angle)

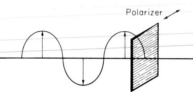

B. Plane of polarization of light and polarizer "crossed" (90° angle)

Figure 15-7. Action of a Polarizer on a Beam of Plane Polarized Light

These situations are illustrated with a pair of schematically drawn polarizers in Figure 15-8.

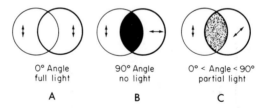

0° Angle full light	90° Angle no light	0° < Angle < 90° partial light
A	B	C

Figure 15-8. Polarized Light Emerging through a Pair of Polarizers

15-2. Optical Activity

In 1811 F. J. Arago, a French physicist and astronomer, discovered that clear quartz crystals had the ability of rotating the plane of polarization of polarized light passing through them. This property could be observed with the aid of a pair of crossed Nicol prisms (Figure 15-9). In the absence of the quartz, the crossed Nicol prisms would transmit no light (Figure 15-8*B*). When the quartz was inserted between the Nicol prisms, a certain amount of light would traverse the system. By rotating one of the Nicol prisms through a certain angle, called α, the **angle of rotation,** the light traversing the system could again be extinguished. At the outset, no light traverses the system, since the polarization planes of the **polarizer Nicol**

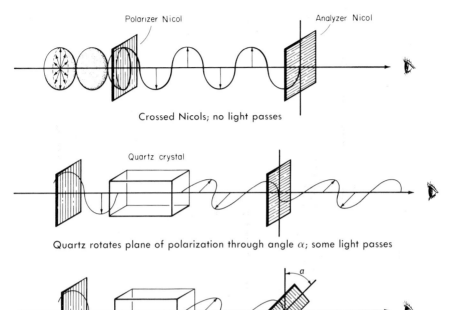

Crossed Nicols; no light passes

Quartz rotates plane of polarization through angle α; some light passes

Analyzer Nicol rotated through angle α; no light passes

Figure 15-9. Demonstration of the Optical Activity of Quartz

and **analyzer Nicol** are at 90°. When the quartz is inserted, the plane of polarization of the light from the polarizer Nicol is rotated into a new plane which is no longer perpendicular to the plane which the analyzer Nicol will stop. Accordingly, some light comes through the system. When the analyzer prism is rotated through the angle α, the two planes again become perpendicular and no light passes. Quartz and other substances capable of rotating the plane of polarization of polarized light passing through them are said to be **optically active.** The phenomenon is referred to as **optical activity.**

Now, two kinds of quartz crystals are known. These differ only in the positions of two small facets on the crystal surface. The facets are located in such a position as to cause the gross crystal structures to be *enantiomeric;* that is, the two crystal forms comprise a pair of nonsuperimposable mirror images, analogous again to a right and left hands. In 1815 the French physicist J. Biot observed that equal thicknesses of each of the enantiomeric types of quartz caused rotations of the plane of polarized light to equal extents, but in opposite directions. The crystal form which rotates the plane of polarization to the right (when the observer is facing the light source) is called **dextrorotatory.** The enantiomeric form rotating the plane of polarization to the left is called **levorotatory.** In the first case, the angle of rotation (α) is positive; in the second case it is negative. Biot also discovered that certain organic materials such as turpentine were optically active by themselves (neat) as well as in solution. Some of these optically active organic substances proved to be dextrorotatory, while others were levorotatory.

15-3. The Polarimeter; Optical Rotation

The angle of rotation of the plane of polarization of plane polarized light caused by a given optically active substance is measured with an instrument called a **polarimeter.** A schematic diagram of this instrument is shown in Figure 15-10. The principles of operation of the polarimeter,

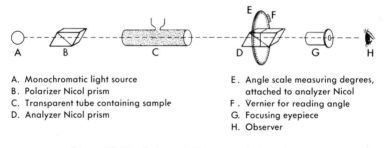

A. Monochromatic light source
B. Polarizer Nicol prism
C. Transparent tube containing sample
D. Analyzer Nicol prism

E. Angle scale measuring degrees, attached to analyzer Nicol
F. Vernier for reading angle
G. Focusing eyepiece
H. Observer

Figure 15-10. Schematic Diagram of a Polarimeter

actually, have been discussed above in connection with the optical activity of quartz crystals, and are illustrated schematically in Figure 15-9. Actual laboratory polarimeters, such as that shown in Figure 15-11, contain optical refinements which permit greater accuracy in measuring the angle of rotation than is possible with the simple "extinction" method illustrated in Figure 15-9.

The angle of rotation caused by an optically active substance depends not only upon the substance itself, but also on such factors as the thickness of the sample, its concentration in solution (if dissolved), the solvent employed (if dissolved), temperature, and the wavelength of the monochromatic light employed in the measurement. These factors are taken into account and specified in the **specific rotation,** symbolized as [α], which is the "intrinsic" optical activity of the substance under the conditions of the

Figure 15-11. A Laboratory Polarimeter

measurement. Specific rotations in solution (the usual practice) are calculated by the following formula:

$$[\alpha]_\lambda^T = \frac{100 \times \alpha}{l \times c}$$

where $\quad \alpha$ = observed rotation in degrees

$\quad\quad l$ = sample tube length in decimeters

$\quad\quad c$ = concentration of solute in grams/100 ml

$\quad\quad T$ = temperature of solution

$\quad\quad \lambda$ = wavelength of light employed

Typical designations for the specific rotations of two representative optically active organic substances are the following:

For α-D-Glucose:

$$[\alpha]_D^{20} = +112.2° \ (c, 4.0; H_2O)$$

For 1,2,3,4-Tetra-O-acetyl-β-D-xylose:

$$[\alpha]_D^{22} = -24.7° \ (c, 5.0; CHCl_3)$$

Notice how the above-mentioned variables are specified in these expres-

sions. The subscript D indicates the wavelength (sodium D line, ~ 5893 Å).
The first compound is dextrorotatory and the second levorotatory. Specific rotation constitutes a unique and characteristic physical constant for
every optically active substance. Optically inactive substances, of course,
have a specific rotation of $0°$.

15-4. Optically Active Organic Compounds

Biot, who first discovered the optical activity of certain organic compounds, also noted that such optical activity persisted when the organic
substance was molten or dissolved in solution. In contrast, the optical
activity of known inorganic compounds disappeared when their crystal
structure was destroyed, that is, when they were melted or dissolved. It
was appreciated, therefore, that optical activity of organic compounds
must be inherent in their molecular structures, while that of the inorganic
compounds then examined must reside in their crystal structure.

In 1848, at the age of 26, the French chemist Louis Pasteur made a most
remarkable discovery in the infant field of organic optical activity. He was
examining two minor by-products of the wine industry: potassium hydrogen tartrate, from tartar (a sludge which accumulates during grape fermentation), and the sodium ammonium salt of racemic acid (Latin:
racemus, grape). The corresponding acids, tartaric acid and racemic acid,
had identical chemical properties and were known to have similar structures ($HOOC—CH(OH)—CH(OH)—COOH$), but had different physi-
cal properties. In particular, tartaric acid was dextrorotatory ($[\alpha]_D^{25} +12°$
(H_2O)), while racemic acid was optically inactive. Pasteur examined
carefully the crystal structures of a number of salts of tartaric acid and
found them all to possess identical hemihedral facets on their surfaces,
causing the crystals to be enantiomeric like the crystals of optically active
quartz. Furthermore, all of the crystals were of the same enantiomeric
structure—all "right-handed." Since Biot had shown that tartaric acid
salts were all dextrorotatory, Pasteur hypothesized that a relationship
might exist between their similar hemihedral crystal habit and their dextrorotatory optical activity. He also suspected that, being optically inactive, the salts of racemic acid should exhibit symmetrical (rather than
hemihedral) crystal habits. Their careful examination, however, revealed
that they too were hemihedral, but that they consisted of *equal quantities*
of "right-handed" and "left-handed" hemihedral forms. Pasteur labori-
ously picked apart the "right-handed" and "left-handed" crystal enantiomers and examined each separately. Both forms proved to be optically
active. Solutions of the "right-handed" crystals from the sodium ammonium salt of racemic acid had a specific rotation equal to that of the cor-

responding salt of natural dextrorotatory tartaric acid (now called (+)-tartaric acid). Solutions of the "left-handed" crystals on the other hand, had specific rotations equal *but opposite in sign* to those of the corresponding salts of (+)-tartaric acid. A mixture containing equal weights of both types of crystals proved to be optically inactive, the dextrorotation of the (+)-tartaric acid salt exactly canceling the levorotation of the newly discovered (−)-tartaric acid salt. The separation of an equimolar mixture of dextrorotatory, (+), and levorotatory, (−), enantiomers into its two optically active components is referred to as **resolution.** Such an equimolar mixture of (+) and (−) enantiomers is called a **racemic mixture,** and is designated as (±) to denote its optical inactivity. Pasteur had thus succeeded in resolving optically inactive (±)-tartaric acid (racemic acid) into optically active (+)-tartaric and (−)-tartaric acids, and in demonstrating that the (+) component was identical with natural dextrorotatory tartaric acid. Pasteur was quite fortunate in his discovery, for it has since proved exceedingly rare for racemates to crystallize in enantiomeric crystal forms which are large enough to permit resolution by hand sorting. Furthermore, it was subsequently found that sodium ammonium racemate crystallizes as a homogeneous molecular compound (**racemic compound** or **racemate**) at temperatures above 28°, and as a mixture of enantiomeric crystals (**racemic mixture**) only below 28°. Pasteur's crystallizations were fortunately conducted below 28°, thus enabling him to discover the existence of the enantiomers. He later discovered a fourth stereomeric tartaric acid, *meso*-tartaric acid, which is discussed in Section 15-7a. The mirror-image crystal structures of the sodium ammonium salts of the enantiomeric tartaric acids are illustrated in Figure 15-12.

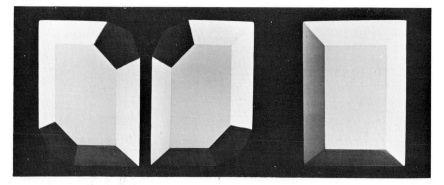

Figure 15-12. Enantiomeric Hemihedral Crystal Structures (left), Compared with a Symmetrical (Holohedral) Crystal Structure (right). Enantiomeric Forms are Models of Sodium Ammonium Tartrate

In the succeeding two decades other investigators added to the growing list of naturally occurring optically active organic substances. Although the fundamental molecular basis of optical activity was not understood at the time, it was appreciated that *all known optically active organic compounds, contained at least one (asymmetric) carbon atom bearing four unlike substituents* (Section 2-8d), and Pasteur himself had early recognized that asymmetric molecular structures of some sort must be involved. It remained for J. H. van't Hoff (22 years old) in Holland and J. A. LeBel (27 years old) in France to propose independently in 1874 their strikingly simple theory of the tetrahedral configuration of carbon atoms in organic compounds (Section 2-8a), and thus to rationalize the puzzling phenomenon of optical

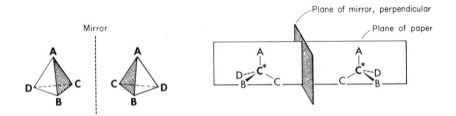

Figure 15-13. Enantiomeric Structures of the Asymmetric Carbon Atom

activity. In Figure 15-13 we emphasize again that *four different groups on a tetrahedral carbon atom give rise to enantiomeric* ("right-" and "left-handed") *molecular structures*. Such structures are simply the molecular equivalent of the enantiomeric crystal structures long known to be associated with the optical activity of certain crystalline inorganic compounds, and accordingly the optical activity of asymmetric organic molecules had a rational analogy. We also understand why the optical activity of organic substances persists in solution and in the liquid or gaseous state; the fundamental asymmetry of the molecular structure is not destroyed by these modifications in the physical state of organic matter.

15-5. The Cause of Optical Activity

Why are enantiomeric structures capable of rotating the plane of polarization of polarized light? This may be understood in terms of the fact that plane polarized lights acts as though it were composed of two oppositely spiraling waves of **circularly polarized light.** Circularly polarized light is light

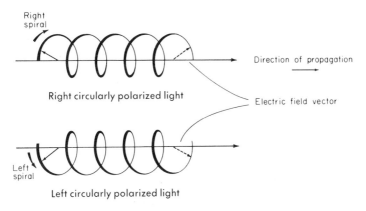

Right spiral

Direction of propagation

Right circularly polarized light

Electric field vector

Left spiral

Left circularly polarized light

Figure 15-14. Right and Left Circularly Polarized Light Waves

whose electric field vectors trace a right- or left-handed spiral path along the axis of propagation, as shown in Figure 15-14. Now, imagine that right and left circularly polarized light waves are traveling exactly in phase along a single path, and visualize the light ray end on as it comes toward you (Figure 15-15). We see that the right and left spiraling electric field

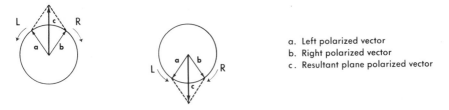

a. Left polarized vector
b. Right polarized vector
c. Resultant plane polarized vector

Figure 15-15. Combination of Right and Left Circularly Polarized Light to Produce Plane Polarized Light

vectors combine to produce a resultant electric field vector which oscillates up and down in a single plane: that is, *right and left circularly polarized lights combine to give plane polarized light.* Now, optically active substances exhibit a phenomenon known as **circular double defraction.** This means that the velocity of right circularly polarized light is *different* than that of left circularly polarized light on passing through the optically active medium. The result is that the left wave, for example, is *slowed down* and lags behind the right wave on emerging from the medium. Now, as seen in

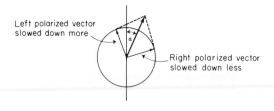

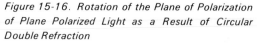

Figure 15-16. Rotation of the Plane of Polarization of Plane Polarized Light as a Result of Circular Double Refraction

Figure 15-16, the recombination of the left and right circularly polarized light produces a resultant plane polarized wave which is *tipped at an angle* from the original plane of polarization shown in Figure 15-15. This is the angle of rotation, α. Actually, right and left circularly polarized light may be produced by a special prism known as a **Fresnel rhomb,** and Fresnel long ago (1825) showed experimentally that right and left circularly polarized lights do indeed traverse optically active media at different velocities. We should note that right and left circularly polarized light waves themselves constitute nonsuperimposable mirror image "structures" (Figure 15-14), just as do right- and left-handed screws. It is understandable that each of these "enantiomeric" waves should interact differently with one enantiomer of an enantiomeric molecular or crystal structure than with the other enantiomer, and should accordingly travel through such asymmetric media at different velocities. A very rough analogy is to recall that a right-hand bolt will go through a right-hand nut, but that a left-hand bolt will not (Figure 15-17).

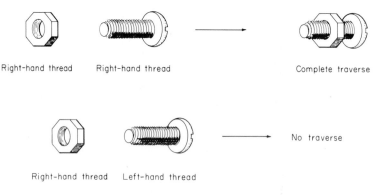

Figure 15-17. Analogy to Circular Double Refraction

15-6. Optical Activity in Compounds with No Asymmetric Carbon Atom

The basic requirement for optical activity in general is the nonsuperimposability of a structure on its mirror image structure. A barrel of right-handed gloves would be optically active if there were a means of making the measurement, and a barrel of left-handed gloves would have an equal but opposite optical rotation. In fact, analogous enantiomeric macro structures (right- and left-handed metal helices) have been shown capable of rotating the plane of polarization of polarized micro waves. It is not surprising, therefore, that certain organic substances besides those containing actual asymmetric carbon atoms are able to meet the criterion of structural nonsuperimposability, and hence may also be optically active. A few such classes of compounds, with their representative enantiomeric structures, are shown in Figure 15-18. By visualizing physical manipulations of these structures

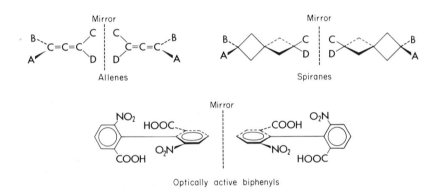

Optically active biphenyls

Figure 15-18. Some Classes of Optically Active Organic Compounds Which Contain No Individual Asymmetric Carbon Atom

in space, we see that the enantiomers shown are indeed nonsuperimposable. The case of the optically active biphenyl derivatives is particularly interesting. One enantiomer can be converted into its mirror image only by holding one of the phenyl rings stationary and *rotating the second ring through 180°* about their connecting bond. This may be prevented from occurring spontaneously by the *bulk* of the groups located on the four *ortho* positions. *Steric hindrance* prevents these groups from rotating past one another, and the 2,2'-dinitro-6,6'-diphenyldicarboxylic acid shown may be resolved into (+) and (−) enantiomers. At higher temperatures, where very energetic molecular motions overcome the steric repulsions of the *ortho* substituents, rotation about the connecting bond can be achieved, and the enantiomers of such compounds will interconvert.

For similar reasons of nonsuperimposability, certain elements other than carbon, when appropriately substituted with other atoms or groups, may act as centers of asymmetry in optically active molecules. Figure 15-19 shows one enantiomeric structure for each of several representative

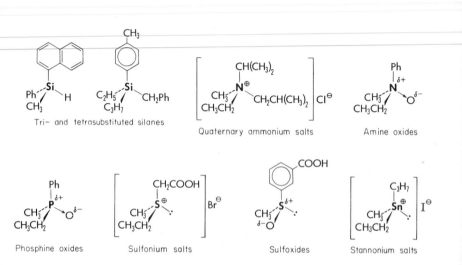

Figure 15-19. *Optically Active Compounds Involving Other Elements as a Center of Asymmetry*

optically active compounds whose asymmetric center involves an element other than carbon. We note that these examples are fundamentally similar to the asymmetric carbon atom; that is, molecular asymmetry in each case is brought about by the presence of *four different groups tetrahedrally disposed* about the central atom. The cases of the sulfonium salts, sulfoxides, and stannonium salts are particularly interesting, as we see in these examples that a *pair of electrons* may sometimes assume the role of the fourth non-identical substituent on the central atom. Trivalent nitrogen is electronically similar to such compounds, as seen in Figure 15-20, and thus in principle should also be capable of permitting two enantiomeric structures when properly substituted. All attempts, however, to resolve simple trivalent nitrogen compounds into enantiomers have failed. The reason for this is that the **energy barrier to inversion** of the trivalent nitrogen atom is so low (5 to 10 kcal/mole) that trivalent nitrogen compounds *invert* spon-

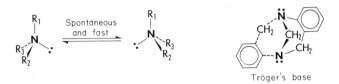

Figure 15-20. Asymmetry around the Trivalent Nitrogen Atom

taneously at room temperature, interconverting their enantiomers (Figure 15-20). We see that this process is completely identical with the *inversion* responsible for the stereochemical instability of carbanions (Section 6-7). The only trivalent nitrogen compound which has been resolved into enantiomers is Tröger's base (Figure 15-20), where the geometrical restriction imposed by the bridge structure prevents inversion of the nitrogen atoms, and where the molecule as a whole is asymmetric. The sulfoxides and sulfonium and stannonium salts in Figure 15-19 are stereochemically stable at room temperature because their energy barriers to inversion are higher. At elevated temperatures they would, of course, undergo similar inversion and interconversion of their enantiomers.

15-7. Molecules with Several Asymmetric Carbon Atoms

We have seen that molecules containing a single asymmetric carbon or other atom (Figure 15-19), as well as molecules of certain other structures (Figure 15-18), are capable of enantiomerism and thus show optical activity. Let us now examine structures containing more than one asymmetric carbon atom with regard to these considerations.

a. Compounds with Two Similar Asymmetric Carbon Atoms. Tartaric acid provides the classic example of a compound containing two *similar* asymmetric carbon atoms. In Figure 15-21 are shown the possible stereochem-

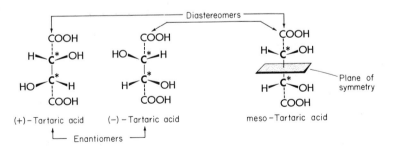

Figure 15-21. Stereochemical Structures of the Tartaric Acids

ical structures of tartaric acid. Each asymmetric carbon (C*) is called "similar," as each has the *same* four dissimilar groups (H, OH, COOH, CH(OH)COOH) attached to it. Table 15-1 summarizes the physical properties of the four known tartaric acids. We note immediately that the

Table 15-1. Physical Properties of the Tartaric Acids

	(+)-Tartaric	(−)-Tartaric	(±)-Tartaric (racemate)	meso-Tartaric
M.p., °C	170	170	206	140
$[\alpha]_D^{25}$ (c, 20; H_2O)	+12.0	−12.0	0.0	0.0
Solubility, g/100 ml H_2O (20°)	139	139	20.6	125
pK_{a_1}	2.93	2.93	2.96	3.11
pK_{a_2}	4.23	4.23	4.24	4.80
Density (20°)	1.760	1.760	1.679	1.666

(+) and (−) enantiomers have identical physical properties except for their specific rotations, which are equal in magnitude but opposite in sign. Racemic (±)-tartaric acid has different physical properties, and is optically inactive for the reasons noted in Section 15-4. Both racemic mixtures and racemates generally have physical properties which differ from those of the two enantiomers which comprise them. These differences are more marked for racemic compounds than racemic mixtures. *meso*-Tartaric acid has still different physical properties, and is also optically inactive. *meso*-Tartaric acid is said to be a **diastereomer** of both (+)- and (−)-tartaric acids. Diastereomers are defined as *optical isomers which are not enantiomers* of each other. *meso*-Tartaric acid is optically inactive because, even though it has individual asymmetric centers, the molecule as a whole does not meet the criterion for nonsuperimposability on its mirror image. Thus if we draw the mirror image of the structure shown in Figure 15-21 for *meso*-tartaric acid, we find that it is superimposable on the structure shown by merely rotating through 180° in the plane of the paper. A quick criterion for this situation is the presence in *meso*-tartaric acid of a plane of symmetry bisecting it; that is, the top half of the molecule is an exact mirror image reflection of the bottom half. All *meso* compounds have an analogous plane of symmetry, and are therefore optically inactive. The four tartaric acids in Table 15-1 are representative of the relationships prevailing in general for compounds containing two *similar* asymmetric centers, that is, we always find two optically active enantiomers, one optically inactive racemic modification, and one optically inactive *meso* diastereomer. Enantiomers, besides having identical physical properties and equal but opposite rotations, react identically chemically and, with symmetrical reagents, at identical rates. Diastereomers generally have different physical properties but show identical chemical behavior, reacting chemically, however at different rates.

b. Compounds Containing Two Dissimilar Asymmetric Carbon Atoms. When a compound has a structure containing two *dissimilar* asymmetric carbon atoms—that is, when the four different groups are *not* identical for each asymmetric center—the situation is different. The stereochemical structures and representative physical properties (arbitrary) of the stereoisomers arising in this situation are shown in Figure 15-22. We notice that

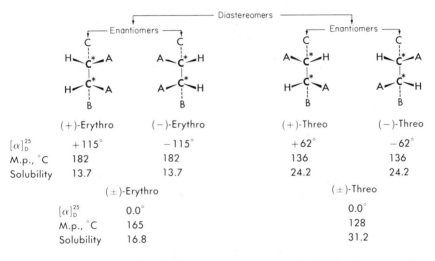

	(+)-Erythro	(−)-Erythro	(+)-Threo	(−)-Threo
$[\alpha]_D^{25}$	+115°	−115°	+62°	−62°
M.p., °C	182	182	136	136
Solubility	13.7	13.7	24.2	24.2

	(±)-Erythro	(±)-Threo
$[\alpha]_D^{25}$	0.0°	0.0°
M.p., °C	165	128
Solubility	16.8	31.2

Figure 15-22. *Stereochemical Structures and Representative Physical Constants of Compounds Containing Two Dissimilar Asymmetric Carbon Atoms*

there are two pairs of enantiomers and two racemic modifications. The (+)- and (−)-*erythro* enantiomers (see below) have identical physical properties, but opposite specific rotations. The same is true for the (+)- and (−)-*threo* enantiomers, whose properties in turn differ from those of the *erythro* diastereomers. The racemic *erythro* and *threo* forms are optically inactive and have physical properties which differ from each other, as well as from any of the two pairs of enantiomers involved. These relationships are generally applicable to compounds having two dissimilar asymmetric centers. Note that no *meso* forms are possible with compounds of this type, since their structures can never have a plane of symmetry.

The terms *erythro* and *threo* designate the configurational arrangements in such structures, that is, the arrangements of their substituents in space. The *erythro* isomers have their two pairs of similar substituents (A and H in Figure 15-22) in a *cis*-type relationship when placed in a conformation which eclipses their nonidentical substituents (B and C). The *threo* configurations involve a *trans*-type relationship of the similar substituents (A and H) when the dissimilar substituents (B and C) are allowed to eclipse. *Erythro* and *threo* designations are derived from the configurations of the four-carbon sugars, **erythrose** and **threose** (see Section 16-3).

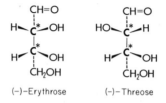

c. *Compounds Containing Many Asymmetric Carbon Atoms.* We have seen above that, with two dissimilar asymmetric carbon atoms, four optically active stereisomers are possible. If we drew out similarly all of the possible stereochemical structures for a molecule containing *three dissimilar* asymmetric carbons, we would find a total of eight optical isomers—four pairs of enantiomers and no *meso* forms. The number of optical isomers arising in compounds containing varying numbers of dissimilar asymmetric carbon atoms is shown in Table 15-2. We see that the number of possible optical isomers increases very rapidly, indeed geometrically, as the number

Table 15-2. Optical Isomerism and Number of Dissimilar Asymmetric Carbon Atoms

Number of Dissimilar C* Atoms	Total Number of Optical Isomers	Number of Racemates
1	2	1
2	4	2
3	8	4
4	16	8
5	32	16
6	64	32
$\vdots$	$\vdots$	$\vdots$
n	2^n	$2^n/2$

of asymmetric carbon atoms in the molecule increases. If any of the asymmetric centers has substituents completely identical with those at any other asymmetric center—that is, if any asymmetric center is completely equivalent to any other—then, as with the tartaric acids, *meso* forms are possible and the total number of optical isomers will be reduced. These polyasymmetric-center situations are encountered among sugar and protein molecules, and will be discussed with specific examples in Chapter 16.

15-8. Resolution of Racemic Modifications

Resolution, we recall, consists in the separation of a (±) racemic form into its (+) and (−) enantiomers. Pasteur's first resolution of racemic tartaric acid involved hand-sorting the enantiomeric crystals in racemic mixtures of certain of its salts. Such mechanical separation, as already mentioned, is not a generally applicable resolution technique because very few racemic mixtures possess enantiomeric crystals of sufficient size to permit hand sorting. In fact, only nine similar examples have been noted since Pasteur's time. Fortunately, alternative resolution methods are available, the two most important of which were also discovered by Pasteur.

Pasteur's second method is referred to as **biological resolution.** If the mold *Penicillium glaucum*, for example, is allowed to act on the ammonium salt of (±)-tartaric acid, its enzymes destroy (metabolize) the ammonium (+)-tartrate component preferentially, and leave the ammonium (−)-tartrate component unchanged. The latter enantiomer may then be isolated from the metabolized mixture. Biological resolution, in general, utilizes a specific microorganism (or an appropriate enzyme from it) to attack selectively one of the enantiomers of a racemic modification, thus permitting subsequent recovery of the unaltered enantiomer. This method, however, has certain inherent disadvantages which limit its utility. In the first place, one of the enantiomers—possibly the desired one—is irrevocably destroyed. Secondly, it may be difficult or impossible to find a microorganism (or enzyme) applicable to a given racemic form. The racemic substrate may be too toxic for the microorganism, may destroy the enzyme, or may simply be indifferent to attack by either. Lastly, yields are low, especially since dilute solutions must be employed. Nevertheless, the procedure of biological resolution is frequently a useful one.

Pasteur's third method, in principle a completely general one, is called **resolution through diasteromers.** This technique involves conversion of the racemic modification into a mixture of two crystalline diastereomers by means of an appropriate chemical reaction with an optically active reagent which is itself a single enantiomer. We recall (Table 15-1 and Figure 15-22) that diastereomers have different physical properties—in particular, different solubilities. The resulting mixture of crystalline diastereomers may accordingly be separated into its two components by **fractional crystallization,** taking advantage of the solubility differences of the two diastereomeric components in a series of systematic recrystallizations. When the two diastereomers are completely separated, each is converted into its original chemical constituents by an appropriate reaction. One of the products from each diastereomer will be an enantiomer from the original racemic form. A schematic diagram of the resolution of a racemic acid by this technique is shown in Figure 15-23. We see that the final stage of the

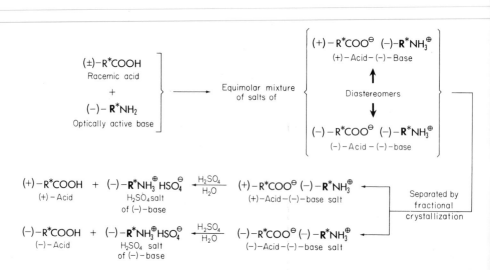

Figure 15-23. Resolution of a Racemic Acid with an Optically Active Base

procedure yields the resolved enantiomers of the acid, and regenerates the original **resolving agent,** the optically active amine base (as its mineral acid salt). Alkaloids such as quinine and cinchonine (see Chapter 16) are naturally occurring optically active amine bases frequently employed as resolving agents in such resolutions of racemic acids. Naturally occurring optically active acids, such as (−)-tartaric acid and (−)-malic acid, $HOOC—CH_2—C*H(OH)—COOH$, from apples, may be used in a similar way as resolving agents for the resolution of racemic amines. This resolution technique is sometimes limited in its application by the noncrystallinity of the mixtures of diastereomers formed in the first stage of the sequence, or by the fact that the diastereomers, even if crystalline, may

have rather similar solubilities and therefore be extremely difficult to separate by fractional crystallization. Resolution through diastereomers, nevertheless, is the most widely used method for the resolution of racemic mixtures. A number of other specialized resolution techniques are known,
including column chromatography (Section 3-5a) with optically active ad-
sorbants, paper chromatography, and gas chromatography (Section 3-5d)
with optically active stationary phases. These techniques are not of broad
applicability, however, sometimes are only partially successful, and are
mainly of theoretical interest.

15-9. Formation of Racemic Modifications

When a laboratory synthesis involving a symmetrical molecule and not
involving asymmetric reagents results in the production of a new asymmetric carbon atom in the molecule, the product is invariably racemic.
This general situation is illustrated in Figure 15-24 with two common re-

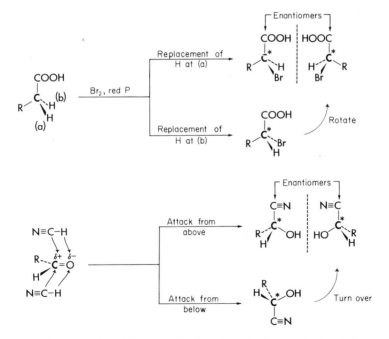

*Figure 15-24. Formation of Racemic Modifications in the Synthesis of Asymmetric
Centers*

actions, the α-bromination of a carboxylic acid (Section 13-4c) and the formation of a cyanohydrin from an aldehyde (Section 12-7j). In the first example we see that either of the two stereochemically equivalent α-hydrogen atoms, (a) and (b), may be replaced during the reaction, leading to enantiomeric α-bromo acids. Since the two hydrogens are chemically identical, there is an equal statistical probability that either hydrogen will be replaced, and the reaction product accordingly contains equal numbers of each enantiomer; that is, it is racemic. In the second example we note that attack by HCN may occur from either "above" or "below" the carbonyl group of the aldehyde, leading to enantiomeric cyanohydrins. Since either mode of attack is equally probable, a racemic form again results.

Racemic modifications also may be formed by a process known as **racemization,** which is defined as the *conversion of one enantiomer of an optically active substance into a racemic mixture.* Racemization is invariably accompanied by a change in optical rotation from a value characteristic of the original enantiomer to a value of zero. In fact, the rates of racemization of optically active materials may be conveniently determined by following the racemization reaction polarimetrically (Figure 15-25). A curve such as shown in Figure 15-25 is known as a mutarotation curve, **mutarotation** being defined simply as a *change in optical rotation with time.*

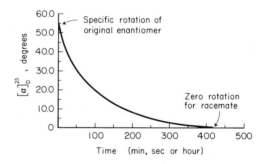

Figure 15-25. Mutarotation of an Optically Active Substance during Racemization

Racemization may be accomplished by a variety of chemical means. The most important chemical mechanisms are shown in Figure 15-26. In the first example, (+)-α-phenylethyl chloride loses HCl when dissolved in liquid SO_2, forming phenylethylene (styrene), which is a stable intermediate having a symmetrical structure. This intermediate is capable of reacting with HCl to regenerate α-phenylethyl chloride, and the attack

may occur with equal probability from either *above* (a) or *below* (b) the
plane of the double bond, thus forming both enantiomers. In the second
example a symmetrical carbonium ion (Section 6-6c) is formed as a transi-

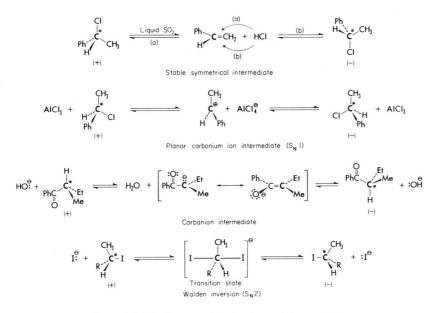

Figure 15-26. Common Mechanisms of Racemization

ent intermediate. This may be subsequently attacked from either side of
its plane, again producing enantiomers. In the carbanion example, removal of the activated α-hydrogen atom from an optically active ketone by
alkali generates a symmetrical, resonance-stabilized carbanion intermediate. This may again undergo attack by H_2O with equal probability from
either above or below its plane of symmetry, again affording enantiomers.
In the last example we note that the enantiomer is formed by a direct S_N2
nucleophilic displacement reaction, involving **Walden inversion** (Section
11-12d) and proceeding through a *symmetrical transition state*. All of the
typical racemization reactions illustrated in Figure 15-26 are reversible
processes. Thus if they are allowed to proceed for a long enough time, the
final equilibrium mixture in each case will be completely racemic.

A process closely related to racemization is **epimerization. Epimers**
are stereoisomers containing more than one asymmetric center and differing in configuration at only *one* of their asymmetric centers. $(-)$-Erythrose

and (−)-threose (Section 15-7b) provide an example of epimers, their configurations at the carbon atom adjacent to the aldehyde function being inverted (that is, having opposite spatial configurations). It should be noted that all epimers are diastereomers, but that all diastereomers are not epimers. Epimerization is thus defined as the *inversion of configuration at one asymmetric center in a molecule containing several asymmetric centers* (Figure 15-27). The mechanisms of epimerization (for example, Figure 15-27) are

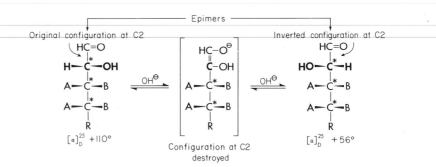

Figure 15-27. An Epimerization Reaction

similar to those of racemization (Figure 15-26), but the equilibrating reaction occurs *only* at the single asymmetric center being inverted, other asymmetric centers being chemically such as not to be involved. It should be emphasized that, although mutarotation occurs during epimerization (the two epimers having different optical rotations), the final equilibrium rotation of the epimerized product will not be (unless fortuitously) zero, as was the case during racemization. Also, in contrast to racemization, the final equilibrium mixture in an epimerization reaction generally contains unequal amounts of the two epimers. Epimerization is an important reaction among the sugars (Section 16-8b), as well as in other branches of organic chemistry.

15-10. Relative Configuration

By *configuration* we mean the arrangement in space of the atoms or groups around an asymmetric center. Suppose we want to compare the configurations of two different optically active compounds, each containing a single asymmetric carbon atom. On what basis can we say that their configurations are "the same" or that they are "opposite"? While configurations of individual asymmetric centers may always be unambiguously designated by models or three-dimensional perspective formulas of the sort used above, a decision as to whether the configurations of two asymmetric centers are "the same" or "opposite" can only be made if arbitrary designations for configuration are agreed upon. The most commonly employed nomenclature for designating configuration uses the prefixes D- and L-. Compounds having a single asymmetric center are drawn with their longest carbon chain vertical, with their number one carbon at the top, and with any ring in the structure written to the bottom (Figure 15-28). For compounds containing a single asymmetric center, *that enan-*

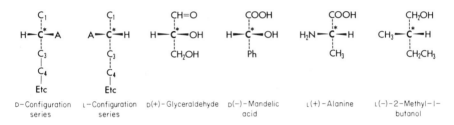

D—Configuration   L—Configuration   D(+)–Glyceraldehyde   D(−)–Mandelic   L(+)–Alanine   L(−)–2–Methyl–1–
series   series   acid   butanol

Figure 15-28. Examples of D and L Configurational Designation

tiomer which has its noncarbon substituent or smallest alkyl group written to the right is said to have the D-configuration and to belong to the D-series. The enantiomer with the corresponding substituent written to the left has the L-configuration and belongs to the L-series. We notice in Figure 15-28 that there is *no correlation between optical rotation* (specified by (+) or (−)) *and configuration.* Some compounds having the D-configuration are dextrorotatory and others are levorotatory, and the same is true for compounds in the L-series. Earlier literature employed the prefixes *d*- and *l*-, sometimes to denote configuration and sometimes the sign of optical rotation. This practice led to considerable confusion, which present practice eliminates by using D and L to denote configuration and (+) and (−) to indicate direction of rotation. D and L configurational nomenclature is applicable to a wide variety of compounds, including those containing several asymmetric centers (in which case each individual asymmetric carbon atom must be designated as either D or L). The system breaks down, however, for compounds of the type $R_1R_2C^*R_3R_4$ (where R's are alkyl or aryl groups), and leads to occasional ambiguities in other cases. There are more complicated configurational nomenclature systems which avoid these difficulties, but their description is beyond the scope of our survey. Other commonly used means

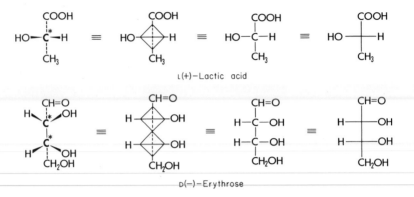

Figure 15-29. Equivalent Configurational Representations

of depicting configurational formulas are shown in Figure 15-29. The last two examples for each compound, called **Fischer projection formulas,** are two-dimensional representations which are understood to imply the three dimensional character of the corresponding perspective drawings or models.

Two compounds having a single asymmetric center are said to have the same **relative configuration** if they belong to the same series (either D or L), and to have opposite configurations if they belong to opposite series. How do we correlate the configurations of two optically active compounds, that is, determine their relative configurations? This is one of the most important tasks of stereochemistry, since such correlations can frequently provide intimate insights into the mechanisms of general organic reactions. The task may be approached by a variety of experimental techniques. Probably the most important and reliable of these involves *chemical inter-conversion* of a compound of known configuration into one whose relative configuration is being sought after (or vice versa). Examples of this method are shown in Figure 15-30. In the first example we see that a $—CH_2COOH$ group in the starting D(+)-3-phenylbutanoic acid (whose configuration, we will assume, is known) is converted into a $—CH_2CH_3$ group in the (+)-2-phenylbutane product whose relative configuration we wish to establish. *Since no bonds to the asymmetric carbon atom are broken during any stage of the overall transformation,* the final $—CH_2CH_3$ group and the original $—CH_2COOH$ group must have identical relative spatial positions around the asymmetric center, and the product must accordingly be of the D-configuration shown. The second example is more complicated in that it involves the overall replacement of a group (—OH) *on the asymmetric center* by another group $(—CH_2CH_2CH_3)$. In fact, the sequence of reactions employed involves

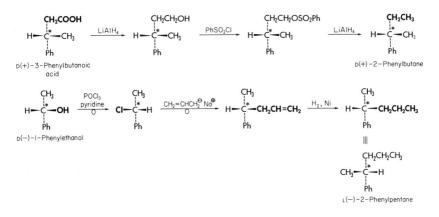

Figure 15-30. Configurational Correlation by Chemical Interconversions

two such replacements (—OH by —Cl and —Cl by —CH₂CH=CH₂). Now it so happens that, by configurational studies on other optically active compounds as well as by other criteria, it is known that both of these nucleophilic displacements are of the S_N2 type and proceed with inversion of configuration (Walden inversion; Section 11-12d). Accordingly, since the stereochemical consequences of each step in the reaction sequence are known, it follows that the final levorotatory product must have the L-configuration indicated. Notice that a looped arrow is used to indicate the occurrence of Walden inversion during a reaction.

We see that configurational correlation by chemical interconversions requires either that the bonds to the asymmetric center are not broken at any stage of the reaction sequence or, if they are, that the stereochemical consequences of the bond-breaking reactions occurring are unambiguously known by other criteria. In principle it is possible to correlate the configuration of any optically active compound with that of any other by such chemical interconversions, and this method has been applied to determine the relative configurations of a very large number of such compounds. In practice, however, such interconversions may be difficult or impossible to carry out in such a way as to meet the above requirements, and configurational relationships may have to be deduced on the basis of less general and often less definitive techniques. These methods, which usually involve a correlation of the optical properties of the compounds to be configurationally related with certain other of their physical properties, are beyond the scope of our chapter. Suffice it to say that they are generally simpler to apply, but are sometimes more open to error, than is the method based on chemical interconversions of optically active compounds.

15-11. Absolute Configuration

In the preceding section we saw that it is both theoretically important and experimentally possible to correlate configurations among optically active compounds. Before the turn of the century, E. Fischer *arbitrarily assumed* that (+)-glyceraldehyde had the D-configuration shown in Figure 15-28, and subsequent relative configurations of other optically active compounds (determined by the methods described above, or others) were therefore ultimately based on this assumed configuration. It was not known, however, whether (+)-glyceraldehyde *actually* did have the D-configuration shown in Figure 15-28, or whether, in fact, it had the enantiomeric L-configuration. In short, the **absolute configuration** (*actual* arrangement in space) of (+)-glyceraldehyde, and therefore also of other optically active compounds, was not known. In 1951 J. M. Bijvoet and co-workers at the University of Utrecht were able to determine experimentally the *absolute* configuration of (+)-tartaric acid, by sophisticated X-ray diffraction measurements on its sodium rubidium salt. Since the relative configurations of (+)-tartaric acid and (+)-glyceraldehyde were known, this experiment also sufficed to establish the *absolute* configuration of (+)-glyceraldehyde, as well as that of all other optically active compounds whose configurations relative to (+)-glyceraldehyde had been determined. Fortuitously, it turned out that the absolute configuration of (+)-glyceraldehyde was in fact the D-configuration previously *assumed* by E. Fischer, and therefore that all known relative configurations were also correct absolute configurations.

15-12. Mechanism and Stereochemistry of Substitution Reactions

When an atom or group attached to an asymmetric carbon atom in an organic molecule is replaced during a chemical reaction by another atom or group, various stereochemical results may occur. Such substitution reactions may in principle follow any one of five stereochemical paths, as illustrated in Figure 15-31. We see that the substitution reaction may proceed by the **100 per cent stereoselective** pathways of complete retention (a) or complete inversion (e) of the relative configurations of the reactant and product, by the **partially stereoselective** pathways of predominant retention (and partial inversion) (b) or predominant inversion (and partial retention) (d) of configuration, or by the **nonstereoselective** path of complete racemization (c). These stereochemical consequences occur, of course, whether the organic reactant undergoing substitution is asymmetric or not. If the reactant is optically active, however, the pathway can be deduced by noting the optical rotations of reactant and product, and by determining (or knowing) their relative configurations, as well as by study-

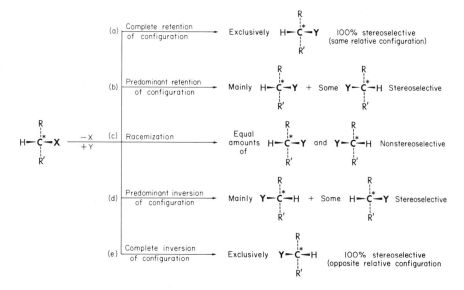

Figure 15-31. Stereochemical Paths of Substitution Reactions

ing polarimetrically the rates of the substitution reaction under varying experimental conditions. Which pathway is followed depends on the reaction mechanism operating in the particular substitution involved. Thus by establishing the **stereochemical course** (path) of a substitution reaction, it is possible to establish the mechanism of the substitution and to determine how it varies under different reaction conditions. Studies of this sort have led to the important general conclusions that:

1. S_N1 *substitutions* (Section 11-12d) *are attended by racemization* (sometimes including partial stereoselectivity toward either inversion or retention of configuration, depending upon the reactant and the reaction conditions).

2. S_N2 *substitutions* (Section 11-12d) *are attended by substantial or complete inversion of configuration.*

3. So-called $S_N i$ *reactions* (substitution nucleophilic internal) *are attended by very predominant retention of configuration.*

In the two examples of an $S_N i$ reaction shown in Figure 15-32, we see that a nucleophilic group within the molecule attacks the center being substituted from the *same side* on which the leaving group is located, and that the resulting product therefore has a relative configuration identical with that of the original reactant. The intermediates 15-**1** and 15-**2,** respectively, in the two reactions shown have, incidentally, been separately isolated. The importance of stereochemical criteria in the study of organic reaction mechanisms may be appreciated from the above generalizations.

Conversion of an alcohol to an alkyl chloride using thionyl chloride (Section 11-7e)

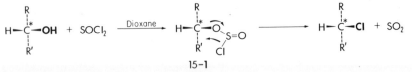

15-1

Hofmann rearrangement of a carboxamide (Section 14-7c)

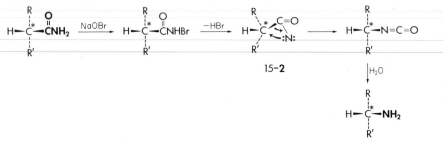

15-2

Figure 15-32. The Stereochemical Course of S$_N$i Reactions

15-13. Stereoselective Syntheses and Asymmetric Syntheses

In Section 15-9 we learned that racemic products were invariably formed when a new asymmetric center was created synthetically in a symmetrical molecule by reaction with a symmetrical reagent. The outcome is different, however, when a new asymmetric center is synthesized in a molecule *already containing* an asymmetric center. The latter situation is illustrated in Figure 15-33, where we see that the reaction of HCN with D(+)-glyceraldehyde results in the formation of a new asymmetric center at the original aldehyde carbon. Depending on whether the HCN adds "above" or "below" the plane of the —CH=O group (see Figure 15-24), however, the new asymmetric center may have either of the alternative configura-

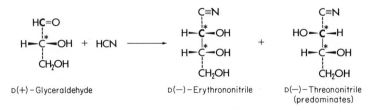

Figure 15-33. Stereoselective Synthesis with an Optically Active Reactant

tions shown for the top C* in the products of Figure 15-33. Since the configuration of the original (bottom) asymmetric carbon atom remains unchanged, two diastereomeric products result, an *erythro* epimer and a *threo* epimer. Now, in contrast to the analogous reaction with a symmetrical aldehyde (Figure 15-24), this synthesis leads to the production of *unequal amounts of the two diastereomeric products*. Such a synthesis, involving the formation of a new asymmetric center in a molecule already containing an asymmetric center, invariably yields diastereomeric products in unequal amounts, and is referred to as a **stereoselective synthesis** of the predominant diastereomer. In situations where the "new" and the "old" asymmetric centers are adjacent to one another in the product, the stereoselectivity in such syntheses may be remarkably high (for example, 5:1 to 9:1). In cases where the "new" and the "old" asymmetric centers are further apart in the product, the stereoselectivity is generally lower. When such syntheses are brought about by enzymes (optically active "biocatalysts" which are involved in the transition state of the reaction), they are frequently 100 per cent stereoselective; that is, one diastereomer is formed to the *exclusion* of the other.

Stereoselective syntheses require only that the reactant contain one or more asymmetric centers, and not that it be optically active (resolved). Thus, stereoselective synthesis is also applicable to racemic mixtures, as shown in Figure 15-34. Here we see that the original $(\pm)$-α-*N*-methylaminopropiophenone yields, on catalytic hydrogenation, two diastereomeric products *each as a racemate*, but that one diastereomeric pair (ephed-

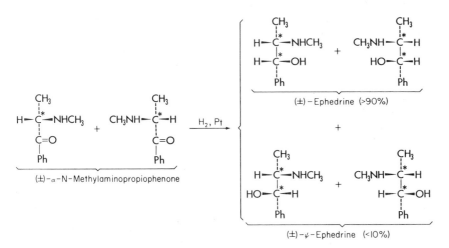

Figure 15-34. Stereoselective Synthesis with a Racemic Reactant

rine) vastly predominates over the other (ψ-ephedrine). Natural (−)-ephedrine, identical with that isolated from the Chinese drug Ma Huang, and used in the treatment of asthma, may be obtained by resolution of the racemic ephedrine diastereomer with optically active mandelic acid.

Now, suppose by some method we are able to remove the "original" asymmetric center in the product of a stereoselective synthesis involving an optically active reactant. We then have left only the "new" asymmetric center and, since the two enantiomers containing it were present in *unequal* amounts, the product will be optically active. Such a sequence of reactions is illustrated in Figure 15-35, where an ester (15-**3**) of an α-keto acid and

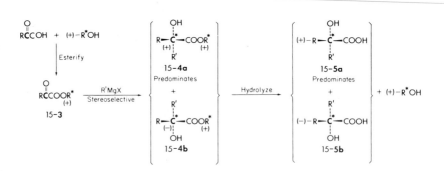

Figure 15-35. Asymmetric Synthesis of an Optically Active α-Hydroxy Acid

an optically active alcohol, (+)-R*OH, is allowed to react with a symmetrical Grignard reagent, R′MgX, to form a new asymmetric center at the α-keto function. The two diastereomeric α-hydroxy ester products (15-**4a** and 15-**4b**) are formed, again as above, in *unequal amounts*. We then saponify the mixture of diastereomers and remove the original optically active alcohol, (+)-R*OH. The remaining α-hydroxy acid product (15-**5a** and 15-**5b**) is an optically active mixture of enantiomers in which one form predominates, namely, that enantiomer which was present as part of the predominant diastereomer in the preceding step. A sequence of reactions which results in the production of an optically active product from an optically inactive starting material (here RCOCOOH) through the temporary intervention of an optically active reagent (here (+)-R*OH) is referred to as an **asymmetric synthesis.** Asymmetric syntheses may also occur under the influence of an asymmetric catalyst or solvent, as well as an asymmetric reagent. Optically active phenylalanine, for example, has been synthesized by the catalytic hydrogenation of ethyl α-acetoxyimino-β-phenylpyruvate using palladium catalyst supported on optically active

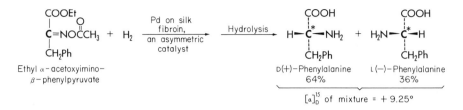

Figure 15-36. Asymmetric Catalytic Hydrogenation

silk fibroin, as shown in Figure 15-36. As described below, asymmetric syntheses may be used to establish absolute configurations in the optically active products arising from them.

Why does an existing asymmetric center impart stereoselectivity to the formation of a new asymmetric center nearby to it? This occurs since the reaction paths leading to the two diastereomeric products have characteristically *different activation energies* (Section 6-8; Figure 15-37). Therefore, that diastereomer arising via the reaction path of lower activation energy will be formed more rapidly and will ultimately predominate in the final product. What is the origin of such activation energy differences? Typical explanations have been given in both steric and electronic terms, with steric rationalizations being perhaps better substantiated experimentally. One representative steric explanation for a stereoselective synthesis is shown in Figure 15-37, where an aldehyde group adjacent to an asym-

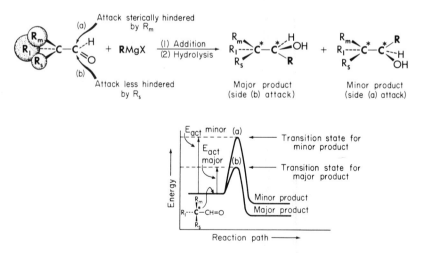

Figure 15-37. Explanation of a Stereoselective Synthesis

metric center is shown to react with a Grignard reagent to form a second-ary alcohol containing a new asymmetric center. Let us assume that the original asymmetric carbon atom of the aldehyde bears a small, medium, and large group (R_s, R_m and R_l, respectively). Assume further, reason-ably, that the aldehyde adopts a preferred conformation with the small and medium size groups flanking the carbonyl function, and the bulkiest group (R_l) in the most distant ("*trans*") position from it. The RMgX may now attack the aldehyde from *above* (path *a*) or *below* (path *b*) the plane of the carbonyl group. Path *a*, however, is subject to greater steric hindrance due to the larger bulk of the R_m group than is path *b* owing to the smaller bulk of the R_s group. The transition state corresponding to path *a* is thus energetically higher than that along path *b* (Figure 15-37), and path *b* is therefore the preferred path which produces the predominant diastereo-mer. Such steric explanations have been able to correlate and predict the stereochemical course of a large number of stereoselective syntheses. We see also how, if we know the absolute configuration of the original asym-metric center in the reactant, such an explanation allows us to predict the absolute configuration of the new asymmetric center in each of the dia-stereomeric products. Reactions analogous to that in Figure 15-37 have thus proved useful as a means of determining absolute configurations.

15-14. Optical Rotatory Dispersion

As early as 1817 Biot recognized that the magnitude of optical rotation shown by an optically active substance depended, among other things, on the wavelength of the monochromatic light used in making its measure-ment. The variation of optical rotation with wavelength is called **optical rotatory dispersion** (ORD). ORD measurements are made with a **spec-tropolarimeter** (Figure 15-38), that is, a polarimeter whose monochro-matic light source can be continuously varied throughout those wave-lengths of the spectrum which are of interest. A typical modern spectro-polarimeter utilizes wavelengths throughout the visible (8000 to 4000 Å) and part of the ultraviolet (4000 to 2100 Å) regions of the spectrum, and, indeed, ORD measurements in the ultraviolet prove to be the most useful and revealing.

A typical ORD curve for a dextrorotatory compound is shown in Fig-ure 15-39. We see that its dextrorotation increases markedly as we go to shorter wavelengths, then reaches a characteristic "peak," starts to fall, becomes negative, reaches a characteristic "trough," and finally begins to rise again. The original monotonic rise in rotation is referred to as **plain ORD,** while the drop and change in sign of rotation is said to occur in the region of **anomalous ORD.** The point (λ_0) in the anomalous region of

Figure 15-38. Spectropolarimeter Used for Optical Rotatory Dispersion Studies

the curve where the line crosses the zero-rotation axis is found at a wavelength very near to the wavelength of maximum absorption (λ_{max}) of one of the bands in the absorption spectrum of the optically active compound (Section 4-7). This band is usually located in the ultraviolet region of the spectrum, and is referred to as the **"optically active" absorption band.**

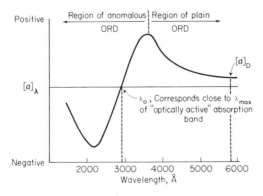

Figure 15-39. Representative Optical Rotatory Dispersion Curve

Other absorption bands whose maxima do not correspond to λ_0 are said to be "**optically inactive**." The enantiomer of the compound producing the ORD curve in Figure 15-39 would produce an ORD curve which is the exact mirror image of the curve shown.

ORD studies are becoming increasingly important as a technique for establishing the location of substituents in complex optically active molecules, for determining absolute configurations, and for obtaining information on the preferred conformations of optically active cyclic structures. Examples of these applications, however, are beyond the scope of our survey, and the reader is referred to the Supplementary Reading list below for more detailed information. The current commercial availability of spectropolarimeters makes the technique of ORD measurement an important one among the very modern physical methods of structural and stereochemical investigation.

15-15. The Origin of Optically Active Compounds

We have seen above how compounds having asymmetric molecular structures may be obtained in an optically active state by the techniques of resolution (Section 15-8) or asymmetric synthesis (Section 15-13). These and related methods, however, rely upon the use of *other optically active substances* obtained (ultimately, at least) from naturally occurring sources. It is most significant that natural products whose molecular structures are asymmetric are *almost invariably optically active in their natural state*, and almost never racemic. There thus arises the interesting question as to the origin of the first optically active compound in nature. This problem is important philosophically, as it bears on the age-old question of the development of life.

Several processes which could account for the spontaneous origin of optically active compounds have been experimentally demonstrated. The first of these is **spontaneous resolution.** Supersaturated solutions containing a racemic solute have been observed on several occasions in the laboratory to deposit one hemihedral crystal form preferentially. This occurs, presumably, by chance innoculation of the solution by a dust particle whose gross structure is such as to act as a "seed" for initiating the crystallization of the particular hemihedral crystal form obtained. Suppose such a process should occur in a large lake, and that a cataclysm such as an earthquake then caused the mother liquors to drain away. The residue on the dry lake bottom would be optically active. The second process involves the intervention of asymmetric inorganic crystals as catalysts (or catalyst supports) in promoting **asymmetric syntheses** or **asymmetric degradations.** Catalytic asymmetric synthesis (with, however, an organic asymmetric catalyst) is typified in Figure 15-36. Catalytic asymmetric degradation is illustrated by the partial thermal decomposition (by dehydration or dehydrogenation at 550°) of racemic 2-butanol, $(\pm)$-$CH_3C^*H(OH)CH_2CH_3$, over nickel catalyst deposited on optically active quartz crystals. One enantiomer decomposes more rapidly than the other under the influence of the asymmetric catalyst, and the undecomposed sample becomes optically active. Such processes, *not* involving an optically active organic reagent, are sometimes called **absolute asymmetric syntheses** or degradations. A third *absolute* process for the spontaneous origin of optical activity involves the intervention in a synthesis of degradation of an external physical force which by nature is itself asymmetric, for example, circularly polarized light (Figure 15-14). If racemic N,N-dimethyl-α-azidopropionamide $(\pm)$-$CH_3C^*HN_3$—$CON(CH_3)_2$, for example, is photochemically decomposed with right or left circularly polarized light of the wavelength 2800 to 3100 Å, one enantiomer is destroyed more rapidly than the other. If the decomposition is not allowed to run to completion, the undestroyed azido compound becomes dextro- or levorotatory, depending on whether right or left circularly polarized light is employed to promote the decomposition. If ordinary light of 2800 to 3100 Å is used, incidentally, both enantiomers are photochemically decomposed at identical rates. Absolute asymmetric syntheses photochemically accomplished with circularly polarized light have also been reported. Now, sunlight reflected from the surface of a body of water becomes somewhat circularly polarized, and it is possible that analogous absolute asymmetric syntheses or degradations might thus have afforded the first optically active compounds in nature.

Once an optically active compound is formed, as we have seen, it will react with symmetrical compounds stereoselectively, thus producing more complex optically active compounds. Furthermore, the more complex an asymmetric molecule is structurally, the greater, generally, is the stereoselectivity with which it reacts. Thus, given an environment in which a variety of chemical reactions may take place, and barring the "degenerative" event of racemization, simpler optically active organic molecules in principle can "grow" into the complex, polymeric and highly stereoselective substances involved in life processes. We shall examine a number of such substances in the following final chapter.

SUPPLEMENTARY READING

1. "Pasteur: The Chemist," H. W. Moseley, *J. Chem. Educ.*, **5**, 50 (1928).
2. "The Liebig-Pasteur Controversy," H. Finegold, *J. Chem. Educ.*, **31**, 403 (1954); G. E. Hein, *J. Chem. Educ.*, **38**, 614 (1961).

3. "Van't Hoff (1852–1911) in Retrospect," H. S. Van Klooster, *J. Chem. Educ.*, **29**, 376 (1952).
4. "My Reminiscences of van't Hoff," A. F. Holleman, *J. Chem. Educ.*, **29**, 379 (1952).
5. "A Student Polarimeter," H. Nechamkin, *J. Chem. Educ.*, **31**, 579 (1954).
6. "A Demonstration Polarimeter," C. S. Spear, *J. Chem. Educ.*, **37**, 230 (1960); H. Burkett, *J. Chem. Educ.*, **26**, 273 (1949).
7. "Inexpensive Polarimeter for Demonstrations and Student Use," J. E. Garvin, *J. Chem. Educ.*, **37**, 515 (1960).
8. "A Model for Optical Rotation," L. J. Jones and H. Eyring, *J. Chem. Educ.*, **38**, 601 (1961).
9. "A Demonstration of Optical Activity with an Eskimo Yo-Yo," E. J. Gill, *J. Chem. Educ.*, **38**, 263 (1961).
10. "The Criterion for Optical Isomerism," H. B. Thompson, *J. Chem. Educ.*, **37**, 530 (1960).
11. "Models Illustrating the Principles of Optical Activity," C. R. Noller, *J. Chem. Educ.*, **24**, 600 (1947).
12. "The Cause of Optical Activity," D. F. Mowery, Jr., *J. Chem. Educ.*, **29**, 138 (1952).
13. "Resolution by the Method of Racemic Modification," F. T. Williams, *J. Chem. Educ.*, **39**, 211 (1962).
14. "Assignment of D and L Prefixes to the Tartaric Acids," C. D. Nenitzescu, *J. Chem. Educ.*, **34**, 147 (1957); J. L. Abernathy, *J. Chem. Educ.*, **34**, 150, 566 (1957); H. B. Vickery, *J. Chem. Educ.*, **34**, 339 (1957).
15. "A Notation for the Study of Certain Stereochemical Problems," M. S. Newman, *J. Chem. Educ.*, **32**, 344 (1955).
16. "Stereoisomerism of Carbon Compounds," W. K. Noyce, *J. Chem. Educ.*, **38**, 23 (1961).
17. "Recent Advances in Stereochemistry—A Survey," D. J. Cram, *J. Chem. Educ.*, **37**, 317 (1960).
18. "The Chemistry of Molecular Shapes," H. C. Brown, *J. Chem. Educ.*, **36**, 424 (1959).
19. "Aspects of Isomerism and Mesomerism. III. Stereoisomerism," R. L. Bent, *J. Chem. Educ.*, **30**, 328 (1953).
20. "Stereochemistry of Simple Ring Systems," J. Figueras, Jr., *J. Chem. Educ.*, **28**, 134 (1951).
21. *Optical Rotatory Dispersion*, C. Djerassi, McGraw-Hill, New York, 1960.
22. "The Origin of Life," G. Wald, *Scientific American*, August, 1954.
23. *The Origin of Life*, J. Keosian, Reinhold Publishing Corp., New York, 1964.

CHAPTER 16

Natural Products

THE TERM **natural products** refers to those organic compounds which are found in nature and are associated with living organisms, either plant or animal. The number and types of organic natural products are immense, indeed, and we have encountered only a few representative examples in previous chapters in connection with our survey of various types of organic compounds.

Natural products serve a bewildering variety of functions in the organisms in which they occur. They may provide the structural substance of the organism; they may be responsible for its color; they may be toxic and serve to protect it from its enemies; they may be involved in the metabolic, reproductive, or other life processes of the organism; or they may constitute curious by-products of no known biological function. Because of their challenging variety and importance, natural products have fascinated organic chemists since the beginning of their science, and many of the important basic discoveries in organic chemistry were made in the field of natural products research. In this chapter we shall examine several of the more important classes of natural products in somewhat greater detail.

CARBOHYDRATES

CARBOHYDRATES comprise a broad category of compounds including the simple **sugars** (polyhydroxy aldehydes and ketones), as well as derivatives and polymers of these. The name is derived from the early observation that many of the simple sugars have the empirical formula $C_n(H_2O)_n$, corresponding to a "hydrate of carbon," as, for example arabinose, $C_5H_{10}O_5$, and glucose, $C_6H_{12}O_6$. Carbohydrates occur widely throughout the plant and animal kingdoms where, in various modifications, they fulfill such diverse functions as being sources of energy (foodstuffs), supporting tissues for plants and some animals, and being precursors of other biological compounds.

16-1. Classes and Properties of Carbohydrates

Simple sugars, or **saccharides,** are crystalline, colorless, odorless, water-soluble compounds having a sweet taste and showing optical activity. Sucrose (common table sugar) is a familiar example. The generic ending -ose designates a simple sugar, such as galactose and maltose. Monomeric sugars which are not hydrolyzable are called **monosaccharides.** Dimeric sugars, called **disaccharides,** are hydrolyzable into two monosaccharide products. **Trisaccharides, tetrasaccharides,** etc., made up of three, four, or more monosaccharide units are also known. Polymeric carbohydrates of high molecular weight are called **polysaccharides.** These are amorphous, water-insoluble solids, of which starch and cellulose (cotton) are familiar examples. On hydrolysis, each polysaccharide molecule affords a large number (100 to 90,000 or so) monosaccharide molecules. Monosaccharides are further classified as **trioses, tetroses, pentoses, hexoses,** etc., depending on the number of carbon atoms in the molecule, and as **aldoses** or **ketoses** depending on whether they possess an aldehyde or ketone function. The latter designations are often combined. Thus an **aldopentose** is a five-carbon monosaccharide having an aldehyde function, while a **ketohexose** is a six-carbon monosaccharide having a keto group. These relationships are summarized in Figure 16-1.

Class	Hydrolytic Behavior
Monosaccharides	$C_nH_{2n}O_n \longrightarrow$ No reaction
Aldose (aldotriose, $C_3H_6O_3$, aldo-pentose, $C_5H_{10}O_5$, etc.)	
Ketose (ketotetrose, $C_4H_8O_4$, keto-hexose, $C_6H_{12}O_6$, etc.)	
Disaccharides	$C_nH_{2n-2}O_{n-1} \longrightarrow$ 2 Monosaccharides
	Example: $C_{12}H_{22}O_{11} + H_2O \longrightarrow 2\,C_6H_{12}O_6$
Trisaccharides	$C_nH_{2n-4}O_{n-2} \longrightarrow$ 3 Monosaccharides
	Example: $C_{18}H_{32}O_{16} + 2\,H_2O \longrightarrow 3\,C_6H_{12}O_6$
Tetrasaccharides, etc. (usually called oligosaccharides)	Yield 4 (or more) monosaccharides
Polysaccharides	Polysaccharide $\longrightarrow$ Many monosaccharides
	Example: $(C_6H_{10}O_5)_n + n\,H_2O \longrightarrow n\,C_6H_{12}O_6$
	$(n = 100\text{–}90{,}000)$

Figure 16-1. Classes of Carbohydrates

16-2. Structures of Aldoses and Ketoses

Let us examine the chemical evidence on which are based the skeletal structures of glucose and fructose, two typical monosaccharides. Each sugar has the molecular formula $C_6H_{12}O_6$. Each reduces Fehling's solution (Section 12-7b) and reacts with phenylhydrazine (Section 12-7g), and therefore must contain either an aldehyde or α-hydroxy ketone grouping. Each reacts with acetic anhydride (Section 13-10b) to form a penta-O-acetate, and thus each must contain five esterifiable —OH groups. The only possible structures which accord with these facts and with Kekulé's valence rules (Section 2-1) are those shown below. Which structure be-

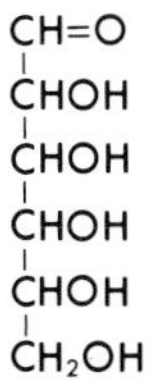

CH=O	CH₂OH	CH₂OH
CHOH	C=O	CHOH
CHOH	CHOH	C=O
CHOH	CHOH	CHOH
CHOH	CHOH	CHOH
CH₂OH	CH₂OH	CH₂OH
16-1	16-2	16-3

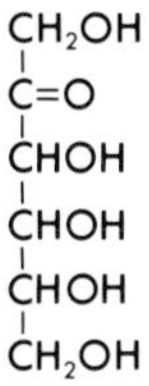

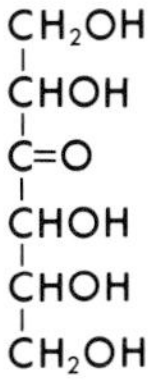

longs to glucose and which to fructose? This question was answered in
1888 by H. Kiliani, who discovered that both sugars add HCN to form a
cyanohydrin (Section 12-7j). When the cyanohydrin from glucose was
hydrolyzed and the resulting hexahydroxy acid was dehydroxylated by
reduction with red phosphorus and hydriodic acid, heptanoic acid was

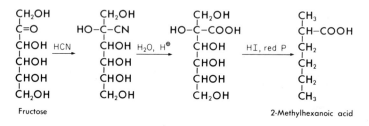

Glucose   Heptanoic acid

obtained, thus establishing the structure of glucose as 16-1. When a similar sequence of reactions was applied to fructose, 2-methylhexanoic acid
resulted, unequivocally establishing the structure of fructuose as 16-2.

$$
\begin{array}{cccc}
CH_2OH & CH_2OH & CH_2OH & CH_3 \\
C=O & HO-C-CN & HO-C-COOH & CH-COOH \\
CHOH & CHOH & CHOH & CH_2 \\
CHOH & CHOH & CHOH & CH_2 \\
CHOH & CHOH & CHOH & CH_2 \\
CH_2OH & CH_2OH & CH_2OH & CH_3
\end{array}
$$

Fructose   2-Methylhexanoic acid

(What would be the final product on applying such a sequence of reactions
to structure 16-3?) Glucose is thus an aldohexose, 2,3,4,5,6-pentahydroxy-
hexanal. It is the most common and important simple sugar, occurring
free in fruits (*grape sugar*), in honey, and in blood (*blood sugar*), and as a
polymer in starch, cellulose, and other polysaccharides. In free or combined form it is probably the most abundant naturally occurring organic
compound. Glucose is dextrorotatory (that is (+)-glucose), and is therefore frequently called **dextrose.** Other aldoses are also straight-chain
polyhydroxy aldehydes skeletally similar to glucose. Fructose, we note, is
a 2-ketohexose. It occurs free in fruits and honey, and combined with glucose in the disaccharide **sucrose** (*cane sugar*, *beet sugar*). Other ketoses are
structurally analogous to fructose, having their keto function at the second
carbon atom in their straight chain. Only two branched-chain sugars
have been found in nature. One is the branched aldopentose **apiose,**
which occurs in parsley.

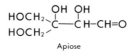

Apiose

16-3. Stereochemical Configurations of Aldoses

In an aldohexose such as glucose, we note the presence of four dissimilar asymmetric carbon atoms (Figure 16-2). Accordingly (see Table 15-2),

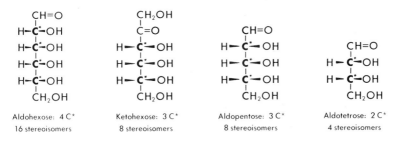

Figure 16-2. Stereoisomerism in Simple Sugars

there must exist $2^4 = 16$ separate stereoisomers of the basic aldohexose structure. In a simple ketohexose such as fructose, there are three dissimilar asymmetric centers, so that $2^3 = 8$ stereoisomers must exist. The same situation prevails with the aldopentoses. With the aldotetroses, we have already encountered the four stereoisomers involving erythrose and threose (Section 15-7b). The stereoisomers of the aldoses are conveniently systematized in the **Rosanoff Classification** (Figure 16-3), where the aldotriose, D-glyceraldehyde, is taken as the parent molecule for aldoses of the **D series.** The D-aldotetroses, D-erythrose and D-threose, are looked upon as arising by a sequence of reactions (capable, incidentally, of being carried out in the laboratory) whereby the —CH=O group at C1 of D-glyceraldehyde becomes the epimeric center at C2 in the aldotetroses. (To abbreviate the pertinent stereochemical features in Figure 16-3, the $H—\overset{*}{C}—OH$ and $HO—\overset{*}{C}—H$ configurations in such structures have been simplified to ⊢ and ⊣, respectively.) The four D-aldopentoses then arise from the two D-aldotetroses by a similar reaction sequence, and so on. Notice in Figure 16-3 that the configuration of the penultimate

H—C—OH group (next to the terminal —CH$_2$OH group) in each of the structures has the same configuration as does D-glyceraldehyde. *Those aldoses and ketoses having the configuration of their penultimate carbon atom similar to that of D-glyceraldehyde are said to belong to the D series of sugars.* Those having the opposite configuration at the penultimate carbon atom belong to the

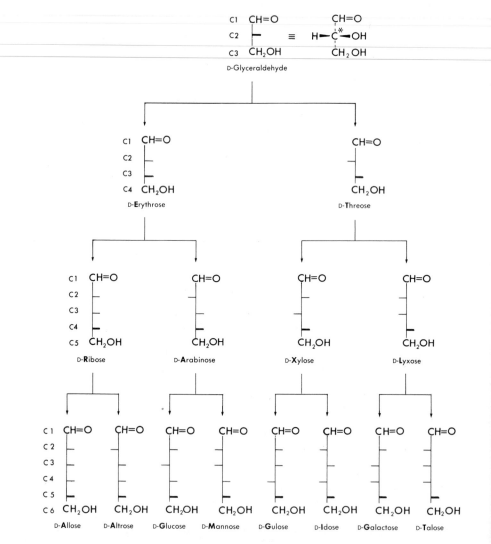

Figure 16-3.   Rosanoff Classification of the D Series of Aldoses

L series; that is, they arise in a similar Rosanoff scheme wherein L-glyceraldehyde is looked upon as the "parent" structure (Figure 16-4). Thus the

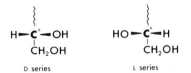

D series   L series

Figure 16-4. Series Designations for Aldoses and Ketoses

D-series classification in Figure 16-3 has a mirror image L- series, and the two series together give the total number of stereoisomers for each class of aldose. It is easy to remember the configurations of the aldoses by recalling the Rosanoff scheme and the mnemonic ET;RAXL;AAGM-GIGT.

16-4. Determination of Carbohydrate Configurations

The establishment of the relative configurations of the aldoses up through the sixteen aldohexoses is probably the greatest triumph of classical stereochemical research. The task was performed almost single-handedly by the great German chemist Emil Fischer (1852–1919) during an eighteen-year period commencing in 1884, earning for him the world's second Nobel Prize in chemistry in 1902. At the time Fischer commenced his studies only three aldohexoses were known in nature: D-glucose, D-mannose, and D-galactose. Fischer established the configurations of the eight aldopentoses and twelve of the sixteen aldohexoses, nine of which he had first to prepare synthetically. How was this titanic task performed? To answer this we must first look at three types of carbohydrate reactions which were key methods in Fischer's investigations.

a. Osazone Formation. In 1884 Fischer discovered the carbonyl reagent phenylhydrazine (Section 12-7g). In applying this reagent to the aldehyde group of aldoses, Fischer noted the curious fact that two phenylhydrazone residues entered the molecule, rather than the usual single residue. These diphenylhydrazones he named **osazones,** a term now generally applied to molecules having two phenylhydrazone residues on adjacent carbon atoms. Fischer found further that the same osazone, D-glucosazone, was obtained from D-glucose, D-mannose, and D-fructose. Since, as subsequently became apparent, the phenylhydrazone residues in osazones were located at C1 and C2 and the original asymmetry at C2 of aldoses was thereby destroyed, this observation indicated that *the stereochemical configura-*

tions at the asymmetric centers below C2 in these sugars must be identical (Figure 16-5). We thus see how osazone formation may be employed as tool for

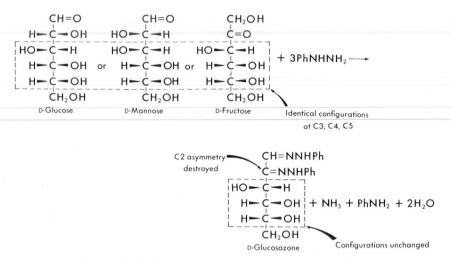

Figure 16-5. Osazone Formation as a Stereochemical Tool

comparing configurations at asymmetric centers below C2 in aldoses and ketoses. The simple C1 phenylhydrazone of D-glucose can be prepared by careful reaction with one mole of phenylhydrazine. D-Glucose phenyl-hydrazone reverts to D-glucosazone in the presence of excess phenylhydra-zine. In 1965 it was shown by NMR spectrometry that osazone structures are best represented as shown below.

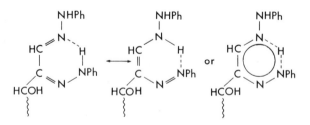

b. Oxidation of Aldoses to Dibasic Acids. When an aldose is treated with strong nitric acid, both its —CH=O group at C1 and its terminal —CH₂OH are oxidized to —COOH. By examining the optical activity or inactivity of the resulting dibasic polyhydroxy acid (class name: **gly-caric acid**), we may determine whether or not the intact asymmetric centers in the product comprise a *meso* structure, thus gaining information as to their relative configurations. This principle is illustrated in Figure 16-6, where we see that D-erythrose gives rise to optically inactive *meso*-tartaric acid, whereas D-threose affords optically active L(+)-tartaric acid.

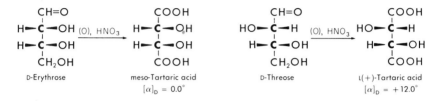

Figure 16-6. *Oxidation of Aldoses to Hydroxy Dicarboxylic Acids*

The configurations in the tartaric acid products thus tell us the configurations in their D-aldotetrose precursors.

c. Kiliani Synthesis and Oxidation. In Section 16-2 we learned how reaction of an aldose with HCN affords a cyanohydrin product one carbon higher, and how this in turn may be hydrolyzed to a polyhydroxy acid (class name: **glyconic acid**). Actually, since a new asymmetric center is generated at C2 during this reaction, a mixture of *two epimeric* cyanohydrins is formed, resulting ultimately in a mixture of two epimeric glyconic acids. Now, suppose we separate the latter and oxidize each in turn to a polyhydroxy dibasic acid, as shown in Figure 16-7. Again, examination of

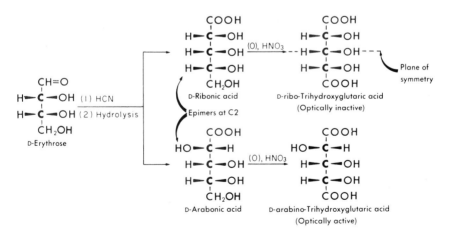

Figure 16-7. *Kiliani Synthesis and Oxidation for Stereochemical Information*

each dibasic acid for optical activity will reveal the presence or absence of *meso* structures, and thus provide information as to the configurations of the asymmetric centers in the dibasic acids and their precursors.

Let us now apply the above reactions to illustrate how Emil Fischer was able to deduce the configurations, for example, of the four D-aldopentoses: D-ribose, D-arabinose, D-xylose, and D-lyxose. Only four stereoisomers are possible in the D series, as shown in the following structures. The question is, which structure corresponds to which aldopentose?

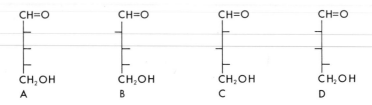

'Experimentally we find the following: (1) D-*Ribose and* D-*arabinose give the same osazone*, and must therefore be configurationally similar below C2. This means that D-ribose and D-arabinose must be either A and B or C and D. This is confirmed by the fact that D-xylose and D-lyxose also give the same osazone, which is different than that from D-ribose and D-arabinose. (2) *On oxidation with nitric acid* D-*arabinose yields an optically active dibasic acid, while* D-*ribose and* D-*xylose afford optically inactive dibasic acids.* Now, as seen in the following equations, structures B and D will give optically active dibasic acids, while A and C yield optically inactive acids. Hence arabinose must be B or D, and ribose and xylose are each either A or C.

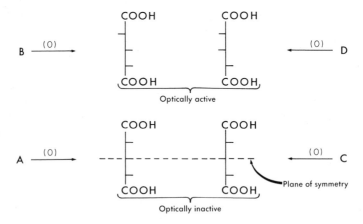

If arabinose is B, ribose is A and xylose must be C, with lyxose (by elimination) being D. Similarly, if arabinose is D, ribose must C, with xylose being A and lyxose (by elimination) being B. (3) *When the Kiliani reaction and oxidation are applied to arabinose, a mixture of two optically active tetrahydroxy dibasic acids is formed.* In the following equations we see the stereochemical consequences of this reaction sequence in terms of structures A, B, C, and D. According to these equations arabinose must be either structure B or C.

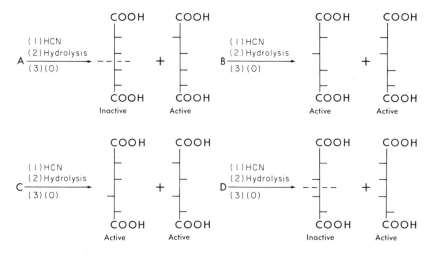

However, by (2) above we know that arabinose is either B or D. Therefore, the structure of arabinose is obviously B, to accommodate both sets of facts. From (1) its epimer, ribose, must be A. Since A is ribose, (2) above requires that xylose have structure C and (by elimination and osazone formation) lyxose have structure D.

Fischer employed similar techniques and reasoning to the configurational problem of the aldohexoses. In addition, he was able to relate these with the aldopentoses by direct interconversions. For example, by application of the Kiliani synthesis to D-arabinose, he obtained a mixture of D-glucose and D-mannose. Knowing the configuration of D-arabinose from above, he thus learned the configurations of C3, C4, and C5 (but not C2) of D-glucose and D-mannose (Figure 16-8). C2 could be established again by the reaction sequence: (*1*) HCN, (*2*) hydrolysis, (*3*) oxidation. D-glucose yielded one optically inactive and one optically active pentahydroxy dibasic acid, while mannose gave two optically active isomers (Figure 16-8). Such experiments led ultimately to the configurational establishment of all of the asymmetric centers in all of the sugars both in the D- and L series. In retrospect, Fischer's researches are even more imposing in view of the fact that he lacked such modern tools as chromatography and infrared analysis to aid in the separation and characterization of his products.

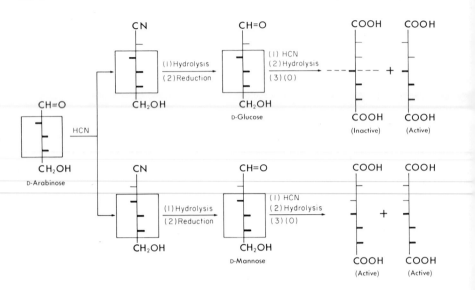

Figure 16-8. *Establishment of the Configurations of D-Glucose and D-Mannose*

16-5. Ring Structure of Sugars

Glucose and other monosaccharides do not behave strictly as simple aldehydes or ketones. For example, in 1893 Fischer attempted to prepare a methyl acetal of glucose by the usual reaction of methanol and HCl with an aldehyde (Section 12-7f):

$$-CH=O + 2\,CH_3OH \xrightarrow{\text{HCl}} -CH(OCH_3)_2 + H_2O$$

The product, however, contained only *one* $-OCH_3$ group, and not the two characteristic of ordinary methyl acetals. Fischer correctly interpreted the structure of the product as a *cyclic acetal*, now called methyl α-D-gluco-pyranoside (Figure 16-9). Notice that this structure contains a *new asymmetric center* at C1, and that accordingly two epimers should exist. The second isomer, called methyl β-D-glucopyranoside, was isolated by van Ekenstein in the following year. Cyclic sugars which are epimers at C1 are called **anomers,** and C1 is referred to as the **anomeric center** of the cyclic structure. Such cyclic structures are drawn either as **Fischer projection formulas** (Section 15-10), with their carbon atoms in a straight line, or as **Haworth projection formulas** depicting a flat six-membered ring (Figure 16-9). Notice that those asymmetric centers whose $-OH$ substituents are written to the *right* in a Fischer projection formula have their substituents written *above* the plane of the ring in the Haworth for-

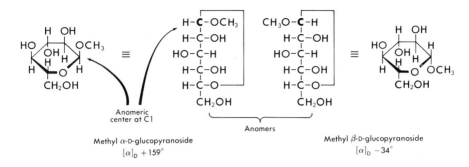

Methyl α-D-glucopyranoside
$[\alpha]_D$ +159°

Methyl β-D-glucopyranoside
$[\alpha]_D$ −34°

Figure 16-9. *Fischer and Haworth Representations of the Anomeric Methyl* *D-Glucopyranosides*

mula (when drawn with its ring oxygen to the front), and those substituents written to the *left* in the Fischer formula appear *below* the ring in the Haworth projection. We shall follow the current practice of using such formulas interchangeably, employing whichever is more convenient in a given situation. Actually, like cycloalkanes (Section 9-6), such cyclic structures are known to exist in chair and boat forms. Chair forms such as 16-4 are again the most stable.

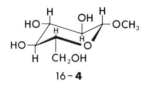

16-4

Another anomaly shown by glucose (and other aldoses and ketoses) is that its aqueous solutions show *mutarotation* (Section 15-9), a characteristic first observed in 1846. A freshly prepared solution of glucose (now called α-D-glucopyranose; see Section 16-6) shows $[\alpha]_D$ + 113°, but on standing $[\alpha]_D$ gradually decreases to 52°. Fischer attributed this mutarotation to reversible hydration of the aldehyde group, but this hypothesis was refuted in 1895 when Tanret isolated an isomeric form of glucose (now called β-D-glucopyranose), by crystallization from hot, concentrated aqueous solution. This isomer showed an initial specific rotation of $[\alpha]_D$ + 19° in water, followed by a gradual mutarotation to the same equilibrium value, $[\alpha]_D$ + 52°. These phenomena are now interpreted in terms of a **cyclic hemiacetal** structure for glucose itself, analogous to the cyclic acetal structures of the methyl D-glucopyranosides above. We now know that α-D-glucopyranose and β-D-glucopyranose, the anomeric cyclic forms, are in *mobile equilibrium* with a *small amount* of open-chain *aldehydo*-D-glucose in

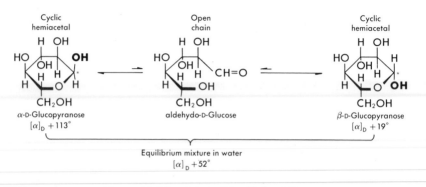

Cyclic hemiacetal   Open chain   Cyclic hemiacetal

α-D-Glucopyranose
$[\alpha]_D +113°$

aldehydo-D-Glucose

β-D-Glucopyranose
$[\alpha]_D +19°$

Equilibrium mixture in water
$[\alpha]_D +52°$

Figure 16-10. Principal Equilibria of Glucose

aqueous solution (Figure 16-10), and that the two crystalline forms of glucose are the cyclic α and β anomers. Mutarotation is caused by the change of either of the cyclic anomers into a final mixture of all of the constituents in solution. Such typical aldehyde reactions as are shown by glucose (oxidation with Fehling's solution; phenylhydrazone, osazone, and oxime formation; etc.) are due to the presence of the small amount of the *aldehydo*-form at equilibrium. As the latter is consumed in reaction with an aldehyde reagent, the equilibrium shifts, and eventually all of the cyclic components end up as aldehyde derivative products. For this reason the anomeric hemiacetal function at C1 in glucose is frequently called a **latent aldehyde group.** Other aldoses also exist as cyclic six-membered hemiacetals analogous to α- and β-D-glucopyranose, while fructose exists as two anomeric six-membered **cyclic hemiketals,** whose structures and names are shown below.

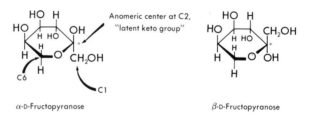

Anomeric center at C2,
"latent keto group"

α-D-Fructopyranose   β-D-Fructopyranose

16-6. Ring Size in Cyclic Sugars

The above anomeric structures for glucose and fructose have been written with six-membered heterocyclic rings. Such structures are called **pyranose** forms to emphasize their structural relationship to their six-membered heterocyclic "parent," *pyran*, and thus to designate their ring

Pyran

size. This nomenclature is carried into specific names, as in the α-D-fructopyranose, methyl β-D-glucopyranoside, and other examples above. Cyclic structures to explain the anomalous properties of glucose and fructose were actually proposed by Tollens as early as 1883, but his farsighted interpretation was discounted for over a decade. He argued that α-D-glucose, for example, had the five-membered hemiacetal structure shown below. Such

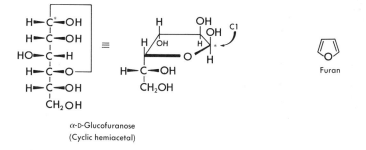

α-D-Glucofuranose
(Cyclic hemiacetal)

Furan

structures are called **furanose** forms to designate their generic relationship to *furan*, their five-membered heterocyclic "parent," and a name such as α-D-glucofuranose accordingly indicates a five-membered heterocyclic ring in the structure. Among the simple sugars and most of their derivatives, we now know that pyranose forms rather than furanose forms are far more common, although α- and β-furanose structures exist to a small extent under equilibrium conditions in aqueous solution. (They should, for example, be included in Figure 16-10 to make it fully accurate.) On what experimental evidence is the pyranose structure based?

One early line of evidence, based on methylation and oxidation experiments performed by Sir Norman Haworth of the University of Birmingham in 1926, is summarized in Figure 16-11. α-D-Glucopyranose was converted into methyl α-D-glucopyranoside, which in turn was fully methylated to give 16-5. The acetal —OCH$_3$ group in 16-5 was then hydrolyzed with dilute acid, leaving the remaining ether —OCH$_3$ groups at C2, C3, C4, and C6 unchanged. The resulting tetra-*O*-methyl-α-D-glucopyranose (16-6) was oxidized with nitric acid, ultimately affording (via 16-7) a mixture of D-dimethoxysuccinic acid and *xylo*-trimethoxyglutaric acid. As indicated by the oxidation sites (a) and (b) in 16-7, these acids could have

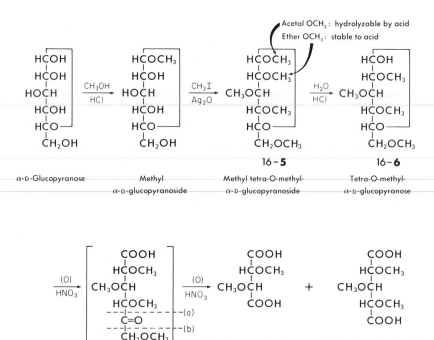

Figure 16-11.   Haworth's Proof of Pyranose Structure

arisen only from an original six-membered ring structure, and their isolation thus established this ring size in α-D-glucopyranose. Other lines of experimental evidence, particularly oxidation with periodic acid (Section 16-7), have since confirmed the pyranose structure of glucose and other simple sugars.

16-7. Configuration at the Anomeric Center

We have seen that the existence of cyclic hemiacetal and hemiketal structures in simple sugars generates a new asymmetric carbon atom at the latent carbonyl group, giving rise to anomers designated as α and β. How do we know the stereochemical configuration at the anomeric center, with respect to the configurations of the remaining asymmetric centers in the sugar molecule?   In cyclic structures such as D-glucopyranose, for example, does the α anomer have its —OH functions at C1 and C2 in a *cis* or *trans* relationship to one another? This important question has inter-

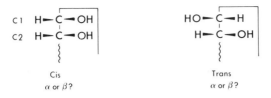

ested a number of chemists over many years, and has been approached experimentally by a variety of techniques, several of which we will examine briefly.

In 1913 J. Boeseken found that *cis-α*-glycols readily form an electrically conducting complex with boric acid in aqueous solution, whereas *trans-α*-glycols do not. When this reaction was applied to α-D-glucopyranose,

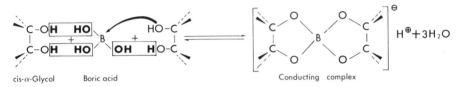

a highly conducting solution resulted, the conductivity of which gradually *decreased* to a constant value. β-D-Glucopyranose, on the other hand, gave a solution of low conductivity, which gradually *increased* to the same value. It was concluded, therefore, that α-D-glucopyranose must have *cis* hydroxyl groups at C1 and C2, that β-D-glucopyranose must have *trans* hydroxyls, and that the changes in conductivity on standing must be due to the gradual interconversion of each anomer to form an equilibrium mixture (Figure 16-10).

Emil Fischer had earlier noted the specificity of certain enzymes in promoting the hydrolysis of glycosides. Thus, the enzyme **maltase** promoted the hydrolysis of methyl α-D-glucopyranoside, but was without action on methyl β-D-glucopyranoside, while the enzyme **emulsin** showed exactly the reverse behavior, hydrolyzing the β-anomer but not the α-anomer. Maltase is thus called an α-**glycosidase** and emulsin a β-**glycosidase.** The specificities of these enzymes were noted during hydrolyses of many other α- and β-glycosides as well, and thus proved useful in determining which glycosides were α and which were β anomers. In 1903 E. F. Armstrong followed such enzymatic hydrolyses polarimetrically, and found that methyl α-D-glucopyranoside initially produced α-D-glucopyranose, while methyl β-D-glucopyranoside afforded β-D-glucopyranose. His inference, subsequently confirmed by other means, was that methyl α-D-glucopyranoside and α-D-glucopyranose were configurationally similar at C1, as were also methyl β-D-glucopyranoside and β-D-glucopyranose.

A direct means for interrelating the anomeric configurations of different methyl glycosides is by oxidation with the glycol-splitting reagent periodic acid (Section 11-8a). In Figure 16-12 are illustrated the reactions of HIO_4

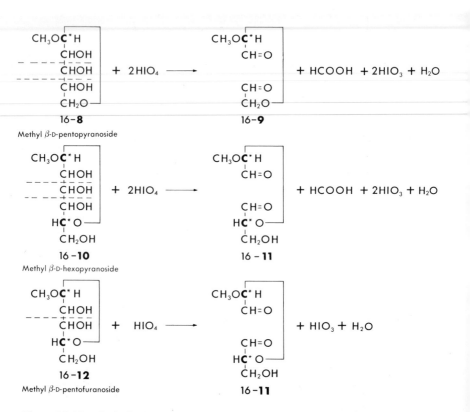

Figure 16-12.   *Periodic Acid in the Determination of Anomeric Configuration and Ring Size in Methyl Glycosides*

with a methyl β-D-pentopyranoside (16-**8**), a methyl β-D-hexopyranoside (16-**10**), and a methyl β-D-pentofuranoside (16-**12**). With 16-**8** we see that *two moles* of HIO_4 cause cleavage between the glycol carbons at C2–C3 and C3–C4, that *one mole of formic acid* is produced from C3 and that a dialde-hyde (16-**9**) is formed which *retains only the asymmetric carbon atom from the original anomeric center.* Thus all methyl pentopyranosides which produce 16-**9** must be configurationally similar at C1, and all methyl pentopyrano-sides having the opposite configuration at C1 will produce the enantiomer of 16-**9**. Methyl D-hexopyranosides such as 16-**10** behave similarly, except that the dialdehyde product (16-**11**) retains the *two* asymmetric centers originally present at C1 and C5. All those methyl D-hexopyranosides having the β configuration at C1 will produce the dialdehyde 16-**11**. Those having the α configuration at C1 yield a diastereisomer of 16-**11**, wherein the configuration of the top asymmetric center is reversed. We thus see the ease with which the anomeric configurations of different glycosides may be related. The simultaneous use of HIO_4 to determine ring size is illustrated with the methyl β-D-pentofuranoside (16-**12**). Note that here only *one mole* of HIO_4 is consumed, and *no formic acid* is produced. Thus by the amount of HIO_4 consumed (one or two moles) and by the presence or absence of one mole of formic acid among the products, we can tell directly the ring size of the glycoside. Periodic acid was first applied to carbohydrate derivatives by C. S. Hudson and E. L. Jackson in 1936. Since then it has proved to be the simplest and most general tool for the determination of ring size and anomeric configuration.

At the present time anomeric configurations of pyranose derivatives may be deduced with fair accuracy merely from optical rotations. It has been found that in the D series, anomers having α configurations are usually more dextrorotatory, while $\dot\beta$ anomers are less dextrorotatory. In the L series α anomers are more levorotatory, and β anomers less levorotatory. While not completely perfect, these generalizations prove valid for a large majority of aldopyranoses and their simple derivatives.

16-8. Reactions of Monosaccharides

Because of their many reactive functional groups, the monosaccharides undergo a wide variety of chemical reactions. Some of these occur in the ring structure and some in the open chain structure. In this section we shall examine some of the more important reactions of monosaccharides and the types of derivatives which result from them.

a. Action of Acids. Monosaccharides are stable toward cold, dilute mineral acids. In hot, concentrated acids, however, they revert to dark, amorphous, resinous "**humins**" of unknown structure. Between these two extremes lie simpler changes, the mechanisms of which are not fully understood. On heating a pentose with 12 per cent HCl, for example, *furfural* is formed, and application of this reaction to the polymeric pentose compo-

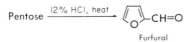

nents (**xylans**) of corn cobs and oat hulls provides our industrial source of this aldehyde. Under similar conditions, hexoses undergo a complex series of changes which ultimately produce *levulinic* and *formic acids*. By using pen-

Hexose $\xrightarrow[\text{heat}]{\text{12\% HCl,}}$ $\left[\text{HOCH}_2\text{—}\underset{\text{O}}{\langle\rangle}\text{—CH=O} \right]$ $\xrightarrow{\text{Other changes}}$ CH$_3$COCH$_2$CH$_2$COOH + HCOOH

Levulinic acid

toses and hexoses labeled at C1 with radioactive carbon, it has been shown
that the aldehyde group in furfural from pentoses and the formic acid from
hexoses arise from the latent aldehyde carbon in these sugars.

b. Action of Alkali.   In the presence of very dilute alkali (for example,
0.02 *N* NaOH), glucose is converted into a mixture of glucose, mannose,
and fructose. Mannose and fructose, under the same conditions, are converted into a similar (but not identical) mixture. This reaction is named
the **Lobry de Bruyn-van Ekenstein conversion,** after its discoverers
(1895). In 1900 A. Wohl explained the conversion on the basis of a common **enediol** intermediate, arising from the carbonyl forms of the sugars.

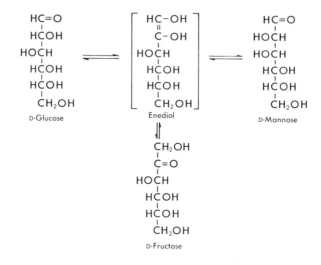

True equilibrium is not achieved, however, as other irreversible changes
also take place. The reaction has been used in the laboratory for preparing
new monosaccharides, and is often called **epimerization,** since an epimer
of the original aldose is produced. Since fructose is a sweeter sugar than
glucose, this reaction has also been used commercially to sweeten corn
syrup, which is principally glucose. In the presence of stronger base,
monosaccharides undergo a poorly understood series of more deep-seated
transformations involving skeletal rearrangements, disproportionation, and
fragmentation, and a complex mixture of products results.

c. Oxidation.   With Fehling's solution (a Cu^{2+}–tartrate complex; Section 12-7b) and Benedict's solution (a Cu^{2+}-citrate complex), monosaccharides and some disaccharides are oxidized to a complex product mixture, and the oxidant is reduced to red, solid Cu_2O. Such oxidations are widely employed in the quantitative analysis for sugars. Glucose in urine, for example, is estimated quantitatively by measuring the amount of Cu_2O formed using these oxidants under carefully standardized conditions. All sugars which are cyclic hemiacetals or hemiketals, that is, those having latent aldehyde or ketone functions, reduce these reagents, and are accordingly referred to as **reducing sugars.** While analytically useful, this oxidation has no preparative value.

Under milder conditions, with bromine water (that is, HOBr) as the oxidant, aldoses are oxidized at their $-CH=O$ function to **glyconic acids.**

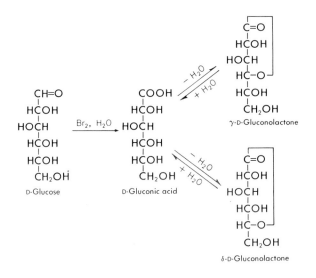

These may be isolated as metal salts or as various carboxylic acid derivatives, but in the free state they spontaneously revert to γ- or δ-lactones (Section 13-15). The γ-lactones are formed more rapidly, but the δ-lactones are more stable and are ultimately isolated. Calcium D-gluconate is used in treating calcium deficiency and in other medical applications.

The general oxidation of aldoses to dibasic acids (**glycaric acids**) with hot HNO_3 has already been discussed in connection with the determination of the configurations of aldoses (Section 16-4b). Glycaric acids form mono- and dilactones.

Other acid derivatives of aldoses are known. The generic name for acids having a terminal $-COOH$ group is **glycuronic acid,** and D-glucuronic acid is the most important member of this series. The animal organism

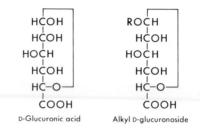

D-Glucuronic acid   Alkyl D-glucuronoside

has the ability to combine certain toxic substances with glucuronic acid and to excrete them in the urine, thus achieving detoxification. Thus a toxic alcohol in the body may combine with glucuronic acid and be excreted as an **alkyl glucuronoside.** Difficult to prepare in the laboratory, D-glucuronic acid is best obtained by feeding the terpene alcohol *borneol* to dogs. Five gram doses may be fed for weeks with no ill effects, and a 50 per cent recovery of borneol as the D-glucuronoside may be achieved by precipitation as its zinc salt from the acidified urine.

A final acid derivative in the carbohydrate series which is of great importance is **ascorbic acid,** the antiscorbutic vitamin C. It occurs naturally in a variety of citrus fruits, which have been known since 1752 to decrease the high incidence of scurvy formerly associated with long sea voyages (hence the slang term "limey" for British sailors). Only in 1917, however, was it recognized as an important dietary factor, and in 1933 its structure was established by E. L. Hirst as the enol of 3-keto-L-gulonolactone. It was synthesized independently in the same year by N. Haworth and T. Reichstein, and it is presently prepared commercially from D-glucose by a later synthesis due to Reichstein.

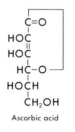

Ascorbic acid

d. Reduction. On reduction with sodium amalgam or certain other reducing agents, aldoses are converted into **alditols,** which are fully hydroxylated, straight-chain alkanes. Thus hexoses afford **hexitols** (hexahydroxyhexanes), while pentoses give **pentitols** (pentahydroxypentanes). Notice in the following example that, since C1 and C6 become structurally similar during reduction, two aldohexoses having appropriate stereochemical configurations will produce the same hexitol. Alditols occur widely

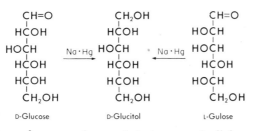

D-Glucose   D-Glucitol   L-Gulose

throughout nature; for example, erythritol occurs in lichens, D-arabitol in certain fungi, D-mannitol in the barks, leaves, and roots of many plants, and D-glucitol in the leaves of the mountain ash and in certain seaweeds.

Another class of alcohol derivative, closely related to the alditols and occurring widely in plant and animal tissues, is the **inositols,** or hexa-hydroxycyclohexanes. There are nine stereoisomeric (*cis-trans*) inositols possible, two of which are optically active and seven of which are *meso* forms. The most common isomer, called **meso-inositol,** is found widely among plants, animals, and microorganisms, in both the free and com-bined state. Note its plane of symmetry in the plane of the paper. It has been suggested that the inositols are formed from sugars in nature, and that they are the precursors of naturally occurring aromatic substances.

meso-Inositol

e. Acetylation. We have already noted (Section 16-2) that glucose re-acts with five moles of acetic anhydride to form a pentaacetate ester. This **acetylation** reaction is a general one for aldoses and ketoses, and the acetate products are generally derived from the pyranose ring form of the sugars. Acetates thus exist as anomeric pairs, typified by those of D-glu-cose below. The two acetates are configurationally similar to the corre-

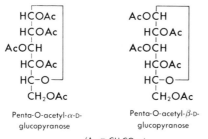

Penta-O-acetyl-α-D-   Penta-O-acetyl-β-D-
glucopyranose   glucopyranose

(Ac ≡ CH₃CO—)

sponding free sugars at their anomeric center, since α-D-glucopyranose yields the α-acetate and β-D-glucopyranose yields the β-acetate on acetylation with acetic anhydride and pyridine at 0°. Moreover, either anomeric acetate may be prepared from either anomeric form of D-glucose by varying the acetylation conditions appropriately. Acetates are important derivatives of the sugars since (1) they are usually crystalline and are thus useful in purifying and characterizing sugars, (2) they are readily converted back to the free sugars by mild alkaline hydrolysis, and (3) they are important starting materials for other synthetic transformations of the sugar molecule. Many other types of esters of the sugars are known, but the acetates are the most generally useful.

   f. Acetylated Glycosyl Halides. An extremely important type of derivative of the above acetylated sugars is the class of compounds known as **poly-O-acetylglycosyl halides.** The syntheses of two such halides from penta-O-acetyl-β-D-glucopyranose are illustrated below. Notice that the

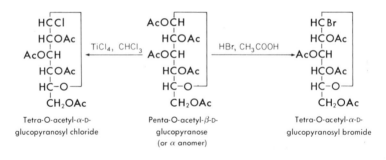

Tetra-O-acetyl-α-D-
glucopyranosyl chloride

Penta-O-acetyl-β-D-
glucopyranose
(or α anomer)

Tetra-O-acetyl-α-D-
glucopyranosyl bromide

anomeric acetoxy group at C1 of the pentaacetate is replaced by halogen, forming an acetylated glycosyl halide having the α configuration at C1. Such halides are generally reactive, crystalline compounds which are stable under very dry conditions, but which decompose rapidly when exposed even to the moisture in the ordinary atmosphere. Their reactivity arises from the lability of their halogen atoms, which are situated as **cyclic hemiacetal halides,** cyclic analogs of the reactive —CH(X)OR function. Several reactions illustrating the synthetic utility of acetylated glycosyl halides are shown schematically in Figure 16-13. Note that Walden inversion occurs in each case, affording products having the β configuration at C1.

   g. Glycoside Synthesis. **Glycosides** are cyclic sugar derivatives wherein the hemiacetal —OH group at the anomeric center of the free sugar has been replaced by —OR, where R may be an alkyl, aryl, or other group. Glycosides with six-membered heterocyclic rings are called **alkyl** (or aryl) **glycopyranosides.** Like the two methyl D-glucopyranosides in Figure

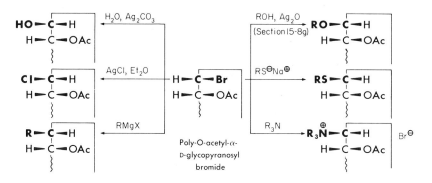

Figure 16-13.   Some Reactions of an Acetylated Glycosyl Bromide

16-9, these exist in all cases as α and β anomers, the configurations of which are analogous to those shown in Figure 16-9. Fischer's method for the synthesis of the methyl D-glucopyranosides (CH_3OH–HCl; Section 16-5) is not generally applicable to the preparation of higher glycosides owing to the insolubility of the aldoses in higher alcohols. One important synthetic use of the above acetylated glycosyl halides is in a general preparation of β-glycosides called the **Königs-Knorr synthesis,** which is illustrated below. The alcohol component in the first step of the synthesis may

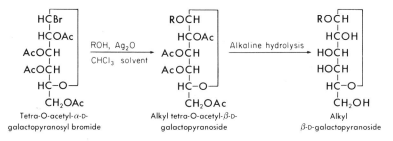

be of the aliphatic, aromatic, or heterocyclic series, and the resulting product is an acetylated β-glycopyranoside. The latter acetate may in turn be deacetylated by alkaline hydrolysis of its ester functions, yielding the free β-glycopyranoside. Note again the Walden inversion which accompanies the replacement of the C1 halogen in the first step. The final glycoside, being an acetal, is stable toward alkali and nonreducing toward Fehling's solution, but is readily hydrolyzable to the parent sugar by dilute acid. Syntheses of glycosides of the α configuration present a more formidable problem, and really general methods are not available. In the aromatic

series, however, α-glycopyranosides may be prepared by fusing acetylated
sugars with molten phenols in the presence of $ZnCl_2$ catalyst.

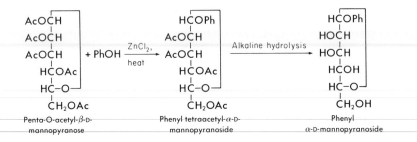

| Penta-O-acetyl-β-D-mannopyranose | Phenyl tetraacetyl-α-D-mannopyranoside | Phenyl α-D-mannopyranoside |

A wide variety of glycosides of alcohols, phenols, and their polycyclic
analogs is found in the plant kingdom. These natural glycosides may be
hydrolyzed either by dilute acid or by the enzyme *emulsin*, the latter hydrolysis indicating that they belong to the β series (Section 16-7). A few
examples of naturally occurring glycosides are shown below. The "alcohol

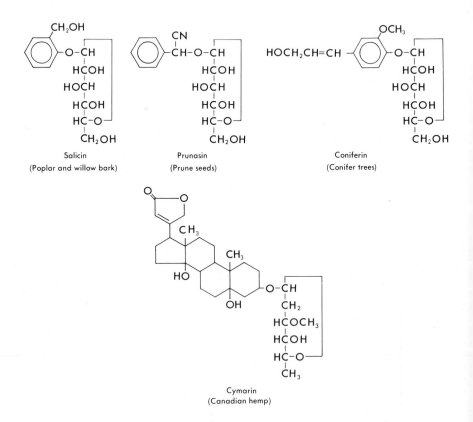

Salicin
(Poplar and willow bark)

Prunasin
(Prune seeds)

Coniferin
(Conifer trees)

Cymarin
(Canadian hemp)

portion" of such glycosides is referred to as the **aglycone.** Natural glycosides are frequently physiologically active, and plant extracts containing such compounds have been used for centuries as medical remedies, ordeal drugs, arrow poisons, and the like.

h. Methylation. We have seen previously (Figure 16-11) that the free —OH groups of methyl α-D-glucopyranoside may be completely methylated to produce the pentamethyl derivative 16-5. Such O-methylation may also be applied to the free sugars, and may be accomplished with $(CH_3)_2SO_4$–NaOH as well as with CH_3I–Ag_2O. The distinction between the *acid-labile glycosidic* —OCH_3 group and the remaining *stable ether* —OCH_3 groups in such structures should again be emphasized (Figure 16-11). Methylation has been widely used to protect permanently the —OH groups of sugars during structural investigations, but it is not a generally useful reaction, since most fully methylated sugar derivatives are syrups.

i. Degradation of the Aldose Chain. Several methods are available for the degradation of an aldose chain, that is, the conversion of an aldose into an aldose having one less carbon atom. Such degradations have been important in interrelating the configurations of hexoses, for example, with pentoses. In this context, they constitute a stereochemical technique which is in essence the reversal of the Kiliani method illustrated in Figure 16-7. One such method, the **Wohl-Zemplen degradation,** is illustrated below.

<pre>
CH=O   CH=NOH   C≡N
 | | |
HCOH   HCOH   HCOAc   CH=O
 | | | |
HOCH   H₂NOH   HOCH   (CH₃CO)₂O   AcOCH CH₃O⊖Na⊕ HOCH
 | ───► | ─────────► | ─────────► |
HCOH   HCOH   (−H₂O)   HCOAc   CH₃OH   HCOH
 | | | |
HCOH   HCOH   HCOAc   HCOH
 | | | |
CH₂OH   CH₂OH   CH₂OAc   CH₂OH

D-Glucose   D-Glucose oxime   Penta-O-acetyl-D-   D-Arabinose
                                  glucononitrile
</pre>

Notice that the last step is in effect a reversal of the cyanohydrin reaction.

j. Increasing the Aldose Chain. The chain length of aldoses may be increased by one carbon atom by several methods. The Kiliani synthesis is one historically important method which has already been discussed (Section 16-4c). A more recent and satisfactory method, the so-called **nitromethane synthesis,** is illustrated below. Note that the first step involves the

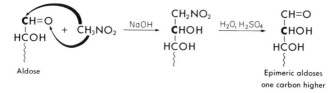

<pre>
CH=O   CH₂NO₂   CH=O
 | | |
HCOH + CH₃NO₂   CHOH   H₂O, H₂SO₄ CHOH
 | ───NaOH──► | ─────────► |
 ⌇   HCOH   HCOH
                   ⌇   ⌇
Aldose   Epimeric aldoses
                                  one carbon higher
</pre>

base-catalyzed condensation of the aldehyde function of the aldose with the activated α-hydrogen atom of nitromethane (Section 12-71) and that the last step is an adaptation of the Nef reaction (Section 14-17e). A mixture of C2 epimers, of course, is formed.

16-9. Disaccharides

Disaccharides are sugars which arise formally by intermolecular dehydration between two monosaccharide molecules:

$$C_6H_{12}O_6 + C_6H_{12}O_6 \longrightarrow C_{12}H_{22}O_{11} + H_2O$$

such syntheses have also been accomplished enzymatically in a few instances. The reverse of this reaction, hydrolysis into two monosaccharides, is a characteristic reaction of disaccharides (Section 16-1). Since such hydrolyses are brought about either by dilute acid or by those enzymes (for example, emulsin and maltase; Section 16-7) capable of cleaving α- or β-glycosides, it is clear that the two monosaccharide units of a disaccharide must be linked together through a **glycoside linkage,** rather than an ether linkage. Disaccharides occur commonly in nature, the most prevalent being *sucrose* (cane sugar, beet sugar), *lactose* (milk sugar), and *maltose* (malt sugar). Structurally, the common disaccharides fall into three classes, depending upon the points of attachment of their glycoside linkages. Members of each of these classes are illustrated below, with their points of attachment numbered in each case.

a. Disaccharides Linked through the Glycosidic Carbon Atom of each Component. *Trehalose* (found in mushrooms and fungi) and *sucrose* (found in sugar cane, beets, sorghum, maple, etc.) are typical examples of this class. Note that the reducing carbon (**glycosidic carbon**) of *each* monosaccharide is tied up in the glycosidic linkage connecting the two. These disaccharides, having no latent carbonyl group, are (like simple glycosides) nonreducing toward Fehling's solution, and are called **nonreducing disaccharides.** For the same reason, they fail to mutarotate in neutral or alkaline solution, form no osazones, and are incapable of forming simple alkyl glycosides. Such compounds are named systematically, as indicated, as **glycosyl-**

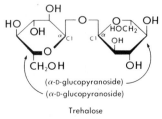

(α-D-glucopyranoside)
(α-D-glucopyranoside)

Trehalose
α-D-Glucopyranosyl-α-D-glucopyranoside

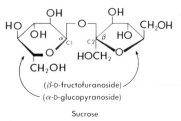

(β-D-fructofuranoside)
(α-D-glucopyranoside)

Sucrose
(α-D-Glucopyranosyl-β-D-fructofuranoside)

glycosides, the glycosyl residue corresponding to the alkyl residue in a simple glycoside.

   b. Disaccharides Linked through C1 of the First and C4 of the Second Component. *Maltose* (obtained from starch) and *lactose* (5 to 8 per cent in mammalian milk) are representative members of this class. We notice that

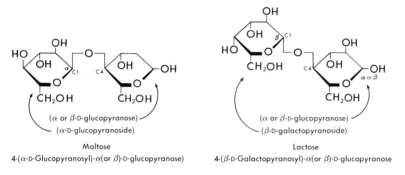

Maltose
4-(α-D-Glucopyranosyl)-α(or β)-D-glucopyranose

Lactose
4-(β-D-Galactopyranosyl)-α(or β)-D-glucopyranose

the reducing carbon at C1 of one monosaccharide, in either an α- or a β-glycoside configuration, is linked through an oxygen bridge to the non-reducing carbon at C4 in the second monosaccharide. The reducing carbon at C1 of the second monosaccharide is unsubstituted, and thus is free to act as a latent aldehyde. Accordingly, such 1,4-disaccharides exist as anomers, reduce Fehling's solution (**reducing disaccharides**), undergo mutarotation in solution, and form osazones (for example, maltosazone), anomeric glycosides (for example, methyl β-maltoside, phenyl α-lactoside), and those other carbonyl derivatives formed by monosaccharides. Another important 1,4-disaccharide is *cellobiose,* which is obtained as its octaacetate by the degradation of cellulose with acetic anhydride containing H_2SO_4. Its structure is similar to that of maltose, except that it has the β configuration at its permanent glycosidic carbon. That is, cellobiose is 4-(β-D-glucopyranosyl)-α(or β)-D-glucopyranose.

   c. Disaccharides Linked through C1 of the First and C6 of the Second Component. *Gentiobiose* and *melibiose* typify this class. We see that these 1,6-

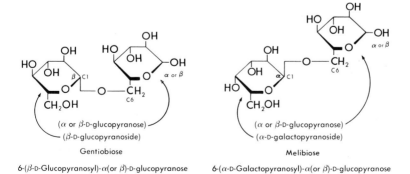

Gentiobiose
6-(β-D-Glucopyranosyl)-α(or β)-D-glucopyranose

Melibiose
6-(α-D-Galactopyranosyl)-α(or β)-D-glucopyranose

disaccharides also have a free latent aldehyde group at C1 in one of their monosaccharide units. They therefore show all of the above-mentioned characteristics of reducing disaccharides. It is noteworthy that D-glucose makes up the "alcohol portion," RO—, of the glycoside unit in all of the above disaccharides.

16-10. Structure Determination of Disaccharides and Trisaccharides

Structural elucidation of the disaccharides is complex, since a number of questions must be answered: (1) what are the two component mono-saccharide units? (2) Which of the monosaccharides is the "alcohol portion" of the glycoside link? (3) What is the stereochemistry (α or β) of the glycoside link? (4) Which oxygen atom of the "alcohol portion" monosaccharide is involved in the glycoside link? (5) What is the ring structure of each monosaccharide component?

Question (1) may be answered by hydrolysis of the disaccharide into its two component monosaccharides, followed by separation and characterization of each. Question (3) is usually answered by enzymatic hydrolysis. If the disaccharide is hydrolyzed in the presence of *emulsin*, a β-glycoside linkage is indicated, while hydrolysis with the α-glycosidase *maltase* suggests an α linkage. Questions (2), (4), and (5) have been answered, generally, by oxidation of the disaccharide, methylation of the resulting glyconic acid, and hydrolysis of the methylated glyconic acid into two partially methylated monosaccharide derivatives. The positions of unmethylated —OH groups in the latter products indicate the points of attachment between the original monosaccharide units, and provide evidence as to the original ring size in these units. Let us illustrate these principles by considering the structure determination of maltose, as shown in Figure 16-14. On acid hydrolysis, maltose yields only D-glucose, indicating that this is the only monosaccharide unit present. Enzymatically, maltose is hydrolyzed by maltase, showing an α-glycoside linkage. Maltose reduces Fehling's solution, indicating the presence of a latent aldehyde function in one of its monosaccharide units. On treatment with HOBr the latent aldehyde carbon of maltose is oxidized to —COOH, affording *maltonic acid*. Methylation of this with $(CH_3)_2SO_4$–NaOH yields the fully methylated ester derivative, methyl octa-O-methylmaltonate. When the latter is hydrolyzed, two products result: 2,3,4,6-tetra-O-methyl-D-glucopyranose from the "glycoside component," and 2,3,5,6-tetra-O-methyl-D-gluconic acid from the "alcohol component" of the original disaccharide. The free —OH groups at C1 and C4, respectively, in these products show that the original glycosidic linkage in maltose involved these carbon atoms, and that the

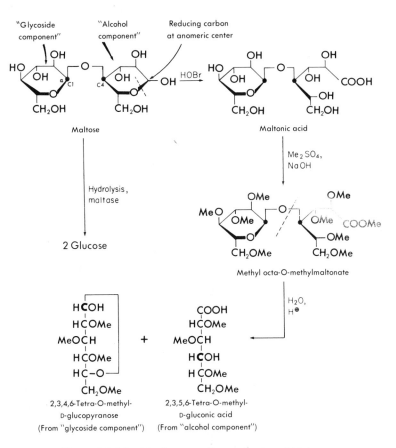

Figure 16-14. The Structure Determination of Maltose

original ring sizes in maltose were not furanose. The structures of other disaccharides have been established by similar types of experiments.

Structures of trisaccharides have been determined largely by partial and selective enzymatic hydrolysis. Let us illustrate the principles involved by examining *raffinose*, a common trisaccharide found in the seeds, leaves, branches, and roots of many plants. Raffinose is a nonreducing sugar, showing that all of its anomeric carbon atoms are tied up in glycosidic linkages. On vigorous acid hydrolysis it yields D-galactose, D-glucose, and D-fructose in equal proportions, indicating the component monosaccharide units. Enzymatic hydrolysis is more selective. Invertase, containing the enzyme β-*fructosidase*, converts raffinose into D-fructose and melibiose, while emulsin, containing the enzyme α-*galactosidase*, hydrolyzes it into sucrose and D-galactose. Knowing the structures of the "overlapping" component disaccharides and the specificities of the enzymes employed, it is possible to formulate the structure of raffinose and interpret its degradations as shown in Figure 16-15. Hydrolysis of fully methylated raffinose yields

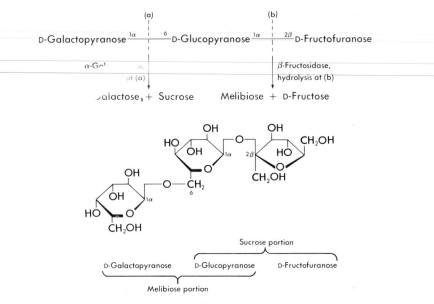

Figure 16-15. The Structure Determination of Raffinose

2,3,4,6-tetra-*O*-methyl-D-galactopyranose,   2,3,4-tri-*O*-methyl-D-glucopy-ranose, and 1,3,4,6-tetra-*O*-methyl-D-fructofuranose, thus confirming the above formulation.

16-11. Polysaccharides

The intermolecular dehydration between monosaccharide units which formally engenders disaccharides and trisaccharides may, in principle, be repeated endlessly to yield long polymers, the **polysaccharides.** In this broad class of compounds, molecular weights are found to range between about 16,000 and 14,000,000; that is, polysaccharide chains may contain from 100 to 90,000 or so monosaccharide units. Polysaccharides made up

of only one kind of monosaccharide unit are called **homopolysaccharides.**
Those derived from several different kinds of monosaccharide unit are
called **heteropolysaccharides.** In this section we shall survey briefly the
more important types of polysaccharides.

    a. Starch. During plant growth, carbohydrates are stored in reserve in
various parts of the plant as microscopic granules of **starch.** Seeds may
contain up to 70 per cent starch, and roots up to 30 per cent. Starch occurs
abundantly in such plants as corn, potatoes, rice, and wheat and constitutes one of the principal foodstuffs (source of energy) of both man and
beast.

    Starch may be separated into two components by fractional precipita-
tion: a microcrystalline substance called **amylose** and an amorphous material called **amylopectin.** Amylose gives a deep blue color with iodine
and absorbs up to 20 per cent of its weight of iodine in the process, forming
a complex in which iodine is held in the central open spaces of a spiral
helix of D-glucose units (see below) which make up the polymer chain.
Amylopectin gives a red-violet color with iodine and absorbs only 0.5 to
0.8 per cent of its weight. Starches from various sources differ widely in
their amylose/amylopectin ratio. Thus corn starch is about 28 per cent
amylose, while sorghum starch is only amylopectin. Both fractions give
only D-glucose on acid hydrolysis, indicating that each is a homopolysac-
charide with D-glucose as the monomer unit. Amylose is hydrolyzed completely to maltose by the enzyme *diastase*, and evidently therefore consists
of a linear chain of glucose molecules linked, as shown, at C4 and C1α.

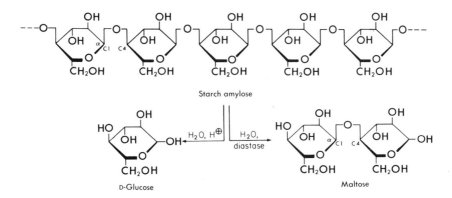

Starch amylose

D-Glucose   Maltose

This formulation is confirmed by the hydrolysis of fully methylated amylose, whereby 2,3,6-tri-*O*-methyl-D-glucopyranose is the principal product
obtained. The molecular weight of amylose varies from 17,000 to 225,000,
indicating a range of 100 to 1400 glucose units in the chain.

    Starch amylopectin consists of molecules in the molecular weight range

200,000 to 1,000,000. Hydrolysis of amylopectin with diastase stops when about half has been converted into maltose. The unhydrolyzed portion is a high molecular weight polymer called **limit dextrin.** Methylation of amylopectin, followed by acid hydrolysis of the fully methylated derivative, yields a mixture of 2,3,6-tri-, 2,3,4,6-tetra-, and 2,3-di-O-methyl-D-gluco-pyranoses, indicating that a branched polymer structure must be present.

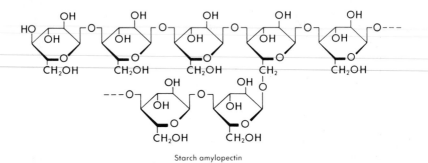

Starch amylopectin

Furthermore, the relative quantities of these three partially methylated glucoses produced in this experiment are such as to suggest that the average chain length of the branches is about 25 glucose units, and that approximately 50 branches must be present in an amylopectin molecule having a molecular weight of 200,000.

   b. Glycogen.   **Glycogen** constitutes the reserve carbohydrate of animals. It is distributed throughout the protoplasm, but it is found principally in liver and muscle tissue, where it exists both in the free state and bound with protein. The acid hydrolysis of glycogen yields only D-glucose, and enzymatic hydrolysis with diastase gives around 30 per cent maltose. Methylation and hydrolysis experiments, as above, indicate that glycogen is a branched polysaccharide quite similar in structure to amylopectin, but with more frequent branches in the polymer chain. The molecular weight of glycogen varies from 4,000,000 to 14,000,000 (25,000 to 90,000 glucose units). This polysaccharide is synthesized in the liver from glucose present in the blood stream.

   c. Cellulose.   A water-insoluble polysaccharide **cellulose** constitutes the bulk of the cell membrane material of higher plants. It makes up over 50 per cent of wood and wood-like plant fibers, and over 90 per cent of cotton fibers. Pure cellulose is obtained from cotton by leaching with organic solvents and dilute alkali, which extract small amounts of fats and other contaminants. Wood consists of cellulose molecules associated with **hemicelluloses,** polymers of related structure, and with **lignin,** a polymeric aromatic material whose structure is not completely known which acts as a matrix binding the cellulose fibers together.

Acid hydrolysis of cellulose, like starch, yields only D-glucose. Acetolysis of cellulose using acetic anhydride and H_2SO_4 affords 40 to 50 per cent of octa-*O*-acetylcellobiose, indicating that cellulose consists of chains of D-glucose units linked between C4 and C1β. Cellulose thus has a structure

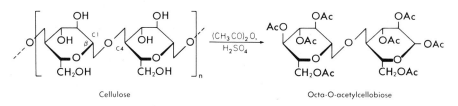

Cellulose   Octa-O-acetylcellobiose

similar to that of starch amylose, except that its glycosidic linkages are β instead of α. This formulation is confirmed by the fact that fully methylated cellulose, like methylated amylose, yields 90 to 95 per cent 2,3,6-tri-*O*-methyl-D-glucopyranose on acid hydrolysis.

d. Modified Cellulose. Cellulose may be modified in a number of ways to meet particular commercial requirements. When cotton fibers under tension are treated with sodium hydroxide solution, the strength of the fibers is increased and their surface irregularities are smoothed. The resulting **mercerized cotton** has a sheen similar to silk, resists shrinkage, and is widely used as a clothing fabric. **Rayon** is a term applied to "synthetic" fibers derived from cellulose. **Viscose rayon** consists of cellulose fibers which have been dissolved as *cellulose xanthate* in a solution of sodium hydroxide and carbon disulfide, then regenerated by treatment with dilute acid (**viscose process**). The cellulose xanthate solution is extruded into

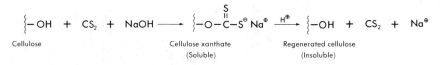

Cellulose   Cellulose xanthate   Regenerated cellulose
                                (Soluble)   (Insoluble)

the acid bath through a baffle of tiny holes, producing fibers of viscose rayon (regenerated cellulose). If the extrusion is performed through a baffle containing a thin slit, sheets of regenerated cellulose are formed. These are treated with lacquers to render them waterproof, then marketed as **cellophane.** Other shapes of extrusion baffles produce regenerated cellulose in the form of sausage casings, artificial straw, and other shapes. During 1960 some 1,179,000,000 pounds of regenerated cellulose were produced in the United States, 63 per cent for rayon and 37 per cent for cellophane. Other commercial processes are known for solubilizing cellulose, then regenerating its fibers from solution, but the viscose process accounts for the bulk of regenerated cellulose produced throughout the world.

e. Cellulose Derivatives. Commercially, the two most important derivatives of cellulose are its acetate and nitrate. When cellulose, pretreated with acetic and sulfuric acids, is treated with acetic anhydride, *cellulose triacetate* is formed. Partial hydrolysis of this yields *cellulose diacetate*, having

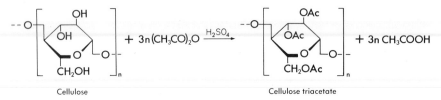

an average of one free —OH group per glucose unit. Both the diacetate and the triacetate are widely employed in fabricating such items as cloth fibers (**acetate rayon**) and photographic film. The acetates are dissolved in appropriate solvents and their concentrated solutions are forced through dies of the desired shape into warm air chambers, where the solvents evaporate to produce threads or sheets of cellulose acetate. The United States production of cellulose acetate in 1961 was about 536,000,000 pounds, of which some 399,000,000 pounds was used in making acetate rayon fibers.

The **cellulose nitrates,** known since the last century, were the first cellulose esters of commercial importance. When cotton is treated with a mixture of nitric and sulfuric acids, its free —OH groups are converted into nitrate esters. If the reaction is pushed to completion, essentially three —NO₂ groups per glucose unit enter the molecule, and *cellulose trinitrate* (guncotton) results. Fabricated into perforated pellets, guncotton

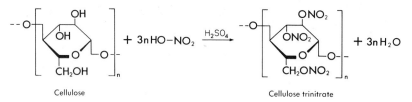

is used as a propellent explosive. When plasticized with nitroglycerin (Section 11-7c), guncotton gives *cordite*, a military explosive. If the above esterification is conducted under less stringent conditions, approximately two —NO₂ groups per glucose unit enter the cellulose chain, resulting in *pyroxylin*. Mixtures of pyroxylin, camphor, and alcohol—kneaded into a dough, compressed in a mold, and allowed to dry—produce *celluloid*. Celluloid, which was originally developed in 1869 as a substitute for ivory in billiard balls, was the principal molding plastic until the 1930's, and was also the basis for early motion picture film and for "artificial leather" (pigmented pyroxylin applied and embossed on a cloth base). Because of their extreme flammability, however, cellulose nitrates have been superseded by the relatively nonflammable cellulose acetates for film, fiber, and fabrication uses. The major use of cellulose nitrates at the present time is as a base for quick-drying lacquers.

Cellulose ethers containing an average of 1 to 2.5 —OCH_3 (**methylcellulose**), —OC_2H_5 (**ethylcellulose**), or —OCH_2COOH (**carboxymethylcellulose**) groups per glucose unit are becoming increasingly important as thickening agents in pastes, cosmetics, sizes, and foodstuffs.

In derivatives such as those described above, the cellulose chain is *degraded* to a certain extent; that is, the average chain lengths are shorter than those found in native cellulose.

f. Other Polysaccharides. Many other varieties of homo- and heteropolysaccharides are found among plants and animals. The main constituents of several important examples of these are illustrated in the structures below. **Mannan** occurs in the vegetable ivory nut and in the cell walls of

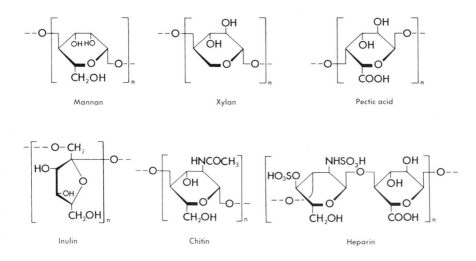

Mannan   Xylan   Pectic acid

Inulin   Chitin   Heparin

many other plants. It hydrolyzes to D-mannose and has a molecular weight of about 13,000. Note its structural similarity to cellulose. **Xylan** is a "hemicellulose" associated with cellulose in wood, corn cobs, straw, etc. It hydrolyzes to D-xylose and has a molecular weight around 30,000. It finds use in the commercial production of furfural (Section 16-8a). **Inulin** is a **fructosan** occurring in Jerusalem artichokes, dandelions, dahlias, and other plants. Its molecular weight is about 5200, and its hydrolysis affords primarily D-fructose. **Pectic acid** occurs in combinations (called **pectins**) with other constituents in the fruits, berries, rinds, and tubers of many plants. Its hydrolysis produces D-galacturonic acid. Pectins are responsible for the gelling of fruit juices in the making of jellies. **Chitin** is found in the shells of crabs and other crustaceans and in the structural substance of insects. It hydrolyzes to 2-amino-2-deoxy-D-glucose and has a molecular weight comparable to that of cellulose. (*Note:* Deoxy sugars lack one or more OH groups as compared to normal sugars. The position of the missing OH group—that is, extra H atom—is indicated by numbering from C1, as in 2-deoxy-D-glucopyranose.) **Heparin** is the blood anti-

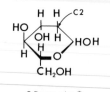

2-Deoxy-α(or β)-
D-glucopyranose

coagulant present in circulatory tissue. It is a sulfated polysaccharide composed of D-glucuronic acid and 2-amino-2-deoxy-D-glucose units containing both —$NHSO_3H$ and —OSO_3H groups. It find use clinically in the prevention of postoperative thrombosis.

16-12. Photosynthesis

Glucose and other sugars were actually prepared synthetically by E. Fischer during the latter part of the 19th century. Oxidation of glycerol, for example, followed by condensation of the three-carbon oxidation products, produced D,L-fructose. Subsequent tedious transformations and fractionations finally afforded D-glucose in very low yield.

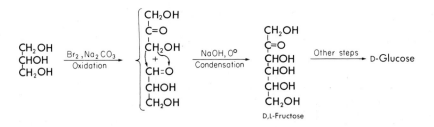

In nature, carbohydrates arise by a more complex and efficient process called **photosynthesis.** Photosynthesis involves the *fixation* of carbon dioxide and water by green plants exposed to sunlight, and results in the formation of carbohydrates and oxygen.

$$n\,CO_2 + n\,H_2O \xrightarrow[\text{green plants}]{\text{Sunlight}} C_nH_{2n}O_n + n\,O_2$$

Since simple carbohydrate derivatives are the natural precursors of poly-saccharides, proteins, and fats, the importance of photosynthesis in pro-viding the building blocks for living matter is apparent. The energy re-quired for photosynthesis is supplied by the sun, and such photosyntheti-cally "trapped" energy becomes manifest when we burn wood, coal, and petroleum, or when we digest foodstuffs. Photosynthesis occurs only in plants and in certain bacteria which contain specific pigments capable of absorbing sunlight. The most common pigment involved in the process is the green pigment **chlorophyll,** which occurs widely among plants and algae. Some fifty years ago R. Willstätter, one of the early pioneers in photosynthesis research and the recipient of the 1915 Nobel Prize in chemistry, demonstrated that chlorophyll contained two pigments, chloro-phyll-a and chlorophyll-b. These differ only with respect to methyl and formyl group at the position indicated in the structure shown below. The

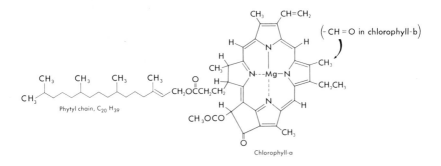

Chlorophyll-a

chlorophylls are *dihydroporphyrins* related in structure to **hemin,** the red pigment in blood cells. Certain purple bacteria having related pigments are also capable of accomplishing photosynthesis, and require light for their growth. The maximum rate of photosynthesis is observed under irradiation with light whose wavelength corresponds to the absorption frequencies of such pigments.

The mechanism of photosynthesis, which has been under investigation for a number of decades, has proved exceptionally complex and elusive, and is only now understood in most of its aspects. While a detailed ac-count of the mechanism is beyond our scope, a few general conclusions might profitably be summarized. The role of light in photosynthesis is to raise certain electrons in the chlorophyll molecule to higher energy levels. The "activated" chlorophyll then transfers this energy to other complex pigment systems in the plant cell. These "activated" pigments in turn pro-vide the energy to split H_2O into $2H^\oplus$ and $\frac{1}{2}O_2$, and to produce **adenosine triphosphate (ATP)** and **reduced triphosphopyridine nucleotide**

(TPNH), represented below in their un-ionized forms. These processes

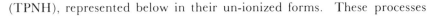

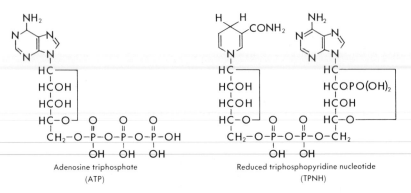

Adenosine triphosphate
(ATP)

Reduced triphosphopyridine nucleotide
(TPNH)

constitute the so-called **light reactions** of photosynthesis, those directly
due to the action of light. ATP is an *energy transfer agent* and TPNH a *reducing agent* in biological systems, and their formation permits the subsequent
occurrence of the so-called **dark reactions** of photosynthesis, those initiated by these particular agents. The overall result of these reactions
is the reversal of normal carbohydrate metabolism (which is: carbohydrate + O_2 → CO_2 + H_2O + energy), and the *fixation* of CO_2 as carbohydrate. A variety of cells devoid of chlorophyll are capable of fixing
CO_2 as carbohydrate provided energy is available in the form of ATP and
TPNH. The function of chlorophyll in the plant is thus to permit the conversion of light energy into chemical energy stored in these transfer agents.
This stored energy is then utilized to "drive" a series of enzyme-catalyzed
"dark reactions" which achieve the conversion of CO_2 to carbohydrates
and amino acids. The details of CO_2 fixation have been elaborated with
the aid of radioactive carbon tracers by Professor M. Calvin at the University of California (Berkeley), who received the Nobel Prize in 1961
for his findings. The initial CO_2 acceptor is a five-carbon sugar derivative, **ribulose diphosphate.** In the presence of the enzyme *carboxydismutase*, this adds CO_2 and H (from H_2O), and cleaves into **3-phosphoglyceric acid.** The latter derivative, containing the incorporated

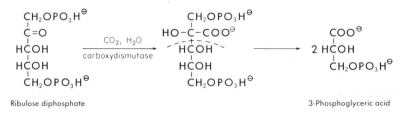

Ribulose diphosphate

3-Phosphoglyceric acid

CO_2, then undergoes a series of over a dozen enzyme-catalyzed condensation and disproportionation reactions, "driven" by the energy carriers ATP and TPNH. These "dark reactions" ultimately result in the formation of carbohydrate and amino acid end products and in the regeneration of ribulose diphosphate, which is again ready to "accept" more CO_2. A highly simplified schematic diagram of the overall process of photosynthesis is shown in Figure 16-16.

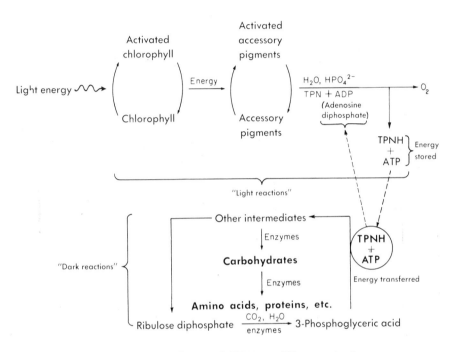

Figure 16-16.   Schematic Diagram of Photosynthesis

AMINO ACIDS

THE AMINO ACIDS constitute a class of compounds which contain both amino and carboxylic acid groups. The simplest amino acids contain one of each function. Proteins, carbohydrates, and fats make up the three major types of food used by man, and every living cell requires a constant supply of amino acids for the synthesis of tissue protein and for other physiological processes. During digestion, food proteins are hydrolyzed in the gastrointestinal tract by so-called **proteolytic enzymes,** affording a mixture of amino acids. In general, animal proteins are more rapidly and completely hydrolyzed than are plant proteins. The resulting amino acids are absorbed through the intestine and are subsequently transformed into tissue protein. Their carbon skeletons also enter into the pathways of carbohydrate and fat metabolism, and they are also involved in a number of other metabolic processes (catabolic reactions) from which their nitrogen atoms finally emerge as urea, the form in which nitrogen is excreted in urine.

16-13. Nomenclature of Amino Acids

Amino acids may be named analogously to the hydroxy acids (Section 13-15), with the amino group designated as α, β, γ, δ, etc., to indicate its position on the chain of the carboxylic acid, which is called by its common name. In the IUPAC system, these compounds are named as amino derivatives of the corresponding acid, with the position of the amino group defined by an appropriate number. However, the most important amino acids are those derived from proteins, and these are most frequently identified by nonsystematic, common names (Table 16-1).

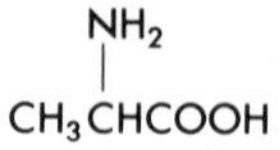

$$\overset{\displaystyle NH_2}{\underset{\displaystyle |}{CH_3CHCOOH}}$$

α-Aminopropionic acid
2-Aminopropanoic acid
Alanine

Table 16-1. Proteinogenous Amino Acids

Name	Abbreviation	Structure	Isoelectric Point
Glycine	Gly	H_2NCH_2COOH	6.0
Alanine	Ala	$CH_3CH(NH_2)COOH$	6.0
Valine[a]	Val	$(CH_3)_2CHCH(NH_2)COOH$	6.0
Leucine[a]	Leu	$(CH_3)_2CHCH_2CH(NH_2)COOH$	
Isoleucine[a]	Ileu	$CH_3CH_2CH(CH_3)CH(NH_2)COOH$	6.0
Proline	Pro	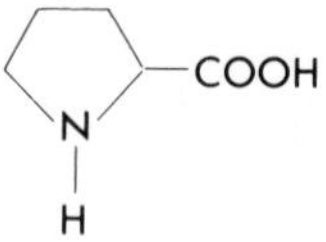	6.3
Hydroxyproline[b]	Hypro	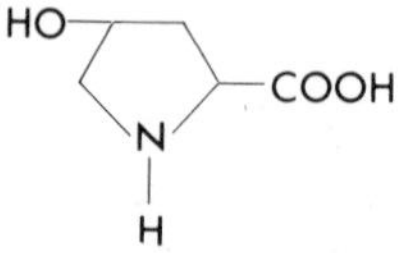	5.7
Phenylalanine[a]	Phe	$PhCH_2CH(NH_2)COOH$	5.5

Table 16-1 (continued)

Name	Abbreviation	Structure	Isoelectric Point
Tyrosine	Tyr	HO—⟨C₆H₄⟩—$CH_2CH(NH_2)COOH$	5.7
Thyroxine[c]	Thy	HO—⟨ring(I,I)⟩—O—⟨ring(I,I)⟩—$CH_2CH(NH_2)COOH$	
Serine	Ser	$HOCH_2CH(NH_2)COOH$	5.7
Threonine[a]	Thr	$CH_3CH(OH)CH(NH_2)COOH$	5.6
Cysteine	CySH	$HSCH_2CH(NH_2)COOH$	5.1
Cystine	CySSCy	$(—SCH_2CH(NH_2)COOH)_2$	5.0
Methionine[a]	Met	$CH_3SCH_2CH_2CH(NH_2)COOH$	5.7
Tryptophan[a]	Try	⟨indole⟩—$CH_2CH(NH_2)COOH$	5.9
Asparagine	Asp–NH₂	$H_2NCOCH_2CH(NH_2)COOH$	5.4
Glutamine	Glu–NH₂	$H_2NCOCH_2CH_2CH(NH_2)COOH$	5.7
Lysine[a]	Lys	$H_2NCH_2CH_2CH_2CH_2CH(NH_2)COOH$	9.6
δ-Hydroxylysine	Lys–OH	$H_2NCH_2CH(OH)CH_2CH_2CH(NH_2)COOH$	9.15
Arginine	Arg	$H_2NC(=NH)NHCH_2CH_2CH_2CH(NH_2)COOH$	11.2
Histidine[d]	His	⟨imidazole⟩—$CH_2CH(NH_2)COOH$	7.5
Aspartic acid	Asp	$HOOCCH_2CH(NH_2)COOH$	2.8
Glutamic acid	Glu	$HOOCCH_2CH_2CH(NH_2)COOH$	3.2

[a] Indispensable for adult man and for all animal species tested.
[b] Constituent of collagen protein only.
[c] Constituent of thyroglobulin protein only.
[d] Required by infants and by all subhuman species tested, but not by adult man.

Notice in Table 16-1 that each amino acid has an amino substituent on the α-carbon atom. We note further that, with the exception of glycine, all of the amino acids listed may exist as enantiomeric D and L forms because of the asymmetry of the α-carbon atom. Now, it is found that all of the proteinogenous amino acids (those derived from proteins) are configurationally related to L(-)-glyceraldehyde, and are accordingly assigned to the L-series (Section 15-10).

Certain amino acids may be synthesized in the body, but others must be furnished in the diet. Those in the first category are called **dispensable** or **nonessential amino acids.** Those in the second category (Table 16-1) are **indispensable** or **essential amino acids.** The latter are those which cannot be synthesized in the body at a rate necessary for normal growth from materials ordinarily available in foodstuffs. It is interesting that the body can utilize completely only the natural L-isomers of the indispensable amino acids.

16-14. Essential Amino Acids

There is no absolute requirement in the body for amino acid, since the need for one essential acid may be influenced by the quantity of others present, as well as by other dietary nutrients. Older men reportedly need twice as much lysine and methionine as younger men, and infants require histidine. The total minimum daily requirement of protein to furnish essential amino acids for maintaining nitrogen balance and other bodily functions is estimated as about 27 grams for young men. The average half-life of amino acids in the body protein of man is 80 days.

Certain genetically controlled metabolic diseases in man are due to specific blocks in amino acid metabolism. One of these is *phenylketonuria*, in which the body is unable to oxidize phenylalanine to tyrosine. Excess phenylalanine and its metabolic product, phenylpyruvic acid, $PhCH_2$—COCOOH, therefore build up to high levels in the blood and urine. The disease is accompanied by feeblemindedness, and 90 per cent of phenylketuronics have IQ's below 50. There has been some success in preventing the onset of mental retardation by employing in the diet protein hydrolyzates low in phenylalanine, to minimize the intake of this particular amino acid.

Glutamic acid, now prepared industrially from beet sugar residues by a microbiological fermentation process, is used in the form of its sodium salt as a condiment and food flavor enhancer.

Although L-amino acids, exclusively, are found in proteins, naturally occurring D-amino acids have been found in a few sources. D-Phenylalanine, for example, occurs in the polypeptide antibiotic gramicidin-S, which was discovered by Russian scientists (hence S for Soviet).

16-15. Zwitterion Structure of Amino Acids

The amino acids generally are crystalline solids of low volatility and high melting point. They are insoluble in nonpolar solvents, but usually soluble in the polar solvent water. They are characteristically amphoteric; that is, they form salts with both mineral acids (at their $-NH_2$ function) and with bases (at their $-COOH$ function). During electrolysis of an acidic solution of an amino acid, it is found that the amino acid migrates as a protonated derivative to the cathode. In alkaline media, electrolysis causes migration of the amino acid to the anode as its anion derivative. These obervations are rationalized in terms of the existance of amino acids as **inner salts,** which are referred to as **dipolar** or **zwitterion** structures. We

$$
\begin{array}{ccccc}
\overset{\oplus}{NH_3}\,Cl^{\ominus} & & \overset{\oplus}{NH_3} & & NH_2 \\
| & \underset{NaOH}{\overset{HCl}{\rightleftharpoons}} & | & \underset{HCl}{\overset{NaOH}{\rightleftharpoons}} & | \\
RCHCOOH & & RCHCOO^{\ominus} & & RCHCOO^{\ominus}\,Na^{\oplus} \\
\text{Cation} & & \text{Zwitterion} & & \text{Anion} \\
\text{(Migrates to cathode)} & & & & \text{(Migrates to anode)}
\end{array}
$$

should note that titration of an amino acid with base actually involves neutralization of the $-NH_3^{\oplus}$ group and not the $-COOH$ group (see 16-13). Conversely, titration of an amino acid with acid involves the $-COO^{\ominus}$ group of the amino acid, and not its amino group, which is tied up as $-NH_3^{\oplus}$ in the zwitterion structure (see 16-**14**). In support of this, it has been shown by electrometric titration of alanine with hydrochloric acid that the ionization constant is typical of $RCOOH$, not of RNH_2.

$$
\begin{array}{ccc}
\overset{\oplus}{NH_3} & & NH_2 \\
| & & | \\
RCHCOO^{\ominus} + OH^{\ominus} & \longrightarrow & RCHCOO^{\ominus} + H_2O
\end{array}
$$
$$
\text{16-13}
$$

$$
\begin{array}{ccc}
\overset{\oplus}{NH_3} & & \overset{\oplus}{NH_3} \\
| & & | \\
RCHCOO^{\ominus} + H^{\oplus} & \longrightarrow & RCHCOOH
\end{array}
$$
$$
\text{16-14}
$$

16-16. The Isoelectric Point

Since the addition of a proton to an amino acid converts it into a cationic species (16-**14**), and the addition of base transforms it into an anionic species (16-**13**), it is evident that there must be one point on the pH scale where the acidic and basic properties of the amphoteric amino acid will be equally balanced. This pH value is called the **isoelectric point.** Since the ionic charges on the amino acid exactly balance each other at the isoelectric point, there being no net positive or negative charge, the amino acid at this pH will not migrate under the influence of an electric current. The solubility of an amino acid also proves to be at a minimum at this point. From earlier discussions regarding the influence of constitution on acidity (Section 13-2) and basicity (Section 14-4), it is not surprising to find that the isoelectric point may vary from one amino acid to another, as is evident in Table 16-1.

The first eighteen amino acids in Table 16-1, ranging from glycine through glutamine, each contain a single amino group and a single carboxyl group. Such amino acids are classed as **neutral amino acids.** The next four amino acids, lysine through histidine, contain an extra basic function and are classed as **basic amino acids.** The last two, aspartic and glutamic acids, have two carboxyl groups but only one amino group, and are called **acidic amino acids.** The general classification of amino acids as neutral, acidic, and basic is seen in Table 16-1 to follow the trend in their isoelectric points.

16-17. Synthesis of Amino Acids

The α-amino acids may be synthesized by several methods. The **Hofmann reaction** (Section 14-6a) utilizes the action of ammonia on an α-halo acid.

$$\overset{\overset{\displaystyle X}{|}}{R}CHCOOH + 2\,NH_3 \longrightarrow \overset{\overset{\displaystyle NH_2}{|}}{R}CHCOOH + NH_4^{\oplus}X^{\ominus}$$

In the **Strecker synthesis,** an aldehyde or ketone is treated with ammonium chloride and sodium cyanide. This forms ammonium cyanide, which

$$NH_4Cl + NaCN \rightleftharpoons NH_4CN + NaCl$$

$$NH_4CN \rightleftharpoons NH_3 + HCN$$

$$RCH{=}O + HCN \longrightarrow \left[\overset{\overset{\displaystyle OH}{|}}{R}CHCN\right] \xrightarrow{NH_3} \overset{\overset{\displaystyle NH_2}{|}}{R}CHCN \xrightarrow{H_2O,\,H^{\oplus}} \overset{\overset{\displaystyle NH_2}{|}}{R}CHCOOH$$

$$16\text{-}15$$

in turn dissociates into ammonia and hydrogen cyanide. The latter adds to the carbonyl group (see Section 12-7j), the resulting cyanohydrin reacts with ammonia, and the amino nitrile (16-**15**) formed is subsequently hydrolyzed to yield an α-amino acid. A third important method involves the **alkylation** of an acetamidomalonic ester. Ethyl malonate is allowed to react with nitrous acid, and the resulting tautomeric C-nitroso derivative (16-**16**) is reduced and acetylated to give ethyl acetamidomalonate (16-**17**). The latter may be alkylated like ethyl malonate itself (Section 13-18), and the resulting C-alkyl ester (16-**18**) is subsequently hydrolyzed and decarboxylated to form the desired α-amino acid.

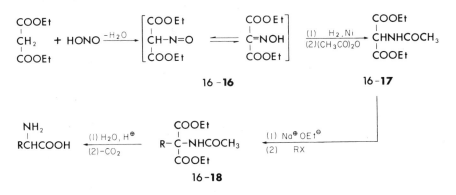

$$16-\textbf{16} \qquad\qquad 16-\textbf{17}$$

$$16-\textbf{18}$$

β, γ, δ, and other types of amino acids may also be synthesized by action of ammonia on the appropriate halo acid. The yields of β-amino acids by this procedure may be low because of the tendency for elimination to occur, resulting in an α,β-unsaturated acid. An alternative procedure for the synthesis of β-amino acids is through the Michael reaction (Section 12-8):

$$RCH = CHCOOH + NH_3 \longrightarrow R\overset{\overset{\displaystyle NH_2}{|}}{C}HCH_2COOH$$

The amino acids resulting from the above synthetic procedures are, of course, racemic. The resolution of such products into their optical isomers may be accomplished by fractional crystallization of diastereomeric salts of their N-acyl derivatives (Section 15-8) or by selective decomposition of one of the members of the racemic pair (Section 15-8). For example, if D,L-alanine is acetylated and the racemic N-acetyl derivative is subjected

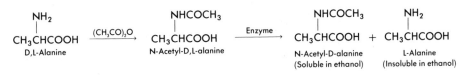

to the action of an enzyme present in hog kidney, the L-acetyl derivative
is preferentially hydrolyzed, and the resulting mixture may be readily separated.

Cautious hydrolysis of appropriate proteins may also provide a source
of particular optically active amino acids, although this procedure cannot
properly be classified as a synthetic method. L-Cystine, for example, can
be obtained by the hydrolysis of human hair with dilute hydrochloric acid.

16-18. Reactions of Amino Acids

The reactions of amino acids are generally those of both the amino
group (Section 14-10) and the carboxyl group (Section 13-4), although
complications may arise from participation of both groups. As an illustration, during the acetylation of the amino group, an **azlactone** may result if excess acetic anhydride is employed or an extended reaction time is
used.

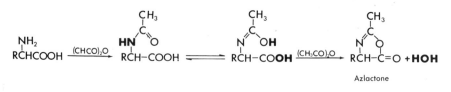

The different classes of amino acids differ in their behavior upon heating
in a manner analogous to that of the hydroxy acids (Section 13-15). The
following behavior of α-, β-, γ-, and δ-amino acids is typical.

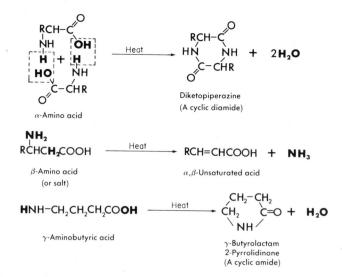

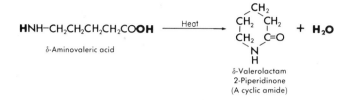

δ-Aminovaleric acid

δ-Valerolactam
2-Piperidinone
(A cyclic amide)

The *N*-vinyl derivative of pyrrolidinone may be polymerized (Section 8-4*l*) to poly-*N*-vinylpyrrolidinone, which is used as a film-forming compound in hair spray.

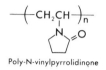

Poly-N-vinylpyrrolidinone

PROTEINS AND PEPTIDES

THE IMPORTANCE of amino acids as a source of proteins for living cells has been previously mentioned. Representatives of this tremendously important class of natural products are synthesized by all forms of life, and are of the utmost significance in biological processes. The seeds of plants contain appreciable quantities of protein, and all mammals are constituted largely of protein (for example, skin, hair, nails, hemoglobin). Antibodies and enzymes and some hormones are proteins, and viruses are in part protein. It is remarkable that no two individuals have identical tissue proteins, except for identical twins. This high degree of specificity results in an important protective mechanism of the body, allowing it to combat invasion by foreign toxic proteins and viruses. On the other hand, allergies and the inability to receive organ transplants also derive from the specificity of tissue protein.

Proteins are high molecular weight polymeric substances derived from amino acid units united by **peptide bonds** (amide bonds). A **peptide** is defined as a substance derived from two or more amino acids united through peptide bonds. A **dipeptide** is derived from two amino acids,

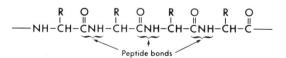

Peptide bonds

Part of a protein or polypeptide chain

$$\begin{array}{ccc} NH_2 & O & R \\ | & \| & | \\ RCH-CNH-CHCOOH \end{array}$$

A dipeptide

$$\begin{array}{ccccc} NH_2 & O & R & O & R \\ | & \| & | & \| & | \\ RCH-CNH-CH-CNH-CHCOOH \end{array}$$

A tripeptide

a **tripeptide** from three, and so on. The term **polypeptide** is used to describe a peptide made up from a large number of amino acid units, and proteins are thus sometimes referred to as polypeptides. However, it is occasionally desirable to make an arbitrary distinction between polypeptides and proteins, and proteins are usually considered to be polypeptides having a molecular weight of 6000 or greater.

16-19. Classification of Proteins

Proteins from various sources are classed as simple or conjugated. **Simple proteins** are derived only from α-amino acids. Examples include ovalbumin of egg white, globulin of egg yolk, keratin of hair, collagen of skin, and elastin of tendons. **Conjugated proteins,** in contrast, contain simple protein molecules united with a nonprotein group. The nonprotein moiety is called a **prosthetic group** (Greek: *prosthetos*, put on). Conjugated proteins are subclassified according to the nature of their prosthetic groups. Thus in a **glycoprotein** (for example, mucin of saliva) the prosthetic group is a carbohydrate, and in a **phosphoprotein** (for example, casein of milk) it is phosphoric acid. **Lipoproteins** have phospholipids, and **nucleoproteins** have nucleic acids (Section 16-30) as prosthetic groups. **Chromoproteins** are conjugated proteins which are colored. A vitally important chromoprotein is the respiratory pigment *hemoglobin*, which combines with oxygen in the lungs and is converted into *oxyhemoglobin*, in which form it transports oxygen through the bloodstream into body tissues. Carbon monoxide is toxic to mammals because its addition compound with hemoglobin is more stable than is oxyhemoglobin. In hemoglobin the protein *globin* is combined with a prosthetic group consisting of a *porphyrin molecule* containing a coordinated ferrous ion. Careful acid hydrolysis of hemoglobin yields globin and the chloride of the prosthetic group, *hemin*. Note the structural similarity between hemin and the porphyrin portion of chlorophyll (Section 16-12).

Proteins may be alternatively divided into two other classes, **fibrous proteins** and **globular proteins.** Fibrous proteins are insoluble in the common solvents, but soluble in strong acids and bases. Collagen and keratin are typical members of this class. Globular proteins are characterized by their solubility in water, or in aqueous solutions of acids, bases, and salts. Examples include ovalbumin, mucin, and the plasma proteins, which occur in blood plasma.

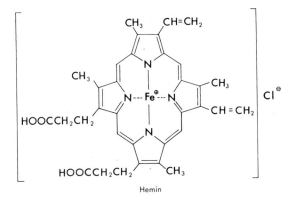

Hemin

16-20. Some Properties of Proteins

The following are some characteristic properties and reactions of proteins.

a. Denaturation. When proteins are heated, exposed to ultraviolet radiation, or treated with a number of solvents or reagents (for example, alcohol, acetone, aqueous potassium iodide), marked changes may occur in their solubility and biological properties. These changes are referred to as **denaturation** of the protein. In some cases the changes are reversible, but more typically they are irreversible. A good example of irreversible denaturation is the familiar change which occurs when a raw egg is heated. X-ray studies indicate that a more random arrangement of the molecules in the protein polymer results on denaturation.

b. Isoelectric Point. We have seen that the backbone of the protein chain consists of a series of amino acid units joined together through peptide bonds. However, because of the presence on the protein chain of additional acidic or basic groups which are not involved in peptide linkages, proteins have isoelectric points in the same way as do the simple amino acids. As with amino acids, these isoelectric points may vary from one protein to another, and a few typical values are listed in Table 16-2. Paral-

Table 16-2. Isoelectric Points of Some Proteins

Hemoglobin	Isoelectric Point
Casein	4.60
Gelatin	4.80–4.85
Insulin	5.30–5.35
Hemoglobin	6.79–6.83

leling the behavior of amino acids, proteins exhibit minimum solubility
and no migration in an electric field at their isoelectric points.

   c. *Color Reactions.*   When concentrated nitric acid is brought into contact with skin, nails, or other proteins, the protein becomes colored deep
yellow. This is known as the **xanthoproteic reaction,** and is presumed to
arise by nitration of the aromatic nuclei of certain amino acids incorporated into the protein chain.

   Upon mixing a dilute solution of cupric sulfate with a weakly alkaline
solution of a protein or peptide, a pink to violet color is developed. This
same color test, known as the **biuret reaction,** is shown by the compound
biuret, $H_2NCONHCONH_2$, from which the reaction gets its name. The
structure of the colored product formed at a section of the protein chain is
represented in 16-**19**.

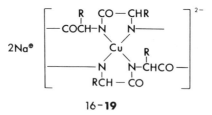

16-**19**

   Ninhydrin (triketohydrindene hydrate) reacts with proteins, peptides,
and α-amino acids with the formation of a characteristic blue color (**ninhydrin reaction**). In addition to this qualitative feature, the reaction is

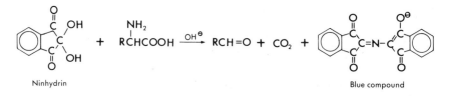

Ninhydrin   Blue compound

useful for the colorimetric estimation of amino acids. Ammonia, ammonium salts, and certain amines also give the blue color under certain conditions.

   d. *Hydrolysis.*   Hydrolysis of proteins and peptides into their constituent amino acids may be accomplished by heating with dilute hydrochloric
or sulfuric acids. Basic hydrolysis can also be used, but alkaline conditions
racemize the resulting amino acids at the same time. Enzymatic hydrolysis
is especially valuable in that it is highly selective and may break the protein only into smaller polypeptide fragments. Thus the digestive enzyme

trypsin breaks a protein chain only at a point where the carboxamide groups of arginine or lysine units occur.

e. Nitrogen Analysis. The total nitrogen content of proteins and peptides may be determined by the Dumas method (Section 4-1b), but is more frequently accomplished by the **Kjeldahl method.** In this procedure, a weighed sample of the protein is digested in hot, concentrated sulfuric acid in the presence of cupric sulfate or other catalysts, whereupon the nitrogen of the protein is converted into ammonium sulfate. When digestion is complete, the mixture is made alkaline with sodium hydroxide, and the liberated ammonia is distilled into a known volume of standard acid. Back titration with a standard solution of sodium hydroxide gives a measure of the amount of ammonia produced, from which the percentage of nitrogen in the sample may be readily calculated. The primary amino groups in proteins or peptides can be determined by the Van Slyke procedure (Section 14-5).

16-21. Isolation and Purification of Proteins

Any method dependent upon volatilization for the isolation and purification of proteins is inapplicable because of the chemical nature and high molecular weights of proteins. Alternative specialized techniques are therefore employed. In one of these, advantage is taken of the different isoelectric points of proteins and their minimum solubility at this pH. A solution of the protein at its isoelectric point is *salted out* (precipitated) by the addition of ammonium sulfate. The protein is then separated from residual electrolyte by **dialysis** through a semipermeable membrane. In this operation a solution of the crude protein is placed in a sac made of a suitable semipermeable material, such as collodion. The sac is placed in running water, and the electrolytes diffuse through the membrane into the surrounding water. The larger protein molecules are unable to pass through the tiny pores of the membrane and are retained within the sac. In a related procedure, alcohol is added to the solution of the protein at its isoelectric point, and the mixture is refrigerated. The crystallization of proteins has been accomplished by both of these processes.

The technique of **countercurrent separation,** developed by L. C. Craig of the Rockefeller Institute for Medical Research, involves carrying out a series of extractions, in which the protein to be purified is successively partitioned between *two immiscible solvents.* This method is especially useful for low molecular weight proteins. Imagine two series of tubes (for example, separatory funnels). The first series all contain a fixed volume of solvent A, and the second series the same volume of solvent B. The substance to be purified is shaken with the immiscible mixture of solvent A and solvent B. After separation, solution A is withdrawn and shaken with fresh solvent B, and solution B is similarly shaken with fresh solvent A. The process is then repeated, as diagrammed in Figure 16-17. The two

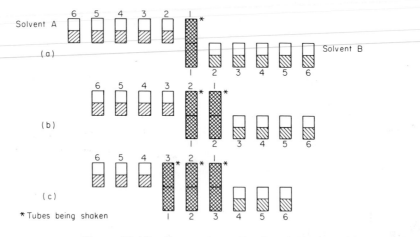

Figure 16-17. Countercurrent Fractionation

sets of tubes in the first partitioning are represented in (a), and the progress of the operation is shown in the succeeding steps, (b), (c), etc. It is seen that the solution in the upper tube of a given pair is next equilibrated with that of a lower tube immediately to its right, and vice versa. The different components in the mixture being separated are generally *partitioned differently* between the two solvents, so that gradually the crude protein, for example, will be separated into its components. Thus a plot of the weight of each component (from a two-component mixture) in the various tubes of the two series having two different solvents might look something like Figure 16-18.

A procedure known as **electrophoresis,** developed by A. Tiselius (Nobel Prize, 1948), is valuable for the determination of the purity of proteins and their separation on a small, but not a large, scale. In this technique a solution of the protein is adjusted to an appropriate pH and placed on a suitable support, such as a gel or filter paper. An electric current is applied, and proteins with different isoelectric points begin to separate.

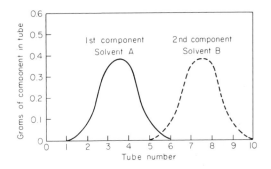

Figure 16-18. Countercurrent Fractionation Pattern of a Two Component Mixture

For example, suppose that three proteins having isoelectric points of 5.5, 6.0, and 6.5 were present in a mixture. If the mixture were buffered at pH 6.0 and an electric current applied, the protein having its isoelectric point at pH 6.0 would remain motionless. The protein having an isoelectric point of 5.5, however, would migrate toward the anode, and that with an isoelectric point of 6.5 would move toward the cathode. The homogeneity of proteins can be determined readily by this method, as well as through the use of an ultracentrifuge (Section 16-22), and by countercurrent distribution.

16-22. Molecular Weights of Proteins

Molecular weights of high polymers such as proteins cannot be determined by the usual methods applicable to low molecular weight compounds (Section 4-3). One of the widely used alternative methods for the determination of the molecular weights of proteins and other high molecular weight polymers is by means of the **ultracentrifuge**, a technique developed largely by T. Svedberg of the University of Uppsala (Nobel Prize, 1962). In this method, a solution of the protein is contained in a small tube which is spun in a centrifuge at very high speeds. Under the action of centrifugal force, the protein moves to the outer end of the tube at a rate which is proportional to its molecular weight. Such **sedimentation rates** may be measured by means of special optical devices built into the ultracentrifuge. Other methods used for determining the molecular weights of proteins include osmotic pressure measurements of their solutions and light-scattering techniques. It should be pointed out that the molecular weights of high polymers obtained by these varying methods are frequently not in very good agreement. The molecular weights of several typical proteins, as determined by their sedimentation rates in the ultra-centrifuge, are shown in Table 16-3.

Table 16-3. Molecular Weights of Some Proteins[a]

Protein	Molecular Weight
Lactalbumin	17,400
Gliadin (wheat)	28,000
Insulin (beef pancreas)	35,000
Ovalbumin (egg white)	44,000
Hemoglobin (man)	63,000
Serum γ-globulin (man)	150,000
Urease (soy bean)	480,000
Yellow fever virus	2,500,000
Tobacco mosaic virus	40,000,000

[a]Many proteins are aggregates held together by relatively weak bonding forces. The minimal molecular weight of a protein is thus often a fraction of the value for the "intact" protein. For example, the minimal molecular weight of insulin is 5733, and of tobacco mosaic virus around 18,000.

16-23. Determination of Protein Structures

The initial problems in the establishment of the structure of a simple protein are the determination of the *amounts of the various amino acids* which it contains and the *sequence of their arrangement* in the protein chain. The total amino acid composition is determined by complete hydrolysis of the protein, followed by quantitative analysis of the hydrolyzate for each amino acid present. The latter may be accomplished in several ways. Thus the amino acids can be separated by means of paper chromatography (Section 3-5c), and their location and estimation can be accomplished through reaction with ninhydrin (Section 16-20c). The amino acids may be separated by means of ion exchange resins (Section 3-6), and a commercial instrument based on this method is available for the quantitative estimation of amino acids. The analysis for a *particular* amino acid may be conducted by **isotopic dilution** techniques. In this procedure a known amount of a C^{14}-labeled variety of the amino acid, whose analysis is sought, is added to the mixture. The chemical properties of the naturally occurring amino acid and its radioactive counterpart (of known radioactivity level) are the same. Therefore, upon isolation of the amino acid and determination of its new level of radioactivity, its quantitative estimation is accomplished. To illustrate, if the radioactivity of the isolated amino acid, after mixing with the labeled sample, were 50 per cent of the radioactivity of the original labeled sample, then the amount of the naturally occurring variety would be equal to the amount of the radioactive variety added to the mixture. The amount of a given amino acid in a protein hydrolyzate may also be determined by means of biological assays. The hydrolyzate is fed to a microorganism which has a specific requirement for a particular amino acid, and its rate of growth is compared with that observed on feeding diets containing known amounts of the amino acid in question.

To determine the amino acid sequence in proteins, the protein is hydrolyzed only partially (using acids or enzymes), or in some instances oxidized, to smaller peptide fragments (di- to heptapeptides). The arrangement of the amino acids in the smaller peptides is then established. From the *overlapping of particular amino acids* observed in the different peptides, and a knowledge of the specificity of any enzymes utilized, the structure of the protein can be deduced. A particularly useful technique in such investigations involves labeling the end amino groups of the smaller peptide fragments by reaction with 2,4-dinitrofluorobenzene (16-**20**). Following the end-functional labeling, the peptide is hydrolyzed, and the terminal amino acid is found as its *N*-2,4-dinitrophenyl derivative (16-**21**). This method

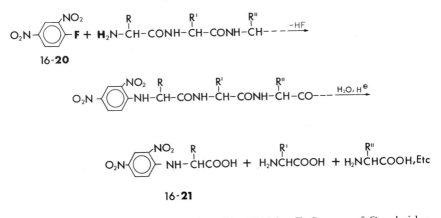

16-**20**

16-**21**

of **end group analysis** was introduced in 1945 by F. Sanger of Cambridge University, who received the Nobel Prize in 1958. An end group analysis for identifying the carboxy-terminal amino acid in peptide chains was developed in 1952 by the Japanese chemist S. Akabori. The peptide is heated with hydrazine, which converts all of the amino acids in the chain, except the carboxy-terminal one, into amino acid hydrazides (16-**22**, 16-**23**). Separation of the free amino acid identifies the carboxy-terminal unit.

$$\underset{\substack{R \\ |}}{H_2NCH}-CONH-\underset{\substack{R' \\ |}}{CH}-CONH-\underset{\substack{R'' \\ |}}{CH}COOH \xrightarrow{H_2NNH_2, \text{ Heat}}$$

$$\underset{\substack{R \\ | \\ 16\text{-}22}}{H_2NCHCONHNH_2} + \underset{\substack{R' \\ | \\ 16\text{-}23}}{H_2NCHCONHNH_2} + \underset{\substack{R'' \\ |}}{H_2NCHCOOH}$$

16-24. Structure of Oxytocin

Oxytocin, a hormone from the posterior pituitary gland, stimulates uterine contraction and is used clinically during labor. The determination of its structure (1953) independently by V. du Vigneaud (Nobel Prize, 1955) and H. Tuppy will serve to illustrate the general principles described above for unraveling the structure of proteins and peptides. The isoelectric point of the hormone is 7.7, suggesting a free amino group. Acid hydrolysis yields eight amino acids (glycine, leucine, isoleucine, proline, cystine, tyrosine, aspartic acid, and glutamic acid) in equimolar amounts, plus three moles of ammonia (corresponding to three $-CONH_2$ groups). The molecular weight of oxytocin is that for an octapeptide. Upon oxidation of oxytocin with performic acid, which is known to oxidize disulfide units to sulfonic acids

$$RSSR \xrightarrow{HCO_3H} 2 RSO_3H$$

a single product is formed having a molecular weight in the range of that of oxytocin, indicating that oxytocin must exist as a ring structure. Hydrolysis of oxidized oxytocin yields two moles of cysteic acid, $HO_3SCH_2CH(NH_2)COOH$, four dipeptides (I–IV) and two tripeptides (V and VI). Treatment of the latter with 2,4-dinitrofluorobenzene, followed by hydrolysis and chromatographic identification of the dinitrophenyl derivatives, establishes the end groups shown in V and VI for these tripeptides. In depicting peptides, the convention of a dash is used to separate the abbreviations for the amino acid units when the order is known, and a comma is used when the sequence is unknown. Also in peptide sequences, the amino acid at the left end of the chain is understood to have a free amino group, whereas that at the right end has a free carboxyl group, unless otherwise indicated.

I	Asp–CySO$_3$H		IV	Ileu–Glu
II	CySO$_3$H–Tyr		V	Tyr–(Glu, Ileu)
III	Leu–Gly		VI	CySO$_3$H–(Leu, Pro)

From the sequence found in IV, that in V must be Tyr–Ileu–Glu, and from II the sequence can be extended to CySO$_3$H–Tyr–Ileu–Glu. From the arrangement of III, that in VI must be CySO$_3$H–Pro–Leu, for the leucine (in VI) must be free to combine with glycine (in III). Adding the glycine to the identified sequence of VI gives $CySO_3H–Pro–Leu–Gly$.

Partial hydrolysis of oxidized oxytocin with a proteinase enzyme from the ubiquitous bacterium *Bacillus subtilis* results in the formation of glycine amide, $H_2NCH_2CONH_2$ ($Gly(NH_2)$), and two acidic tetrapeptides (VII and VIII). Their hydrolysis, identification of their amino acids by chromatography, and their end group analysis with 2,4-dinitrofluorobenzene show the tetrapeptides to be the following. The amino acids in VII correspond

VII $CySO_3H–(Glu, Tyr, Ileu)$ VIII $Asp–(CySO_3H, Leu, Pro)$

to those in the sequence already established, $CySO_3H–Tyr–Ileu–Glu$, and addition of aspartic acid to the sequence found for VI gives $Asp–CySO_3H–Pro–Leu$ for VIII. The isolation of glycine amide points to its presence as an end group, so that the sequence becomes $Asp–CySO_3H–Pro–Leu–Gly(NH_2)$, which is related to the previously described sequence, $CySO_3H–Pro–Leu–Gly$, from the hydrolysis of oxidized oxytocin. The sequence of amino acids in oxidized oxytocin then must be as follows, with the indicated points of hydrolysis by bacterial proteinase:

$$CySO_3H–Tyr–Ileu–Glu(NH_2)⫫Asp(NH_2)–CySo_3H–Pro–Leu⫫Gly(NH_2)$$

Oxidized Oxytocin

It will be recalled that three amide groups were indicated by the initial hydrolysis of oxytocin. The terminal glycine amide accounts for one of these, and transformation of those carboxyl groups of aspartic and glutamic acid which are not involved as peptide bonds into amide functions permits assignment of the other two. From the structure of oxidized oxytocin and the aforementioned mode of cleavage of disulfide bonds with performic acid, oxytocin itself must have the following structure.

$Cy–S–S–Cy–Pro–Leu–Gly(NH_2)$
    | |
Tyr $Asp(NH_2)$
    | |
$Ileu$———$Glu(NH_2)$

Oxytocin

The exact sequence of amino acids in proteins has profound biological implications, even in very closely related proteins. A striking example of this is the comparison of normal hemoglobin (hemoglobin A) with that (hemoglobin S) which accompanies the inherited genetic disease known as sickle cell anemia. This disorder, arising from a mutant gene, is characterized by sickle-shaped red blood cells, which are normally spherical. Each hemoglobin molecule consists of some 8000 atoms and is made up of two identical halves, each containing about 300 amino acid units of some

19 different kinds. The difference in the two hemoglobins lies in the fact that at one point in the chain, a glutamic acid unit in normal hemoglobin is replaced by a valine unit in the abnormal one. This is shown below in the representation of the single polypeptide (out of 28 obtained from various hydrolyses of each type of hemoglobin) which contains the variant amino acid.

Polypeptide from Hemoglobin A: His–Val–Leu–Leu–Thr–Pro–<u>Glu</u>–Glu–Lys

Polypeptide from Hemoglobin S: His–Val–Leu–Leu–Thr–Pro–<u>Val</u>–Glu–Lys

One of the most complex proteins so far elucidated structurally (F. Sanger, 1955) is insulin, the pancreatic hormone required for normal metabolism of carbohydrates. Insulin deficiency results in diabetes mellitus, a hereditary or developmental disorder in carbohydrate metabolism which may be controlled by injection of insulin obtained from cattle pancreas.

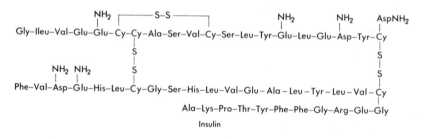

Insulin

16-25. Conformation of Proteins

Besides the complex problem of the sequence of amino acids in proteins, there is the additional difficult problem of the manner in which the protein chains are arranged. In one classification of overall structural features, the sequence of amino acids in the protein chain is called the **primary structure,** the conformation of the chains the **secondary structure,** and the way in which the secondary structural units are arranged in the natural protein (folded, refolded) is called the **tertiary structure.** X-ray diffraction studies have been especially important in revealing the secondary and tertiary structure of proteins.

A secondary structure found in peptides and a number of proteins, particularly of the fibrous type, is the so-called α-**helix.** This structure, simultaneously proposed in 1951 for α-keratin proteins (hair) by L. Pauling (Nobel Prizes, 1954, 1964) and R. B. Corey of the California Institute of Technology and by F. H. C. Crick (Nobel Prize, 1962) of Cambridge

University, arises as a consequence of resonance in the peptide linkage (16-24) and hydrogen bonding (16-25) between —NH— and $>$C=O groups along the protein chain. In this structure, the chain of amino acids

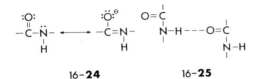

16-24   16-25

is arranged in a helical coil, referred to as an α-helix. As shown schematically in Figure 16-19, the helix has about 3.6 amino acids per turn, and a distance of 5.4 Å between turns. Hydrogen bonds such as 16-25

Figure 16-19. Schematic Representation
of the α-Helix

3.6 amino acid units, 5.4 Å

Hydrogen bonds

exist between the whorls of the spiral, and involve amino acid units separated by four peptide bonds in the chain. These hydrogen bonds run essentially parallel to the long axis of the coil, and serve to maintain the spacing between the turns. This small helix is in turn part of a larger helix (Figure 16-20), which has about 13 turns of the small helix for every

Figure 16-20. Spiraling of α-Helices

Small α-helices

One turn of
large helix

turn of the larger helix. Strands of these larger helices, in turn, intertwine to make up the fibrous protein (Figure 16-21). Globular proteins often

Figure 16-21. Strand of Fibrous Protein

contain helical and nonhelical parts to their structures. Silk fibroin and related fibrous proteins are thought to have their adjacent peptide chains running "in opposite directions," as shown schematically in Figure 16-22.

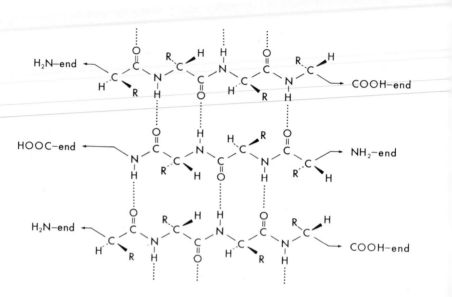

Figure 16-22.   Proposed Structure of Silk Fibroin

It is also considered probable that β-keratin, exemplified by stretched hair, has a structure related to that of silk fibroin, except that the chain sequences are parallel rather than antiparallel.

16-26. Synthesis of Peptides

In one of the first general methods for the synthesis of polypeptides, Emil Fischer (1901–1903) allowed an α-halo acyl chloride (16-**26**) to react with the ester of an amino acid (16-**27**). The ester group of the product was then selectively hydrolyzed under mild alkaline conditions, and the halo group was replaced with an amino group by reaction with ammonia, yielding a dipeptide (16-**28**). Esterification of the dipeptide, followed by reaction with another α-halo acyl chloride, and so forth, then produced a

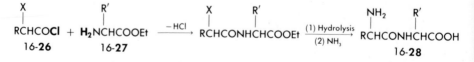

tripeptide. Fischer actually prepared the octadecapeptide Leu–(Gly)₃–
Leu–(Gly)₃–Leu–(Gly)₉ by this method. The synthesis of naturally occurring peptides is complicated by the need for reactions which will not favor
racemization, and which take place in high yield. For example, if the yield
of each step in a five-step sequence of reactions is 50 per cent, the overall
yield for the sequence would be only 3.1 per cent! Such considerations
have motivated the development of improved synthetic methods. Let us
consider several of these.

In the **mixed anhydride synthesis,** developed in 1950–1951, the amino
group of an amino acid is protected by reaction with *carbobenzoxy chloride,*

$$PhCH_2OH \ + \ COCl_2 \ \xrightarrow{\ -HCl\ } \ PhCH_2OCOCl$$
Benzyl alcohol   Phosgene   Carbobenzoxy chloride

to form the carbobenzoxy derivative 16-**29.** This is converted into its triethylammonium salt (16-**30**), which is allowed to react with ethyl chloro-
formate, ClCOOEt, to form the mixed anhydride 16-**31.** Acylation of an
amino acid ester with the latter compound yields the carbobenzoxy derivative (16-**32**) of a dipeptide, which may be converted into the free dipeptide
ester (16-**33**) by catalytic hydrogenolysis.

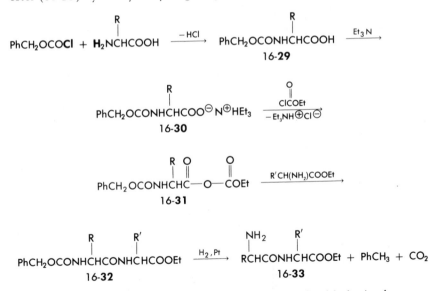

Another type of peptide synthesis involves simple *dehydration* between
protected amino acid units. The intermolecular dehydration, for example,
between an *N*-carbobenzoxy-protected amino acid (16-**29**) and an amino
acid ester, using *N,N*-dicyclohexylcarbodiimide (16-**34**) as a dehydrating
agent, produces the carbobenzoxy derivative (16-**32**) of a dipeptide ester.

The dehydrating agent 16-34 is converted into N,N'-dicyclohexylurea (16-35) in the process, which precipitates quantitatively in the solvents employed (tetrahydrofuran, acetonitrile, methylene chloride). The dipeptide derivative 16-32 may again be converted into the free dipeptide by catalytic hydrogenolysis, followed by hydrolysis.

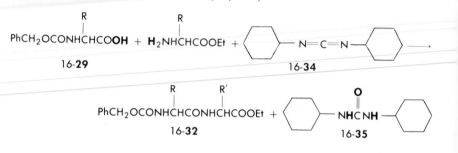

16-27. Enzymes

We have seen previously that enzymes (Greek: *en zyme*, in yeast) are simple or conjugated proteins of natural origin, which are capable of catalyzing specific chemical reactions both *in vivo* and *in vitro*. Their high specificity and the mild conditions under which they react are noteworthy. The first enzyme to be crystallized was *urease* (J. B. Sumner, 1926; Nobel Prize 1946), which catalyzes the hydrolysis of urea into ammonia and carbon dioxide. Today hundreds of enzymes are known in the pure (or practically pure) state.

Enzymes are often named by adding the suffix -*ase* to a stem name which reflects the nature of the substrate upon which they act, or the type of reaction which they catalyze. Thus hydrolytic enzymes (**hydrolases**) include **glycosidases,** which catalyze the hydrolysis of glycosides; **esterases,** which promote the hydrolysis and formation of esters; **proteinases,** which hydrolyze proteins; **lipases,** which hydrolyze fats; and **phosphatases,** which act upon phosphates. *Catalase* is a widely occurring hemoprotein capable of decomposing hydrogen peroxide into water and oxygen. It thus serves to protect the organism against hydrogen peroxide formed during biological processes. The interconversion of α-amino acids and α-keto acids during life processes is promoted by enzymes called **transaminases.**

$$\underset{\text{RCHCOOH}}{\overset{\overset{\displaystyle NH_2}{|}}{}} + \underset{\text{R'CCOOH}}{\overset{\overset{\displaystyle O}{||}}{}} \xrightarrow{\text{Transaminase}} \underset{\text{RCCOOH}}{\overset{\overset{\displaystyle O}{||}}{}} + \underset{\text{R'CHCOOH}}{\overset{\overset{\displaystyle NH_2}{|}}{}}$$

Transaminases specific for aspartic and glutamic acids contain pyridoxal phosphate or pyridoxamine phosphate in their prosthetic groups. These two heterocyclic bases are related to pyridoxine, vitamin B_6

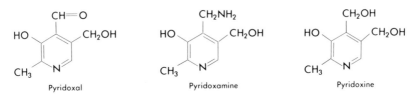

Pyridoxal   Pyridoxamine   Pyridoxine

The **proteolytic enzymes** act upon proteins, and important examples are found in the digestive tract: pepsin, trypsin, chymotrypsin, and carboxypeptidase. Such enzymes are usually excreted in the body as inactive precursors (for example, pepsinogen, trypsinogen), which are subsequently activated by other enzymes. Trypsin, which attacks central peptide bonds in a protein, is referred to as an **endopeptidase**. Enzymes which cause the hydrolysis of only the *N*-terminal amino acid and *C*-terminal amino acid units of peptides are called **aminopeptidases** and **carboxypeptidases**, respectively.

In 1913 L. Michaelis suggested that enzyme action was initiated through the formation of an enzyme–substrate complex, and subsequent research has completely substantiated his contention. The catalytic activity of enzymes appears to be limited to one or a very few specific portions of the enzyme molecule, called the **active sites** of the enzyme. In most enzyme systems the active sites responsible for catalytic activity are not yet known. Furthermore, many enzymes react with a substrate only in the presence of a second substance, referred to as a **coenzyme**. Coenzymes are generally nonprotein in nature, and frequently they prove to be nucleotides (Section 16-29).

16-28. Depsipeptides

A group of cyclic compounds derived from α-amino acids and α-hydroxy acids are called **depsipeptides**. These compounds exhibit antibiotic properties to varying degrees. Two examples of this group of compounds are *enniatin B*, isolated from strains of the fungus *Fusarium*, and *esperin*, an antibiotic produced by *Bacillus mesentericus*.

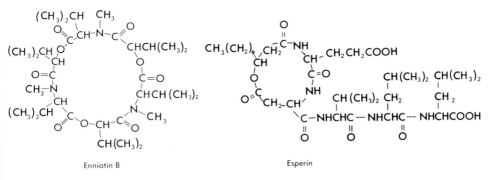

Enniatin B   Esperin

NUCLEIC ACIDS AND NUCLEOTIDES

THE MOST IMPORTANT conjugated proteins in nature are the **nucleoproteins,** which are found in every cell of every living species. The prosthetic groups of nucleoproteins are complex polymeric molecules known as **nucleic acids.** Nucleic acids of high molecular weight (above one million) are involved in carrying the genetic information which guides cell reproduction along the lines of exact replication necessary for cell differentiation, and are themselves believed to be capable of self-reproduction. It is not known with certainty how the protein portion and the nucleic acid portion of nucleoproteins are combined, but the two may be separated readily.

16-29. Components of Nucleic Acids

The hydrolysis of nucleic acid polymers breaks them initially into monomeric units called **mononucleotides.** Further hydrolysis of mononucleotides splits them into phosphoric acid and a class of compounds called **nucleosides.** Final hydrolysis of nucleosides yields a five-carbon sugar (either D-ribose or 2-deoxy-D-ribose) plus a heterocyclic nitrogen base which is either a **purine** or a **pyrimidine** derivative. This hydrolytic behavior is summarized in Figure 16-23.

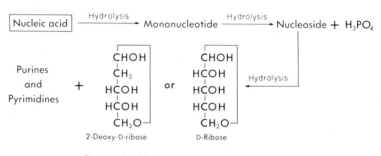

Figure 16-23. *Hydrolysis of Nucleic Acids*

Nucleic acids are divided into two groups, **ribonucleic acids** (RNA) and **deoxyribonucleic acids** (DNA). RNA, which affords only D-ribose among its final hydrolysis products, is found in cell cytoplasm, may be prepared from yeast cells, and is generally the less abundant nucleic acid in cell nuclei. DNA, which yields 2-deoxy-D-ribose on hydrolysis, may be obtained from thymus gland, and is the chief component of cell chromosomes. The purine and pyrimidine bases obtained on complete hydrolysis of DNA and RNA are shown in Figure 16-24.

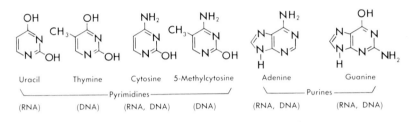

Figure 16-24.   Nitrogen Bases from Nucleic Acids

As noted in Figure 16-23, partial hydrolysis of the nucleic acids DNA and RNA yields phosphoric acid plus the corresponding **nucleosides**, in which the sugar component is still linked to the purine or pyrimidine bases shown in Figure 16-24. The following structures are typical of the five nucleosides which are obtainable from DNA, and the four from RNA.

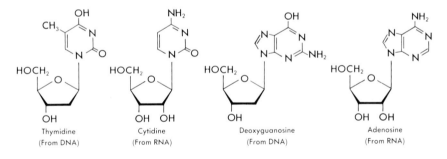

16-30. Structure of Nucleic Acids

The DNA molecule is a polymer containing more than 5000 mononucleotide units. How are these individual mononucleotide units arranged in the intact nucleic acid macromolecule? As a result of researches by the English chemist Sir Alexander R. Todd of Cambridge University (Nobel Prize, 1957) and others, the structures of nucleic acid molecules are now believed to be similar to those represented in the accompanying formulas.

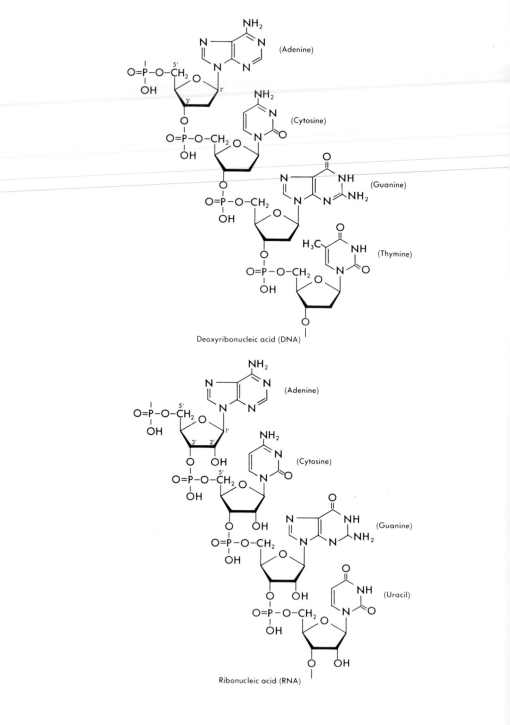

Deoxyribonucleic acid (DNA)

Ribonucleic acid (RNA)

The "backbone" of each polymer is comprised of repeating D-ribose (or 2-deoxy-D-ribose) and phosphoric acid ester units, with each pentose molecule attached to one of the purine or pyrimidine bases in Figure 16-24 through N-glycoside linkages. Note that in DNA the pentose unit is exclusively 2-deoxy-D-ribose, whereas in RNA it is exclusively D-ribose, and that the phosphate linkages attach at carbon atoms 3′ and 5′ of the pentose units. Notice also that the bases involved in the intact nucleic acids are tautomeric forms of the free bases shown in Figure 16-24. It is believed that the tautomeric forms shown are favored in the intact nucleic acid because of the requirements of hydrogen bonding, as described below.

In 1953 J. D. Watson and F. H. C. Crick (shared Nobel Prize, 1962) proposed, on the basis of X-ray analysis and other data on crystalline DNA, a "secondary structure" (Section 16-25) for the DNA macromolecule. Their proposal has substantially withstood subsequent critical scrutiny. They suggested that the DNA polymer chain consists of a *double coiled*, right-handed helix, with the two individual strands running in *opposite* directions from the viewpoints of the mononucleotide sequences in each strand (Figure 16-25). Approximately ten mononucleotide units

Figure 16-25. Schematic Representation of the Double Helix of DNA (Watson-Crick)

constitute a complete turn of the helix of each strand, and the "backbone" of each strand (consisting of 2-deoxyribose and phosphate units) lies outside the helix of each strand, while the nitrogen bases in each strand lie toward the center of each helix (Figure 16-26). The Watson-Crick repre-

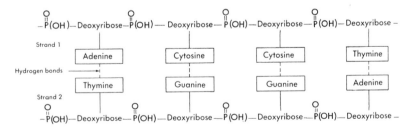

Figure 16-26. Segment of the Double-Stranded Helix of DNA

sentation of the DNA molecule is shown as a molecular model in Figure 16-27.

Hydrogen bonds between the heterocyclic bases in each of the two strands of DNA (Figure 16-26) constitute the forces of attraction which hold the two strands together. By considering the mole ratios in which

Figure 16-27. Model of the DNA Molecule. Courtesy Dr. A. Hodge of California Institute of Technology and Dr. A. Kornberg of Stanford University. Dr. Kornberg shared the Nobel Prize in medicine in 1959 for his enzymatic synthesis of DNA

the individual bases occur in DNA, and the geometry of these bases with respect to the size of each helix, it has been deduced that in the DNA molecule adenine must be hydrogen-bonded to thymine, and cytosine to guanine, as shown in Figure 16-26, and in greater detail in Figure 16-28.

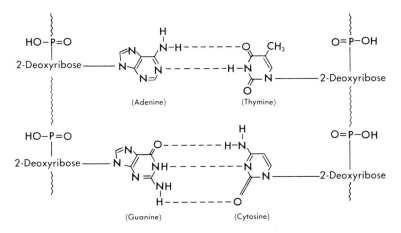

Figure 16-28.   Hydrogen Bonding between Specific Bases in DNA

The structure of RNA, except for the difference in its pentose units (D-ribose) and the heterocyclic bases involved (Figure 16-24), is believed to be similar to that of DNA. RNA, however, appears capable of existing not only as a double-stranded helix (like DNA), but as a single-stranded helix as well.

16-31. Function of Nucleic Acids

Mention has been made that nucleic acids are responsible for imparting the "genetic message" which causes living cells to reproduce true to their prototype. What is the mechanism of this remarkable feat of nature, and how is it interpreted in terms of the known structural features of nucleic acids? In the example of sickle cell anemia (Section 16-24), we have seen also that the amino acid sequence in proteins determines the nature and function of the protein, so that the question might better be put: "How are specific amino acid sequences genetically built into proteins during their biological syntheses?"

It is generally agreed that genes are DNA units, but the mechanisms by which DNA achieves its genetic function are not yet fully understood. It is currently thought that a double-stranded DNA unit acts as a *template* to direct the synthesis of **messenger RNA units** from monomeric ribonucleotide molecules in the nucleus of the cell, as shown in Figure 16-29.

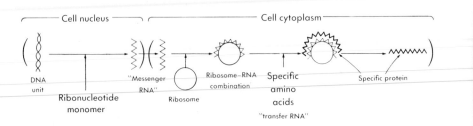

Figure 16-29. Schematic Diagram of Specific Protein Synthesis

The unique messenger RNA polymer, which is "coded" with a particular sequence of nitrogen bases along its chain (complementary to the sequence in the original DNA), migrates from the nucleus of the cell to the cytoplasm, where it combines with a cellular ribosomal particle. This combination in the cell cytopolasm becomes the site of protein synthesis, and the messenger RNA dictates, presumably through highly specific hydrogen bonding of **transfer RNA** combined with amino acid monomers or small peptides, what amino acid sequence will prevail in the resulting enzymatically synthesized protein. Figure 16-29 shows a highly simplified schematic diagram of a specific protein synthesis "directed" by nucleic acids.

The phenomenon of gene replication in cells also involves DNA. A simplified schematic diagram of the overall result of this vital process of genetic control is shown in Figure 16-30. The double helix of DNA is thought to separate, and the individual strands are able to bind in sequence their complementary free nucleotides (adenine–thymine and cytosine–guanine; Figure 16-28) through specific hydrogen bonding, and simultaneously to form in similar sequence phosphate ester linkages by enzyme catalysis. The result is two polymeric molecules of the original DNA double helix.

In view of the countless billions of conceivable sequences of purine and pyrimidine bases which are possible in a DNA molecule containing 5000 or so mononucleotide units, it is understandable how the above mechanisms can specifically reproduce the billions of individual proteins which are encountered throughout nature. The emerging science of **molecular**

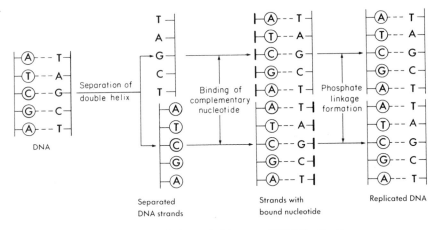

Figure 16-30. Schematic Diagram of DNA Replication

biology concerns itself with the intimate details of these fascinating vital phenomena.

STEROIDS

STEROIDS INCLUDE a wide variety of natural products containing the **cyclo-pentenophenanthrene** ring system present in cholesterol. On dehydrogenation with selenium (Section 10-3), cholesterol and other steroids yield 3'-methyl-1,2-cyclopentenophenanthrene (the so-called **Diels hydrocarbon,** 1927) thus revealing their basic ring system. Among steroid deriva-

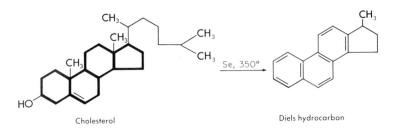

Cholesterol   Diels hydrocarbon

tives are found plant and animal sterols, adrenal hormones, sex hormones, bile acids, cardiac aglycones, toad poisons, and steroid sapogenins. Because of their widespread occurrence and physiological importance, steroids have been extensively investigated chemically, and many of the reactions and generalizations of organic chemistry were initially developed in connection with steroid research.

16-32. Cholesterol and Other Sterols

Sterols are crystalline alcohols (Greek: *steros*, solid + *ol*) which are found in animals and plants. Cholesterol is the most important animal sterol (**zoosterol**), occurring in all parts of the body, but concentrated in the brain and spinal cord tissues. The total cholesterol in a 170-pound man is around 250 grams. It was first obtained by Conradi in 1775 from gallstones, but its currently accepted structure was not fully elucidated until 1932. Cholesterol is prepared commercially from the spinal cords of cattle by alkaline hydrolysis followed by solvent extraction, as well as by similar isolation from wool grease. It is used as a starting material for the preparation of other important steroid derivatives. In the animal organism cholesterol is thought to be a precursor of all other physiologically important steroids found in the body, into which cholesterol may be converted metabolically.

Cholesterol is found only in animals. Plants, however, contain a number of closely related steroid alcohols (**phytosterols**), of which *stigmasterol* from soy bean oil and *ergosterol* from ergot and yeast are representative.

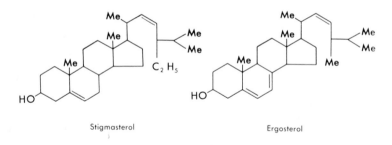

Stigmasterol   Ergosterol

Irradiation of ergosterol with ultraviolet light transforms it into a number of products, among which is *calciferol*, or vitamin D_2. This and related D vitamins control the quantity and balance of calcium and phosphorus in

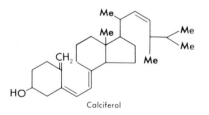

Calciferol

body fluids. In the absence of D vitamins, the disturbance in calcium and phosphorus metabolism results in soft bones, a deficiency disease known as *rickets*.

16-33. Bile Acids

A number of steroid acids, referred to as **bile acids,** occur combined (through amide linkages) with glycine, H_2NCH_2COOH, and taurine, $H_2NCH_2CH_2SO_3H$, in human and animal bile. Salts of these combined acids (**bile salts**) act as emulsifying agents for ingested fats, and promote their hydrolysis and absorption through the intestine. Free bile acids are obtained by the alkaline hydrolysis of such bile salts. The most abundant bile acids from human bile are *cholic acid* and *deoxycholic acid*, structures of which are shown below.

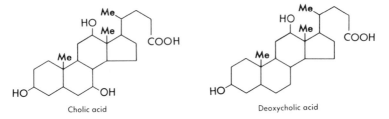

Cholic acid   Deoxycholic acid

16-34. Sex Hormones

Sex hormones control the sex characteristics and processes of animal organisms. These steroids are elaborated in the male testes and female ovaries under the influence of the gonadotropic hormones, which are secreted by the anterior lobe of the pituitary gland. Steroid sex hormones are classed as **androgens,** or male hormones, and **estrogens,** or female hormones. They are responsible for the development of sex characteristics, sexual drive, ovulation, and other related phenomena.

The principal androgen, *testosterone*, is secreted by the testes, and controls male sexual development. A related androgen, *androsterone*, is a metabolic product of testosterone, and is excreted in male urine (about 1 mg per liter).

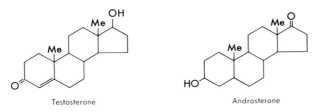

Testosterone   Androsterone

The most important estrogens are *estradiol*, which controls female sex characteristics and initiates the menstrual cycle, and *progesterone*, which prepares the uterus for the implantation of the fertilized ovum.   Progesterone is employed clinically in the prevention of abortion.

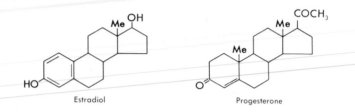

Estradiol   Progesterone

16-35. Corticosteroids

The adrenals are two small glands, situated in the body, one above each kidney.   Their outer layer (adrenal cortex) elaborates a series of important steroidal hormones called **corticosteroids,** which have broad regulatory influence over physiological processes in the body.   Such diverse phenomena as kidney function, electrolyte balance, resistance to disease and stress, growth, and the metabolism of foodstuffs appear to be under control of the adrenal hormones, and the details of their widespread physiological action are only beginning to be understood today.   Of the forty or so steroid compounds which have been isolated from the adrenal cortex, *cortisone, hydrocortisone,* and *aldosterone* are among the most important biologically.   Cortisone, administered as its acetate, is employed in the treatment of acute inflammatory diseases of the eye, skin, and mucosa, and hydrocortisone finds similar broad medical application.   Aldosterone is used in the treatment of Addison's disease, a pathological condition caused by adrenocortical atrophy.

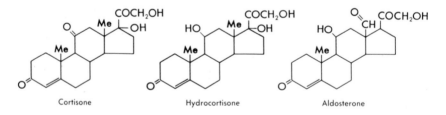

Cortisone   Hydrocortisone   Aldosterone

16-36. Steroid Sapogenins

The **saponins** (Latin: *sapa,* soap) comprise two groups of plant *glycosides* which form soapy solutions in water and are toxic to fish.   As the active principles of many soap roots and soap barks, they have found use by native tribes as soap substitutes and in fishing, since their action stuns fish, but does not render them inedible. The sugar component of saponins may be monosaccharides such as glucose, galactose, and xylose, or it may be a higher saccharide. The aglycone of the saponin, called a **sapogenin,** may be a pentacyclic triterpene (Section 16-51) in the **terpenoid saponins** or a steroid derivative in the **steroid saponins.** Hydrolysis of steroid saponins affords steroid sapogenins, two examples of which are shown below. *Sarsasapogenin* is obtained from the sarsaparilla root (*Similax medica* and related species), while *diosgenin* occurs in various species of yams (*Dioscorea tokoro*, etc.). These and other steroid sapogenins are used as

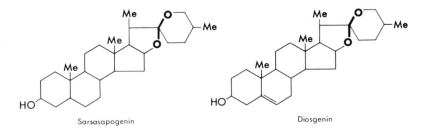

Sarsasapogenin   Diosgenin

starting materials in the production of progesterone and other medically important steroid derivatives. Notice the bicyclic acetal side chain in these structures, a characteristic of the steroid sapogenins.

16-37. Cardiac Glycosides and Toad Poisons

Cardiac glycosides are a group of natural glycosides having a powerful and specific action on heart muscle. *Digitalis*, a preparation from the seeds of purple foxglove (*Digitalis purpurea*), contains the glycoside *digitoxin*, and is widely used in the treatment of heart disease. *Strophanthin*, occurring in *Strophanthus kombé* seeds, is one of the toxic glycosides in African arrow poisons, and 0.00007 gram of this glycoside will stop the heart of a 20-gram mouse within minutes. The red squill (sea onion, *Scilla maritima*) contains the glycoside *scilliroside*. It is highly and specifically toxic to rodents, and the use of red squill as a rat poison was described in Arabia as early as the thirteenth century. Hydrolysis of such glycosides yields various types of sugars, of which at least twenty have been isolated. The aglycones of such glycosides, referred to as **genins,** are steroid derivatives characteristically having an unsaturated lactone side chain. The aglycones from digitoxin, strophanthin, and scilliroside, respectively, are shown below.

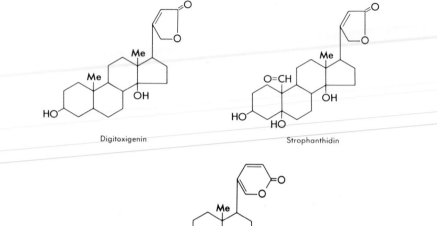

Digitoxigenin   Strophanthidin

Scillirosidin

Closely related to the steroidal cardiac aglycones are the toad venoms, which are secreted from the skin glands of various species of toads. The Chinese drug Ch'an Su, used for centuries as a folk remedy, is prepared from the skin of the Chinese toad, *Bufo bufogargarizans*, and powdered toad skins were early used in Western medicine in the treatment of dropsy. *Bufotalin* and *gamabufotalin* are representative genins among the toad poi-

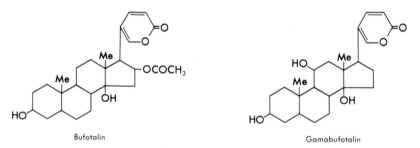

Bufotalin   Gamabufotalin

sons. In the intact toxin the steroid nucleus is connected through ester linkages to complex carboxylic acid moieties, such as suberylargenine.

$$HOOC(CH_2)_6CONHCH(CH_2)_3NHCNH_2$$

with COOH on the CH and NH / ‖ on the C, NH₂

Suberylargenine

16-38. Stereochemistry of Steroids

Examination of the structurel formula of cholesterol reveals the presence of eight asymmetric carbon atoms, whose positions and numbers are shown below. 5 α-Cholestan-3β-ol, the hydrogenation product of cholesterol,

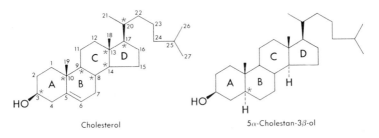

Cholesterol   5α-Cholestan-3β-ol

has an additional asymmetric center at C5. In principle, there are thus $2^8 = 256$ stereoisomers for cholesterol and $2^9 = 512$ for 5α-cholestan-3β-ol (Section 15-7c). The geometrical restrictions of the fused ring systems in the steroid molecule, however, severely limit the number of stereoisomers possible and, in fact, only two epimeric (at C5) series of steroids are found in nature. These are the **cholestane type** (5α type) of steroid, having rings A and B in a *trans* fusion, and the **coprostane type** (5β type), with the A and B rings *cis*. These configurational types are shown in Figure 16-31, both as "flat" structures with wedged lines indi-

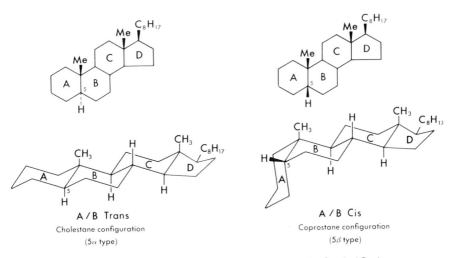

A / B Trans   A / B Cis
Cholestane configuration   Coprostane configuration
(5α type)   (5β type)

Figure 16-31. Stereochemical Configurations in the Steriod Series

cating projection in front of the "plane" of the steroid nucleus and dashed lines indicating projection behind the plane of the nucleus, and as the fused chair conformation rings actually believed to prevail in steroid molecules. In steroid nomenclature, substituents projecting behind the "plane" of the nucleus (dashed lines) are referred to as α **substituents,** while those projecting in front of the nucleus (wedged or solid lines) are called β **substituents.** Notice that the C3 hydroxyl group, the angular methyl groups at C10 and C13, and the side chain at C17 in cholesterol are all β substituents, and that the ring junctions at B/C and C/D are *trans*. In nature, most steroids vary in their nuclear configuration only at C5 (A/B *cis* or A/B *trans*), with all other configurations at ring junctions being identical. In the cardiac aglycones and the toad poisons, however, the C13 angular methyl group and the C14 hydroxyl group are *cis* and β; that is, the C/D ring junction is *cis*, rather than *trans* as in other steroids. Substituents at various positions about the steroid nucleus may adopt either α or β configurations, but the preferred configurations are generally those which allow the substituent to be in an *equatorial* rather than an axial orientation (see Figure 9-14).

16-39. Steroids in Medicine

In previous sections we have noted the profound physiological effects produced by many of the naturally occurring steroids, and reference has been made to the medical usage of a number of these substances. In recent years chemical research in the steroid field has gone hand in hand with clinical investigation to develop a wide variety of steroid derivatives, not found in nature, which have specific physiological action and medical application. Small variations in the structure of steroid molecules frequently engender wide variations in physiological activity, and hundreds of such steroid derivatives have been tested in a variety of medical contexts in the search for new drugs having enhanced potency, broader applicability, lower toxicity, and fewer undesirable side effects. Steroid therapy is becoming increasingly important in modern medicine, and runs the gamut from preventing abortion to arresting certain cancers, from controlling pregnancy to treating arthritis, and from correcting hormonal abnormalities to treating dermatitis. A detailed survey of the clinical applications of steroids is beyond our scope, but mention might be made of a few important synthetic steroid drugs. *Dexamethasone*, a fluorine-containing steroid, is used in treating inflammations, the acetylenic derivative *19-norethisterone* exerts control over the menstrual cycle and is used as an oral contraceptive, and the triketone *prednisone* finds general application in the field of cortisone therapy.

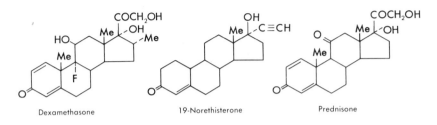

Dexamethasone   19-Norethisterone   Prednisone

ALKALOIDS

THE TERM **alkaloid,** meaning alkali-like, is applied to naturally occurring basic nitrogen compounds of plant origin. Typical alkaloids have marked physiological action in animals or man, and alkaloid preparation have been used for centuries in folk medicine and as ordeal drugs. Alkaloid bases are found in the bark, leaves, seeds, or roots of a wide variety of plants, and each site in the plant may contain several alkaloids of closely related structure. For historical reasons and because of their structural complexity, the nomenclature of alkaloids has not been systematized. The names of alkaloids are therefore usually derived from the plant in which they are found, or from the physiological action which they induce.

16-40. Extraction and Structure Elucidation of Alkaloids

The isolation of alkaloids from their plant sources is usually not difficult. A typical scheme for the extraction of crude alkaloids from a plant is diagrammed in Figure 16-32. Notice how the basic alkaloids are separated from neutral plant constituents by virtue of the solubility of the alkaloids in dilute acid through salt formation. The resulting crude alkaloid mixture

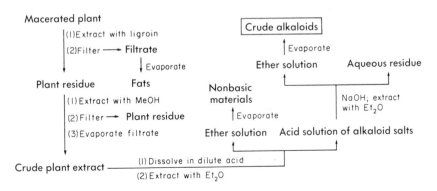

Figure 16-32.   Typical Procedure for the Isolation of Alkaloids from Plants

is then subjected to fractional crystallization, column chromatography, gas chromatography, or other techniques for separation into its individual pure components.

Because of their physiological action, alkaloids have interested organic chemists since the early days of the science. Their frequent molecular complexity has made the structure determination of alkaloids both tedious and challenging, and it is beyond our scope to examine this fascinating field in detail. Suffice it to say that one of the most powerful degradative tools in alkaloid structural investigations has been quaternization of the alkaloid base using methyl iodide (Section 14-11), followed by Hofmann degradation (Section 14-12) of the quaternary ammonium base. The application of this technique to the structure determination of the alkaloid mescaline, from mescal buttons, has already been discussed (Section 14-13), and serves to illustrate the principles involved.

Alkaloids are so numerous and involve such a variety of molecular structures that their systematic classification is difficult. We shall limit our brief survey to a discussion of several representative alkaloid types of increasing structural complexity.

16-41. Phenylalkylamine Derivatives

The Chinese herb Ma Huang (*Ephedra equisetina*), used for a variety of ailments for over 5000 years, contains a number of bases of which the simple β-phenylalkylamine derivative (−)-*ephedrine* is the most important. Now produced synthetically, it is widely used as a nasal decongestant and in the treatment of allergies. Its diastereomer, (+)-ψ-*ephedrine*, occurs in related plant species. Notice the structural similarity of these simple alkaloids with *adrenalin* (epinephrine), the blood-pressure-increasing substance elaborated in the adrenal glands, and to mescaline (Section 14-13).

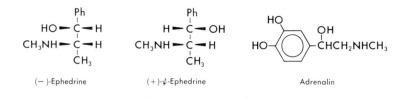

<table>
<tr><td>(−)-Ephedrine</td><td>(+)-ψ-Ephedrine</td><td>Adrenalin</td></tr>
</table>

16-42. Pyrrolidine Derivatives

Representatives of this class include *hygrine* and *cuscohygrine*, oily bases found in the leaves of the Peruvian cusco bark tree (*Erythroxylon coca*).

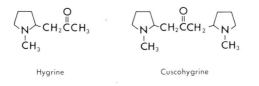

Hygrine   Cuscohygrine

16-43. Piperidine Derivatives

Isopelletierine, named as a derivative in honor of the French alkaloid chemist P. J. Pelletier (1788–1842), occurs in the bark of the pomegranate tree (*Punica granatum*). *Lobeline*, from the seeds of Indian tobacco (*Lobelia inflata*), is used medically as a respiratory stimulant and tobacco substitute. *Piperine*, extractable from the black pepper plant (*Piper nigrum*), is used occasionally in flavoring, and as an insecticide.

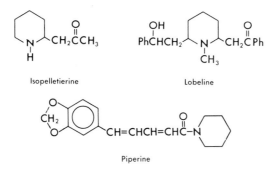

Isopelletierine   Lobeline

Piperine

16-44. Pyridine-Pyrrolidine and Pyridine-Piperidine Derivatives

Nicotine, the principal alkaloid of tobacco (*Nicotiana tabacum*), finds widespread commercial use as an agricultural insecticide. It is one of the most toxic alkaloids known, a fatal dose for man being about 40 mg. *Myosmine* also occurs in tobacco, and is partially responsible for the aroma of tobacco smoke. *Anabasine* is the chief alkaloid in the poisonous Asiatic plant, *Anabasis aphylla*. Oxidation of nicotine and such related alkaloids yields *nicotinic acid* (pyridine-3-carboxylic acid) or *niacin*, the pellagra-preventing

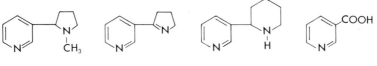

Nicotine   Myosmine   Anabasine   Nicotinic acid

factor in yeast, milk, liver, alfalfa and other cereals, and legumes. Nicotinamide was formerly referred to as vitamin B_3, and is used in the treatment
of pellagra, a deficiency disease characterized by skin lesions, gastrointestinal disturbance, and nervous symptoms.

16-45. Alkaloids with Condensed Ring Systems

Besides occurring as the simple rings we have seen in the alkaloids
described above, pyrrolidine, pyridine, and piperidine nuclei more frequently are found in *condensed* (fused) ring systems. The majority of
alkaloids have these more complex fused-ring structures, and the examples
given below are representative of the types of structures encountered in
the hundreds of alkaloids whose structures have been determined. The
more complex alkaloids shown here are arranged roughly according to
their increasing molecular complexity, rather than according to chemical
class or plant origin.

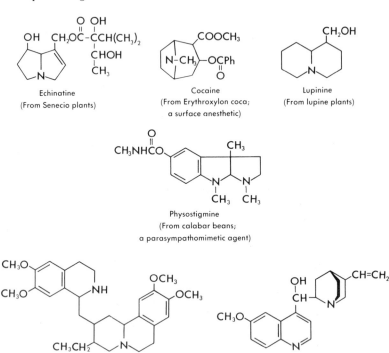

Echinatine
(From Senecio plants)

Cocaine
(From Erythroxylon coca;
a surface anesthetic)

Lupinine
(From lupine plants)

Physostigmine
(From calabar beans;
a parasympathomimetic agent)

Emetine
(From Uragoga ipecacuanha root;
used for amebic disorders)

Quinine
(From Cinchona tree bark;
an antimalarial agent)

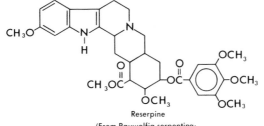

Reserpine
(From Rauwolfia serpentina;
a tranquilizer and sedative)

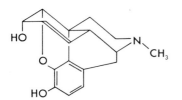

Morphine (conformational formula)
(From opium poppies; an analgesic and sedative)

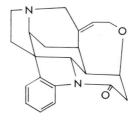

Strychnine (conformational formula)
(From Strychnos nux vomica seeds;
a circulatory stimulant in shock)

TERPENES

THE FRAGRANT CONSTITUENTS of plants, mixtures called **essential oils,** may be isolated by steam distillation, solvent extraction, or other treatment of the plant. These volatile, ambrosial oils have been investigated since the sixteenth century because of their value in perfumery, and the pure components isolated from them are called **terpenes**. The term terpene originally designated mixtures of isomeric $C_{10}H_{16}$ hydrocarbons found in turpentine and other essential oils, but the term is currently applied to all oxygenated and/or unsaturated compounds from plant sources which are derived from the molecular formula $(C_5H_8)_n$. Terpenes rival carbohydrates, steroids, and alkaloids in the chemical interest which they have stimulated, and again many of the fundamental reactions and generalizations of organic chemistry—for example, the Wagner-Meerwein rearrangement (Section 8-3a) and Bredt's rule (Section 8-3c)—were discovered during the course of terpene research.

16-46. The Isoprene Rule

The unifying structural characteristic of terpenes is their derivation from one monomeric structural unit, **isoprene** (C_5H_8; Section 8-5b). Thus the common terpenes are skeletally divisible into from two to eight **isoprene units** (Section 8-5b). As in rubber, vitamin A, and β-carotene (Section 8-5b), the isoprene units in terpenes are usually joined in *head-to-tail linkages*, although tail-to-tail linkages are occasionally encountered. The isoprene units making up several common terpenes are illustrated in Figure 16-33. The divisibility of terpene structures into isoprene units is

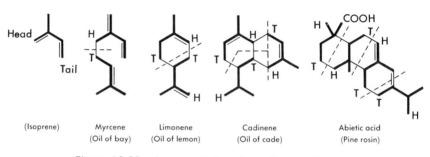

| (Isoprene) | Myrcene (Oil of bay) | Limonene (Oil of lemon) | Cadinene (Oil of cade) | Abietic acid (Pine rosin) |

Figure 16-33. Isoprene Units in Some Common Terpenes

referred to as the **isoprene rule,** and was first pointed out in 1887 by O. Wallach of the University of Göttingen, who received the Nobel Prize in chemistry in 1910. The isoprene rule has been of great value as a working hypothesis in the structural elucidation of terpenoid compounds.

16-47. Classification of Terpenes

Terpene molecules are classified on the basis of the number of isoprene units which they contain. The classes found in nature are listed in Table 16-4. Classes containing five or seven isoprene units are not found among natural terpenes. In the following sections we shall examine briefly representative members of each of these classes.

16-48. Monoterpenes

A monoterpene hydrocarbon, $C_{10}H_{16}$, has six hydrogen atoms less than the corresponding saturated alkane, $C_{10}H_{22}$. The deficiency of six hydrogen atoms in monoterpenes may be accommodated in four structural

Table 16-4. Classes of Terpenes

Class	Number of Carbon Atoms	Number of Isoprene Units
Monoterpenes	10	2
Sesquiterpenes	15	3
Diterpenes	20	4
Triterpenes	30	6
Tetraterpenes	40	8
Polyterpenes	$5n$	n

types: (1) acyclic monoterpenes with three double bonds, (2) monocyclic monoterpenes with two double bonds, (3) bicyclic monoterpenes with one double bond, and (4) tricyclic monoterpenes with no double bonds. Oxygenated and/or hydrogenated derivatives of each of these types are known, as seen in the following examples.

a. Acyclic Monoterpenes (see also myrcene, Figure 16-33).

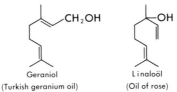
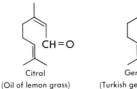

Citral	Geraniol	Linaloöl
(Oil of lemon grass)	(Turkish geranium oil)	(Oil of rose)

b. Monocyclic Monoterpenes (see also limonene, Figure 16-33).

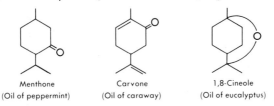

Menthone	Carvone	1,8-Cineole
(Oil of peppermint)	(Oil of caraway)	(Oil of eucalyptus)

c. Bicyclic Monoterpenes. This important class of monoterpenes contains a wide variety of skeletal types. Derivatives of each of the following *bicyclic saturated hydrocarbons* have been characterized. Dotted lines separate the two isoprene units involved in each structure.

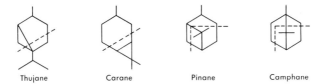

| Thujane | Carane | Pinane | Camphane |

Isobornylane   Isocamphane   Fenchane

Several important monoterpene representatives of these hydrocarbon types are the following, shown in both flat and perspective formulas.

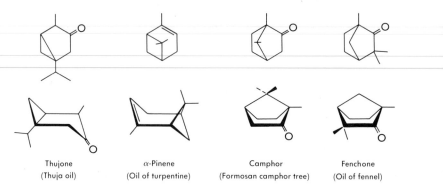

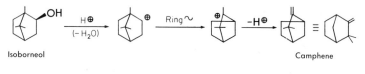

| Thujone | α-Pinene | Camphor | Fenchone |
| (Thuja oil) | (Oil of turpentine) | (Formosan camphor tree) | (Oil of fennel) |

It is among this group of monoterpenes, particularly, that the prevalence of molecular rearrangements during organic reactions first became apparent. The Wagner-Meerwein rearrangement during the dehydration of the camphane derivative *isoborneol* to the isocamphane derivative *camphene* is typical of the rearrangements which occur in these systems.

Isoborneol   Camphene

d. Tricyclic Monoterpenes.

Tricyclene   Cyclofenchene
(Obtained synthetically   (Obtained synthetically
from camphor)   from fenchone)

16-49. Sesquiterpenes

Sesquiterpenes, derived from $C_{15}H_{26}$, are known in nature mainly as acyclic, monocyclic, and bicyclic structures. The following sesquiterpenes, with their isoprene units indicated, are illustrative of each type.

   a. *Acyclic Sesquiterpenes.*

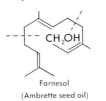

Farnesol   Nerolidol
(Ambrette seed oil)   (Oil of neroli)

b. *Monocyclic Sesquiterpenes.*

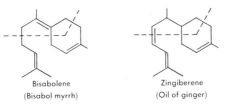

Bisabolene   Zingiberene
(Bisabol myrrh)   (Oil of ginger)

   c. *Bicyclic Sesquiterpenes.* These sesquiterpenes fall into several series, depending upon the type of aromatic hydrocarbon derivative which they yield on dehydrogenation with selenium (Section 10-3). The **cadalene series** yields *cadalene* (1,6-dimethyl-4-isopropylnaphthalene) on dehydro-

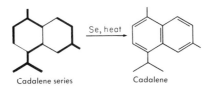

Cadalene series   Cadalene

genation, while the **eudalene series** affords *eudalene* (1-methyl-7-isopropyl-naphthalene), undergoing aromatization with expulsion of its angular

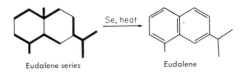

Eudalene series   Eudalene

methyl group. Note the different arrangement of isoprene units in each series.

Naturally occurring representatives of each series, respectively, are *cadinene* (cadalene type) from oil of cade (Figure 16-33) and *β-selinene* and *β-eudesmol* (eudalene type).

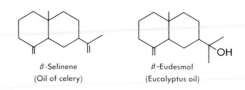

β-Selinene
(Oil of celery)

β-Eudesmol
(Eucalyptus oil)

A third type of bicyclic sesquiterpene is found in the **azulene series,** which contains the bicyclo[5.3.0]decane ring system, and which yields violet or blue azulene derivatives (Section 10-9) on dehydrogenation. The structure and dehydrogenation of two bicyclic sesquiterpenes of the azulene series are shown below, with isoprene units indicated in each. Azulene

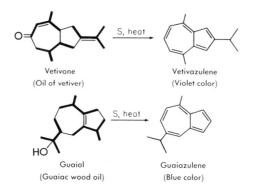

Vetivone
(Oil of vetiver)

Vetivazulene
(Violet color)

Guaiol
(Guaiac wood oil)

Guaiazulene
(Blue color)

hydrocarbons themselves also occur in certain natural oils. Thus vetivazulene has been isolated from vetiver oil, and chamazulene causes the blue color of chamomile oil.

An unusual bicyclo[7.2.0]undecane ring system was encountered in the sesquiterpene hydrocarbon *caryophyllene* (from oil of cloves), the final structure of which was deduced by D. H. R. Barton of Imperial College, London, in 1953. Several tricyclic sesquiterpenes are also known. *Copaene,* from African copaiba balsam, and *cedrol,* from cedar wood, are representative.

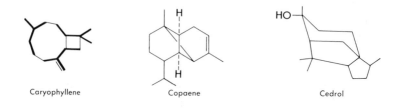

Caryophyllene

Copaene

Cedrol

16-50. Diterpenes

These C_{20} terpenoid compounds also occur as acyclic, monocyclic, bi-cyclic, and tricyclic derivatives. The most important *acyclic* diterpene is the alcohol *phytol*, $C_{20}H_{39}OH$, which occurs esterified in the chlorophyll of green plants (Section 16-12). The most important *monocyclic* diterpene is the fat-soluble compound *vitamin A* (Section 8-5b), which is required for good vision and which aids in resistance to infection. *Agathic acid*, $C_{20}H_{30}O_4$, from natural resins such as Manila copal and kauri copal, a fossil resin from New Zealand, is a typical *bicyclic* diterpene, while

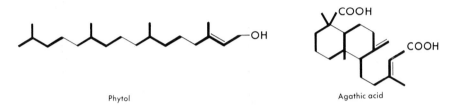

Phytol   Agathic acid

abietic acid from pine rosin (Figure 16-33) is representative of *tricyclic* diterpenes.

16-51. Triterpenes

The acyclic triterpenoid hydrocarbon *squalene*, $C_{30}H_{50}$, comprises up to 90 per cent of the liver oil of certain species of sharks of the family *Squalidae*. Squalene is made up of six isoprene units, joined in the manner Tail-Head, T-H, T-T, H-T, H-T. This gross structure was confirmed in 1931 by P. Karrer of the University of Zürich (Nobel Prize, 1937), who synthesized squalene from two molecules of the sesquiterpene bromide farnesyl bromide. The four central double bonds in squalene could, in

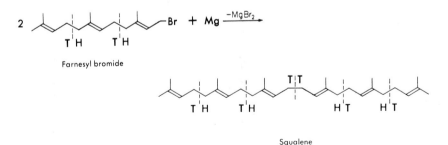

Farnesyl bromide

Squalene

principle, each be of either a *cis* or *trans* configuration, permitting a total of sixteen possible stereoisomers. X-ray diffraction studies involving

squalene, however, indicate that each of the central double bonds has a
trans configuration; that is, squalene has the all-*trans* geometrical structure
shown in Figure 16-34. The key position of squalene in the biogenesis of
complex terpenes and steroids is discussed in Section 16-53.

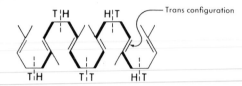

Figure 16-34.   Geometrical Configuration of Squalene

Triterpenes in nature are usually polycyclic in structure.   Mono- and
bicyclic triterpenes are not known, but *ambrein* from whale ambergris is
representative of the very rare class of **tricyclic triterpenes.   Tetracyclic
triterpenes** are found somewhat more plentifully, and *lanosterol*, which
occurs along with cholesterol in wool fat, is typical of this class.   **Penta-**

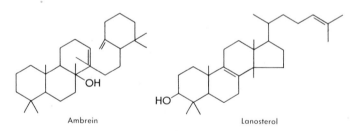

Ambrein   Lanosterol

cyclic triterpenoids, on the other hand, are of very widespread occurrence
in plants, where they may occur either in the free state or combined (as
aglycones) with various sugars.   Glycosides derived from pentacyclic triterpenes constitute one class of saponins (Section 16-36), and their aglycones are referred to as **triterpenoid sapogenins.** *α-Amyrin* from Manila
elemi resin and *oleanolic acid* from olive leaves, guaiac bark, and sugar beets

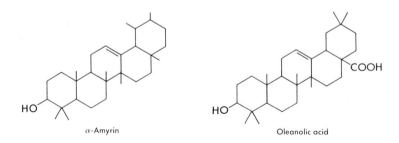

α-Amyrin   Oleanolic acid

are but two examples of the numerous pentacyclic triterpenoid compounds which have been isolated from a wide variety of plant sources.

16-52. Tetraterpenes—The Carotenoids

The **carotenoids** are reddish yellow pigments occurring in plants and animals. They are principally classed as **tetraterpenoid** compounds, which are oxygenated and/or highly unsaturated acyclic, monocyclic, and bicyclic C_{40} molecules derived from eight isoprene units. Carotenoids found in animals are either identical with, or derived from, the more plentiful members found among plants. Carotenoids of similar structure usually occur together in the same source, and their separations rely heavily on chromatographic procedures. In fact, the techniques of column chromatography (Section 3-5a) were chiefly developed during the course of early carotenoid research.

The most important *acyclic* tetraterpene is *lycopene*, $C_{40}H_{56}$, the red pigment in ripe tomato and watermelon. One kilogram of fresh tomato yields about 20 mg of lycopene. Its catalytic hydrogenation results in the uptake of 13 moles of hydrogen, and yields perhydrolycopene, $C_{40}H_{82}$. Hence lycopene contains no rings. In 1931 P. Karrer of Zürich established the structure of lycopene by synthesizing perhydrolycopene via the coupling of two units of dihydrophytyl bromide. Like squalene, lycopene is known to have all-*trans* configurations of its interior double bonds.

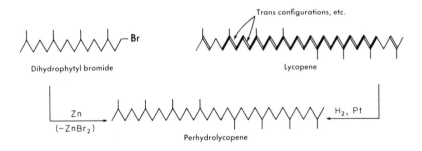

Trans configurations, etc.

Dihydrophytyl bromide   Lycopene

Zn
(−ZnBr₂) H_2, Pt

Perhydrolycopene

The prototypical *bicyclic* carotenoid hydrocarbon *carotene*, $C_{40}H_{56}$ (m.p. 168°), was first isolated in 1831 by H. W. F. Wackenroder, as red crystals from carrots. For a century carotene was considered to be a homogeneous substance, until the German chemist Richard Kuhn (Nobel Prize, 1938) separated it chromatographically into three isomers, α-carotene (m.p. 188°), β-carotene (m.p. 184°), and γ-carotene (m.p. 178°). Carotene from carrots contains about 15 per cent α-carotene, 85 per cent β-carotene (Section 8-5b), and a trace (0.1 per cent) of γ-carotene. Subsequent investigations by R. Kuhn, L. Zechmeister, H. Brockmann, and others have disclosed that the three carotenes are the structurally similar, all-*trans* mono- and bicyclic tetraterpenes shown below. The intestines and liver of

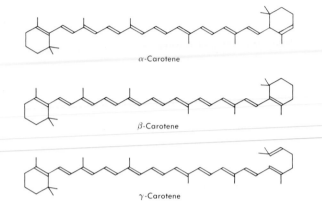

α-Carotene

β-Carotene

γ-Carotene

animals have the ability to cleave and hydroxylate β-carotene at its central double bond, producing two molecules of vitamin A. Thus β-carotene is a precursor of vitamin A in the body.

A number of oxygenated derivatives of monocyclic and bicyclic tetraterpenes are known. Referred to as **xanthins,** these compounds make up the red and yellow pigments of many plants, and of the parts of some animals. The following three examples represent typical xanthins.

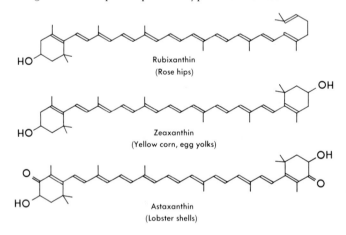

Rubixanthin
(Rose hips)

Zeaxanthin
(Yellow corn, egg yolks)

Astaxanthin
(Lobster shells)

16-53. Biogenesis of Natural Products

The origin of complex natural products from simple molecules in animals and plants has intrigued chemists speculatively for several decades.

In recent years, however, with the advent of radioactive tracers, this fascinating problem has been approachable experimentally, and the biosyntheses of many complex natural products are now substantially understood. While a detailed examination of biogenesis is beyound our scope, it is instructive to survey briefly the biogenetic schemes leading to some of the types of natural products we have encountered.

Coenzyme A (abbreviated HSCoA) occurs as part of an enzyme which catalyzes biological acetylation reactions, and appears to be implicated in all biosynthetic processes which proceed by way of two-carbon units. Its structure was elucidated during 1948–1953, and its synthesis was accom-

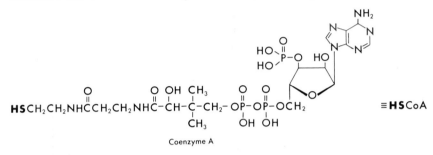

Coenzyme A

plished by H. G. Khorana in 1961. Coenzyme A is intimately involved in carbohydrate metabolism, and from this, with the subsequent biosynthesis of fatty acids, terpenes, and steroids in plants and animals. Its S-acetyl derivative, *acetylcoenzyme A*, $CH_3COSCoA$, has a highly reactive C–S bond, and the first step in biosynthesis is the self-condensation of $CH_3COSCoA$ to form *acetoacetylcoenzyme A*. By subsequent enzymatically

$$CH_3COSCoA + H-CH_2COSCoA \rightleftharpoons CH_3COCH_2COSCoA + HSCoA$$

Acetoacetylcoenzyme A

catalyzed reduction, dehydration, and hydrogenation, acetoacetylcoenzyme A may be converted into butyrylcoenzyme A. Similar condensation

$$CH_3COCH_2COSCoA \xrightarrow{(H)} CH_3\overset{OH}{\underset{|}{CH}}CH_2COSCoA \xrightarrow{-H_2O}$$

$$CH_3CH=CHCOSCoA \xrightarrow{(H)} CH_3CH_2CH_2COSCoA$$

Butyrylcoenzyme A

of the latter with more $CH_3COSCoA$ yields butyroacetylcoenzyme A (16-36). Repetition of these sequences of reactions builds the chain length of 16-**36** up progressively by two carbon units, and ultimately affords the long chain fatty acids. This sequence explains why natural fatty acids are usually straight chain and contain even numbers of carbon atoms.

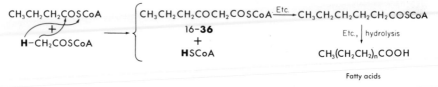

In other biological reactions catalyzed by other enzyme systems, acetyl-coenzyme A and acetoacetylcoenzyme A may condense to form the intermediate 16-**37**. Under the influence of reduced triphosphopyridine nucleotide (TPNH; Section 16-12), 16-**37** is ultimately converted into *mevalonic acid* (16-**38**), the key intermediate in terpene and steroid biosynthesis.

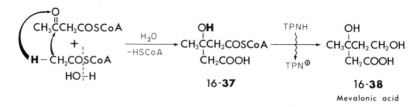

Mevalonic acid is next converted, under the influence of adenosine triphosphate (ATP; Section 16-12), into its 5-phosphate (16-**39**) and 5-pyrophosphate (16-**40**). Spontaneous decarboxylation and dehydration of 16-**40** leads to isopentenyl pyrophosphate (16-**41**) and β,β-dimethylallyl pyrophosphate (16-**42**), which are the "active forms," so to speak, of *iso-*

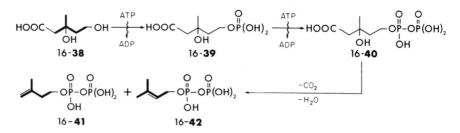

prene in terpene and steroid biosyntheses. Enzymatic condensation of 16-**41** with 16-**42**, for example, affords the monoterpene *geraniol*, as its pyrophosphate. Similar condensation of the latter with 16-**41** yields the acyclic sesquiterpene alcohol *farnesol*, as its pyrophosphate. Continued such additions, followed by cyclizations, oxidations, dehydrations, and the like, produce the variety of terpene derivatives which we have surveyed briefly above.

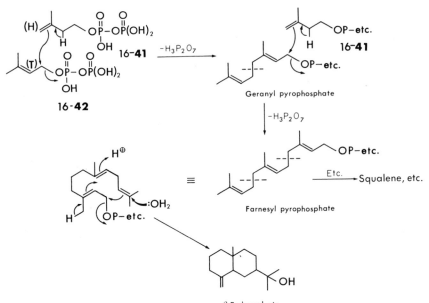

Geranyl pyrophosphate

Farnesyl pyrophosphate

Etc. → Squalene, etc.

β-Eudesmol, etc.

One of the key products in the above biosynthetic scheme for terpenes is the triterpene hydrocarbon *squalene* (Section 16-51). Through isotopic labeling experiments, conducted by K. E. Bloch of Harvard University (Nobel Prize, 1964) and others, it has been shown that squalene is biologically converted by cyclization reactions into the tetracyclic triterpene *lanosterol*. The latter, undergoing various small molecular changes brought about enzymatically in the animal or plant, is the precursor of *cholesterol*, from which all other natural steroidal substances are biogenetically derived.

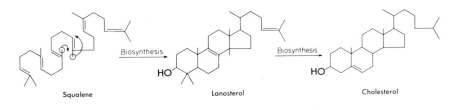

| Squalene | Lanosterol | Cholesterol |

SUPPLEMENTARY READING

Carbohydrates
1. *Structural Carbohydrate Chemistry*, E. G. V. Percival, J. Garnet Miller Ltd., London, 1962.

2. *The Monosaccharides*, J. Stanek, M. Cerny, J. Kocourek, and J. Pacak, Academic, New York, 1963.
3. *Recent Advances in the Chemistry of Cellulose and Starch*, J. Honeyman, Heywood and Co. Ltd., London, 1959.
4. "The Basic Work of Fischer and van't Hoff in Carbohydrate Chemistry," C. S. Hudson, *J. Chem. Educ.*, **30,** 120 (1953).
5. "Emil Fischer's Discovery of the Configuration of Glucose," C. S. Hudson, *J. Chem. Educ.*, **18,** 353 (1941).
6. "Emil Fischer," L. Darmstaedter and R. E. Oesper, *J. Chem. Educ.*, **5,** 37 (1928).
7. "The High Points in the Development of Cellulose Chemistry since 1876," E. Heuser, *J. Chem. Educ.*, **29,** 449 (1952).
8. "Cellulose, Glycogen and Starch," T. J. Schoch, *J. Chem. Educ.*, **25,** 626 (1948).
9. "Symposium on Wood as a Chemical Raw Material," *J. Chem. Educ.*, **35,** 482–506 (1958).

Photosynthesis

1. *The Photosynthesis of Carbon Compounds*, M. Calvin and J. A. Bassham, Benjamin, New York, 1962.
2. "Advances in Photosynthesis," R. B. Park, *J. Chem. Educ.*, **39,** 424 (1962).
3. "The Path of Carbon in Photosynthesis," J. A. Bassham, *Scientific American*, June, 1962.
4. "New Aspects of Photosynthesis," J. A. Bassham, *J. Chem. Educ.*, **38,** 151 (1961).
5. "The Role of Light in Photosynthesis," D. I. Arnon, *Scientific American*, November, 1960.
6. "Photosynthesis," J. A. Bassham, *J. Chem. Educ.*, **36,** 548 (1959).
7. "Photosynthesis in Cell-free Systems," C. A. Kind, *J. Chem. Educ.*, **33,** 530 (1956).
8. "Isotope Studies in Photosynthesis," J. A. Bassham, A. A. Benson and M. Calvin, *J. Chem. Educ.*, **30,** 274 (1953).
9. "Progress in Photosynthesis," E. I. Rabinowitch, *Scientific American*, November, 1953.
10. "The Relationship of Plant Pigments to Photosynthesis," J. H. C. Smith, *J. Chem. Educ.*, **26,** 631 (1949).
11. "ATP," P. K. Stumpf, *Scientific American*, April, 1953.
12. "The Origin of Life," G. Wald, *Scientific American*, August, 1954.

Proteins

1. *The Chemistry and Function of Proteins*, F. Haurowitz, Academic, New York, 1963.
2. "The Chemical Structure of Proteins," W. H. Stein and S. Moore, *Scientific American*, February, 1961.
3. "The Three-Dimensional Structure of a Protein Molecule," J. C. Kendrew, *Scientific American*, December, 1961.
4. "Collagen," J. Gross, *Scientific American*, May, 1961.
5. "Proteins," P. Doty, *Scientific American*, September, 1957.

6. "Models of the α-Helix Configuration in Polypeptides," T. A. Wheeler, *J. Chem. Educ.*, **34,** 136 (1957).
7. "The Structure of Protein Molecules," L. Pauling, R. B. Corey and R. Haywood, *Scientific American*, July, 1954.
8. "Potentialities of Protein Isomerism," I. Asimov, *J. Chem. Educ.*, **31,** 125 (1954).
9. "Discovery of Insulin: Frederick Banting," A. B. Garrett, *J. Chem. Educ.*, **40,** 211 (1963).
10. "The Insulin Molecule," E. O. P. Thompson, *Scientific American*, May, 1955.
11. "Plasma Expanders," R. T. Merrick, *J. Chem. Educ.*, **30,** 368 (1953).
12. "Liebig and Proteins," H. B. Vickery, *J. Chem. Educ.*, **19,** 73 (1942).
13. "Countercurrent Distribution," M. Verzele and N. Schamp, *J. Chem. Educ.*, **39,** 97 (1962).
14. "Electrophoresis," G. W. Gray, *Scientific American*, December, 1951.
15. "An Introduction to Electrophoresis," R. A. Alberty, *J. Chem. Educ.*, **25,** 426, 619 (1948).
16 "Separation of Peptides by Paper Electrophoresis and Chromatography," P. Kasimer and H. J. Morowitz, *J. Chem. Educ.*, **39,** 430 (1962).
17. "Identification of Amino Acids in a Protein Hydrolysate by Paper Chromatography," L. B. Clapp and C. Hausch, *J. Chem. Educ.*, **37,** 293 (1960).

Enzymes

1. *Outlines of Enzyme Chemistry, 2nd Edition,* J. B. Nielands and P. K. Stumpf, John Wiley and Sons, Inc., New York, 1958.
2. "Progress in Enzyme Chemistry," J. B. Neilands and S. Rogers, *J. Chem. Educ.*, **39,** 154 (1962).
3. "Enzymes and Metaphor," I. Asimov, *J. Chem. Educ.*, **36,** 535 (1959).
4. "Transformation of Organic Compounds by Microorganisms," D. Perlman, *J. Chem. Educ.*, **36,** 60 (1959).
5. "The Kinetics of Enzyme Catalyzed Reactions," W. H. R. Shaw, *J. Chem. Educ.*, **34,** 22 (1957).
6. "Enzymes, the Basis of Life," J. B. Sumner, *J. Chem. Educ.*, **29,** 114 (1952).

Nucleic Acids

1. *The Chemistry of Nucleosides and Nucleotides,* A. M. Michelson, Academic, New York, 1963.
2. "Ribonucleic Acid, the Simplest Information-transmitting Molecule," H. Fraenkel-Conrat, *J. Chem. Educ.*, **40,** 216 (1963).
3. "Messenger RNA," J. H. Hurwitz and J. J. Furth, *Scientific American*, February, 1962.
4. "Ribonucleic Acid and Protein Synthesis," J. S. Roth, *J. Chem. Educ.*, **38,** 217 (1961).
5. "How Cells Make Molecules," V. G. Allfrey and A. E. Mirsky, *Scientific American*, September, 1961.
6. "Nucleic Acids and Proteins," M. B. Hoagland, *Scientific American*, December, 1959.

7. "Nucleic Acids, Genes and Viruses," J. L. Fairley, *J. Chem. Educ.*, **36,** 544 (1959).

8. "The Duplication of Chromosomes," J. H. Taylor, *Scientific American*, June, 1958.

9. "Nucleic Acids," F. H. C. Crick, *Scientific American*, September, 1957.

10. "The Structure of the Hereditary Material," F. H. C. Crick, *Scientific American*, October, 1954.

Steroids

1. *Steroids*, L. F. Fieser and M. Fieser, Reinhold Publishing Corp., New York, 1959.

2. *Steroid Drugs*, N. Applezwieg, McGraw-Hill Book Co., Inc., New York, 1962.

3. "Some Recent Advances in the Field of Steroids," R. E. Beyler, *J. Chem. Educ.*, **37,** 491 (1960).

4. "Steroids," L. F. Fieser, *Scientific American*, January, 1955.

5. "Cortisone and ACTH," G. W. Gray, *Scientific American*, March, 1950.

Alkaloids

1. *The Alkaloids*, K. W. Bentley, Interscience, New York, 1957.

2. "Alkaloids—the World's Pain Killers," R. L. Ray, *J. Chem. Educ.*, **37,** 451 (1960).

3. "Determination of Alkaloid Structure," A. W. Sangster, *J. Chem. Educ.*, **37,** 454, 518 (1960).

Terpenes

1. *Mono- and Sesquiterpenoids*, P. de Mayo, Interscience, New York, 1959.

2. *The Higher Terpenoids*, P. de Mayo, Interscience, New York, 1959.

3. "Nature of Essential Oils. I. Production," F. S. Sterrett, *J. Chem. Educ.*, **39,** 203 (1962).

4. "Nature of Essential Oils. II. Chemical Constituents, Analysis," F. S. Sterrett, *J. Chem. Educ.*, **39,** 246 (1962).

5. "Tall Oil and Terpene Derivatives," G. H. Eick, *J. Chem. Educ.*, **34,** 613 (1957).

6. "Indispensable Leaf Yellow," H. H. Strain, *J. Chem. Educ.*, **23,** 262 (1946).

7. "Otto Wallach: The First Organizer of the Terpenes," W. S. Partridge and E. R. Schierz, *J. Chem. Educ.*, **24,** 106 (1947).

Biosynthesis

1. *The Biosynthesis of Steroids, Terpenes and Acetogenins*, J. H. Richards and J. B. Hendrickson, Benjamin, New York, 1964.

2. *Biogenesis of Natural Compounds*, P. Bernfeld, The Macmillan Co., New York, 1963.

3. *The Biosynthesis of Proteins*, H. Chantrenne, Pergamon, New York, 1961.

Miscellaneous

1. *The Natural Pigments*, K. W. Bentley, Interscience, New York, 1960.

2. "Structural Variety of Natural Products," W. R. Roderick, *J. Chem. Educ.*, **39,** 2 (1962).

3. "Chemical Structure and Biological Activity," A. Burger, *J. Chem Educ.*, **35,** 142 (1958).

4. "The Chemistry of Flower Color Variation," T. A. Geissman, *J. Chem. Educ.*, **26,** 657 (1949).

Questions

Questions for Chapter 1

1-1   List three general natural sources of organic compounds.

1-2   What element must be present in an organic compound?

1-3   What other elements are found most frequently in organic compounds?

1-4   Describe the "vital force" theory and explain its origin. Why has it been abandoned?

1-5   Why is there such a large number of compounds of carbon, compared to those of any other element?

Questions for Chapter 2

2-1   Define each of the following terms and illustrate each with an example: (a) acyclic compound, (b) aliphatic compound, (c) aromatic compound, (d) bicyclic compound, (e) heterocyclic compound, (f) isoelectronic, (g) stereoisomers, (h) geometrical isomers, (i) optical isomers, (j) van der Waals forces.

2-2   Distinguish between or among the following: (a) empirical, molecular, and structural formulas: (b) ionic, covalent, and coordinate covalent bonds: (c) permanent and induced dipoles.

2-3   Name the functional group present and write general formulas for the following types of compounds: (a) alkene, (b) alcohol, (c) carboxylic acid, (d) amide, (e) ketone, (f) nitrile, (g) alkyl bromide.

2-4   Write Kekulé and electron dot formulas for the following molecular formulas: (a) H_2CO_3, (b) HNO_3, (c) $SOCl_2$, (d) C_2H_5Br, (e) $CHCl_3$, (f) C_3H_8, (g) C_3H_6, (h) C_2H_2, (i) CH_2O, (j) CH_2O_2, (k) CH_5N.

2-5   Write structural formulas for the first six members of the homologous series of straight chain aldehydes.

2-6   Write structural formulas for all of the compounds having each of the following molecular formulas: (a) C_5H_{10}, (b) C_3H_8O, (c) C_4H_5Cl.

2-7   Write condensed structural formulas for each of the following: (a) all isomeric four-carbon alkenes, (b) all isomeric five-carbon alcohols.

2-8 State and explain the difference in boiling points of ionic and covalent compounds. State and explain the difference in melting points.

2-9 Are racemates optically active? Why?

2-10 Draw a three-dimensional representation showing the spatial distribution of the atoms in carbon tetrachloride and in *cis*- and *trans*-Cl—CH=CH—Cl.

2-11 Which of the following structures correspond to molecules which will have geometric isomers? (a) $(CH_3)_2C=CHC_2H_5$, (b) $ClCH_2CH=CHCH_3$, (c) $ClCH_2CH=CHCH_2Cl$, (d) $HOOCC\equiv CCOOH$, (e) $CH_2=CHCH_2COOH$, (f) $HOOCCH_2CH=CHCOOH$,

(g) $CH_3CH_2CH_2COOH$, (h) ⟨ ⟩—CH_3, (i) CH_3—⟨ ⟩—CH_3.

2-12 Indicate the asymmetric carbon atom, if any, in each of the following structures: (a) $CH_3CHBrCH_2CH_3$, (b) $DCH_2CH(OH)CH_3$, (c) $HC\equiv C(CH_2)_6CH_3$, (d) $CH_2=C(Br)CH_3$, (e) $BrClCHCOOH$, (f) $(CH_3CH_2)_2CHCOOH$, (g) $CH_3CH_2CH(CH_3)COOH$.

2-13 Which of the isomeric five-carbon alcohols in Question 2-7(b) has an asymmetric carbon atom? Make a perspective drawing of the enantiomers of each such isomer.

2-14 Draw Newman projection formulas for all nonequivalent conformations of $CH_3CH_2CH_2CH_3$, considering rotation about the *central* carbon-carbon bond. Are the nonbonded interactions greater in the eclipsed form(s) of this compound than in ethane? Explain. Why is it that conformational isomers of neither compound have been isolated?

2-15 Which bond in each of the following pairs has the greater degree of ionic character? Why? (a) B—N or C—N, (b) C—F or C—O, (c) Si—Cl or P—S.

2-16 What are the characteristics which make C^{14} a useful isotope for tracer experiments?

2-17 Explain how the use of C^{14} dating may be employed to determine the age of a piece of cloth found in an archeological excavation.

Questions for Chapter 3

3-1 Define each of the following terms: (a) mother liquor, (b) eluate, (c) adsorbent, (d) R_f value, (e) boiling point, (f) melting point.

3-2 Distinguish clearly between: (a) distillation and sublimation, (b) column chromatography and thin layer chromatography, (c) chromatography and ion exchange.

3-3 Describe each of the following processes and indicate why each works: (a) fractional distillation, (b) vapor phase chromatography, (c) extraction.

3-4 Under what circumstances would you employ vacuum distillation in the isolation or purification of a compound? When would you employ an ion exchange resin?

3-5 What are the necessary conditions for the use of steam distillation in the isolation of a substance? How does steam distillation differ from ordinary distillation?

3-6 Why is it often necessary to crystallize a compound several times before it is pure?

3-7 What methods are employed to determine experimentally whether a compound is pure?

Questions for Chapter 4

4-1 Explain the difference between the partial synthesis and the total synthesis of a compound.

4-2 Describe the process used in the qualitative analysis of organic compounds for nitrogen, sulfur, and halogens. In what form of inorganic salts do these elements appear for subsequent detection?

4-3 Describe the main features of the quantitative procedures used in the analyses of organic compounds for carbon, hydrogen, nitrogen, sulfur, and halogens.

4-4 Explain how the molecular weight of an organic compound may be determined by means of mass spectrometry. How does the value obtained by this method compare in accuracy with the value obtained by other means?

4-5 What is the general effect of the "natural abundance" of C^{13} on the mass spectrum of an organic compound?

4-6 Explain how x-ray diffraction is used in studying the structures of organic substances.

4-7 Distinguish between: (a) stretching and bending vibrations, (b) absorption band and absorption spectrum, (c) ground states and excited states.

4-8 Explain the basis for the absorption of energy in the ultraviolet-visible, infrared, and nuclear magnetic resonance regions of the radiant energy spectrum.

4-9 What is the difference between monochromatic light and ordinary light in the visible region of the spectrum?

4-10 Why is ultraviolet light more energetic than infrared light?

4-11 Explain why the chemical shift of a hydrogen atom bonded to nitrogen is different than that of a hydrogen bonded to carbon. What is the cause of spin-spin splitting?

4-12 How many major types of signals would you expect in the NMR spectrum of the following compounds, and what would the relative intensities of the signals

$$O$$
$$\|$$

be? (a) $CH_3CH{=}O$, (b) CH_3CCH_3, (c) $(CH_3)_2CHOH$,

$$O$$
$$\|$$

(d) $CH_3CH_2CH_2CH_3$, (e) $CH_3CH_2COCH_3$.

4-13 Suggest a means of distinguishing between: (a) an ether and an ester, (b) an aldehyde and a carboxylic acid, (c) an alkyl halide and an alkene.

4-14 A compound of unknown identity has a molecular weight of 141 ± 3 and yields $(CH_3)_2CHCH_2CH{=}O$ as the only product upon ozonolysis. What are the possible structural formulas for the compound?

4-15 How could you distinguish between $CH_3CH{=}CHCH_2CH_2CH_3$ and $(CH_3)_2C{=}CHCH_2CH_3$?

4-16 (a) A 0.528 g sample of a compound, A, when dissolved in 10 g of benzene, gives a solution which boils at 82.2°. What is the molecular weight of A?
(b) Borneol melts at 204° and has a molal freezing point constant of 35.8°. It is found that a mixture of 20.00 mg of compound B and 1.000 g of borneol melts at 200°. Calculate the molecular weight of compound B.
(c) Exaltone, a C_{15} cyclic ketone used in perfumery, melts at 65.6° and has a molal freezing point constant of 21.3. A mixture of 40.0 mg of compound C and 1.000 g of exaltone melts at 63.6°. Calculate the molecular weight of C.

4-17 Calculate the empirical formulas for the compounds shown by analysis to contain: (a) C, 58.84; H, 4.09; and N, 11.38 per cent: (b) C, 51.80; H, 3.62; and N, 10.07 per cent: (c) C, 39.32; H, 8.25; and S, 26.24 per cent: (d) C, 45.84; H, 4.49; N, 8.91 and S, 20.40 per cent.

4-18 A compound was found to contain 58.05 per cent C, 6.48 per cent H, and 22.60 per cent N. Its molecular weight is 124. Calculate the molecular formula of the compound.

4-19 Analysis of compound X shows it to contain C, 19.67; H, 4.92; and N, 22.95 per cent. A solution of 0.250 g of X in 100 g of ethylene dibromide (freezing point 10.0°; molal freezing point constant 10.5) freezes at 9.58°. Calculate the molecular formula of X.

4-20 The combustion of a 10.000 mg sample of compound Y yielded 29.550 mg of CO_2 and 5.289 mg of H_2O. Qualitative analysis eliminated the presence of other elements except oxygen. A mixture of 0.0119 g of Y in 1.000 g of camphor was found to melt at 1.82° lower than pure camphor. Calculate the molecular formula of compound Y.

4-21 Qualitative analysis of compound Z eliminated the possible presence of any elements other than carbon, hydrogen and oxygen. The combustion of 8.000 mg of compound Z afforded 15.623 mg of CO_2 and 7.951 mg of H_2O. Molecular weight measurements by the freezing point method gave a value of 92 ± 4 for compound Z. Calculate its molecular formula. Could Z be an alcohol? A carboxylic acid? An ether? Explain. How could you confirm your decision?

Questions for Chapter 5

5-1 Define and illustrate each of the following terms: (a) atomic orbital, (b) molecular orbital, (c) canonical structure, (d) delocalization energy (e) nodal plane in a molecular orbital, (f) resonance energy.

5-2 What are the circumstances under which a resonance hybrid may be expected to exist?

5-3 What is the condition for bond formation according to molecular orbital theory?

5-4 State three general consequences of resonance.

5-5 Explain two experimental methods for estimating resonance energy.

5-6 Distinguish between or among the following, using examples to illustrate your answers: (a) s and p orbitals, (b) digonal, trigonal, and tetragonal hybridizations.

5-7 Draw pictorial representations of a σ and a π bond.

5-8 Compare the relative stabilities of: (a) $RC\equiv N:$, $R\overset{\ominus}{\underset{..}{C}}=\overset{\oplus}{N}:$, and $RC=\overset{\oplus}{N}\overset{\ominus}{\underset{..}{:}}$,

(b)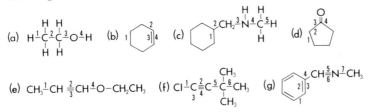

5-9 The length of the central carbon-carbon bond in butadiene, $CH_2=CH-CH=CH_2$, is 1.46 Å, whereas that expected for an ordinary carbon-carbon bond is 1.54 Å. Explain.

5-10 The heat of hydrogenation of butadiene is 57.1 kcal/mole. Calculate its resonance energy.

5-11 Draw a diagram of the molecular orbitals available to the π electrons of butadiene.

5-12 Show the major canonical structures involved in the resonance hybrid of each of the following: (a) $CO_3{}^{2-}$, (b) $NO_3{}^{\ominus}$, (c) $RCOO^{\ominus}$, (d) CO_2, (e) RNO_2, (f) $CH_2=CHCH=O$, (g) $CH_2=CHCH=CHCH=CH_2$, (h) $CH_2=CHCH_2{}^{\oplus}$.

5-13 Define the type of molecular orbitals in the numbered bonds of each of the following structures:

Questions for Chapter 6

6-1 Give a brief definition for each of the following terms: (a) addition reaction, (b) carbene, (c) condensation reaction, (d) elimination reaction, (e) Lewis acid, (f) Lewis base, (g) paramagnetism, (h) substitution reaction, (i) reaction mechanism.

6-2 Distinguish clearly between: (a) activation energy and heat of reaction, (b) homolytic and heterolytic bond cleavages, (c) transient intermediate and transition state.

6-3 Explain how ionic and free radical reactions may be distinguished in terms of their experimental characteristics.

6-4 What qualitative relationship exists between reaction rate and activation energy for a given reaction?

6-5 What can you say concerning the maximum value of the activation energy of an endothermic reaction and the heat of this reaction?

6-6 Cite evidence supporting the existence of free radicals, carbonium ions, and carbanions.

6-7 Compare the configurations of $(CH_3)_3C^{\oplus}$, $(CH_3)_3C:^{\ominus}$, and $(CH_3)_3C\cdot$.

6-8 Predict and explain the relative ease of dissociation of the members of each of the following groups of organic chlorides into carbonium ions and chloride ions: (a) $CH_3CH_2CH_2Cl$, $(CH_3CH_2)_2CHCl$, and $(CH_3CH_2)_3CCl$; (b) Ph_3CCl, $PhCH_2Cl$, and $PhCH_2CH_2Cl$; (c) $CH_3CH_2CH_2Cl$, $CH_3CH=CHCl$, and $CH_2=CHCH_2Cl$.

6-9 Why is an α hydrogen easier to remove than a β or γ hydrogen from
$$\overset{\gamma}{CH_3}-\overset{\beta}{CH_2}-\overset{\alpha}{CH_2}-CH=O$$ upon reaction with NaOEt? What would be the configuration of the carbanion obtained on removal of the α hydrogen?

6-10 Write formulas for the initial product or products from each of the following pairs of reactants. Use electron dots to show the new bond resulting in each reaction. (a) $AlCl_3$ and $CH_3OCH(CH_3)_2$, (b) $CH_3CH_2C\equiv N$ and H_2SO_4 (c) CH_3CH_2Br and $FeBr_3$, (d) $ZnCl_2$ and $(CH_3)_2CHCH=O$, (e) CH_3OH and BF_3, (f) $(CH_3CH_2)_2C=O$ and HCl, (g) HBr and $(CH_3)_2NH$.

6-11 Why is it that silver ion will form a complex with $RCH=CHR$ but not with RCH_2CH_2R?

6-12 Place the following substances in order of their increasing ease of dissociation into free radicals. Explain the reason for your choice.

(a) $(CH_3)_3CC(CH_3)_3$, (b) Ph_3CCPh_3, (c)

6-13 What products would result on heating tetrapropyllead, $(CH_3CH_2CH_2)_4Pb$, at 800°?

6-14 Indicate the type of reaction mechanism (carbonium ion, carbanion, or free radical) prevailing during each of the following transformations, and suggest the individual steps for each mechanism.

(a) When shaken with concentrated hydrochloric acid, t-butyl alcohol, $(CH_3)_3COH$, forms t-butyl chloride, $(CH_3)_3CCl$.

(b) Triphenylmethane, Ph_3CH, reacts with potassium amide, KNH_2, in liquid ammonia to form an orange solution, from which the potassium salt of triphenylmethane may be recovered by evaporation.

(c) Methane and bromine yield methyl bromide, CH_3Br, on irradiation with ultraviolet light.

(d) When the vapors of acetone, CH_3COCH_3, are brought into contact with a red hot wire (700–750°), methane and a valuable compound known as ketene, $CH_2=C=O$, are formed as the principal products.

6-15 Which of the following would you expect to yield free radicals of the greatest half-life in a Paneth experiment? $Pb(CH_3)_4$, $Pb(C(CH_3)_3)_4$, or $Pb(CH(CH_3)_2)_4$.

6-16 Consider the following consecutive reaction:

$$A \xrightarrow{E_{act} = 20 \text{ kcal/mole}} B \xrightarrow{E_{act} = 10 \text{ kcal/mole}} C$$

Which is the rate-controlling step in the conversion of A to C? Why?

6-17 Calculate the heat of reaction for each of the following, and state whether the reaction is endothermic or exothermic (see Table 2-7).

(a) $CH_3CH_3 + Br_2 \rightarrow CH_3CH_2Br + HBr$

(b) $HC\equiv CH + H_2 \xrightarrow{\text{Catalyst}} CH_2=CH_2$

(c) $CH_3CH_2CH_2Br + HI \rightarrow CH_3CH_2CH_2I + HBr$

(d) $(CH_3)_3COH + HCl \rightarrow (CH_3)_3CCl + H_2O$

(e) $CH_3I + HI \rightarrow CH_4 + I_2$

6-18 Draw an energy diagram for the reaction in Question 6-17(a).

6-19 The combination of chlorine atoms occurs with zero activation energy. Draw an energy diagram representing the dissociation of chlorine molecules into atoms.

Questions for Chapter 7

7-1 Write IUPAC names for the following alkyl groups:

a. $CH_3-\overset{\overset{\displaystyle CH_3}{|}}{CH}-CH_2CH_2-$

c. $CH_3\overset{\overset{\displaystyle H_3C}{|}}{\underset{\underset{\displaystyle CH_2}{|}}{C}}-\overset{\overset{\displaystyle CH_3}{|}}{CH}-$
$\quad\quad\quad\quad CH_3$

b. $CH_3CH_2\overset{\overset{\displaystyle}{|}}{\underset{\underset{\underset{\displaystyle CH_3}{|}}{CH_2}}{C}}(CH_3)CH_2-$

d.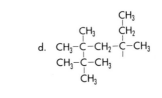

7-2 Give IUPAC names for the following and draw the structural formulas for the compounds where these are not given.

a. The isomeric straight-chain (noncyclic) hexanes

b. The isomeric straight chain heptanes

c. $CH_3CH_2\overset{\overset{\displaystyle}{|}}{\underset{\underset{\displaystyle CH_3}{|}}{CH}}CH_2\overset{\overset{\displaystyle}{|}}{\underset{\underset{\displaystyle CH_3}{|}}{CH}}CH_3$

e. $CH_3CH_2CH_2CH_2\overset{\overset{\displaystyle}{|}}{CH}CH_2CH_2CH_3$
$\quad\quad CH_3CH_2CH_2CH_2CHCH_2CH_2CH_3$

d. $CH_3\overset{\overset{\displaystyle}{|}}{\underset{\underset{\displaystyle CH_3}{|}}{CH}}CH_2\overset{\overset{\displaystyle}{|}}{\underset{\underset{\underset{\displaystyle CH_3}{|}}{CH}CH_3}{CH}}CH_3$

f. $CH_3\overset{\overset{\displaystyle}{|}}{\underset{\underset{\displaystyle Cl}{|}}{CH}}CH_2CH_2\overset{\overset{\displaystyle}{|}}{\underset{\underset{\displaystyle CH_2CH_3}{|}}{CH}}CH_3$

g. $CH_3CH[C(CH_3)_3]_2$

i.

$$CH_3 \quad CH_3$$
$$\backslash CH /$$
$$CH_3 \qquad\qquad CH_3$$
$$CH-C-CH$$
$$CH_3 \qquad\qquad CH_3$$
$$CH$$
$$CH_3 \quad CH_3$$

h. $CH_3CH_2CH_2CH_2CHCH_2CH_2CHCH_3$
$\qquad\qquad\qquad\quad CH_2 \qquad NO_2$
$\qquad\qquad\qquad\quad CH_3CH$
$\qquad\qquad\qquad\qquad CH_3$

7-3 Draw structural formulas for:

a. 3,4-Dimethyl-5-ethyloctane   d. 4,4-Di(2-chloroethyl)octane

b. 4-Methyl-6-ethyl-5-isobutyldecane   e. 2,5-Dimethyl-3-isopropyl-3-chlo-

c. 5-Chloro-2-nitro-4-isopropylheptane   rohexane

7-4 Describe the difference between the following:

a. An alkylaromatic hydrocarbon and a cycloalkane

b. Polymerization and alkylation

c. Thermal and catalytic cracking

d. The Bergius and the Fischer-Tropsch processes

7-5 How are lubricating oil, paraffin wax, and Vaseline isolated from petroleum?

7-6 How is the octane rating of a gasoline decided? What organometallic compound is added to improve the octane rating of gasoline?

7-7 Write equations for the following reactions:

a. Isomerization of an alkane

b. The water gas reaction

c. Pyrolysis of an alkane

d. Formation of carbon black

e. The formation of carbene

7-8 Explain the increase in the boiling points of the homologous straight-chain alkanes with increasing molecular weight. Why does a branched-chain alkane boil at a lower temperature than the isomeric straight-chain compound?

7-9 Provide the information requested for each of the following:

a. The structural formulas for the products from the pyrolysis of pentane

b. The structural formulas and names of the monosubstitution products from the reaction of heptane with chlorine at 300°.

c. The structural formulas and names of the mononitroalkanes from the vapor phase nitration of butane at 420°

d. The structural formula and name of the product formed from the reaction

$$\qquad\qquad\qquad\qquad\qquad\qquad\qquad\qquad O \qquad O$$
$$\qquad\qquad\qquad\qquad\qquad\qquad\qquad\qquad \parallel \qquad \parallel$$
of excess hydrazine and sodium ethoxide with $\quad CH_3C-CH-CCH_3$
$$\qquad\qquad\qquad\qquad\qquad\qquad\qquad\qquad\qquad CH_3CHCHO$$

e. The structural formula and name of the products from the reaction of carbene with 2,2,4-trimethylpentane (note that this compound is commonly known as isooctane).

7-10 Write equations for the following:

    a. Two different procedures for the synthesis of butane from a ketone

    b. Three different methods for the conversion of 1-bromo-4-methylhexane to 3-methylhexane

    c. Five different procedures for the synthesis of 2,2-dimethylbutane (commonly known as neohexane)

    d. The synthesis of 2-methylpentane from three different carbonyl-containing compounds.

7-11 Write equations for each of the following:

    a. The photobromination of ethane to yield two different compounds having the formula $C_2H_4Br_2$

    b. The formation of 2,2- and 2,3-dimethylbutanes from the catalytic alkylation of isobutane with ethylene

7-12 An alkene C_4H_6 was isolated from an alkane-cracking experiment. A 5 ml sample of the gas was mixed with 100 ml of hydrogen over a platinum catalyst. At the end of the reaction the new volume was 95 ml. Suggest a structural formula for the alkene. What is the alkane produced?

7-13 A gas is known to be methane, ethane, or propane. A 10 ml quantity of the gas was mixed with 100 ml of oxygen. After igniting the mixture and drying the resultant gaseous mixture, the volume was found to be 80 ml. Which of the three alkanes is at hand?

Questions for Chapter 8

8-1 Distinguish clearly between (among) the following:

    a. Allyl halide and an allene

    b. Conjugated and cumulated unsaturation

    c. Hydroboration and hydroxylation

    d. Bullvalene and vulcanization

    e. Bathochromic and photoexcited

    f. Buna S and Buna N

    g. Polyene and polymer

    h. Head-to-tail and stereospecific

    i. Polymer and copolymer

    j. Primary, secondary, and tertiary hydrogens

    k. Primary, secondary, and tertiary alkyl halides

    l. Atactic, isotactic, and syndiotactic

8-2 Which of the compounds listed in Table 8-1 are capable of geometric isomerism? Draw the structural formulas for each possible pair of such isomers.

8-3 Write equations that show the mechanism for each of the following:

    a. $E1$ and $E2$ reactions of an alkyl halide with a base

    b. Addition of halogen to an alkene

    c. Acid-catalyzed dehydration of an alcohol

    d. Allylic halogenation

    e. Propagation step in free radical polymerization of an alkene

8-4 Which compound in each of the following pairs would yield an olefin more readily under the proper conditions?

a. $CH_3CH_2CH_2OH$ *or* $CH_3CH(OH)CH_3$

b. $CH_3CH(CH_3)CH_2OH$ *or* $CH_3CH_2CH_2CH_2OH$

c. $CH_3\overset{\overset{\displaystyle CH_3}{|}}{\underset{\underset{\displaystyle OH}{|}}{C}}CH_3$ *or* $CH_3CH_2CH(OH)CH_3$

d. $CH_3CH(CH_3)CHBrCH_3$ *or* $CH_3CH(CH_3)CHClCH_3$

e. $CH_3CH_2CH_2CH_2Cl$ *or* ⬡-Cl

8-5 Write formulas and IUPAC names for the principal products obtained from the dehydration of the following alcohols:

a. $(CH_3)_3COH$

b. $CH_3CH_2CH_2CH(OH)CH_3$

c. $(CH_3)_2CHC(CH_3)CH_2CH_3$
$\qquad\qquad\quad\underset{\displaystyle OH}{|}$

d. $CH_3CH_2CH(OH)CH_2CH_2CH_3$

e. $CH_3CH_2CH(CH_2CH_3)C(CH_3)_2$
$\qquad\qquad\qquad\qquad\quad\underset{\displaystyle OH}{|}$

8-6 Give a theoretical explanation for:

a. Bredt's rule

b. Saytzeff's rule

c. The differences noted in the heats of hydrogenation of compounds **8-10**, **8-11**, and **8-12**

d. The role of the catalyst in catalytic hydrogenation

e. The formation of 4,5-dichloro-2-hexene and 2,5-dichloro-3-hexene from the reaction of chlorine with $CH_3CH=CH-CH=CHCH_3$

8-7 What readily measurable physical and chemical properties may be used to distinguish qualitatively between an alkane and an alkene?

8-8 Which group of compounds would you expect would exhibit a greater bathochromic effect, if any, with increasing values of n:

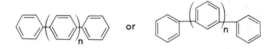

8-9 Offer an explanation for the termination of cationic polymerization of an alkene.

8-10 Would the same product result from the reaction of hydrogen bromide with 1-pentene if carried out (a) in the presence and (b) in the absence of peroxides? Explain.

8-11 Which would be more soluble in a solution of silver nitrate: 1-butene or isobutane? Explain.

8-12 The formation of dihalides from alkenes and chlorine or bromine is carried out in the dark. Why?

8-13 In the acid-catalyzed dehydration of 1-butanol, $CH_3CH_2CH_2CH_2OH$, and depending upon reaction conditions, varying amounts of 2-butene are formed with 1-butene. Write equations that explain the formation of both products. Suggest a means to circumvent the formation of 2-butene as a by-product.

8-14 Gutta-percha, which is obtained from the leaves of hybrids of *Palaquium* and is used as a covering for golf balls and submarine cable, has a similar structure but a different configuration than natural rubber.   Draw a possible stereochemical picture of the gutta-percha molecule.

8-15 What would you expect would be the principal product(s) from the reaction of cyclopentene with bromine when carried out in the presence of a large excess of nitrate ion? Explain.

8-16 Predict the chemical and stereochemical courses of the following reactions with 1-methylcyclopentene:
   a. Ozonolysis
   b. Oxidation with potassium permanganate
   c. Hydroxylation with osmium tetroxide
   d. Hydroxylation with performic acid

8-17 Show the products which would result on complete ozonolysis of vitamin A. In what ratio would these be formed?

8-18 Write equations that show how you could accomplish the following:
   a. Conversion of a primary alcohol to a secondary alcohol
   b. Conversion of a secondary alcohol to a primary alcohol
   c. Synthesis of tertiary butyl alcohol from isobutylene
   d. Synthesis of isobutyl alcohol from isobutylene
   e. Synthesis of 2-methyl-2-hexene from five different starting compounds

8-19 Write equations that show how you could synthesize each of the following compounds starting with 1-butene:
   a. $CH_3CH_2CH_2CH_2OH$
   b. $CH_3CH_2CH(OH)CH_3$
   c. $CH_3CH_2CH_2CH_3$
   d. $CH_3(CH_2)_6CH_3$
   e. $CH_3CH_2CH(OH)CH_2I$
   f. $CH_3CH_2CH_2CH=O$
   g. $CH_3CH_2CH_2CH_2MgBr$
   h. $CH_3CH_2CHClCH_2Cl$
   i. $CH_3CH_2CHClCH_3$
   j. $CH_3CH=CHCH_2Br$

8-20 Calculate the heats of addition of bromine and chlorine to ethylene.

8-21 The heat of hydrogenation of cyclopentene is 26.9 kcal/mole, whereas that of 1,3-cyclopentadiene is 50.9 kcal/mole. Calculate the resonance energy of the latter.

Questions for Chapter 9

9-1 Are 1-pentyne, 2-pentyne, and 3-pentyne proper names according to the IUPAC system?

9-2 Draw electron dot structures for ethane, ethene, and ethyne and indicate the bond angles and bond lengths in each molecule.

9-3 Explain clearly and illustrate what is meant by each of the following:
   a. Saddle conformation of cyclooctane
   b. Ring strain
   c. Axial and equatorial bonds
   d. Nonbonded repulsion
   e. Ethylation
   f. Vinylation
   g. Transannular effect
   h. *Cis* addition of a dieneophile
   i. Acetylenic Grignard reagent
   j. 1,2 cycloaddition

9-4 Offer an explanation for the fact that the melting point of 2-butyne ($-24°$) is greater than that of 1-butyne ($-122°$).

9-5 Draw structural formulas for the tautomeric forms of acetaldehyde, acetone, and methyl ethyl ketone.

9-6 Calculate the valence angle distortion in cyclononane according to the Baeyer theory. Criticize the significance of this number.

9-7 Give IUPAC names for each of the following:

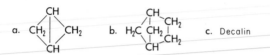

a. b. c. Decalin

9-8 Draw:

    a. A three-dimensional formula for adamantane

    b. Newman projection formulas for the chair and boat conformations of cyclohexane as viewed from one end

    c. Three-dimensional formulas for the most stable conformations of the *cis* and *trans* isomers of decalin showing the direction of the bonds for the two hydrogens on the carbon atoms shared by the two rings. Which isomer the more stable?

    d. Three-dimensional formulas for the most stable conformations of *cis*- and *trans*-1,3-dimethylcyclohexanes. Which isomer would you expect would be the more stable? Why?

9-9 Which would be the more stable, *cis*- or *trans*-1,2-dichlorocyclobutane? Why?

9-10 Which isomer would dehydrohalogenate ($E2$) more readily, *cis*- or *trans*-4-bromo-*t*-butylcyclohexane? Explain.

9-11 Why is it that the chair and boat conformations of cyclohexane are capable of coexistence? Which conformational isomer is the more stable? Why? Why have the individual conformational isomers not been isolated?

9-12 Why is it that acetylene burns with a luminous flame?

9-13 Write equations for the following:

    a. Three reactions common to alkenes and alkynes

    b. Two reactions of a 1-alkyne not shown by a 2-alkyne

    c. A reaction expected of $CH_2{=}CH{-}CH{=}CH{-}CH_2{-}CH_3$ but not of $CH_2{=}CH{-}CH_2{-}CH{=}CHCH_3$

9-14 Draw a flow diagram that shows how you could separate by chemical means and recover the components of a mixture of pentane, 1-pentene, and 1-pentyne.

9-15 Explain clearly how you distinguish qualitatively by spectral means between 5-methyl-2-octene and 5-methyl-2-octyne.

9-16 How could you distinguish through qualitative chemical methods between:

    a. 1- and 2-hexynes

    b. Propene and cyclopropane

9-17 Write equations that show the mechanism of:

    a. Conversion of an enol to a keto form (show the canonical forms of the intermediate)

b. Base-catalyzed isomerization of 1-pentyne to 2-pentyne including the formation of any expected by-product

c. The transformation

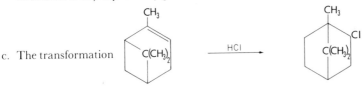

9-18 Write equations, including general conditions and catalysts, to show how the following could be synthesized from acetylene:

a. Acetaldehyde
b. Vinylacetylene
c. Benzene
d. Chloroprene
e. Cyclooctatetraene
f. Vinyl iodide
g. 1-Heptyne
h. $CH_3C\equiv CK$

i. Nonane
j. *cis*-2-Hexene
k. 1,1-Dibrompropane
l. 1-Bromo-2-chloropentane
m. 1,2-Dichlorobutane
n. 2,3-Dibromo-2,3-dichlorooctane
o. $CH_3COCH_2CH_3$

9-19 Write equations, including general conditions and catalysts where possible, that show how the following transformations could be accomplished:

a. 1-Butene $\longrightarrow$ 1-Butyne
b. Stilbene (PhCH=CHPh) $\longrightarrow$ Diphenylacetylene
c. The separate conversion of each of three different starting compounds to 1-decyne
d. Cyclopropane $\longrightarrow$ Propyl hydrogen sulfate ($CH_3CH_2CH_2OSO_3H$)
e. A ketone $\longrightarrow$ 2-Hexyne
f. 1-Butyne $\longrightarrow$ $CH_3CH_2CH(OH)CH_3$
g. Acetylene $\longrightarrow$ Chloroprene $\longrightarrow$ A rubber
h. Phenol $\longrightarrow$ Cyclohexene

i.

$\longrightarrow$ Decalin

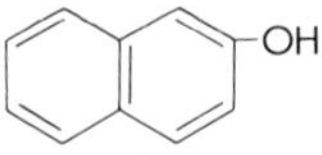

β – Naphthol

j.
OH

$\longrightarrow$ 1,2-Dibromo-4-methylcyclohexane

CH_3

P – Cresol

k. Any compounds containing no more than six carbon atoms $\longrightarrow$

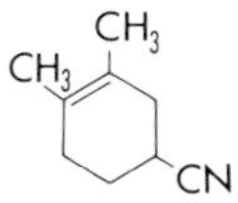

l. Any compounds containing no more than six carbon atoms $\longrightarrow$

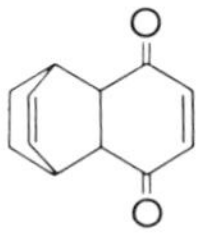

m. Calcium carbonate + Coke ⟶ Cyclohexane

Questions for Chapter 10

10-1 Define each of the following:
  a. Arene
  b. Annulene
  c. Birch reduction
  d. Destructive distillation of coal
  e. Dehydrogenation
  f. Phenonium ion
  g. π complex
  h. Polynuclear aromatic compound
  i. Nitronium ion

10-2 Write structural formulas for each of the following:
  a. Toluene
  b. Benzoic acid
  c. Biphenyl
  d. *o-*, *m-*, and *p*-xylenes
  e. Ethylbenzene
  f. Naphthalene
  g. Azulene
  h. Ferrocene
  i. Pyrrole
  j. Thiophene
  k. Furan
  l. Indole
  m. Quinoline
  n. Anthracene
  o. *p*-Bromotoluene
  p. 3,5-Dichlorophenol
  q. 2,4,6-Trinitrobenzoic acid
  r. *o*-Dinitrobenzene
  s. *m*-Cyano-*s*-butylbenzene
  t. Di(*p*-nitrophenyl)methane
  u. 1-Bromo-7-isopropylnaphthalene
  v. 1,8-Dinitronaphthalene
  w. 3-Ethyl-6-bromophenanthrene
  x. 9,10-Dihydroxyanthracene
  y. 2-(9-Phenanthryl)-2-pentene
  z. *cis*-1,4-Di(4-bromophenyl)cyclohexane

10-3 Name the compounds represented below:

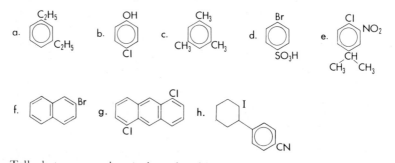

10-4 Tell what you can about valence bond isomers of benzene that have been synthesized. What bearing do these compounds have on the structure of benzene proposed by Kekulé?

10-5 Give examples of free radical and nucleophilic aromatic substitutions. What can you say about the orientation of substituents in these reactions?

10-6 What factors influence the ratio of isomers formed in electrophilic aromatic substitution? Where possible, give examples that show the nature of the influences.

10-7   State Hückel's rule and show its application to three non-benzenoid aromatic
       compounds.

10-8   How do you account for the fact that nitrobenzene is sometimes used as a sol-
       vent for Friedel-Crafts reactions although it contains five potentially replace-
       able hydrogen atoms?

10-9   Explain why the nitration of toluene gives a higher o/p substitution ratio than
       found for t-butylbenzene under the same conditions.

10-10 Write formulas for five Friedel-Crafts catalysts, arranging in order of decreas-
       ing activity. What is there about the electronic structure of all of these that
       results in their common catalytic behavior?

10-11 Arrange the following compounds in the order of decreasing ease of sulfona-
       tion: acetophenone, toluene, phenol, chlorobenzene, N,N,N-trimethylanilin-
       ium chloride $(PhN(CH_3)_3^{\oplus} Cl^{\ominus})$.

10-12 Assume that ferrocene is monoacetylated and the product is then converted
       to a diacetyl derivative. Write equations showing reagents and conditions
       that could be employed for these transformations and the structural formulas
       of the products.

10-13 The ring bromination of a dipropylbenzene yields three isomeric monobromo
       derivatives. Identify the dipropylbenzene. What are the names and structures
       of the monobromo derivatives? Give the names and structures of the dibromo
       products which might have been formed simultaneously.

10-14 The ozonolysis of benzene affords three moles of glyoxal, $O{=}CH{-}CH{=}O$.
       Illustrate the course of this transformation with equations.

10-15 Ozonolysis of o-xylene yields diacetyl, $CH_3{-}CO{-}CO{-}CH_3$, methyl-
       glyoxal, $CH_3{-}CO{-}CHO$, and glyoxal, $O{=}CH{-}CH{=}O$, in a ratio of
       $1{:}2{:}3$. How may this observation be explained?

10-16 Offer an explanation for the fact that 1,6-methanocyclodecapentaene (I) is an
       aromatic compound although it contains no benzene rings. Does it follow
       necessarily that cyclodecapentaene (II) would also be an aromatic compound?
       (Use suitable models if available to help you reach a decision.)

I   II

10-17 Draw structural formulas of the geometrical isomers obtained on chlorination
       of benzene under the influence of ultraviolet irradiation.

10-18 Show the products that would be formed from the exhaustive hydrogenation of
       m-xylene. Draw all possible conformations of these products. Which product
       and which conformations would you expect to predominate? Why?

10-19 Predict the major product, or products, expected from each of the following
       ring substitution reactions:
       a. Nitrations of (1) p-hydroxytoluene, (2) 1-naphthol, (3) ethylbenzene, (4) ni-
          trobenzene

   b. Brominations of (1) m-methylbenzoic acid, (2) p-hydroxydiphenylmethane, (3) acetanilide, $PhNHCOCH_3$, (4) p-methoxychlorobenzene

   c. Sulfonations of (1) m-xylene, (2) phenylcyclohexane, (3) o-nitrodiphenylmethane, (4) m-ethylphenol

   d. Acylations $(RCOCl/AlCl_3)$ of (1) diphenyl ether, (2) cyanobenzene, (3) tetralin, (4) diphenyl

10-20 Offer an explanation for the driving force for conversion of the Dewar form of the trimer of t-butylfluoroacetylene to 1,2,3-trifluoro-4,5,6-tri-t-butylbenzene.

10-21 Give equations that show the formation of the major product, or products, from each of the following reactions (if more than one major product is formed, indicate the principal one):

   a. Nitration of cumene (isopropylbenzene)
   b. Chlorination of phenol
   c. Sulfonation of toluene
   d. Reaction of ethylbenzene with CH_3Cl and $AlCl_3$
   e. Oxidation of m-xylene with CrO_3
   f. Reaction of α-methylnaphthalene with 1,3,5-trinitrobenzene

10-22 Offer an explanation for the following:

   a. The principal product from the alkylation of benzene with isobutyl bromide is t-butylbenzene

   b. When a mixture of toluene and benzene is stirred and heated with concentrated sulfuric acid, it is found upon examination after some time that the unreacted hydrocarbon layer is chiefly benzene.

   c. When the sulfuric acid layer from b (above) is mixed with water and the mixture is boiled, a compound, C_7H_8, separates from solution. Oxidation of this product with sodium dichromate–sulfuric acid mixture yields benzoic acid. What is C_7H_8? Write equations describing all of the chemical changes that have occurred. What can you say concerning the reversibility of the sulfonation process? What other aromatic substitution reaction has this characteristic?

10-23 Write equations, including general conditions and catalysts, to show how you could accomplish each of the following conversions in the laboratory.

   a. Benzene $\longrightarrow$ m-Benzenedisulfonic acid
   b. Benzene $\longrightarrow$ m-Nitrobenzoic acid
   c. Benzene $\longrightarrow$ Lindane
   d. Benzene $\longrightarrow$ m-Nitroacetophenone
   e. Benzene $\longrightarrow$ Terephthalic acid
   f. Benzene $\longrightarrow$ 1-Isopropyl-4-t-butylcyclohexane

   g. Naphthalene $\longrightarrow$

   i. Cyclohexane $\longrightarrow$ Norcaradiene

10-24 Write equations showing the mechanism of each of the following reactions:
   a. Benzene $\longrightarrow$ Benzenesulfonic acid

b. Butylbenzene $\longrightarrow$ *o*- and *p*-Chlorobutylbenzenes

c. Naphthalene $\longrightarrow$ 1-Nitronaphthalene

d. Benzene $\longrightarrow$ Ethylbenzene

e. Benzene + PhCOCl $\longrightarrow$ Benzophenone

10-25 The compound $C_{11}H_{14}$ was isolated during the course of an experiment. The oxidation of $C_{11}H_{14}$ yielded $C_{10}H_{12}O$, which, upon heating with hydrazine and and sodium ethoxide, was converted to $C_{10}H_{14}$; vigorous oxidation of $C_{10}H_{14}$ yielded $C_8H_6O_4$; and nitration of $C_{10}H_{14}$ gave two compounds, both having the formula $C_{10}H_{13}NO_2$. Write the possible structural formulas for $C_{11}H_{14}$ and the other compounds listed. Write equations for the transformations involved, supplying the reagents that could be used, where these are not given.

Questions for Chapter 11

11-1 Define and illustrate each of the following:

a. Azeotrope

b. Anthocyanin

c. Benzyne

d. Chelate ring

e. Denatured

f. Desulfuration

e. Erlenmeyer's rule

f. Enzyme

g. Fusel oil

h. Glycol

i. 80 proof

j. Oxonium salt

k. Tetritol

l. Wood alcohol

m. Walden inversion

11-2 Write structural formulas for:

a. *s*-Butyl alcohol

b. 3-Bromocyclohexanol

c. *p*-Chlorophenol

d. α-Naphthol

e. 2-Pentanol

f. 4-Methyl-5-decanol

g. Allyl sulfide

h. 1,3-Dioxacyclohexane

i. Ethanesulfonic acid

j. Tetrahydrofuran

11-3 Give the IUPAC name for each of the following:

a. $(CH_3)_2CHCH_2CH(C_2H_5)CH(OH)CH_3$

b. $(CH_3)_2CHCH(OH)CH(CH_3)_2$

c. $PhCH(CH_3)CH_2CH(OH)CH_3$

d. $(CH_3CH_2CH_2)_2CHCH(OH)CH_2CH_2CH_3$

e. $EtOCHMeCH_2Me$

f. $EtCCl_2CH(OMe)Me$

g. *t*-BuOH

h. Pr_2Zn

i.

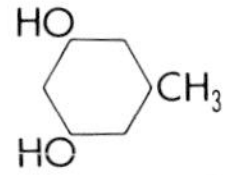

j.

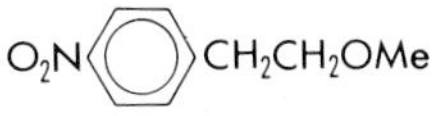

k.

l.

11-4 Cite an important commercial use of:
    a. Tri-*o*-cresyl phosphate   e. Ethyl alcohol
    b. Ethylene glycol   f. Phenol
    c. Methanol   g. Glycerol
    d. Ethyl ether   h. 1,1,1-Trichloro-2,2-di(*p*-chlorophenyl)ethane

11-5 Write equations, including general conditions and catalysts, to illustrate each
    of the following transformations:
    a. An alcohol $\longrightarrow$ A carboxylic acid
    b. An alcohol $\longrightarrow$ An ether
    c. An alcohol $\longrightarrow$ An ester (two methods)
    d. An alcohol $\longrightarrow$ An alkyl chloride (two methods)
    e. An alkyl halide $\longrightarrow$ A nitrile
    f. An alkyl halide $\longrightarrow$ An ester
    g. An alkyl halide $\longrightarrow$ An alcohol
    h. An alkyl halide $\longrightarrow$ An alkyl sulfide
    i. A mercaptan $\longrightarrow$ An alkanesulfonic acid
    j. A mercaptan $\longrightarrow$ A disulfide
    k. An alkyl sulfide $\longrightarrow$ A sulfone
    l. An arylsulfonic acid $\longrightarrow$ A phenol

11-6 Write equations giving general conditions and catalysts for:
    a. Claisen rearrangement
    b. Lucas test
    c. Finkelstein reaction
    d. Allylic rearrangement
    e. Pinacol rearrangement
    f. Zeisel analysis
    g. Alfol process
    h. The industrial preparations of phenol, glycerol, ethylene glycol, methanol,
       and ethanol.

11-7 Describe a qualitative chemical test by which you could distinguish between
    or among:
    a. Propyl ether and 1-propanol
    b. Ethyl bromide and heptane
    c. Cyclohexanol and phenol
    d. 3-Methyl-1-pentanol, 2-methyl-3-pentanol, and 3-methyl-3-pentanol

11-8 Arrange the following in the requested order (show your order clearly and ex-
    plain your choice):
    a. Increasing boiling point: (1) pentane, methyl ethyl ether, and *n*-butyl alco-

hol; (2) 1-butanol, methyl sulfide, and *n*-propyl mercaptan; (3) 1-chloro-octane, 1-bromopentane, methyl iodide, decane, and 1 nonanol (*Hint:* comparison with homologs shows that the magnitude of the differences among the alkyl halides listed cannot be attributed to the slight differences in their molecular weights); (4) methyl chloride, ethyl bromide, and methyl iodide

b. Increasing melting point: butyl, isobutyl, and *t*-butyl alcohols

c. Decreasing water solubility: (1) *n*-butyl alcohol and *n*-butyl mercaptan; (2) glycerol, 2-methyl-2-butanol, 1-pentanol, and 2-methyl-1-butanol

d. Decreasing acidity: *m*-nitrophenol, 2,4-dinitrophenol, phenol, *p*-methylphenol, and cyclohexanol

e. Increasing rate of ether formation upon reaction with potassium methoxide: propyl chloride, propyl bromde, and propyl iodide

f. Increasing rate of alkaline hydrolysis: *p*-chlorotoluene, 4-methylcyclohexyl chloride, and phenylchloromethane

11-9   Giving your reasons, predict the structure of the principal product from the pinacol rearrangement of each of the following glycols: 2-methyl-2,3-pentanediol, 2-methyl-3-phenyl-2,3-butanediol, 3,4-diphenyl-3,4-hexanediol, 1,1-diphenyl-2-methyl-1,2-propanediol.

11-10   Write the structural formula(s) for the new product(s), if any, expected from from reaction of the following:

a. Butyl ether and aluminum chloride

b. Phenyl ethyl sulfide and excess hydrogen peroxide

c. Cyclohexyl bromide and thiourea

d. Benzyl bromide and potassium cyanide

e. Phenyllithium and acetone

f. *n*-Butyl chloride, thionyl chloride, and pyridine

g. Acetaldehyde and lithium aluminum hydride, followed by hydrolysis

h. Pinacol and lead tetraacetate

i. Cyclohexanol and phosphorus pentachloride

j. 3-Methyl-1-chlorobutane and aqueous sodium hydroxide

k. Phenylmagnesium bromide and ethanol

l. *p*-Bromotoluene, potassium amide, and ammonia

m. Tetrahydrofuran and hydrogen iodide (two moles) (heat)

n. Mercuric acetate and *p*-cresol

o. $CH_3C{\equiv}CK$ and propyl iodide

p. *m*-Methylphenol and zinc dust (heated strongly)

q. Phosphorus oxychloride and methyl alcohol

r. Methyl ethyl sulfide and propyl iodide

s. $CH_3COCH_2CH_2CH(CH_3)_2$ and isopropylmagnesium bromide, followed by hydrolysis

t. 1-Bromopentane and mercurous fluoride

u. Trimethylene glycol and excess hydrogen bromide

v. $\left(Me\langle\bigcirc\rangle\right)_2C(OH){-}C(OH)Me_2$ and a small amount of sulfuric acid

w. Diethylmercury and hydrochloric acid

x . Isobutyl alcohol, ⟨○⟩CO₂H and a small amount of sulfuric acid
        Cl

y. 1-Phenoxy-2-butene (heated)

z. Ethyl iodide and excess ammonia

11-11 Tell how you could accomplish the following (explain your choice of reagents and physical method used, and write equations for chemical changes involved, where possible):

a. Synthesize ethyl *t*-butyl ether

b. Prepare absolute ether from commercial ether known to contain peroxides

c. Remove isobutylene, *t*-butyl alcohol, and water by chemical means from a crude sample of *t*-butyl chloride

d. Prepare absolute ethanol from starch

11-12 What characteristic differences would you expect in the infrared spectra of the pairs of compounds in Question 11-7a and b which would permit their distinction in each case?

11-13 The OH absorption band appears at longer wavelengths for concentrated solutions of alcohols in nonhydroxylic solvents than for dilute solutions. Why?

11-14 *o*-Nitrophenol and *p*-nitrophenol may be separated by steam distillation. Which isomer would you predict would be volatile with steam and why?

11-15 Write equations that show the formation of five different products that may result from the reaction of ethyl alcohol with concentrated sulfuric acid.

11-16 Which elements are generally involved in hydrogen bonding?

11-17 Explain the different stereochemical consequences of S_N1 and S_N2 reactions.

11-18 Show how the rate expressions for S_N1 and S_N2 reactions differ.

11-19 Write equations showing the mechanism of each of the following reactions:

a. Williamson synthesis by an S_N2 process

b. The pinacol–pinacolone rearrangement

c. $(C_2H_5O_2C)_2CHNa + CH_3CHClCH=CH_2 \longrightarrow$
$$(C_2H_5O_2C)_2CHCH_2CH=CHCH_3$$

d. $(CH_3)_3CCH(OH)CH_3 \xrightarrow{H_2SO_4}$
$(CH_3)_2C=C(CH_3)_2 + (CH_3)_2CHC(CH_3)=CH_2 + (CH_3)_3CCH=CH_2$
(Major product)   (Minor products)

e. $CH_3CH=CHCH_2Cl + KO_2CCH_3 \longrightarrow$
$$CH_3CH=CHCH_2O_2CCH_3 + CH_3CHCH=CH_2$$
$$\qquad\qquad\qquad\qquad\qquad\qquad | $$
$$\qquad\qquad\qquad\qquad\qquad O_2CCH_3$$

f. $PhC\equiv CK + CH_3CH_2CH_2I \longrightarrow$
$$PhC\equiv CCH_2CH_2CH_3 + PhC\equiv CH + CH_3CH=CH_2$$

11-20 Illustrate each of the following reactions with an equation, including general conditions and catalysts:

a. Nitration of *o*-cresol

b. Bromination of *p*-ethylphenol

c. Sulfonation of catechol

d. Grignard synthesis of the following alcohols starting with benzene or any aliphatic compound containing no more than four carbon atoms: (1) 3-methyl-1-butanol; (2) 2-methyl-2-pentanol; (3) 4-methyl-4-heptanol; (4) 2,2-dimethylpropanol; (5) 2-phenylethanol

e. Conversion of propylene into the following compounds: (1) 1-chloro-2-propanol; (2) methyl isopropyl ether; (3) isopropyl ether; (4) n-propyl isopropyl sulfide

11-21   Write equations, including general conditions and catalysts, to show how you could accomplish the following transformations (assume any reagents needed are available):

a. Ethyl chloride $\rightarrow$ Tetraethyllead

b. Phenol $\rightarrow$ Phenol–formaldehyde resin

c. Glycerol $\rightarrow$ Nitroglycerin

d. n-Propyl alcohol $\rightarrow$ n-Propyl iodide

e. Butyl bromide $\rightarrow$ Butylmagnesium bromide

f. α-Naphthol $\rightarrow$ Methyl α-naphthyl ether

g. n-Propyl alcohol $\rightarrow$ Isopropyl alcohol

h. Benzaldehyde $\rightarrow$ Benzyl bromide

i. 2,3-Epoxybutane ($CH_3CHCHCH_3$ with $\overset{O}{\overset{/\backslash}{}}$) $\rightarrow$ Acetaldehyde

j. 1-Butanol $\rightarrow$ 2-Chlorobutane

k. Benzene $\rightarrow$ $PhO_2CCH_2CH_3$

l. Benzene $\rightarrow$ $Ph_2C(OH)CH_3$

m. Benzene $\rightarrow$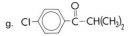

n. $CH_3CH_2CH_2CO_2CH_2CH_3$ $\rightarrow$ n-Butyl alcohol

Questions for Chapter 12

12-1   Name each of the following:

a. $CH_3(CH_2)_6CHO$

b. $CH_3CHPhCH_2CHO$

c. $(CH_3)_3CCOCH_3$

d. $Ph_2CHCOCH_2CH_3$

e. $(CH_3CH_2)_2CO$

f. $CH_3(CH_2)_2CH(CH_3)CHO$

g.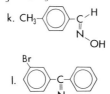

h. $PhCH_2CH_2COCH_2CH_2Ph$

i. $(CH_3)_2CHCOCH_2CH_2CHO$

j. $CH_3COCHClCHClCHO$

k. $CH_3\!-\!\langle\bigcirc\rangle\!-\!\overset{H}{\underset{\underset{OH}{N}}{\overset{\|}{C}}}$

l. $\underset{\underset{HO}{N}}{Br\text{-}\langle\bigcirc\rangle\text{-}\overset{\|}{C}\text{-}\langle\bigcirc\rangle}$

12-2 Define each of the following:
a. Paraformaldehyde
b. Hydroformylation
c. Crossed Cannizzaro reaction
d. $p \longrightarrow \pi^*$ transition
e. Principle of vinylogy
f. Schiff test
g. Trioxane
h. Benedict's solution

i. Schiff base
j. Metaldehyde
k. Thioketal
l. Anil
m. Tautomerism
n. Conjugate addition
o. Tropolone

12-3 Assume that the dehydrogenation of 1-heptanol is 20 per cent complete upon passage over a catalyst. How could you separate the components of the mixture and recover these through chemical means?

12-4 How are formaldehyde, acetaldehyde, acetone, and methyl ethyl ketone synthesized industrially?

12-5 Is the reaction commonly called a benzoin condensation named according to the general definitions given in Section 6-1?

12-6 Write equations for six reactions shown by aldehydes which are not shown by ketones.

12-7 Write equations for six reactions shown by both aldehydes and ketones.

12-8 Describe a qualitative chemical test by which you could distinguish between the members of each of the following pairs:

a. Hexanal and cyclohexanone,
b. 2-Heptanone and 3-heptanone
c. 3-Pentanone and ethyl propyl ether
d. 2,3-Butanediol and 1,3-butanediol
e. Cyclobutanone and butanone
f. Acetone and isopropyl alcohol
g. $PhCOCH_2COPh$ and $PhC{=\!=}CHCOPh$ with OH group
h. 1,1-Dimethoxypropane and 1,3-dimethoxypropane

12-9 Write an equation to illustrate each of the following:
a. Reformatsky reaction
b. Benzoin condensation
c. Knovenagel condensation
d. Meerwein-Ponndorf reaction
e. Baeyer-Villiger reaction
f. Claisen condensation
g. Rosenmund reduction

12-10 Offer an explanation for the following:
a. When gaseous formaldehyde is dissolved in water and the solution is then evaporated, a white solid remains.
b. The rate of furfural semicarbazone formation is greater at pH 3.13 than at a higher or lower pH.
c. If aldolization of acetone is attempted in the presence of deuterium oxide and the reaction is interrupted after a time, it is found that deuteroacetone can be detected even though very little of the aldol has formed.
d. Heating isobutyraldehyde with barium hydroxide produces no aldol, but barium isobutyrate and isobutyl alcohol are formed in quantitative yields.

e. The difference observed in the behavior of *syn*- and *anti*-aldoxime acetates upon treatment with sodium carbonate.

f. Benzil reacts with *o*-phenylenediamine (1,2-diaminobenzene) to yield a red crystalline compound, $C_{20}H_{14}N_2$, but dibenzoylmethane, $(PhCO)_2CH_2$, does not.

g. Under the same conditions the yield of bisulfite addition product from cyclohexanone is 35 per cent, whereas that from methyl isopropyl ketone is 3 per cent.

h. The differences you might expect in the infrared spectra of 50:50 solutions of acetaldehyde and ethanol and of acetone and ethanol.

i. Ethyl mesoxalate, $(C_2H_5O_2C)_2C{=}O$, is a colorless liquid, which upon standing in an open container in the laboratory is converted to a white crystalline solid, $C_7H_{12}O_6$. Suggest the nature of the product and how you would expect its infrared spectrum to differ from that of ethyl mesoxalate.

j. The difference expected in the tendencies to enolize of $CH_3COCH_2COCH_3$ and $CH_3COCH_2CH_2CH_3$. How could you determine the amount of enol in each case?

k. The tendency for phenol to exist in an enol form is greater than for phloroglucinol.

l. The aromatic character of tropylium chloride.

12-11 Write equations including general conditions and catalysts, to show how you could accomplish the following transformations in the laboratory:

a. An aldehyde to an alkane having the same carbon skeleton
b. A *gem*-dihalide, RCX_2R, to a ketone having the same carbon skeleton
c. A ketone to a secondary alcohol having the same carbon skeleton
d. An acid chloride to an aldehyde having the same carbon skeleton
e. An aldehyde to a carboxylic acid having the same carbon skeleton
f. An alcohol to an aldehyde having the same carbon skeleton (two methods)
g. An aldehyde to an acetal
h. A ketone to an alkene in one step
i. A ketone to an ester in one step

12-12 Estimate the equilibrium constant for the keto $\rightleftharpoons$ enol system for butanone at 25°

12-13 What evidence is there supporting the idea that the Cannizzaro reaction occurs by an intermolecular hydride shift?

12-14 What features are common to the Claisen condensation, Knovenagel condensation, and the aldol reaction?

12-15 How do you explain the pronounced reactivity of epoxides over that of ordinary ethers?

12-16 Predict and explain the effect of increasing hydrogen ion concentration on the rate of aldehyde cyanohydrin formation. What complicating factor would you expect at high pH values?

12-17 Tell what you can about the type, industrial uses, and natural occurrences of quinones.

12-18 What feature, or features, do you find common to the Cannizzaro reaction and benzilic acid rearrangement?

12-19 What advantage is associated with the use of sodium borohydride over lithium aluminum hydride as a reducing agent?

12-20 Write the formulas for the principal organic product (or products) expected from the following:

 a. Diethyl ketone plus magnesium amalgam followed by hydrolysis
 b. 2-Phenylbutanal and diaminesilver hydroxide
 c. 2,3-Epoxybutane plus sodium ethoxide followed by hydrolysis
 d. Acetophenone and sodium hypoiodite
 e. p-Methylbenzaldehyde and ammonia
 f. Camphor and semicarbazide
 g. 4-Chlorocyclohexanone and aluminum isopropoxide
 h. 5-Decanone and triphenylphosphinemethylene
 i. 3,4-Dimethoxybenzaldehyde and sodium bisulfite
 j. 3-Hexanone and Caro's acid
 k. Acetone and 2,4-dinitrophenylhydrazine
 l. Muscone and Girard's reagent
 m. 3-Pentanone and diazomethane
 n. Phenylacetaldehyde, $PhCH_2CHO$, and sodium hydroxide
 o. $CH_3CH{=}CH{-}CH(OH)CH_2Ph$ plus acetone and aluminum t-butoxide
 p. Propanal plus propanol and a small quantity of concentrated sulfuric acid
 q. Furfural, $\overset{\underset{O}{}}{\bigsqcup}{-}CHO$, and concentrated sodium hydroxide
 r. syn-p-Chlorophenyl-α-naphthyl ketoxime and dry HCl in ether
 s. 2-Methyl-3-hexanone plus ethyl 2-bromopropanoate and zinc followed by careful hydrolysis
 t. Nitroethane plus acetaldehyde and sodium ethoxide
 u. p-Ethylbenzaldehyde plus acetophenone and sodium hydroxide
 v. 4-Methylhexanal and Fehling's reagent
 w. $PhCH_2CN$ plus pentanal and potassium methoxide
 x. Stilbene oxide, $Ph\overset{\overset{O}{\diagup\diagdown}}{CHCH}Ph$, plus a dilute solution of acidified methanol
 y. Methyl vinyl ketone plus diethylmalonate and sodium ethoxide
 z. Paraldehyde, heated with a small quantity of sulfuric acid.

12-21 Write an equation to illustrate the mechanism of each of the following reactions:

 a. Beckman rearrangement   h. Michael reaction
 b. Acetal formation   i. Epoxidation of an alkene with a peracid
 c. Haloform reaction   j. Wittig reaction
 d. Aldol reaction   k. Oppenauer oxidation
 e. Hydrazone formation   l. Perkin reaction
 f. Claisen-Schmidt reaction   m. Acid- and base-catalyzed enolizations
 g. Reimer-Tiemann reaction

12-22 Give an equation for the course of the reaction involving each of the following and name the principal product in each case:

 a. Propionaldehyde and phenylhydrazine

b. Benzophenone and hydroxylamine
c. Clemmensen reduction of phenyl benzyl ketone
d. HCN and benzaldehyde
e. Sulfuric acid and 2,3-dimethyl-2,3-butanediol
f. CrO_3–H_2SO_4 and ethyl p-nitrophenyl ketone
g. Pyrolysis of calcium propionate, $(CH_3CH_2CO_2)_2Ca$
h. Cyclohexanone and phenylmagnesium bromide followed by hydrolysis
i. Cyclopentanone and lithium aluminum hydride followed by hydrolysis.

12-23 Explain in detail how you could prove, other than by synthetic means, the correctness of each of the following structural formulas:

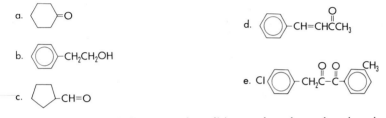

12-24 Write equations, including general conditions and catalysts, that show how the
following could be accomplished (assume that any reagents needed are available):

a. Synthesis of butanal (five methods)
b. Synthesis of dibenzyl ketone (five methods)
c. N,N-Dimethylaniline $[(CH_3)_2NC_6H_5]$ $\rightarrow$ p-N,N-Dimethylamino-
   benzaldehyde
d. Propionaldehyde $\rightarrow$ 2-Methyl-1,3-pentanediol
e. Cyclohexanone $\rightarrow$ Methyl cyclohexyl ether
f. Benzaldehyde $\rightarrow$ 1-Phenyl-3-methyl-1-butanol
g. Methyl iodide $\rightarrow$ Acetophenone
h. Benzene $\rightarrow$ Benzophenone oxime
i. Acetophenone $\rightarrow$ 2-Phenyl-3-methyl-2-butanol
j. $Cl(CH_2)_3CHO$ $\rightarrow$ $PhCO(CH_2)_3CHO$
k. Propanoic acid $(CH_3CH_2CO_2H)$ $\rightarrow$ $(CH_3CH_2)_2C(OH)C(OH)(CH_2CH_3)_2$
l. p-Nitroacetophenone $\rightarrow$ p-Nitrobenzoic acid
m. Benzaldehyde $\rightarrow$ $PhCH=CHCH_2OH$

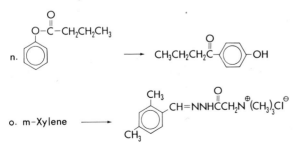

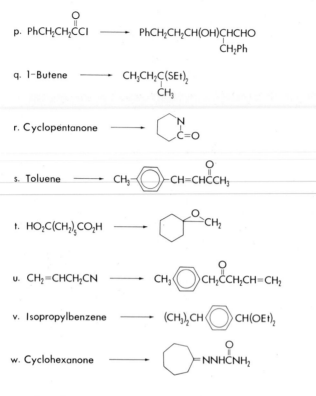

p. PhCH₂CH₂CCl → PhCH₂CH₂CH(OH)CHCHO
                                              CH₂Ph

q. 1-Butene → CH₃CH₂C(SEt)₂
                                    CH₃

r. Cyclopentanone →

s. Toluene → CH₃—⟨ ⟩—CH=CHCCH₃

t. HO₂C(CH₂)₅CO₂H →

u. CH₂=CHCH₂CN → CH₃⟨ ⟩CH₂CCH₂CH=CH₂

v. Isopropylbenzene → (CH₃)₂CH⟨ ⟩CH(OEt)₂

w. Cyclohexanone → =NNHCNH₂

Questions for Chapter 13

13-1   Give IUPAC names for the following:
 a. CH₃(CH₂)₂CO₂H
 b. PhCH₂CH₂CHClCO₂H
 c. CH₃CH₂CH(CH₃)CH₂CO₂CH(CH₃)₂
 d. CH₃CH₂CPh₂CO₂CH₂Ph

 e. CH₃NHO₂S⟨ ⟩

 f. Br⟨ ⟩OCCHBrCHBrCH₃
                              ‖
                              O

 g. CH₃CH₂COBr

 h. O₂N
        ⟨ ⟩COCl
         Cl

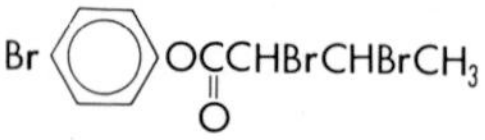

 i. ⟨ ⟩CONMe₂

 j. CH₃(CH₂)₄SO₃H
 k. (CH₃)₃CSO₃H

 l. HO⟨ ⟩SO₃H

 m. CH₃O₃S⟨ ⟩CH₃

 n. (CH₃CH₂CO)₂O
 o. [(CH₃)₂CHCH₂CO]₂O

              Ph
 p. CH₃CHCH₂CO
                         O
       (CH₃)₃CCO

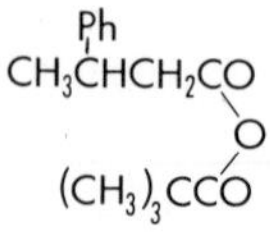

 q. CH₃CHCH₂CN
                   O
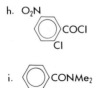

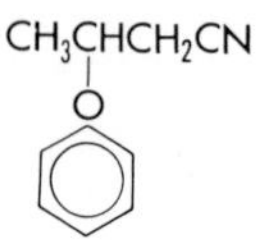

r. CH_3⟨◯⟩$CH_2CH(OH)CO_2H$

s. $CH_3CH(OH)CH_2CH_2CO_2Na$
t. $PhCO_2NHCH_3$
u. $HO_2C(CH_2)_3CO_2H$
v. $MeSO_2NEt_2$

w. $CH_3\overset{\overset{O}{\|}}{C}(CH_2)_4CO_2Bu$

x. $\underset{\underset{CH_2CO_2H}{|}}{\overset{\overset{CHBrCO_2H}{|}}{CH_2}}$

y. $CH_3CH(OEt)CH_2COCl$
z. $CH_3CHPhCH_2O\overset{\overset{}{}}{C}\underset{\underset{O}{\|}}{H}$

13-2　Write structural formulas for: (a) aspirin, (b) an ortho acid, (c) a glycolide, (d) an alkyd resin, (e) oxalic acid, (f) a barbiturate, (g) saccharin, (h) the tosylate group, (i) sulfanilimide, (j) an hydroxamic acid, (k) a δ-lactone, (l) a thioncarboxylic acid, (m) a fat, (n) a soap, (o) two types of detergents other than soap.

13-3　Tell what is meant by: (a) transesterification, (b) cyanoethylation, (c) Blanc's rule, (d) surface active, (e) hydrophobic, (f) saponification, (g) drying oil, (h) iodine number.

13-4　Write equations, including general conditions and catalysts, that illustrate general methods for the synthesis of each of the following: (a) an acid by four methods, (b) an acyl halide from a carboxylic acid using two different reagents, (c) a carboxylic acid anhydride, (d) an ester by four different methods, (e) an amide by four different methods, (f) a nitrile by two different methods, (g) an ortho ester, (h) an α-hydroxy acid, (i) an α-keto acid, (j) a γ-keto acid, (k) a peroxy acid, (l) an arylsulfonic acid, (m) an arylsulfonyl chloride, (n) an aryl sulfonate, (o) an aryl cyanide, (p) a ketal.

13-5　Write equations that show how the following transformations could be accomplished, giving general conditions and catalysts: (a) an orthoester to an aldehyde through the Grignard reagent, (b) a carboxylic acid to an aldehyde through three different schemes, (c) two general methods for converting a primary alkyl halide, RX, to the next higher homolog, RCH_2X, (d) the synthesis of three different types of compounds each from an ester, an acyl halide and an anhydride.

13-6　Write equations for the following:
a. The reaction of ketene with: (1) water, (2) butanoic acid, (3) isopropyl alcohol, (4) diethylamine, $(C_2H_5)_2NH$.
b. The reaction of diazomethane with: (1) hydroquinone, (2) stearic acid, (3) enolized ethyl acetoacetate.
c. The use of the malonic ester synthesis leading to: (1) ethyl ethylmalonate, (2) pentanoyl chloride, (3) 3-phenylpropanoic acid, (4) isobutyramide, (5) 2-methylbutanoic acid.
d. The conversion of ethyl acetoacetate to: (1) methyl isopropyl ketone, (2) 4-phenyl-2-butanone, (3) 3-methyl-2-hexanone, (4) $CH_3CO(CH_2)_2$-$COCH_3$, (5) $CH_3CO(CH_2)_6COCH_3$, (6) 2-propylhexanoic acid.
e. The action of phenylmagnesium bromide on: (1) benzoic acid, (2) methyl isobutyrate, (3) propanenitrile, (4) γ-butyrolactone.

13-7　Distinguish clearly among fat, ester wax, and ester oil.

13-8 Describe the cleansing action of a detergent. What advantage do synthetic detergents have over soap?

13-9 Give a brief description of the preparation of soap from a fat.

13-10 Iodine numbers are used in determining the degree of unsaturation of ester oils. How could the reaction of these oils, or fats, with sodium hydroxide be used to evaluate the average molecular weight of the acids from which these are derived?

13-11 Describe how you could decide through qualitative chemical tests between: (a) ethyl propanoate and methyl butanoate, (b) cyclohexanecarboxylic acid and phenol, (c) 3-methoxypropanoic acid and methyl propanoate, (d) 4-chlorohexanoic acid and hexanoyl chloride.

13-12 Write the formula for the main organic product, or products, from the following: (a) sodium propionate and acetyl chloride, (b) the reaction of succinic anhydride, toluene and aluminum chloride followed by hydrolysis, (c) p-toluenesulfonic acid and potassium permanganate, (d) α-naphthalenesulfonyl chloride and ammonia, (e) phthalic anhydride and p-cresol, (f) benzoyl chloride and dibutylcadmium, (g) pentanoyl chloride and sodium ethylmercaptide, (h) isobutyronitrile is hydrolyzed with sodium hydroxide, (i) δ-valerolactone and ethyl alcohol, (j) ethyl glutarate plus sodium methoxide and a large excess of methanol, (k) the reaction of 2-phenylbutylmagnesium bromide and carbon dioxide followed by hydrolysis, (l) acetic propionic anhydride and water, (m) lithium aluminum hydride and ethylbenzoate, (n) isobutyric acid, bromine and a small quantity of red phosphorous, (o) linoleic acid and lithium aluminum hydride, (p) mesitoic acid (2,4,6-trimethylbenzoic acid) is dissolved in concentrated sulfuric acid and the mixture is carefully added, with cooling, to a large volume of methanol, (q) ammonium pentanoate is heated, (r) propanamide is heated with phosphorus pentoxide, (s) α-naphthalenecarboxylic acid is heated with soda lime, (t) ethyl orthoformate and butylmagnesium bromide, (u) 4-hydroxyhexanoic acid is heated, (v) acetoacetic acid is heated, (w) phosgene and isopropyl alcohol, (x) sodium p-toluenesulfonate and sodium cyanide are heated together, (y) N,N-dimethylpentanamide and lithium diethoxyaluminum hydride, (z) pimelic acid, $HO_2C(CH_2)_5CO_2H$, is heated.

13-13 Write equations for the following, giving general conditions and catalysts: (a) Fischer esterification, (b) Schotten-Baumann reaction, (c) Pinner reaction, (d) Hell-Volhard-Zelinsky reaction,

13-14 Describe one use for the following in connection with the chemistry of carboxylic acids, analogs, and derivatives: (a) sodium hydroxide, (b) red phosphorus, (c) acetic anhydride, (d) cobalt salts, (e) urea, (f) Raney nickel, (g) lithium triethoxyaluminum hydride, (h) barium hydroxide, (i) concentrated sulfuric acid, (j) fluoroboric acid, (k) potassium ethoxide, (l) chromic anhydride, (m) diazomethane, (n) phosphorus tribromide, (o) a dialkyl cadmium, (p) acrylonitrile, (q) hydrogen peroxide, (r) soda lime, (s) ethyl malonate, (t) a Grignard reagent, (u) iodine monobromide, (v) ethyl acetoacetate, (w) lithium aluminum hydride, (x) ammonia, (y) thionyl chloride, (z) chlorosulfonic acid.

13-15 Write equations for the synthesis of the following, giving general conditions and catalysts: (a) ketene, (b) diazomethane, (c) ethyl acetoacetate, (d) phenobarbital, (e) phosgene, (f) ethyl orthoformate, (g) urea, (h) phthalic anhydride, (i) Dacron, (j) a glyptal resin, (k) Nylon, (l) benzoyl peroxide, (m) saccharin, (n) formic acid, (o) oxalic acid, (p) maleic acid, (q) ethyl malonate, (r) adipic acid, (s) terephthalic acid.

13-16 Write equations that illustrate the mechanism for the following: (a) saponification of an ester, (b) alkylation of ethyl malonate, (c) Newman esterification, (d) chromic acid oxidation of a secondary alcohol, (e) Claisen ester condensation.

13-17 Calculate the equivalent weight (**neutralization equivalent**) of the following acids: (a) butyric acid, (b) succinic acid, (c) aspirin, (d) citric acid.

13-18 The **saponification equivalent** of an ester is its equivalent weight in basic hydrolysis. Thus the saponification equivalent of ethyl acetate is 88.1. Could you decide between the following by measuring their saponification equivalents? Explain. (a) methyl heptanoate and ethyl heptanoate, (b) methyl butanoate and isopropyl propanoate, (c) ethyl propenoate and ethyl adipate, (d) α-valerolactone and the glycolide (also called a lactide) from 2-hydroxypentanoate.

13-19 Cite evidence for resonance in the carboxylate group.

13-20 Compare acid-base, oxidation-reduction, and electrophilic aromatic substitution reactions. Describe common features.

13-21 What are the most probable oxidizing species in acidic solution and the reduced forms of HNO_3, H_2O_2, CrO_3, $KMnO_4$, and $HOCl$?

13-22 Ordinary methods of esterification of tertiary alcohols with carboxylic acids and anhydrides are unsuccessful because of the ease of dehydration of the alcohol; the reaction of the alcohol with an acid chloride may lead to a tertiary chloride. Suggest a possible practical method for the synthesis of esters of tertiary alcohols.

13-23 Offer an explanation for the following:

   a. The predicted relative rates of acid hydrolysis of:

     (1) $CH_3CH(CH_3)CO_2Et$, $CH_3CH_2CH_2CO_2Et$, and $(CH_3)_3CCO_2Et$

     (3) $BuCO_2CH(CH_3)CH_2CH_3$, $BuCO_2(CH_2)_3CH_3$ and $BuCO_2C(CH_3)_3$

   b. The relative boiling points of esters and carboxylic acid of the same molecular weight

   c. The fact that benzoic acid is a stronger acid than acetic acid

   d. The extraordinary boiling points of nitriles

   e. The "sawtooth" nature of the melting points of the homologous straight-chain carboxylic acids

   f. The relative basicities of ethoxide and malonate anion

g. The following pK_a values

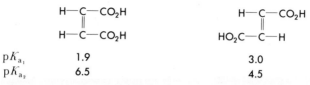

pK_{a_1}	1.9	3.0
pK_{a_2}	6.5	4.5

h. The rise in the oxidation potential (oxidizing strength) of oxidants with decreasing pH of the medium

i. The formation of t-butyl methyl ether upon prolonged reflux of t-butyl benzoate in methanol, although the ether is not formed if a mixture of t-butyl alcohol, methanol, and benzoic acid is refluxed for the same time.

13-24 Offer a mechanistic interpretation for:

a. The C-acylation of a nitrile using an ester and sodium amide

b. The Dieckmann condensation

c. $Et_2CHCHO + CH_2{=}CHCN \xrightarrow{\;OH^{\ominus}\;}$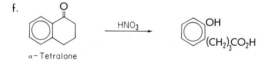

d. The conversion of cyclohexanol to cyclohexanone with chromic anhydride in acetic acid

e. The acid catalyzed hydrolysis of an ester (Hint: According to the **principle of microscopic reversibility,** if a given sequence of steps exists for the forward reaction, the reverse sequence obtains for the reverse reaction.)

f.

α-Tetralone

13-25 In one adaption of the **Arndt-Eistert reaction** a carboxylic acid is converted to its next higher homolog through a decomposition of a diazomethyl ketone in the presence of water. The decomposition is thought to proceed through an aldoketene. Offer a mechanistic interpretation for the several steps.

$$RCO_2H \xrightarrow{SOCl_2} RCOCl \xrightarrow{CH_2N_2}$$

$$RCOCHN_2 \xrightarrow{H_2O/Ag,\ Cu,\ or\ Pt} \underset{\text{An aldoketene}}{(RCH{=}C{=}O)} \longrightarrow RCH_2CO_2H$$

13-26 Tell specifically how you could decide by means of infrared spectrometry and without recourse to reference compounds between the following? (a) butanamide and N,N-dimethylbutanamide, (b) methyl 2-methylhexanoate and and 2-methylhexanamide, (c) isobutyric acid and methyl propanoate.

13-27 Suggest a spectral means by which you could distinguish between methyl isobutyrate and methyl butyrate without utilizing reference compounds.

13-28 Ketene dimerizes spontaneously to diketene, which is known to have the structure shown below. What chemical and physical properties could be used to support this structure?

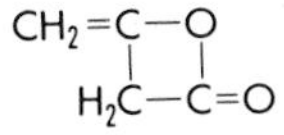

Diketene

13-29 Dimethylketene is converted to a dimer which may have either structure I or II (below). Its NMR spectrum shows a single resonance signal. Which structure is correct? Explain.

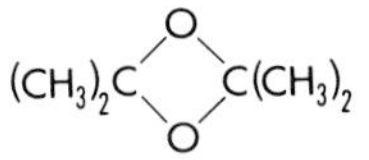

I 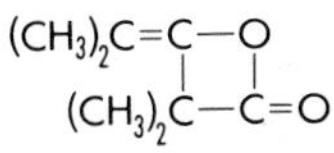   II

13-30 The reaction of methyl mercaptan with vinyl acetate may yield $CH_3CO_2CH_2$-CH_2SCH_3 or $CH_3CO_2CH(SCH_3)CH_3$. Describe how the NMR spectra for these two compounds would be expected to differ.

13-31 Write balanced net equations for the following reactions:

a. 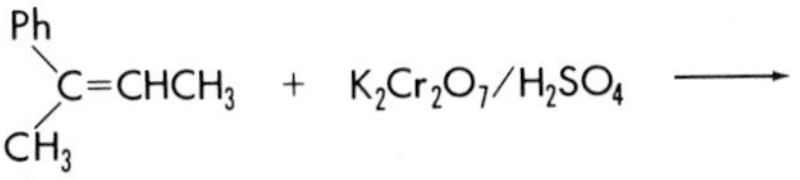   Ph
      \
       C=CHCH₃   +   K₂Cr₂O₇/H₂SO₄   ⟶
      /
     CH₃

b.   RSH   +   HNO₃   ⟶   RSO₃H   +   NO₂

c.    ⬡CH=CH₂   +   KMnO₄/HO₂CCH₃   ⟶

d. 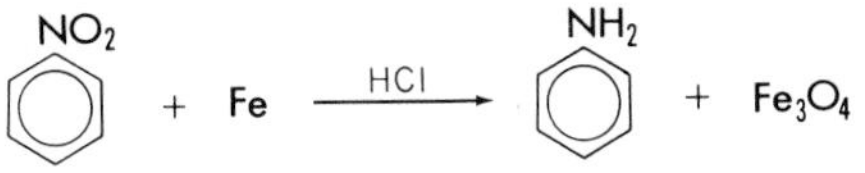   NO₂   NH₂
     ⬡   +   Fe   —HCl→   ⬡   +   Fe₃O₄

e. 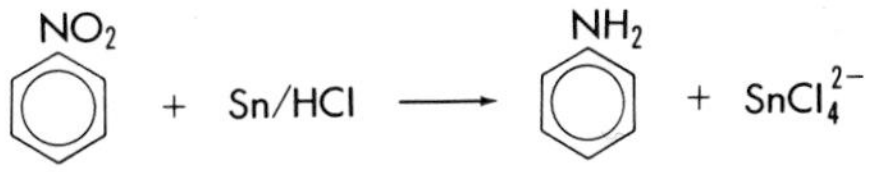   NO₂   NH₂
     ⬡   +   Sn/HCl   ⟶   ⬡   +   SnCl₄²⁻

f. 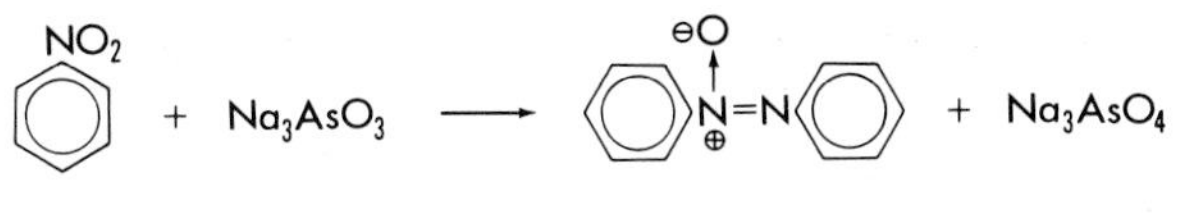   NO₂   ⊖O
                                 ↑
     ⬡   +   Na₃AsO₃   ⟶   ⬡N=N⬡   +   Na₃AsO₄
                                 ⊕

g. 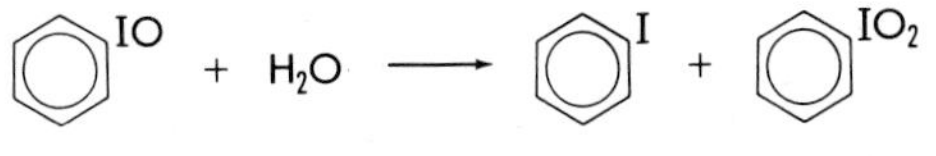   ⬡IO   +   H₂O   ⟶   ⬡I   +   ⬡IO₂

h. 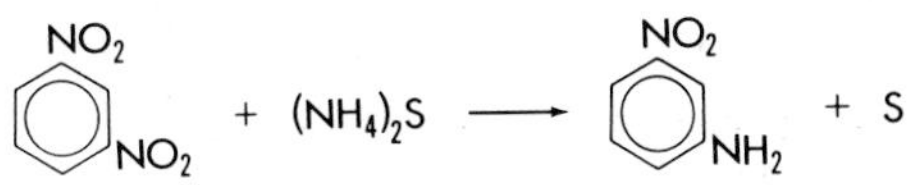   NO₂   NO₂
     ⬡NO₂   +   (NH₄)₂S   ⟶   ⬡NH₂   +   S

13-32 Write equations that show how you could accomplish the following conversions giving general conditions and catalysts: (assume that any reagents needed are available).

a. Ethylbenzene $\longrightarrow$ p-Ethylbenzenesulfonamide

b. Toluene $\longrightarrow$ p-Methoxybenzoic acid

c. Propanol $\longrightarrow$ Phenyl propyl ketone

d. Benzoic acid $\longrightarrow$ p-Cyanophenyl methyl ether

e. Propanoic anhydride $\longrightarrow$ $CH_3CH_2CH_2SCCH_3$
$$\overset{\|}{O}$$

f. Methyl pentanoate $\longrightarrow$ 1-Bromopentane

g. Propyl chloride $\longrightarrow$ Isobutyl butyrate

h. 2-Methylpropanamide $\longrightarrow$ 1,1-Di-p-tolyl-3-methyl-1-butanol

i. Benzene $\longrightarrow$

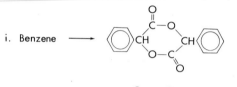

j. Benzene $\longrightarrow$

k. Adipic acid $\longrightarrow$

l. Acetic acid and $KC^{14}N$ $\longrightarrow$ $(CH_3)_2CHC^{14}O_2H$

m. $C^{14}H_3I$ $\longrightarrow$ $PhCH_2C^{14}H_2CO_2CH_3$

n. $(CH_3)_2C=CH(CH_2)_3CO_2H$ $\longrightarrow$

13-33 Identify the starting compound and transformation products for each of the following and write equations for the chemical changes described:

a. $C_8H_6O_2$ is insoluble in water, but upon heating with sodium hydroxide is converted to a water-soluble compound. Acidification of the hydrolysis mixture yields a product which reacts with diazomethane to form $C_9H_{10}O_3$. Upon treatment with acetic anhydride $C_9H_{10}O_3$ is converted to $C_{11}H_{12}O_4$. Oxidation of $C_8H_6O_2$ converts it to $C_8H_6O_4$. The latter is nitrated with some difficulty yielding two mononitro derivatives.

b. C_8H_{14} reacts with hydrogen chloride to form a single product $C_8H_{15}Cl$ and upon oxidation C_8H_{14} is converted to a carboxylic acid having the empirical formula $C_4H_7O_2$. (There are two possible answers.)

c. Ozonolysis of $C_{10}H_{16}O_4$ yields a single product $C_5H_8O_3$. Hydrolysis of the latter yields an acid and an alcohol. Upon heating the acid, carbon monoxide is evolved and the alcohol gives a positive test with iodoform. Hydrolysis of $C_{10}H_{16}O_4$ results in the formation of an acid, A, which slowly forms $C_6H_6O_3$ upon heating. This new compound reacts with water to yield an acid having the same molecular formula as A, but a different melting point; the latter isomer readily reverts to $C_6H_6O_3$ on heating.

Questions for Chapter 14

14-1   Give IUPAC names for:
a. $CH_3CH_2CH_2NH_2$
b. $CH_3CH(CH_3)NO_2$
c. $CH_3CH(OC_2H_5)CH_2CH(NH_2)CH_3$
d.

e.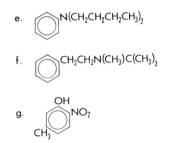

f.

g.

14-2   Define and illustrate: (a) ambident ion, (b) diazotization, (c) reductive amination, (d) urethane, (e) enamine, (f) invert soap, (g) "FBI" effect, (h) mordant, (i) phospholipid, (j) Hinsberg reaction, (k) Van Slyke determination, (l) Zerevitinoff analysis, (m) "red, white, and blue" reaction, (n) polynitroarene complex.

14-3   Write a brief description of the different types of dyes based upon their structure and upon their method of application. Give examples where possible.

14-4   Briefly describe the origin of color in dyes and the role of chromophores and auxochromes. Give examples of these two types of groups.

14-5   Explain: (a) the greater stability of aryldiazonium salts compared to alkyldiazonium salts, (b) the greater acidity of imides compared to amides, (c) the greater stability of *trans*-azobenzene compared to *cis*-azobenzene, (d) why guanidine is such a strong base, (e) the absence of a carbonyl stretching band

in the infrared spectrum of an acidic solution of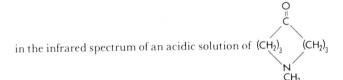

(f) how the different factors involved contribute to the acidity of primary and secondary nitroalkanes, (g) why the C–N–C bond angle in trimethylamine is so much greater than that expected for a $C-sp^3-sp^3-N$ bond, (h) why 2,4-dinitrochlorobenzene can be readily hydrolyzed to yield 2,4-dinitrophenol by simply refluxing with aqueous sodium carbonate, whereas phenyl chloride is very difficult to hydrolyze.

14-6   Write equations, giving general conditions and catalysts, for the following:
a. Ten different ways to synthesize propylamine
b. Three different ways to synthesize dipentylamine
c. Two different ways to synthesize (1) triethylamine, (2) trimethylpropylammonium hydroxide, (3) aniline

d. The synthesis of (1) urea from carbon dioxide, (2) isocyanic acid from urea, (3) cyanamide from calcium carbide

e. Gabriel synthesis

f. The reactions: (1) Leuckart, (2) Sandmeyer, (3) Gatterman, (4) Gomberg, (5) Mannich

g. The rearrangements: (1) benzidine, (2) Demjanov

14-7 Give two different examples of: (a) hydrogenolysis, (b) an ylide (only one of each is described in Chapter 14).

14-8 Describe how you could use isotopic labeling to establish that the benzidine rearrangement occurs intramolecularly.

14-9 Would you expect diphenylnitromethane readily to undergo H-D exchange upon treatment with sodium ethoxide in C_2H_5OD? Explain.

14-10 Write electron dot formulas for the two most important canonical forms of an isonitrile.

14-11 Discuss the factors influencing the boiling points and the water solubilities of amines.

14-12 Describe what you would expect to be common and distinguishing features of the infrared spectra of propylamine and 1-nitropropane.

14-13 Compare and explain the expected basicity differences between: (a) aniline and cyclohexylamine, (b) 2,6-diisopropyl-N,N-diethylaniline and 3,5-diisopropyl-N,N-diethylaniline, (c) 3,4-dimethylaniline and 3,4-dimethoxyaniline, (d) ethylamine and ammonia, (e) 3-dimethylamino-1-propanol and trimethylethylammonium hydroxide.

14-14 Calculate pK_b for the following: (a) isobutylamine, $K(25°) = 2.6 \times 10^{-4}$; (b) dimethylbenzylamine, $K(25°) = 8.5 \times 10^{-6}$; (c) β-naphthylamine, $K(25°) = 1.29 \times 10^{-10}$

14-15 Write structural formulas for the principal products expected from the pyrolysis of (a) dimethylethylphenylammonium hydroxide, (b) methyldipropylisobutylammonium hydroxide, (c) the quaternary base derived through exhaustive methylation of pyrrolidine, (d) methylethylpropylsulfonium hydroxide.

14-16 Describe how you could distinguish qualitatively between the following through chemical properties: (a) p-toluidine and 1-amino-4-methylcyclohexane, (b) 1- and 2-nitropropanes, (c) N,N-dimethylaniline and p-ethylaniline, (d) tetrabutylammonium hydroxide and tributylamine, (e) 2-methyl-2-nitropentane and 3-methyl-2-nitropentane.

14-17 Write equations that show the mechanism of each of the reactions listed: (a) Hofmann rearrangement, (b) conversion of $R_2C=CHNR_2$ to $R_2CHCH=\overset{\oplus}{N}R_2$, (c) alkylation of ammonia, (d) Cope elimination reaction, (e) Curtius reaction, (f) hydrolysis of benzenediazonium hydrogen sulfate.

14-18 Write the formula(s) for the principal product (or products) expected from the following: (a) ethylamine, chloroform, and concentrated sodium hydroxide, (b) methylisopropylamine and nitrous acid, (c) o-toluidine, sodium nitrite, and hydrochloric acid at 0°, (d) 1-amino-4-methoxybutane, p-toluenesulfonyl chloride, and sodium hydroxide, (e) butanamide and lithium aluminum hydride, (f) triethylamine and hydrogen peroxide, (g) p-ethylbenzenediazonium chloride and p-isopropylaniline, (h) benzalaniline, $PhCH=NPh$, and butylmagnesium bromide followed by hydrolysis, (i) isopropyl isothiocyanate and methyl mercaptan, (j) a solution of benzenediazonium chloride and potassium iodide is heated, (k) benzyltrimethylammonium iodide and silver hydroxide, (l) benzenediazonium bromide and o-cresol, (m) propylmagnesium chloride and isopropylamine, (n) hexanoic acid, hydrazoic acid, and concentrated sulfuric acid followed by dilution with water and the addition of excess sodium hydroxide, (o) p-chlorobenzenediazonium hydrogen sulfate and hypophosphorus acid, (p) heating benzenediazonium chloride with cuprous cyanide, (q) p-cresol, formaldehyde, and diethylamine, (r) phenylisocyanate and water, (s) benzenediazonium fluoroborate and sodium nitrite, (t) dimethylethylamine and benzyl bromide, (u) propanamide, sodium hypobromite, and water, (v) p-nitroisopropylbenzene, tin, and hydrochloric acid, (w) ethyl acetoacetate and p-bromobenzenediazonium bromide, (x) benzylamine and nitrous acid, (y) 2-naphthalenediazonium chloride, stannous chloride, and hydrochloric acid, (z) an alkaline solution of nitroethane and bromine.

14-19 Tell which reaction, or reactions, may contribute to lowering the yield in: (a) the Gatterman synthesis of an aryl chloride, (b) the reductive amination of an aldehyde, (c) the synthesis of a primary amine from an alkyl halide by the Hofmann reaction, (d) the synthesis of a primary amine by the reduction of a nitrile, (e) the synthesis of an isonitrile from an alkyl halide and silver cyanide.

14-20 Write the equations for the following conversions, giving general conditions and catalysts:

a. Benzenediazonium bromide to: (1) bromobenzene by two procedures, (2) potassium diazobenzoate, (3) cyanobenzene, (4) potassium benzenearsonate, (5) biphenyl, (6) p-hydroxyazobenzene.

b. Propanol to: (1) $CH_3CH=CH_2N$ ⬠   (2) N-propylpyrrolidine

c. 1-Nitropentane to:
   (1) pentylamine, (2) butanal, (3) pentanoic acid, (4) 4-nitro-3-octanol

d. p-Nitrotoluene to: (1) p-toluidine, (2) p,p'-dimethylhydrazobenzene, (3)

p-nitrosomethylbenzene, (4) CH_3⬡$\overset{\overset{\displaystyle O}{\uparrow}}{N}=N$⬡$CH_3$

e. Phenyl isocyanate to: (1) PhNHCONHPh, (2) PhNHCOOEt

f. Ethyl isocyanide to: (1) propanenitrile, (2) methylethylamine, (3) ethyl isothiocyanate

14-21 Write equations that show how the following transformations may be accomplished, giving general conditions and catalysts:

a. Nitromethane $\rightarrow CH_3CH_2CH(OH)CH_2NH_2$

b. $(CH_3)_2CH\overset{\displaystyle O}{\overset{\|}{C}}NH_2 \longrightarrow (CH_3)_2CHN^{\oplus}(C_2H_5)_3OH^{\ominus}$

c. Aniline $\longrightarrow$ 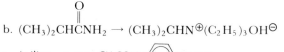 CH$_3$CONH⟨◯⟩SO$_3$C$_2$H$_5$

d. Aniline $\longrightarrow$ o-Bromofluorobenzene

e. Nitrobenzene $\longrightarrow$ p-Aminobenzoic acid

f. Nitrobenzene $\longrightarrow$ ⟨◯⟩N=C=O
                           Br

g. Nitrobenzene $\longrightarrow$ p-Nitroaniline

h. m–Dinitrobenzene $\longrightarrow$ H$_2$N⟨◯⟩—⟨◯⟩NH$_2$
                                    CH$_3$O   OCH$_3$

i. m-Iodoaniline $\longrightarrow$ 1-Phenylethanol

j. Bromobenzene $\longrightarrow$ Br⟨◯⟩—⟨◯⟩CH$_3$

k. p–Ethylbenzoic acid $\longrightarrow$ Et⟨◯⟩N=CH⟨◯⟩

l. 1-Chloropentane $\longrightarrow$ Butylamine

m. Isopropyl bromide $\longrightarrow$ Isobutylamine

14-22 Identify the compounds in the following and write equations for the chemical changes described:

a. Reduction of C_9H_9N with sodium and alcohol yields $C_9H_{13}N$, which yields a water-soluble sulfonamide from the Hinsberg reaction. Hofmann degradation of $C_9H_{13}N$ gives C_9H_{10}. Vigorous oxidation of C_9H_{10} yields benzoic acid, and one of the products from its ozonolysis gives a positive haloform test.

b. Reaction of $C_6H_{13}NO_2$ with nitrous acid results in a blue-colored solution. Upon reduction with hydrogen and a palladium–charcoal catalyst an amine is formed. Exhaustive methylation of the amine, conversion to the quaternary base, and pyrolysis yield C_6H_{12}. Oxidation of C_6H_{12} with potassium permanganate yields two acids, one of which is found to be acetic acid. When the second acid is converted to an amide and subjected to the conditions for a Hofmann rearrangement, isopropylamine is formed.

c. A vile stench results when $C_8H_{11}NO$ is treated with chloroform and concentrated sodium hydroxide. Its reaction with acetyl chloride leads to the formation of $C_{12}H_{15}NO_3$, which yields two isomeric compounds, $C_{12}H_{14}N_2O_5$, upon nitration. Hofmann degradation of $C_8H_{11}NO$ yields C_8H_8O.

Questions for Chapter 15

15-1   Define and illustrate: (a) optical activity, (b) racemic mixture, (c) absolute asymmetric synthesis, (d) asymmetric degradation, (e) optically active absorption band, (f) plane of symmetry.

15-2   Distinguish clearly between: (a) configuration and constitution, (b) epimerization and racemization, (c) plane and circularly polarized light, (d) epimer and diastereoisomer, (e) *meso* and racemic compound, (f) stereoselective and nonstereoselective, (g) mutarotation and optical rotatory dispersion, (h) the notations D,L and (+), (−), (i) plain and anomalous ORD.

15-3   Explain schematically how a pair of polaroid sunglasses reduces the glare reflected from the surface of a lake.

15-4   What is a necessary condition for optical activity?

15-5   Briefly describe the general methods used for the resolution of racemic mixtures.

15-6   Make a schematic sketch of the component parts of a polarimeter and explain how the instrument operates.

15-7   What are the factors that influence the specific activity of a solution of an optically active compound?

15-8   Compare the properties of enantiomers with those of a racemic mixture and a racemic compound, which might be derived from the enantiomers.

15-9   How do the properties of diastereomers differ from those of enantiomers?

15-10   Give examples of: (a) six types of compounds which owe their optical activity to an asymmetric atom other than carbon, (b) three types of compounds capable of existing in optically active forms, but not having an asymmetric atom.

15-11   Offer an explanation for optical activity.

15-12   What explanations are offered for the origin of optically active compounds?

15-13   Why does the presence of an asymmetric center in a molecule impart stereoselectivity upon the introduction of a second asymmetric center?

15-14   Show a scheme (flow sheet) for the resolution of racemic ephedrine.

15-15   When 1.5 g of an optically active compound is dissolved in 25 ml of chloroform at 25°, the optical rotation of the solution, observed in a 2 dm polarimeter tube using a sodium D-line light, is −4.8°. What is the specific rotation of the compound?

15-16   Why does mutarotation proceed to zero in a racemization reaction, but not generally to zero in an epimerization reaction?

15-17   Draw a mutarotation curve which might be typical for an epimerization reaction.

15-18   Draw three-dimensional formulas for all of the stereoisomers of 3-phenyl-2-butanol. Indicate which are *erythro* and which are *threo*.

15-19   Draw three-dimensional formulas for the two four-carbon sugars erythrose and threose. Name each isomer. Now, suppose the —CH=O group in each of these compounds is reduced to —CH$_2$OH using lithium aluminum hydride. Draw the three-dimensional formulas for the products.

15-20 How could you resolve a racemic alcohol?

15-21 How could you prepare optically active α-bromopropionic acid from propionic acid?

15-22 Biphenyl derivatives having methyl rather than nitro substituents in the 2 and 2' positions racemize more rapidly upon heating than do the isomers shown in Figure 15-18. Why?

15-23 Quaternary ammonium salts of the type $R_1R_2R_3R_4N^{\oplus} X^{\ominus}$ are capable of resolution, but salts of the type $R_1R_2NH_2^{\oplus}X^{\ominus}$ are not. Why?

15-24 What would be the total number of stereoisomers possible for the following quaternary ammonium salts?

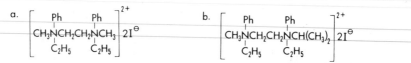

15-25 The steroid cholestanol possesses nine dissimilar asymmetric carbon atoms. How many stereoisomers of this substance may exist? How many racemates? (Only two of these isomers are found in nature!)

15-26 Predict the number of isomers possible for each of the following compounds. Draw three-dimensional and Fischer projection formulas for each isomer. Label active forms, *meso* forms, and racemic pairs. Indicate two diasteromers wherever such forms may exist.

a. $CH_3CHClCH_2CN$

b. $CH_3CHBrCH_2CHBrCH_2$

c. $CH_3CHBrCHBrCH_2CH_2$⟨⟩CH_3

d. $CH_3CHClCH_2CO_2CH_2CH_3$

e. $CH_3CH(OH)CH(OH)CH_2OH$

f. $CH_3CH{=}CHSCH(CH_3)CH_2CH_3$

g. $CH_2{=}CHCHPhCHClCH_3$

15-27 It has been found that optically active (+)-phenylpropionic acid is converted in the Schmidt reaction to (+)-phenylethyl alcohol (1-phenylethanol) with 99.6 per cent retention of configuration. What can you say concerning the mechanism of this reaction?

15-28 Show with perspective drawings why the action of a Grignard reagent on an unsymmetrical ketone leads to a racemic alcohol.

15-29 Can either *cis-* or *trans*-1,3-dimethylcyclohexane or *cis-* or *trans*-1,4-dimethylcyclohexane exist in racemic forms? Explain and illustrate your answer with perspective drawings.

15-30 S_N2 reactions are accompanied by inversion of configuration. Yet the S_N2 reaction in Figure 15-26 is attended by racemization. Why?

15-31 If the iodide ion in the S_N2 reaction of Figure 15-26 were replaced by radioactive iodide ion ($I^{*\ominus}$), what would you predict regarding the relationship between the rates of inversion, racemization, and uptake of radioactivity by the alkyl iodide?

15-32 The conversion of an optically active secondary alcohol, R_1R_2C*HOH, into its alkyl chloride using $SOCl_2$ occurs with retention of configuration in dioxane but with inversion of configuration in pyridine. How do you account for this mechanistically?

15-33 How could you correlate the configuration of D (−)-atrolactic acid (2-hydroxy-2-phenylpropanoic acid), $CH_3CPh(OH)CO_2H$, $[\alpha]_D$ −86°, with that of dextro atrolactamide, $[\alpha]_D$ 9°?

15-34 Predict the stereochemical course of the reaction between methylmagnesium iodide and 2-phenylpropanal.

15-35 Contrast the stereochemical courses of the reactions of phenylmagnesium bromide with propanal and with 2-methoxypropanal.

15-36 Which reaction of methylmagnesium iodide should proceed with greater stereoselectivity, that with 2-methoxybutanal or that with 3-methoxybutanal? Why?

15-37 How could you resolve the sulfoxide shown in Figure 15-19?

15-38 How could you obtain optically active 1-phenyl-3-hydroxy-3-methyl-2-pentanone from optically active 4-phenyl-3-hydroxy-2-butanone through synthesis?

Questions for Chapter 16

16-1 What assumption is implicit in Kiliani's structure proof for glucose and fructose?

16-2 How would you establish the skeletal structure of apiose? Name all products involved.

16-3 Draw the Rosanoff classification for the L- series of aldoses.

16-4 How would you determine which structure is D-glucose and which is D-mannose in Figure 16-8.

16-5 Redraw Figure 16-9 to include the α- and β-D-glucofuranose forms which are present to a minor extent at equilibrium.

16-6 What assumptions are implicit in Haworth's establishment of the pyranose ring size in glucose (Figure 16-11)?

16-7 Illustrate the application of Haworth's methylation-oxidation technique (Figure 16-11) to methyl α-D-glucofuranoside.

16-8 Neutral solutions of sucrose show no mutarotation, but acid solutions do. Why?

16-9 Give an alternate systematic name for sucrose.

16-10 What final methylated degradation products would result if the "alcohol component" of maltose were furanose, with its glycoside linkage at C5? Would HIO_4 serve to distinguish between this structure and that actually possessed by maltose?

16-11 Show how you could establish the structures of cellobiose, lactose, and gentiobiose.

16-12 Illustrate with an equation the hydrolysis of fully methylated raffinose.

16-13 Why does a mouthful of bread develop a sweet taste on prolonged chewing?

16-14 Give complete equations for the following reactions: (a) the methylation of methyl α-D-mannopyranoside, (b) the acetylation of D-xylose with Ac₂O–H₂SO₄, (c) the oxidation of maltose with NaOBr solution, (d) the oxidation of L-lyxose with HNO₃, (e) the Kiliani synthesis applied to D-galactose, (f) the oxidation of methyl β-D-glucofuranoside with HIO₄, (g) the reaction of tetra-*O*-acetyl-α-D-glucopyranosyl bromide with sodium thiophenylate, (h) the oxidation of calcium D-arabinonate with H₂O₂ in the presence of FeSO₄.

16-15 Draw the stereoisomers of inositol, and indicate which are optically active.

16-16 Show how you could convert D-glucose into: (a) methyl tetra-*O*-acetyl-β-D-glucopyranoside, (b) δ-D-gluconolactone, (c) phenyl-α-D-glucopyranoside, (d) coniferin, (e) tetra-*O*-acetyl-β-D-arabinose.

16-17 Describe and distinguish among: (a) amino acid, (b) essential amino acid, and (c) nonessential amino acid.

16-18 Describe alternate ways by which you might resolve (±)-phenylalanine.

16-19 Show the forms in which the following amino acids will exist in solutions of low pH, medium pH, and high pH: (a) valine, (b) proline, (c) lysine, (d) aspartic acid.

16-20 Describe the characteristics of amino acids and proteins at their isoelectric points.

16-21 Illustrate three methods for the synthesis of: (a) alanine, (b) valine.

16-22 Show the conversion of: (a) tyrosine into its azlactone, (b) proline into its diketopiperazine.

16-23 What is meant by the following terms: (a) prosthetic group, (b) phosphoprotein, (c) nucleoprotein, (d) porphyrin, (e) denaturation.

16-24 What are the following techniques, and how are they useful in purifying proteins: (a) dialysis, (b) countercurrent fractionation, (c) electrophoresis.

16-25 Explain how paper chromatography might be useful in establishing the amino acid constituents of a polypeptide.

16-26 Indicate with an equation the course of the following reactions: (a) the action of acetyl chloride on the sodium salt of proline, (b) the action of excess methyl iodide and silver oxide on hydroxyproline, (c) the action of excess Raney nickel in refluxing ethanol on cystine, (d) the action of excess potassium permanganate in alkali on phenylalanine, (e) the action of sodium hydroxide on thyroxine, (f) the action of benzenediazonium chloride on tyrosine.

16-27 How could a sample of radioactive phenylalanine be utilized to establish the phenylalanine content of a crude protein hydrolyzate?

16-28 What is meant by "end-group analysis," and how is the technique useful in the investigation of proteins?

16-29 Write the structures of the following polypeptides:
a. H–Try–Tyr–Pro–Pro–Leu–Val–Gly–Gly–Lys–Ser–OH
b. Arginylserylphenylalanyldiglycylhydroxyproline

16-30 Starting with carbobenzoxy chloride, any desired amino acids, and any other reagents, show how you would accomplish the synthesis of: (a) H–Val–Phe–OH, (b) H–Ala–Leu–Pro–Gly–OH

16-31 Draw the structures of: (a) an *N*-terminal hydroxyproline unit in a protein, after reaction of the protein with 2,4-dinitrofluorobenzene, followed by hydrolysis; (b) a carboxy-terminal glutamic acid unit in a protein, after reaction of the protein with hydrazine, followed by hydrolysis.

16-32 A tetrapeptide contains Val, Gly, Leu, and Pro in unknown sequence. Its reaction with 2,4-dinitrofluorobenzene, followed by hydrolysis, affords the N-2,4-dinitrophenyl (DNP) derivatives of Gly and the dipeptide Gly–Pro. Its reaction with hydrazine, followed by hydrolysis, yields Leu. What is the structure of the tetrapeptide?

16-33 A pentapeptide containing two moles of Gly and one each of Leu, Ser, and Phe per mole in unknown sequence, gives the DNP derivative of Leu after reaction with 2,4-dinitrofluorobenzene and complete hydrolysis. Partial hydrolysis of the DNP-pentapeptide yields the DNP derivative of a dipeptide Leu–Phe, and a tripeptide. Conversion of the latter to its DNP derivative followed by partial hydrolysis, affords DNP–Gly–Gly. What is the amino acid sequence in the original pentapeptide?

16-34 Elemental analysis of hemoglobin shows an iron content of Fe, 0.342 per cent. What is the minimum molecular weight of the hemoglobin molecule associated with a single iron atom? How many such subunits must be contained in the hemoglobin molecule?

16-35 Show the results of the following sequence of reactions starting with deoxycholic acid: (a) esterification with CH_3OH, $H^\oplus$, (b) reaction of the resulting ester with PhMgBr, (c) dehydration of the product from (b), (d) oxidation of the product from (c).

16-36 Show how a repetition of the sequence of reactions (**Barbier-Wieland degradation**) in Question 16-35 could be used to establish the structure of the side chain in deoxycholic acid.

16-37 Show the structures of the product(s) you would obtain from the following reactions: (a) the ozonolysis of calciferol, (b) the action of bromine on cholesterol, (c) the reaction of acetic anhydride with cortisone, (d) the action of sodium hypoiodite on progesterone, (e) the reaction of hydroxylamine with androsterone, followed by PCl_5 in ether, followed by hydrolysis, (f) the hydrolysis of bufotalin.

16-38 Devise a scheme to degrade the ergosterol molecule so as to establish its structure. Show the reagents for each reaction and the structure of each degradation product.

16-39 Distinguish between steroid sapogenins and terpenoid sapogenins.

16-40 Illustrate degradation reactions which could be used to establish the structure of nicotine.

16-41 Construct three-dimensional models of quinine, morphine, and strychnine.

16-42 Starting with any desired C_6 or C_7 aromatic or heterocyclic derivative, any small aliphatic compounds, and any desired inorganic reagents, devise syntheses for: (a) adrenalin, (b) vitamin B_3 (nicotinamide), (c) piperine, (d) hygrine.

16-43 Indicate the isoprene units in the following terpenoid compounds: (a) geraniol, (b) camphor, (c) fenchone, (d) β-eudesmol, (e) cedrol, (f) ambrein, (g) lanosterol, (h) α-amyrin.

16-44 Show the products and the number of moles of each which would be obtained
       by the ozonolysis of the following: (a) lycopene, (b) perhydrolycopene, (c)
       squalene, (d) agathic acid, (e) rubixanthin, (f) ambrein.
16-45 Indicate the formal steps which must be accomplished for the biosynthetic
       conversion of squalene into: (a) cholesterol, (b) progesterone, (c) cortisone.

Index

Abietic acid, 583
Absorption spectrum, 70
Acetaldehyde, 299, 308
Acetals, 316–17
Acetamides, 369
Acetic acid, 344, 349
Acetone, 299, 308
Acetonitrile, 371
Acetophenone, 299
Acetylation, 515–16
Acetylcholine, 424
Acetylcholinesterase, 424
Acetylene, 185–86
Acetylenes, 183. *See also* Alkynes
Acids, Lewis definition of, 105–06, 401
Acrylonitrile, 372
Activation energy, of reaction, 114–15
Acyclic compounds, 18
Acylals, 317–18
Acylation, 362–63, 366, 418, 420–21
Acyl halides, 352–53
Acyloins, 331
Addition reactions, 97
　of aldehydes and ketones, 325–27
　of alkenes, 154–64
　of alkynes, 190–91
　of aromatics, 224–25
　of cycloalkanes, 207–10
　of dienes, 175–76
Adenosine triphosphate (ATP), 531, 532, 588
Adipic acid, 379
Adrenalin, 574
Adsorbents, definition of, 47
Agathic acid, 583

Aglycone, 519
Alchemy, 2
Alcohols, 248–76
　nomenclature of, 248–50
　properties of, 250–54
　reactions of, 264–72, 275–76, 316–18
　sources and uses of, 255–58
　sulfur analogs of, 294–95
　synthesis of, 258–63
Alcoholysis, 365
Aldehydes, 298–341
　distinguished from ketones, 311–13
　isomeric forms of, 309–11
　nomenclature of, 299–300
　properties of, 300–02
　reactions of, 309–36
　sources of, 299
　synthesis of, 302–05, 308
　unsaturated, 336–39
Aldimine, 318
Alditols, 514
Aldol condensation, 327–30
Aldonic acids, 513
Aldoses, 494, 495–99
Aldosterone, 568
Alfol process, 258, 259
Alicyclic compounds, 195. *See also* Cycloalkanes
Aliphatic compounds, 19, 119
　of nitrogen, 433–34
Alkaloids, 573–77
　condensed ring systems in, 576–77
　isolation of, 573–74
　structure of, 427, 574–75

Alkanes, 119, 120, 121–42
  nomenclature of, 121–23
  properties of, 123–26
  reactions of, 136–42
  sources and uses of, 126–31
  synthesis of, 131–36
Alkenes, 119, 143–81
  nomenclature of, 144, 145
  properties of, 145
  reactions of, 154–74
  sources of, 145
  synthesis of, 146–54
Alkyd resins, 381
Alkylation, 130
  of alkenes, 169
  of alkynes, 187–88
  of amines, 410–11, 417, 418
  of nitroalkanes, 433
Alkyl aromatics, 120
Alkyl glycopyranosides, 516–17
Alkyl halides. *See* Halides, organic
Alkyne rearrangements, 192
Alkynes, 119, 183–94
  nomenclature of, 184
  properties of, 184–85
  reactions of, 188–94
  sources of, 185–86
  synthesis of, 186–88
Allene, 174, 192
Allylic halogenation, 168–69
Allylic rearrangements, 284–85
Ambident ion, 432, 449
Ambrein, 584
Amides, 367–70
Amination, reductive, 411–13
Amines, 369, 397–422
  and aldehydes, 319
  basicity of, 401–08
  characterization of, 408–09
  nomenclature of, 397–99
  preparation of, 324
  properties of, 400–01
  reactions of, 418–22
  structure of, 399
  synthesis of, 409–17
Amino acids, 533–41
  nomenclature of, 534–36
  occurrence of, 536–37, 550–57
  reactions of, 540–41
  structure of, 537
  synthesis of, 538–40
  see also Proteins

Aminobenzene, 398
Aminopeptidases, 557
Ammonia, 318–21, 397, 399. *See also* Amines
Ammonolysis, 365
Amylopectin, 525
Amylose, 525
Amyrin, 584
Anabasine, 575
Analytical chemistry, 3
Androgens, 567
Androsterone, 567
Anhydrides, carboxylic, 353–54
  cyclic, 379–81
Aniline, 398
Anils, 319
Anthocyanins, 292
Apiose, 496–97
Arndt-Eistert reaction, 432, 449
Arenesulfonic acids, 226
Aromatic hydrocarbons, 19, 119–20
  benzene derivatives of, 241
  nomenclature of, 216–18, 219–20
  non-benzenoid derivatives, 241–43
  properties of, 216–18
  reactions of, 224–39
  sources of, 220–23
  structure of, 216–18, 219–20, 239–41
  synthesis of, 223–24
Aromatic nitrogen compounds, 432, 434–39
Aronium ion, 440
Aroyl halide, 352
Aryl halides. *See* Halides, organic
Ascorbic acid, 514
Aspirin (acetylsalicylic acid), 345
Atactic, 173
Atom, and bonding, 11
  carbon, 4–5
  configurations of, 478–82
  and formulas, 9–11
  free rotation of, 31–32
  orbitals of, 89–91
Autoxidation, 293
Auxochromes, 445
Aza derivatives, 398
Azeotrope, definition of, 256–57
Azobenzene, 437
Azo derivatives, 444
Azulene series, terpenes, 582

Baeyer test, 165
Baeyer-Villiger reaction, 334–35
Barbier-Wieland degradation, 633

Barbiturates, 385–86
Bart reaction, 441
Bases, Lewis definition of, 105–06, 401
Bathochromic, 178
Beckmann rearrangements, 321–24
Benedict's solution, 312
Benzaldehyde, 299, 319, 331–32
Benzene, 19, 86, 93–94, 119
Benzidine rearrangement, 437–38
Benzilic acid rearrangements, 332
Benzoin condensation, 331–32
Benzoquinone, 339
Benzyne intermediates, 286–87
Bergius process, 130
Bile acids, 567
Biochemistry, 1, 3
Biosynthesis, 586–89
Birch reduction, 224
Biuret reaction, 544
Blanc's rule, 380
Boiling point, 53
    of alcohols, 250–51
    of alkanes, 124–25
    of alkenes, 145
Boiling point elevation, 61, 62
Bond, chemical, 11–16
    coordinate covalent, 14
    covalent, 11, 13–14
    energy of, 32–33
    in formulas, 9–10
    heat of formation of, 33
    homolytic and heterolytic cleavage of, 98–99
    ionic, 11, 12, 14–15
    length of, 25–26
    multiple, 16
    nature of, 85–94
    orbital theory of, 89–94
    pi (π), 91, 435
    and properties, 17–18
    and reaction mechanisms, 97–99
    resonance theory of, 85–89
    sigma (σ), 91
Bredt's rule, 153, 577
Bromination, 433
Buna rubber, 176, 177
Butanedioic acid, 378

Cadelene series, terpenes, 581, 582
Calciferol, 566
Cannizzaro reaction, 332–34
Canonical structures, 87, 103, 108

Carbamide, 449
Carbanions, 98
    configuration of, 113
    stability of, 111–12
    transient, 112–13
Carbene insertion, 141–42
Carbenes, 99
Carbocyclic compounds, 18
Carbohydrates, 494–533
    classes and properties of, 494–95
    configurations of, 499–504
    ring size of, 506–08
    ring structure of, 504–06
Carbon, 1
    atom of, 4–5
    bond lengths, 25
    character of, 4–5
    graphite structure of, 228–29
    isotopes of, 33–34
    quantitative analysis of, 56–59
    tetrahedral, 24, 464
Carbonation, 349–40
Carbonic acid, 377
Carbonium ions, 98
    configurations of, 110–11
    isomerization of, 137–38
    stable, 106–08
    transient, 108–10
Carbonyl compounds, 258–60, 298, 309
Carboxamides, 367–70
Carboxylic acids, 344–52
    acidity of, 347–49
    and amino acids, 533
    anhydrides of, 353–54
    nitrogen analogs of, 387–90
    nomenclature and properties of, 345–46
    reactions of, 351–52
    sulfur analogs of, 387–90
    synthesis of, 349–50
Carboxypeptidases, 557
Carnauba wax, 355–56
Caro's acid, 334
Carotene, 178, 585–86
Carotenoids, 585–86
Catalase, 556
Cellobiose, 521
Cellophane, 527
Celluloses, 526–29
Chelates, 254
Chemical engineering, 3
Chitin, 529
Chlorophyll-a, 55, 531

Cholesterol, 566, 589
Cholic acid, 345, 567
Choline, 423–24
Chlorophyll, 55–56, 531
Chlorosulfonation, 389
Chromatography, 47–51
Chromic acid oxidation, 393–95
Chromophores, 70, 444
Chromoproteins, 542
Chugaeff reaction, 150, 427
Citric acid, 344, 376
Claisen rearrangement, 293–94
Claisen condensation, 366
Claisen-Schmidt condensation, 328–29
Clemmenson reduction, 136, 314
Cocaine, 576
Coenzyme A, 587–88
Coenzymes, 557, 587–88
Collagen, 542
Column chromatography, 47–48
Complex formation, 228–29, 435
Condensation reactions, 97, 327–33, 365–67,
    381–82
Conformational analysis, 31–32
Cope rearrangement, 180, 427
Copolymerization, 171
Corticosteroids, 568
Cortisone, 568
Countercurrent separation, 545–46
Coupling reactions, 206–07, 443–44
Cracking process, 129
Creatine, 451
Creatinine, 451
Crystallization, 45–46
Curtius reaction, 416
Cuscohygrine, 574, 575
Cyamelide, 451
Cyanamide, 450
Cyanamide process, 450
Cyanic acid, 451
Cyanides, 371. See also Nitriles
Cyanoethylation, 372
Cyanohydrins, 326
Cyanuric acid, 451
Cyclic anhydrides, 379–81
Cyclic compounds, 18–19
Cycloalkanes, 119, 195–213
    nomenclature of, 195–96
    properties of, 195
    reactions of, 210–14

ring strain and geometry of, 197–200
sources and uses of, 196–97
synthesis of, 205–10
Cyclodecarboxylation, 380
Cycloparaffins, 195. See also Cycloalkanes
Cyclopentenophenanthrene, 565

Decarbonylation, 382–83
Decarboxylation, 378
Degradation reactions, 64–65, 424–27, 519
Dehalogenation, 146, 152–54
Dehydration, 146–50, 269, 290
Dehydrogenation, 223–24, 267–68, 302
Dehydrohalogenation, 146, 150–52, 186–87,
    279
Demjanov rearrangements, 418, 419–20
Denaturation, 256, 543
Denatured alcohol, 256, 257
Deoxycholic acid, 7, 567
Deoxyribonucleic acids (DNA), 558, 559–65
Depsipeptides, 557
Destructive distillation, 220–22
Desulfuration, 296
Detergents, 357–59, 389
Dexamethasone, 572
Dextrin, 526
Dextrose, 496
Diastase, 525
Diastereomer, 470
Diazoamino compounds, 443–44
Diazo compounds, 444–48
Diazomethane, 335, 363–64, 433
Diazonium salts, 418, 438–44
Diazotization, 420, 438–39
Dicarboxylic acids, 376–82
Dichroism, 456–57
Dieckmann condensation, 367
Diels-Alder reaction, 207–09, 340
Diels hydrocarbon, 565
Dienes, 174–78
Digitalis, 569
Dimerization, 172
Diols, 263–64
Diosgenin, 569
Dipole moments, 15, 17–18
Disaccharides, 494, 495, 520–24
Displacement reactions, 96. See also Substi-
    tution reactions
Disproportionation reactions, 333, 433–34
Distillation, 38–44, 220–22

Diterpenes, 583
Dyestuffs, 444–48

Echinatine, 576
Electrochemistry, 3
Electromagnetic spectrum, 67
Electronegativity, 15
Electron sharing, 11
Electron transfer, 11
Electrophilic substitutions, 230–38
Electrophoresis, 546–47
Elemental analyses, 56–60
Elimination reactions, 96–97, 146, 151–52, 424–27
Emetine, 576
Empirical formulas, 60–61
Emulsin, 509, 522
Enamines, 421–22
Enantiomers, 27, 454, 459–60, 462–64
End group analysis, 549
Endopeptidases, 557
Endothermic reaction, 114
Enols, 309–11, 313
Enzymes, 255, 509, 556–57
    hydrolytic, 556
    proteolytic, 533, 557
Ephedrine, 574
Epimerization, 477–78, 512
Epinephrine, 574
Epoxides, 288, 335–36, 341–42
Equilibrium, of reaction, 113
Ergosterol, 566
Erlenmeyer's rule, 263
Essential oils, 577
Esterases, 556
Esterification, 359–62, 365
Esters, 266–67
    carboxylic, 367
    keto, 382–86
    natural, 355–57
    nomenclature and properties of, 354–55
    ortho, 373–74
    reactions of, 364–67
    synthesis of, 359–64, 384–86
Estradiol, 568
Estrogens, 567
Ethanol, 255–57
Ethers, 287–94
    nomenclature, properties, and characterization of, 287–89

occurrence and uses of, 289–90
reactions of, 291–94
sulfur analogs of, 295–96
synthesis of, 290–91
Ethylene oxide, 341–42
Ethylenes, 143. See also Alkenes
Endalene series, terpenes, 581, 582
Exothermic reaction, 114
Extraction, 37–38

Farnesol, 588
Fats, 356–57
Fatty acids, 356–57
Fehling's solution, 312
Fermentation, 255
Fischer projection formulas, 480, 504
Fischer-Tropsch process, 131
Fluorocarbons, 279
Formaldehyde, 299, 308, 319, 324, 450
Formalin, 308, 324
Formic acid, 349
Formulas, 8–11
Formylation, 304–05
Fractional distillation, 40–42, 127–29
Free energy, 116
Free radicals, 98
    configurations of, 104–05
    reactions of, 99–100
    stable, 100–02
    substitution by, 238–39
    transient, 102
Freezing point depression, 61, 62
Fresnel rhomb, 466
Friedel-Crafts reaction, 226–27, 276, 306–07
Fries reaction, 307–08
Fructose, 495–96
Fuels, 126–31
Fulminic acid, 451–52
Functional groups, 19–21, 63–64
Furanose, 507

Gabriel synthesis, 414
Gallic acid, 344–45, 429
Gas chromatography, 49–51
Gattermann reaction, 440
Gattermann-Koch synthesis, 305
Genins, 569, 570
Gentiobiose, 521
Geometric isomerism, 28–30, 321
Geraniol, 588

Girard's reagent, 320
Globin, 542
Glucose, 495–96
Glutaric acid, 379
Glycaric acid, 500–01
Glycerol, 264
Glycogen, 526
Glycols, 163, 263, 269–72
Glyconic acid, 501
Glycoprotein, 542
Glycosidases, 556
Glycosides, 509–11, 516–19, 568–570
Glycosyl-glycosides, 520–21
Glycuronic acids, 513
Gomberg reaction, 442
Grignard reagents, 134–36
    and acetylene, 189
    and alcohols, 260–63
    and aldehydes, 304
    and amines, 418
    carbonation of, 349–50
    and esters, 364
    and ketones, 306
    and organometallic compounds, 279–80
    and Schiff bases, 417
Guanidine, 450–51

Halides, organic, 276–87
    nomenclature, properties, and characteri-
        zation of, 277–78
    reactions of, 279–83
    structure and reactivity of, 283–87
    synthesis of, 278–79
Haloform reaction, 312–13
Halogenation, of alkanes, 138–41
    of alkenes, 168–69
    of aromatics, 226
    of carboxylic acids, 351–52
Haworth projection formulas, 504
Heat of Reaction, 114
Hell-Volhard-Zelinsky reaction, 352
Hemiacetals, 316
Hemin, 542
Hemoglobin, 551–52
Heparin, 530
Heterocyclic compounds, 17, 243–47
Hexitols, 264, 514
Hexoses, 494
Hinsberg reaction, 409, 418, 428
Hofmann reaction, 410–11, 414–16, 424–27,
    538
Homologous series, 21–22

Hormones, 565, 567–68
Hückel's rule, 241
Hybridization, 91–94
Hydration, 17
    of alkenes, 162–63, 257, 260
    of alkynes, 191–92, 302
Hydrazobenzene, 437
Hydrazones, 319
Hydroaromatics, 120
Hydroboration, 167–68, 260
Hydrocarbons, 19
    classes of, 119–20
    nomenclature of, 120–23
    see also Alkanes; Alkenes; Aromatic hydro-
        carbons
Hydrocortisone, 568
Hydroforming reaction, 197, 222
Hydrogenation, of alkanes, 131–32, 133
    of alkenes, 155–57
    of alkynes, 189–90
    of cycloalkanes, 205–06, 210–11
    heats of, 88–89, 155–57
Hydrogen bonding, 251–54
Hydrogenolysis, 304, 417
Hydrohalogenation, 159–62
Hydrolysis, 134–36, 162
    of alkyl halides, 260
    of dihalomethylarenes, 304
    of esters, 359, 365
    of keto esters, 383, 385
    of nitriles, 350
    of nitroalkanes, 433–34
    of nucleic acids, 558
    of proteins, 544–45
    see also Saponification
Hydroxy acids, 374–76
Hydroxylation, 163–64, 302
Hygrine, 574, 575
Hyperconjugation, 103, 109

Indicators, 448
Inductive effect, 238, 348, 403, 426
Infrared spectrometry, 53, 71–72
Ingrain dyes, 447
Inorganic chemistry, 3
Inositols, 515
Insulin, 552
Inulin, 529
Invertase, 523
Iodination, 226
Ion exchange, 52
Ion exchange resins, 52

Ionization, 17
Isocyanates, 451–52
Isocyanic acid, 451
Isocyanides, 408, 418, 448
Isoelectric point, 538, 543–44
Isomerism, 23–30
    cis-trans, 29
    functional, 23–24
    geometric, 28–30, 321
    optical, 27–28, 454–91
    positional, 23
    skeletal, 22
Isomerization, of alkanes, 138–39
    of alkenes, 179–81
    of cycloalkanes, 212
    and keto-enol forms, 191, 309–11
Isonitriles, 448–49
Isoprene, 177, 178, 578
Isotactic, 173
Isothiocyanates, 452
Isotopes, 33–34
Isotopic dilution, 548

Kekulé conventions, 9–11
Keratin, 542, 554
Ketals, 317
Keto acids, 382–86
Keto-enol tautomerization, 191, 309–11, 431
Ketones, 298–342
    distinguished from aldehydes, 311–13
    isomeric forms of, 309–11
    nomenclature of, 299–300
    properties of, 300–02
    reactions of, 309–36
    sources of, 299
    synthesis of, 302–03, 305–08
    unsaturated, 336–39
Ketoses, 494, 495–97
Kiliani synthesis, 501–03, 519
Kjeldahl method, 545
Königs-Knorr synthesis, 517
Korner's "Absolute method," 240

Lactic acid, 376
Lactones, 374–76
Lactose, 520, 521
Lanosterol, 584, 589
Lecithins, 424
Leuckart reaction, 412–13
Light, 454 ff.
    circularly polarized, 464–66

    plane polarized, 454–58
Lignin, 526
Lipases, 556
Lithium aluminum hydride, 134, 258
Lobeline, 575
Lobry de Bruyn-van Ekenstein conversion, 512
Lucas test, 268
Lupinine, 576
Lycopene, 585

Malic acid, 376
Malonic acid, 378
Maltase, 509, 522
Maltonic acid, 522
Maltose, 520, 521, 522–23
Mannan, 529
Mannich reaction, 417
Markownikoff's rule, 160
Mass spectrometry, 53, 63, 77–79
Meerwein-Ponndorf reduction, 306, 314
Melibiose, 521
Melting point, 53
    of alcohols, 251
    of alkanes, 125–26
    of alkanes, 125–26
    of alkenes, 145
Melting point depression, 61
Mercaptans, 294–95
Mercuration, 276
Mescaline, 428–29, 574
Metal acetylides, 188–89
Metal alkoxides, 265
Metaldehyde, 325
Methane, 78, 119
Methanol, 255
Methylation, 427, 428, 519
Mevalonic acid, 588
Michael reaction, 338
Microscopic reversibility, 622
Molecular complexes, 228, 235
Molecular formulas, 8–9, 60–61
Molecular structure, 9
    determination of, 55–83
    models, 26
    and optical activity, 462–64
    and physical properties, 123–24
    see also Atom
Molecular weights, determination of, 61–63
Monocyclic compounds, 120
Mononucleotides, 558
Monosaccharides, 494, 495, 511–20

Monoterpenes, 578–80
Mordant dyes, 447
Morphine, 577
Mucin, 542
Mustard oils, 452
Myosmine, 575

Naphthenes, 196
Natural gas, 126, 127
Nef reaction, 434, 520
Neoprene, 176
Neutralization, acid-base, 105
Neutralization equivalent, 621
Niacin, 575–76
Nicol prism, 456
Nicotine, 575
Nitration, 141, 225–26
Nitriles, 370–72
Nitrobenzene, 430
Nitro compounds, 429–38
    aliphatic, 433–34
    aromatic, 434–39
    nomenclature and uses of, 429–30
    structure and properties of, 430–31
    synthesis of, 431–33
Nitrogen, 397–52
    and carboxylic acids, 387–90
    in proteins, 545
    quantitative analysis of, 59
    see also Alkaloids; Nitro compounds
Nitromethane synthesis, 519–20
Nitrosobenzene, 437
Nitrous acid, 418–20, 434
Nomenclature, general, 120–23
Norethisterone, 572
Nuclear magnetic resonance spectrometry, 53, 74–77
Nucleic acids, 558–65
    components of, 558–59
    function of, 563–65
    structure of, 559–63
Nucleophilic substitutions, 238–39, 281–83, 434–35
Nucleosides, 558
Nucleotides, 558–65

Octane number, 129–30
Oils, 356–57
Oleanic acid, 584
Olefins, 119, 143. See also Alkenes

Oppenauer oxidation, 305–06, 314
Optical activity, 27–28, 458–91
    and asymmetric syntheses, 584–88
    cause of, 464–66
    and molecular structure, 462–64
    resolution of, 463, 473–75
    rotatory dispersion in, 488–90
    specific rotation in, 460–61
    and stereoselective syntheses, 484–86
Optical isomerism, 27, 454–91
Organic chemistry, 1–4
    definition of, 1, 3
    development of, 2–4
Organic compounds, 4
    and criteria of purity, 52–53
    functional groups of, 21
    homologous series of, 21–22
    isolation and purification of, 36–53
    number of, 4
    optical activity of, 463–91
    principal series of, 18–19
    properties of, 16–18
    sources of, 5–6
    transformations of, 6
Organic reactions, 96–117
    activation energy of, 114
    energy relations in, 113–17
    equilibrium of, 113
    intermediates of, 99
    mechanisms of, 97–99
    oxidation-reduction, 390–95
    rate-determining step in, 116
Organometallic compounds, 134, 279–81, 306
Ortho acids, 373
Ortho esters, 373–74
Osazones, 332, 499–500
Ovalbumin, 542
Oxacycloalkanes, 289
Oxalic acid, 378
Oxidation, of alcohols, 267–68, 302, 305–06, 349
    of aldoses, 500–01
    of alkanes, 136–37
    of alkenes, 164–65, 350
    of amines, 421
    of chromic acid, 393–95
    of saccharides, 512–14
Oxidation-reduction reactions, 390–95
Oximes, 319, 320, 321–22

Oxonium salts, 265, 291–92
Oxytocin, 550–51
Ozonization, 165–67, 302
Ozonolysis, 65, 167, 428

Paper chromatography, 48–49
Paraffins, 119. *See also* Alkanes
Paraformaldehyde, 324
Paramagnetism, 101
Pectic acid, 529
Pectins, 529
Pentitols, 264, 514
Pentoses, 494
Pepsin, 557
Peptides, 541–57
  definition of, 541–42
  synthesis of, 555–56
  see also Proteins
Peroxides, 293
Peroxy acids, 387
Petroleum, 126–30, 222–23
Phenolphthalein, 448
Phenols, 272–76, 313
Phenylalkylamine derivatives, 574
Phenylhydrazones, 319, 320
Phosphatases, 556
Phosphoglyceric acid, 533
Phospholipids, 424
Phosphoprotein, 542
Photosynthesis, 55, 530–33
Phthalic acid, 379
Physical chemistry, 3
Physostigmine, 576
Phytol, 583
Phytosterols, 566
Pi (π) complexes, 228, 435
Pinacol rearrangements, 271–72
Pinner reaction, 374
Piperidine derivatives, 575
Piperine, 575
Polarimeter, 460–61
Polycyclic compounds, 120
Polyenes, 178–79, 179–81
Polyethylene, 170
Polymerization, 130, 169
  addition, 382
  of aldehydes, 324–25
  of alkenes, 169–74
  of alkynes, 193–94
  anionic, 172–74

cationic, 172
condensation, 381–82
of dienes, 176–77, 382
free radical, 169–72
Polyols, 263–64
Polysaccharides, 494, 495, 524–30
Polysubstitution, 323–38
Porphyrin, 542
Prednisone, 572
Progesterone, 568
Proteinases, 556
Proteins, 541–57
  classification of, 542
  isolation and purification of, 545–47
  molecular weights of, 547–48
  properties of, 543–45
  structures of, 548–54
  see also Amino acids; Nucleic acids
Pyranose, 506–07
Pyridine derivatives, 575–76
Pyrolysis, 137, 303, 424–28
Pyrrolidine derivatives, 574–75

Quantitative analysis, 56–59
Quantum theory, 66–69
Quaternary ammonium compounds, 422–29
Quinine, 576
Quinones, 339–40

Racemate, 27, 463
Racemic acid, 462, 463
Racemization, 27–28, 476–78
Raffinose, 523, 524
Rayon, 527
Reactions. *See* Organic reactions
Reduction, 132, 134, 136, 390–95
  of aldehydes and ketones, 313–15, 411
  of aldoses, 514–15
  of alkyl halides, 279
  bimolecular, 315
  of carbonyl compounds, 258–60
  of carboxylic acids, 351
  of diazonium salts, 442
  of esters, 364
  of nitroarenes, 435–38
  of nitrogen derivatives, 413–14
Reformatsky reaction, 327
Refractive index, 53
Reimer-Tiemann reaction, 305
Replacement reactions, 268–69, 439–42

Reserpine, 577
Resonance theory, 85–89, 103, 109
Ribonucleic acids (RNA), 558–59, 562, 563–65
Ribulose diphosphate, 532
Ring strain, theory of, 197–205
Rosanoff classification, 497, 498
Rosenmund reduction, 303–04
Rubber, 176–78

Saccharides, 494, 495
Sandmeyer reaction, 440
Sapogenins, 568–69
Saponification, 357
Saponins, 568–69, 584
Sarsasapogenin, 569
Saturated hydrocarbons. *See* Alkanes
Saytzeff rule, 147–48, 150
Schiemann reaction, 441
Schiff bases, 319, 411, 417, 421
Schiff reagent, 311
Schmidt reaction, 416
Schotten-Baumann reaction, 362
Scilliroside, 569
Semicarbazones, 319, 320
Sesquiterpenes, 580–82
Side-chain oxidation, 229–30
Silk fibroin, 554
Simmons-Smith reaction, 209–10
Soaps, 357–59, 423
Solubility, 126
Solution, saturated, definition of, 45
Solvation, 109
Spectrometers, 69–71
Spectrometry, 66–69
    infrared, 53, 71–72
    mass, 53, 63, 77–79
    nuclear magnetic resonance, 53, 74–77
    ultraviolet, 53, 73
    visible, 73
Spectropolarimeter, 488, 489
Squalene, 583, 589
Starch, 525–26
Steam distillation, 43–44
Stereochemistry, 24–32, 469–72, 482–84
Stereoisomerism, 24–32, 497–99
Steric effects, 101–02, 404–07
Steric hindrance, 360, 467–68
Steroids, 565–73
Sterols, 566–67

Stigmasterol, 566
Strecker synthesis, 538
Strophanthin, 569
Structural formulas, 9–11
Strychnine, 577
Sublimation, 44–45
Substitution reactions, 96, 225–27, 230–41, 482–84
Succinic acid, 378–79
Sucrose, 496, 520
Sulfa drugs, 389
Sulfides, organic, 295–96
Sulfonamides, 389
Sulfonation, 226
Sulfones, 296
Sulfonic acids, 388–90
Sulfoxides, 296
Sulfur, 59–60, 387–90
Surface chemistry, 3
Syndiotactic, 173
Synthesis, 6, 83

Tartaric acids, 376, 462, 463, 469–70
Tautomerization, 191, 309
    aci-nitro, 431
    keto-enol, 191, 309–11, 431
Terephthalic acid, 379
Terpenes, 196, 577–89
Testosterone, 567
Tetrasaccharides, 494, 495
Tetraterpenes, 585–86
Tetritols, 264
Tetrodotoxin, 451
Tetroses, 494
Thin layer chromatography, 48
Thioacetals, 317
Thioketals, 317
Tollen's reagent, 311–12
Tosylates, 390
Transaminases, 556
Trehalose, 520
Triols, 264
Trioses, 494
Trioxane, 324
Triphosphopyridine nucleotide (TPNH), 531–32, 588
Trisaccharides, 494, 495, 522–24
Triterpenes, 583–85
Tropolones, 340–41
Trypsin, 557

Ultracentrifuge, 547
Ultraviolet spectrometry, 53, 73
Unsaturated hydrocarbons, 143. *See also*
    Alkenes
Urea, 449–50
Urease, 556

Vacuum distillation, 43
Valence, 9–11, 180–81
Van der Waals forces, 17–18
Van Slyke methods, 408, 545
Vat dyes, 447
Vinylation, 192–93
Vinylology, principle of, 338–39
Vinyl polymers, 170
Vitamin A, 178, 583, 586
Vitamin B_{12}, 82

Wagner-Meerwein rearrangements, 283, 577
    of alcohols, 269
    in alkene synthesis, 149

and amines, 419
of cycloalkanes, 211
and terpenes, 580
Walden inversion, 481, 516, 517
Williamson synthesis, 291
Wittig reaction, 334
Wohl-Zemplen degradation, 519
Wolff-Kishner reduction, 136, 314, 319

Xanthates, 150, 527
Xanthins, 586
Xanthoproteic reaction, 544
X-ray diffraction, 79–82
Xylan, 529

Ylides, 344, 426

Zeisel analysis, 293
Zerevitinoff method, 418, 428
Zinc dust distillation, 275
Zoosterols, 566